Ship Operation Automation

Computer Applications in Shipping and Shipbuilding

Volume 1

Ship Operation Automation

Proceedings of the IFAC/IFIP Symposium
Oslo, Norway, July 2-5, 1973

Edited by

Yuzuru FUJITA
University of Tokyo

Kjell LIND
The Ship Research Institute of Norway

Theodore J. WILLIAMS
Purdue University

NORTH-HOLLAND PUBLISHING COMPANY - AMSTERDAM · OXFORD
AMERICAN ELSEVIER PUBLISHING COMPANY, INC. - NEW YORK

Library of Congress Catalog Card Number: 74-84736
North-Holland ISBN: 0 7204 2815 7
American Elsevier ISBN: 0 444 10735 5

Published by:
NORTH-HOLLAND PUBLISHING COMPANY — AMSTERDAM
NORTH-HOLLAND PUBLISHING COMPANY, LTD. — OXFORD

Distributors for the U.S.A. and Canada:
American Elsevier Publishing Company, Inc.
52 Vanderbilt Avenue
New York, N.Y. 10017

First edition 1974
Second printing 1975

PRINTED IN THE NETHERLANDS

CONTENTS

FOREWORD

The future dominance of the automation practices of the shipbuilding and ship operation industries by the digital computer and by computer-based techniques has been admirably forecast by the presentations which were made at the two International Conferences on these industries held during the summer of 1973 in Oslo, Norway, and in Tokyo, Japan, which are reported in the two volume series on *Computer Applications in Shipping and Shipbuilding* of which this Volume is a part. Only a continued growth in the application of these techniques will permit each of these industries to maintain their recent expansions and developments in the face of the critical personnel shortages and the fast rising costs which are facing them.

The International Federation for Information Processing (IFIP) and the International Federation of Automatic Control (IFAC) cooperated in organizing and presenting these Conferences. *The IFAC/IFIP Symposium on Ship Operation Automation* held in Oslo, Norway, on July 2—5, 1973, whose Proceedings are reported in this present Volume, presented a total of 62 papers on the automation of bridge, engine room, cargo handling, and ship administrative functions to over 550 attendees from 30 countries. *The IFIP-IFAC-JSNA Joint Conference on Computer Applications in the Automation of Shipyard Operation and Ship Design* held in Tokyo, Japan, on August 28—30, 1973, and whose Proceedings are reported in the companion Volume of this Series, had 353 attendees from 24 countries and included 54 papers on computer-based ship design and computer automation techniques in the shipyard itself, such as flame cutting, plate bending, welding, overall planning, and work scheduling. The Society of Naval Architects of Japan (JSNA) ably served as the Local Organizers of the Tokyo Conference and as Cosponsors along with the two International Federations, IFIP and IFAC.

The papers and discussions of the Oslo Symposium showed that computer-based automation systems can readily assume all the operational aspects of engineroom control and of the navigational functions of a ship at sea. With a proper modification of present national and international laws and regulations and a successful completion of current research investigations, these computer-based systems will also be able to handle these same control tasks in restricted areas such as harbors, straits, and rivers. Such developments should eventually permit a major reduction in crew sizes in ships of all types. Almost all major maritime nations now have programs in operation or under active development for investigating the possibilities and potentials of such crew reductions. This concern is based upon the recent severe reductions in the availability of qualified individuals who wish to make

seafaring a lifetime career. Computer-based techniques have certainly appeared on the world scene at an appropriate time in this regard.

The recent major expansions in the numbers and sizes of ocean-going vessels has occurred because of the mushrooming needs for energy and the closing of important trade routes. This factor has greatly accelerated the needs of the naval architect and of the shipyards themselves for computer-based aids to their work. The very large size of the new tankers, the highly critical design factors necessary for the recent large liquified natural gas carriers, and the very high performance requirements of the new container ships all have demanded sophisticated design techniques of the naval architect which could only be carried out in a reasonable period of time by the use of computer methods. Likewise, the very complex problems arising in the construction of such complex vessels under very accelerated schedules again have demanded computer-based shipyard planning and operational techniques for their successful completion. Fortunately these techniques are available as evidenced by the papers of the Second Conference.

The Local Organizing Committees of both Conferences are to be congratulated for their superb organization of both Conferences, for their admirable handling of the larger than expected attendance, and for their organization of a set of very appropriate social programs and technical visits.

In view of the success of the 1973 Conferences, plans are now under way to repeat them in 1976. A Second Conference on Computer Applications in the Automation of Shipyard Operation and Ship Design will be held at Chalmers University, Gothenberg, Sweden, in June 1976. A Second Symposium on Ship Operation Automation is planned for Tokyo, Japan, in August of that same year. By that time there should be several further significant developments in computer applications to both ship building and ship operation to report in the second dual volume of Proceedings of this series.

In addition to their sponsorship by IFIP and IFAC, the present Conferences enjoyed the following additional Sponsorships and Committee Memberships.

1. *IFAC/IFIP Symposium on Ship Operation Automation*
    a. Organizing Societies:
       The Swedish National Committee for IFAC.
       Swedish Society for Information Processing.
       Danish Automation Society.
       Norwegian Computer Society .
       Norwegian Society for Automatic Control
          (Local Organizer).

b. Local Organizing Committee:

Mr. I. Høivold, Chairman	Norway
Mr. K. Lind, Secretary	Norway
Mr. O. Bakkevig	Norway
Mr. H.V. Ellingsen	Norway
Mr. S.T. Lyngsø	Denmark
Mr. H.P. Klemmetsen	Norway
Mr. A. Madesaeter	Sweden
Mr. L. Monrad-Krohn	Norway
Mr. J. Stefenson	Sweden
Mr. O. Tveit	Norway

c. International Program Committee:

Prof. T.J. Williams, Chairman	USA
Dr. N. Yonehara	Japan
Mr. P. Obresumov	USSR
Mr. S.T. Lyngsø	Denmark
Mr. J. Stefenson	Sweden
Mr. I. Høivold	Norway

2. *IFIP-IFAC-JSNA Joint Conference on Computer Applications in the Automation of Shipyard Operation and Ship Design*

a. Organizing Societies:
Information Processing Society of Japan
Society of Instrument and Control Engineers
The Society of Naval Architects of Japan
(Local Organizer)

b. Local Organizing Committee:
Dr. M. Kinoshita, Chairman
Prof. Y. Fujita, Secretary
Prof. E. Goto
Mr. T. So
Prof. M. Terao
Prof. A. Nomoto
Prof. S. Motora
Prof. T. Iwata

c. Honorary Chairman:

Prof. Dr. H. Kihara	Japan

d. International Organizing Committee:

Prof. T.J. Williams, Co-chairman	USA
Dr. M. Kinoshita, Co-chairman	Japan
Prof. A.S. Douglas	UK
Prof. H. Benford	USA

(Plus Members of Local Organizing Committee)

e. International Program Committee:

Prof. Y. Akita, Chairman	Japan
Dr. E.G. Baker	USA
Dr. H. Goodman	UK
Prof. F. Hiramoto	Japan
Prof. J. Sujara	Japan
Prof. G. Sawaragi	Japan

(Plus Members of Local Organizing Committee)

YUZURU FUJITA
KJELL LIND
THEODORE J. WILLIAMS

AN EVALUATION OF THE
PRESENT STATUS OF SHIP AUTOMATION

Theodore J. Williams
Purdue Laboratory for Applied Industrial Control
Purdue University
West Lafayette, Indiana 47907 USA

The members of the International Program Committee, who are listed on your program, join me in hoping you will enjoy the lectures and papers of the Symposium. We hope that they, plus the individual contacts which you will make here, will be very helpful to you in the development of your own area of ship operation automation. We hope also that the Symposium itself will serve to promote the field of the automation of ship operations at sea in which we all are so vitally interested.

We also wish to thank the authors of the papers for their contributions to the program. Without them, of course, there would be no symposium such as this.

I personally am grateful for the opportunity of addressing you here this morning and of presenting to you in a few brief sentences my own personal impressions of where our field finds itself now at the start of our IFAC/IFIP Symposium on Ship Operation Automation here at Oslo in Mid-1973.

INTRODUCTION AND STATEMENT OF PRESENT STATUS

As the authors of the papers of this Symposium will tell us during our Symposium, essentially every task involved in shipboard operation has already been carried out by automated means using analog or digital computer systems or is now in the process of being so implemented.

The way is then clear, I believe, for us at any time we desire, to fit out a fully automated ship in which at least all of the at-sea and dock-side functions will be placed under the operation of a hands-off automation system. No one should seriously question our technological capability of doing this. We may, however, seriously question whether we can or should do this as a general practice at present for several important reasons

1. First and most important - we still have serious questions about the overall reliability of the several components of the necessary automation system - sensors, the data transmission network, the data presentation devices and even of the computers themselves.

2. The payout of automation systems seems to be mainly in the subjective rather than in the directly measurable economic areas. At present systems costs, it is difficult to show a real payout for these systems from measurable quantities alone. We know that such systems can increase ship safety, that they can promote crew preferences for service on vessels equipped with them, that they can help decrease maintenance costs, and many other benefits. But, we do not know as yet how to put a real monetary value on many of these factors.

3. Hardware which can be used for automated ship functions is now in a rapid state of development. What type of this equipment, then, will we eventuelly standardize for our preferred installations?

4. Even assuming the final success of automation techniques, we have not worked out the best trade-offs between manpower and automation techniques in the sea going environment. We still must evaluate many things in this area. Among them are:

   a. Man's true position as a back-up device for automation devices versus the use of redundancy or other related techniques.

   b. Man's value for maintenance at sea versus the carrying out of all such functions in part or in dry dock.

   c. The social problems of small crews on long voyages - their pay, their duties and the hours of watch standing, their use of off-duty time, the question of the carrying of families on board etc.

   d. The training required of the personnel of these ships must be established. Actually, of course, solution of the earlier problems will make plain the requirements in this latter area.

A REVIEW OF COMPUTER CONTROL
STATUS TODAY

In a recent rather severe review of the field of
digital computer control as applied to all industry,
the following list of conclusions concerning the
history of the field to date has been collected in
Table I. They are also applicable to many of the
early installations on shipboard or may potentially apply to those to be made in the future, if
the proper precautions are not taken.

Despite this indictment of the early history of
the digital computer control field (due mainly
to overenthusiasm and overconfidence in the
face of inexperience) and the questions raised
earlier, I believe we will all agree that further
automation of the world's shipping is inevitable.
I believe also that we agree that the digital computer or its variants are a major factor in the
development. How then can we achieve this increase most easily and painlessly?

TABLE I -
A SUMMARY OF MANAGEMENT CONCLUSIONS
CONCERNING INDUSTRIAL (AND SHIPBOARD)
COMPUTER APPLICATIONS

1. Computers are facinating and intellectually
   inspiring subjects with which to work. Their
   proponents tend to be extremely enthusiastic
   concerning the computer's capabilities as
   well as their own individual skills. As a
   result there is a tendency to overestimate the
   rate of progress possible in completing projects. A similar tendency exists regarding
   the development of solutions to application
   problems which may arise. Likewise, these
   individuals tend to underestimate the difficulties, and the amount of equipment and time
   needed for these projects and these problem
   solutions.

2. Early computer equipment was quite unreliable.
   In addition, the tendencies mentioned above
   often resulted in projects being too large, too
   complex, and requiring too much machine
   speed and memory for the avialable devices.
   The reliability and speed problems have
   largely been corrected. However, thoughts
   of these earlier failures are hard to erase
   from the minds of our industry's management.

3. Computer enthusiasts have completely misjudged the degree of acceptance of computer
   systems by their uniniated compatriots. They
   also tend to underestimate the amount of
   training which is required to correct the resulting situation. Because of the small size of
   the usual "computer group" involved in most
   installations, complete acceptance by the ship's
   crew is absolutely necessary to assure the continuity of a project once the members of the
   computer installation group leave the project
   for their next assignment.

4. In many cases the extremely flexible and very
   sophisticated systems envisioned by early
   workers have not been necessary to accomplish
   the tasks required.

5. A corollary to this last Item is the fact that
   there are generally other solutions which are
   available for most situations requiring any
   except the most sophisticated of computer
   control installations. These other solutions,
   being extensions of presently available techniques, are more readily accepted by the non-
   computer trained individual. In fact, they are
   often sought out by him as counter factors to
   proposed computer applications.

6. The type of person who is most intrigued by
   computers tends to be the one who is most
   likely to be enthusiastic, innovative, and
   creative. These individuals see a ready opportunity to fulfill their creative needs through
   applications in the computer field. The
   result has been a very great proliferation of
   new computer designs, new codes, and of
   new programming languages. Most serious
   of all - there have been many new reworkings
   of already solved problems for the sake of
   innovations alone or for only minor technical
   or economic gains.

7. Our machine-oriented ethics of efficiency
   and of low costs cause us to be overconcerned
   as to whether our computer systems are
   planned and programmed so that their duty
   efficiency is high, that their memories are
   full, and that as many ship operations as
   possible are forced into them. Experience
   is tempering these factors. However, this
   condition plus those mentioned earlier still
   prevail in far too many cases. We then have
   the expected effects of increasing programming
   manpower requirements. Likewise we increase the difficulties of the deciphering of
   programming errors and of making programming updates.

8. The area where these results combine to cause
   the most problems in project completion and
   in user acceptance is in the area of programming management. Except for rare cases,
   projects still tend to be understaffed. This
   results in project delays and overruns. Likewise, innovations and the desire for efficiency
   and completeness combine to make project
   programming a much more difficult task than
   it need to be otherwise.

9. Contrary to the expectations and predictions
   of their proponents, digital systems have not
   been as truly flexible as originally planned.
   Particularly, the changing and updating of
   their programs have proved to be much more
   difficult and more errorprone than can be
   tolerated in industrial situations.

10. In general the documentation of the programs of most systems has been woefully, sometimes totally deficient. This is particularly so when it comes to making it possible for a new engineer to pick up and modify a partially completed project.

SYSTEM RELIABILITY

As we mentioned earlier, a major problem for the designer and installer of future shipboard automation systems is that of achieving and (perhaps equally as important) demonstrating a satisfactory level of overall system reliability.

In this context a major disappointment to those of us observing the field of industrial control has been the lack of really significant development in sensors for industrial control systems. As has been indicated above, we have had spectacular developments in computers and in their directly associated devices in the past few years. In most cases, however, we are still depending on the same types of sensors and transducers that were used ten, twenty, and more years ago. The same, of course, applies to the ship operation field.

It would appear that a major world-wide development effort is needed in order to achieve the necessary long-life capability in the marine and in severe industrial environments. Almost every class of sensors can stand considerable work. Many of them are especially vulnerable to failures at present. Among these are, of course, radars, sonars, flow measurements of various materials, vibration sensing, level measurements in large tanks, and temperation measurement of rotating components.

The setting and acceptance world-wide of a set of standard specifications for the performance and operations requirements for these sensors would be a necessary first step in such a development as we have envisioned. The proposed standards of the British Ship Research Association (BSRA) and of Det norske Veritas, to name only two, are an excellent start in this area. We, however, need a universally accepted code if that is at all possible.

ONE POSSIBLE AID TO FURTHER DEVELOPMENT IS A STANDARDIZED SHIP BOARD COMPUTER SYSTEM

In developing future ship-board computer systems a major consideration must be the reduction of the personnel requirements needed to implement an installation. This involves all phases of a project: the original engineering layout, the mathematical modelling and control strategy development, the coding in an appropriate programming language, and finally the checkout and testing of the final installation.

Other important considerations are developing the maximum overall reliability of the resulting system, as just mentioned, as well as the minimum total cost at final commissioning, and a maximum flexibility and ease of making post commissioning changes. Standardization has long been recognized as one means by which such results can be obtained.

Our industry must be prepared to accept standards, and to use them, before this method can succeed.

In order to readily achieve our main object, which is that of reducing overall systems costs and of simplifying greatly the engineering, the installation, and the commissioning of a shipboard control system, it is necessary to modify greatly the previously common organization of the data collection and conversion and the control correction output distribution parts of the system.

In place of the formerly common methods of using separate pairs of leads between each sensor or each final actuator, the computer, we wish to adopt the concepts recently perfected by the aerospace industry. This is to use a set of remote multiplexers and a single "data highway" carrying only digital signals between these multiplexers and the computer itself.

Such a concept has been technically possible for some time. However, integrated circuitry has only recently made remote multiplexers and multiple A/D converters economically practical. It has also helped to make computer systems fast enough to handle the data load which is necessary for the method of operation which is described here.

Figure 1 diagrams one possible form of data collection and conversion part of the system under discussion. It should be noted here that critical elements of the data path such as its multiplexer switches and the A/D converters themselves are dual.

This allows independent operation so that the failure of any single element will not disable a particular input. We specify also that the switches should "fail open" by design. This is in contrast to the usual operation of reed relays. These elements should also be capable of being tested independently during preventive maintenance procedures.

Maximum reliability at the computer end of the data acquisition system can be achieved by the use of a set of dual computers, one in a use, the other in a standby status.

Again, the drastic price reduction of capable small computer mainframes has made economically practical a concept which is not new in other industries or even in shipping.

In considering such a system as we have just outlined, the so-called micro computer and all of its ramifications becomes vitally important. You are all undoubtedly aware of the recent appearance of its so-called "computer on a chip" at prices which are minute fractions of previously well accepted costs and with potential reliabilities vastly exceeding those possible previously. Certainly, they are going to have a vital role in future marine systems - where and to what extent, however, is not yet completely clear.

Here again, a cooperative study project would be particularly rewarding since it would save to prevent many of the false steps that are sure to occur as various chip configurations are tried for several different applications.

Likewise, standard digital process control programming languages are under active development in worldwide coordinated efforts.

I am happy to report to those of you who are not already familiar with it, that one of these is conducted by my own organization, Purdue University, and is receiving wide acceptance. Certainly, use of one or the other of these standard languages must also be part of our future method of development of shipboard systems.

As a set of conclusions to our discussion and as a counter to the developments listed earlier, we can state that under most circumstances we should strive to achieve the following in our computer-based ship data collection and control systems:

1. They should be kept as simple as possible, consistent with the result expected.

2. For large tasks, functions should be distributed among a group of small computers or other small devices. Each should carry out only a few relatively simple jobs. Work should not be concentrated in one large system. This principle will become ever more important as the costs of the small systems continue to decrease. Each of the small systems should have the capability of communicating with its fellows and with a larger central system if present.

3. The computer language used by the engineer or programmer in developing a new system should be as near to a natural language as possible. This will permit self-documenting of the program to the maximum extent. This is incompatible with the small computers of our last item. Therefore, host-system compiling will probably be necessary.

4. The computer system's source program should be transportable to other types of computer systems. This will help avoid the necessity of reprogramming should the computer hardware be changed or a further application be made of the same technique to a new ship.

5. The question of whether a particular computer is being efficiently used should not be a pertinent question in the systems analysis. The only valid question is whether that particular application makes the proper economic payout considering both manpower and hardware costs.

6. We should be sure that proposed systems have a sufficient growth potential to allow for the inevitable expansion of the system. Such expansion need not burden the present configurations of both hardware and software.

7. Acceptable industry standards for programming languages and for interface systems designs should be developed and adopted as rapidly as possible.

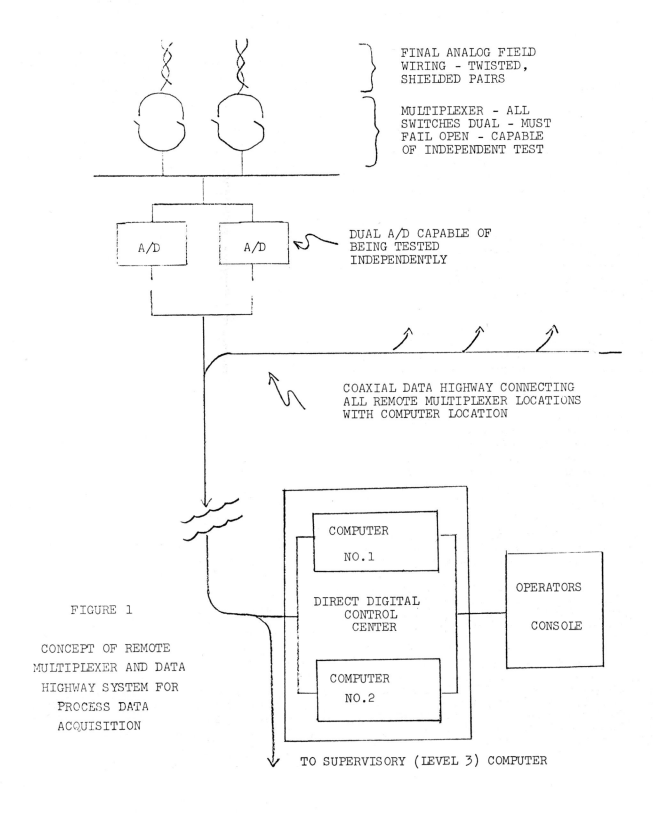

FINAL ANALOG FIELD
WIRING - TWISTED,
SHIELDED PAIRS

MULTIPLEXER - ALL
SWITCHES DUAL - MUST
FAIL OPEN - CAPABLE
OF INDEPENDENT TEST

A/D   A/D

DUAL A/D CAPABLE OF
BEING TESTED
INDEPENDENTLY

COAXIAL DATA HIGHWAY CONNECTING
ALL REMOTE MULTIPLEXER LOCATIONS
WITH COMPUTER LOCATION

COMPUTER
NO.1

DIRECT DIGITAL
CONTROL
CENTER

OPERATORS
CONSOLE

COMPUTER
NO.2

FIGURE 1

CONCEPT OF REMOTE
MULTIPLEXER AND DATA
HIGHWAY SYSTEM FOR
PROCESS DATA
ACQUISITION

TO SUPERVISORY (LEVEL 3) COMPUTER

INTEGRATED NAVIGATION SYSTEMS
FOR THE
VERY LARGE CRUDE CARRIER

Thomas D. Mara
Director, Market Development
Sperry Marine Systems
Sperry Rand Corporation
Charlottesville, Virginia 22901

ABSTRACT

Many advanced "systems" are in use onboard VLCC's, including positioning, collision avoidance, speed logs, and docking systems. However, the coming generation of VLCC are to use integrated systems that incorporate all today's "systems" as subsystems. The integrated system utilizes dual computers with common interface to all subsystems. The results are improved operator information and system availability. System availability as high as 98 percent of ship operating time has been guaranteed with properly designed systems. This paper describes several of today's primary subsystems and an Integrated Navigation System being delivered to Scandinavian Ship operators. The concept of availability and requirements for high system availability are also reviewed.

INTRODUCTION

The state-of-the-art in marine navigation is presently open to innovation and application of advanced techniques for both antigrounding and anticollision. Ship operators have recognized that even the most experienced seaman can and will use every available navigation aid. The very large crude carrier's (VLCC) deck officer is typically a highly trained man with years of experience and proved decision skills. The potential for increased safety and increased operational efficiency outweighs the former traditional conservatism and application of navigational arts. The science of navigation is being formalized. Progressive ship operators have recognized the potential of advanced knowledge of navigation. Advances in the science of navigation are represented through the technology of collision avoidance, speed log, doppler docking, satellite navigation, and Omega.

To date, the number of installations for all these "systems" is in hundreds. Industry recognizes that this technology will continue to develop for several years. Many operators have evaluated equipment representing the new technology over the past several years. These operators have watched the initial problems be overcome and they have seen a need for integrating these equipments to achieve a higher level of navigational science.

To date, marine systems are categorized at three levels of sophistication for convenience. The most basic level of sophistication is the stand-alone system. An example of this system is the Collision Avoidance or Satellite Navigation System. This level is the most common.

The second level of sophistication incorporates multiple "systems" (subsystem) in an integrated system. Typical of these systems is the general purpose computer. The general purpose computer integrates collision avoidance, satellite navigation, speed log, radar, and gyro to provide continuous anticollision and position data.

The third level of sophistication is the system that incorporates all the previous subsystems (previously discussed) and additional navigation subsystems. This level strives for increased reliability through redundancy, provides derivative high order information, and controls ship handling. Doppler docking and Decca Navigator are frequently incorporated in the Integrated Navigation System. These systems improve the restricted water capability of the system. Improved reliability of the system is also achieved through redundancy of fundamental inputs such as dual gyros. Dual computers are frequently incorporated as well. Higher order derivative information (presently "sensed" or calculated by the navigator, such as drift) may be determined from integration of the gyro, doppler docking, and position data. This information can then be displayed to the operator. Finally, system information, such as heading to steer, may be displayed or automatically presented as output to the autopilot.

The third level of system is the system given prime consideration herein. Attention is also given to the new concept of hardware "availability".

The next sections of this paper briefly describe the subsystems of an Integrated Navigation System supplied by Sperry Marine to several Scandinavian ship operators. The concept of availability and the guarantee that Sperry is able to offer, through the use of hardware redundancy, is also outlined in this paper.

Collision Avoidance Subsystem

Sperry has delivered over twenty collision avoidance subsystems, including numerous Scandinavian operators. The photograph presented in Figure 1 shows the system in use aboard a H.M. Wrangell tanker.

In investigations, begun in 1968, it was clear that an immediate presentation of course alternatives was necessary. These course alternatives should be available to the deck officer. Target data, such as course, speed, future position, closest point of approach (CPA), and the like, were only valuable insofar as the data was necessary to determine threat situations and avoidance alternatives.

The objective of the Sperry system is to automatically calculate the point at which own ship could collide with each target, assuming own ship maintained speed, while the target maintained course and speed. In effect, Sperry calculates the intercept point of each target. Conversely, this point is also the avoidance point. This point is then displayed as the end of a true vector orginating at each respective target. As this is the one point that own ship could hit the target, the bearing between own ship and the intercept point is the one course own ship must avoid to avoid a collision.

Sperry enclosed this point of possible collision (PPC) with a danger area that represents the safe passing distance designated by the deck officer. This area is typically elliptical for moving targets and circular for stationary targets. Avoidance of elliptical areas, shown graphically in Figure 2, will result in a safe passing. Should own ship's heading intersect an ellipse, or an intercept point, a potentially unsafe passing or collision exists, respectively. The display concept is illustrated by the target on own ship's forward starboard quarter, which is on a collision course, and the target on the forward port quarter, which will pass within the officer's designated safe passing distance.

The Sperry collision avoidance display presents the threat and the maneuver alternatives simultaneously on one display. No other information is necessary for the officer to determine his alternatives. He must simply select any heading that does not intersect the end of a target vector or the elliptical safe passing distance he has designated.

The computer is continuously analyzing target data and will update the display automatically. Thus, through only two operator actions -- designation of target to be tracked and entry of acceptable safe passing distance -- the computer and display have been harnessed to aid the officer in decision-making.

The system also has a series of alarms to warn of collision danger from tracked targets. A danger area can be selected by the deck officer in which any new target will set off an audible alarm.

One additional display feature allows Sperry to present chart data, such as channel or shoal information, superimposed on the collision avoidance display. This capability aids the deck officer in the selection of collision avoidance maneuvers that are also acceptable for navigation purposes. Figure 3 demonstrates how this concept allows the deck officer to easily determine any avoidance maneuver that will take own ship outside the navigable channel. This display concept is already in use on a Swedish tanker, the "Jarl Malmros". To date, computer programs are already available for primary deep draft ports in Northern Europe, the Malacca Straits, and other areas of the world.

Navigation Satellite Subsystem

The Navy Navigation Satellite System, called Transit, has been available to commercial maritime operators since July 1967. The system consists of 3 elements: the satellites, the ground tracking stations, and the user equipment. At this time, there are five operational Transit satellites. Each satellite is in a circular polar orbit circling the earth at approximately 105 minute intervals.

These satellites transmit continuously at 150 and 400 megahertz. However, the commercial or merchant satellite receiver receives only the single 400-megahertz frequency. The satellite signals are phase modulated with information providing precise time marks and describing the orbital path of the satellite. The radiated power is approximately 1 watt. Four ground stations are used to track each satellite. The tracking data is processed by a ground computer where future orbit predictions are made. This orbit prediction is then transmitted to the satellite, stored in the satellite memory system, and retransmitted continuously by the satellite as it proceeds in its orbit. Fresh orbit prediction data is transmitted to each satellite approximately once every 12 hours.

Shipboard equipment consists of an antenna and receiver, a digital computer, and display system with keyboard and optional teletype. This equipment is completely passive and fully automatic after start up. Transmitted satellite signals are received, decoded, and transferred to the computer. Range changes between the satellite and the ship are computed by measuring the doppler shift of the satellite signal. Computation of a position fix is performed automatically by the digital computer, using the doppler shift data and the decoded satellite message. The fix and time of fix is automatically displayed.

Computation of a precise fix requires that the ship's speed and heading be known accurately and be input to the computer. Inaccurate speed and heading inputs represent the greatest potential source of fix errors. Speed input errors are reflected as fix errors on the order of 120 feet for each 0.1 knot of speed error. Assuming a speed input error of 1/4 knot, a fix accuracy of better than 0.15 nautical miles will be obtained at sea.

Dead-reckoning can be performed by the system continuously. Inputs for dead-reckoning are made automatically through log and gyro interfaces. The time and dead-reckoned (DR) position can be continuously displayed on a cathode-ray tube (CRT) or on a teletype at fixed intervals and on demand. Dead-reckoned position is automatically updated with each new satellite fix.

Program options for this system also include estimated time of arrival (ETA), Great Circle or rhumb line course, and distance to any selected destination. The present DR position is used to continuously compute the above values. This feature can provide a display of any required course change in real-time.

Omega Subsystem

Omega is a long baseline, hyperbolic-line navigation system similar in principle to Loran. Because of very low frequency transmission employed in Omega, baseline lengths are in the order of one-quarter the circumference of the earth (approximately 5400 nautical miles), and propagation is such that only 8 stations are required for worldwide coverage. Current coverage and geographical accuracies are shown in the Omega coverage diagram shown in Figure 4. The 8 stations are identified by the letters A through H, and are located as follows:

Station

A	Norway	Operational at low power (full power in 1973)
B	Trinidad	Operational at 1 kilowatt (full power in 1975)
C	Hawaii, U.S.A.	Operational at 1.5 kilowatt (full power in 1973)
D	North Dakota, U.S.A.	Fully operational at full power.
E	L'Reunion Is.	Operational by 1975.
F	Argentina	Operational by 1974.
G	Australia	Operational by 1975.
H	Japan	Operational by 1973.

Each station will transmit at 10.2, 11-1/3, and 13.6 kilohertz in a specified format. A receiver tuned to a single frequency will receive signals in a preset commutation pattern (Table 1).

Table 1

Omega Commutation Pattern

Station	A	B	C	D	E	F	G	H
Length of Transmission (seconds)	0.9	1.0	1.1	1.2	1.1	0.9	1.2	1.0

In order to prevent ambiguity that would arise if any of the stations radiated more than halfway around the world, the transmission from each station will be tailored to restrict coverage so that at least 2 of the 8 stations will be inaudible at any one point. An Omega receiver must be initially synchronized with the Omega transmitter commutation pattern in Table 1. Circuits can be designed to synchronize a receiver automatically using the basic 10.2, 11-1/3, and 13.6-kilohertz pulse commutation pattern, but the signal levels required for positive automatic synchronization are greater than that for normal manual audio/visual synchronization and receiver operation. Thus, manual acquisition is recommended until station construction is complete.

The lane created by 10.2-kilohertz transmission from a pair of stations is 8 miles wide along the baseline. The resulting coverage pattern is ambiguous every 8 miles, requiring the navigator to know his position with ±4 miles in order to establish an initial lane count on an Omega receiver. If the 13.6-kilohertz carrier is also received, the difference between 13.6 and 10.2 (3.4-kilohertz) establishes a 24-mile lane along the baseline. Omega navigation charts are plotted so that every third 10.2-kilohertz lane is numbered; these numbered lines are also the zero-phase lines for the 3.4-kilohertz difference frequency, and thus identify the 24-mile wide lanes as well.

The Sperry SR-500 Omega Receiver will simultaneously receive signals from any four existing or proposed Omega transmitters and continuously track phase differences of the selected two pairs. The resulting two Lines of Position (LOP's) are displayed on two servo-driven, six-digit counters on the front panel. The internal master crystal oscillator is phase locked (synchronized) to a selected transmitter by a small servo. Use of servos for these functions prevent complete loss of synchronization and LOP data during momentary loss of signal.

To operate the subsystem, the operator first examines an Omega chart for the area of interest and determines the stations he will use. The navigator then positions the station selector switches on the SR-500 receiver for the desired stations. With only minimal experience, the navigator can determine from the chart what audio pattern he will hear -- which stations will have strong signals and which will be weak. Even with eight stations transmitting, the two on the far side of the earth will always be inaudible.

At the time the receiver is initiated in a particular area, the initial lane count corresponding to ship's known position must be obtained and manually set into the LOP counters. This is performed by determining the Omega coordinates of known ship's position from the Omega chart, applying the sky-wave corrections from published tables, and obtaining the resultant lane count. As the lanes are ambiguous every eight miles, the ship's position must be known within ±4 miles (with single frequency reception) in order to determine the correct original lane count.

Having selected the desired stations, the navigator turns on the SR-500 receiver power. He synchronizes to the received signals by releasing the "sync" pushbutton as he hears the audible signal from the station selected to be the master station. One-half hour after synchronization, the receiver "ready" lamp will illuminate, indicating that the receiver is ready for use. Whenever a position fix is desired, the navigator simply reads the two LOP's from the "lanes" counters, adds the sky-wave corrections, and plots the resultant readings on the Omega chart. The intersection of the two lines is own ship's position. A two pen chart recorder is also available to record LOP's and time mark every half-hour.

Doppler Speed Log Subsystem

The Sperry Doppler Speed Log transmits a 2-megahertz signal in a pulse mode and obtains its signals from reflections of the transmitted energy from the natural scatterers in the water mass. This ability gives the speed log an all ocean capability. All other doppler speed logs measures vessel speed relative to the ocean floor that serves as the reflector for the transmitted sonar energy.

The Sperry equipment (mounted in a three-inch gate valve) operates as a water speed log even when other water speed logs (EM, pitot, impeller) must retract their sensing probes and cease to operate. The log automatically switches to bottom lock mode at approximately 10 feet of water below the keel and continues to operate until the vessel has virtually no water remaining beneath the hull.

The Sperry doppler log has an accuracy of 1 percent over the entire speed range. Test data shows that actual performance is in the order of 0.5 percent. The achieved accuracy is obtained without any shipboard calibration as speed data is obtained with respect to water scatterers 10 feet to 15 feet out from the hull. This distance is well beyond the ship's boundary layer and, therefore, calibration is not dependent upon the status of the boundary layer that is affected by draft, fouling, trim, and the like.

The system provides ship speed to the nearest tenth of a knot and distance traveled on three remote displays and the master display. In addition, data transmission is available that provides distance input to a true motion radar at 200 pulses normally opened (NO) or normally closed (NC) relay contact actuations per nautical mile, and digital outputs (binary coded decimal) for interfacing with any navigation, satellite, or other computer.

Doppler Docking Subsystem

Doppler Docking Subsystems are an aid to the captain or pilot of large vessels during low speed maneuvers such as docking or anchoring. The high resolution velocity display, available with this system, is required because the very large mass of the modern supertanker requires approach speeds of such small magnitude as to be nearly imperceptible to the human eye. The system can also supply highly accurate speed over the ground data in restricted water and coastal navigation in water depths of up to 450 and 600 feet.

Two sets of transducers, one located forward and the other aft, measure the total ship velocity component. A fifth transmitting transducer is used to achieve bottom lock at depths greater than 250 feet. Bow and stern velocity are presented digitally with arrows indicating whether the velocity is in a port or starboard direction. Ship velocity, forward or aft, is also presented. Velocity is presented in feet per second, meters per second, or knots. The accuracy of this system is one percent.

The system can drive up to three remote displays that provide information similar to the wheelhouse unit. Outputs for true motion radar and computerized system are also available.

INTEGRATED NAVIGATION SYSTEM

The Integrated Navigation System can be provided in many different configurations. This is obvious if one considers the variety of features available in individual subsystems. Primary differences in system concepts lie in the number of sensors (dual radars, single or dual computer), method of interfacing and interswitching of computer (manual or automatic switchover of computer load at the failure of one computer), and the number of types of displays.

Controversy also exists over the approach to computer utilization. Should the primary bridge functions be stored such that collision avoidance subsystems and positioning subsystems utilize individual computers, leaving the operator to select the more critical function in the event of a single computer failure? Or, should there be sufficient computer memory supplied with both data processors so that all functions are integrated in software and can be performed simultaneously on either of two computers? This would leave the only question - whether both computers should be in use simultaneously or one used as a standby machine. It is felt that these questions will be answered in time through operational experience, as cost should not be a significant factor. At present, it would typically cost 5% or less of the total system cost to provide sufficient computer memory for one machine to perform the total workload, allowing a standby capability.

Sperry has, to date, proposed a rather conservative approach in its Integrated Navigation System to keep costs at a minimum and provide high system availability.

The system, representative of several to be supplied for Scandinavian ship operators, is presented in Figure 5.

The system includes dual radars, gyros, and speed sensors. Without the continual availability of inputs from these sensors, the system capability is seriously degraded. Therefore, the radars have an interswitch capability, and either radar can be selected as the source of collision avoidance data.

The fact that big ships carry both a docking system and a speed log frequently makes alternative speed courses available. Dual gyros also are becoming increasingly common and are highly recommended. Inaccurate heading information makes both collision avoidance and navigation systems useless. It is also recommended that a comparator be fitted to the gyro installation. The gyros can then be monitored automatically and an alarm sounded when a present deviation exists (for example, a 3-degree difference between gyros). The selection of sensor inputs to the computer system is left to the deck officer.

The integrated system also includes dual general-purpose computers. The gyro and log inputs are interfaced to both computers, while the computer interface to radars or navigation receivers can be interswitched by manual changeover.

The basic system concept uses the dual computers for only one subsystem function at any one time, that is, one for position fixing and one for collision avoidance. In the event of a computer failure, only one function can be performed at any one time, requiring a decision of necessity. Tape cassettes, used for program entry, allow rapid entry and change of subsystem programs. Simplicity in system design and high reliability are achieved with this concept.

A more sophisticated system can also be provided to increase system capability in case of computer failure. An increase of computer memory to double the capacity of the basic system, that is, a 16-K memory, will allow fully integrated hardware and software. The higher memory capacity and interface of all sensors to both computers allow one computer to be used as a standby machine, or both computers to be used simultaneously at half capacity until the failure of either computer. The switchover of computers can be automatic, although a manual switch is suggested to keep maximum simplicity and high reliability.

SYSTEM AVAILABILITY

With the redundancy of system elements and interswitching included in the system design, the measure of available is more meaningful than traditional measures such as reliability. Availability takes into consideration the mean-time-between-failures (MTBF) and the mean-time-to-repair (MTTR) as shown in the following formula.

$$\text{Availability} = \frac{\text{MTBF}}{\text{MTBF} + \text{MTTR}}$$

If effect, availability deals with the ship's operational schedule rather than equipment design. If one specifies an availability of 95 percent, the system must be operational 95 percent of a ship's total yearly time underway. If an equipment has a MTBF of 1200 hours, the system could fail in the first hour of a 30-day voyage several times a year.

The Sperry Integrated Navigation System offers a high degree of functional availability. In order to achieve a high availability, the equipment must possess a low failure rate, adequate spares must be available aboard ship, the design must be modular and a crew member must receive special vendor training. This training enables trained onboard personnel the capability to perform normal maintenance. Redundancy of equipment enhances the availability and allows for those instances when onboard repairs become more difficult to implement.

With its present Integrated Navigation System, Sperry has guaranteed several customers an availability of 98 percent. To achieve this level of availability, Sperry has selected components with low failure rates and has run a system burn-in period of 1500 hours to guard against infant mortality. In this burn-in period the system is run under a variety of environmental conditions.

If a component fails, the failure is recorded, the part replaced, and the test resumed. Should the component fail a second time, a new component is selected and the total 1500-hour burn-in test reinitiated. Sperry has also specified the shipboard spares inventory and is responsible for training a crew member. Modular equipment design has been applied in such a manner that spares are minimized, replacement and training simplified. Maximum availability is a function of good design, sufficient predelivery testing, adequate spares, and most important -- training. Only through ease of shipboard replacement can high availability be guaranteed.

Figure 1. Sperry Collision Avoidance System
Onboard H. M. Wrangell Tanker

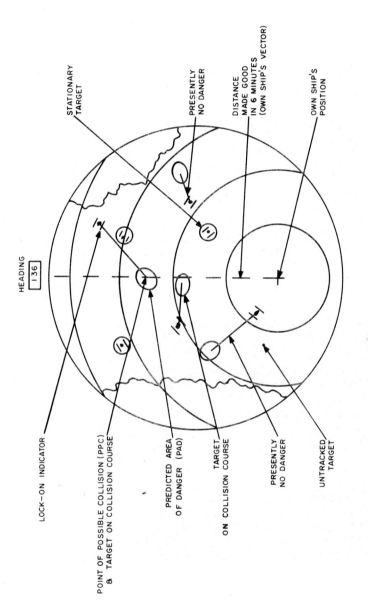

HEADING
136

STATIONARY
TARGET

PRESENTLY
NO DANGER

DISTANCE
MADE GOOD
IN 6 MINUTES
(OWN SHIP'S VECTOR)

OWN SHIP'S
POSITION

LOCK-ON INDICATOR

POINT OF POSSIBLE COLLISION (PPC)
& TARGET ON COLLISION COURSE

PREDICTED AREA
OF DANGER (PAD)

TARGET
ON COLLISION COURSE

PRESENTLY
NO DANGER

UNTRACKED
TARGET

Figure 2.   Sperry Collision Avoidance Display

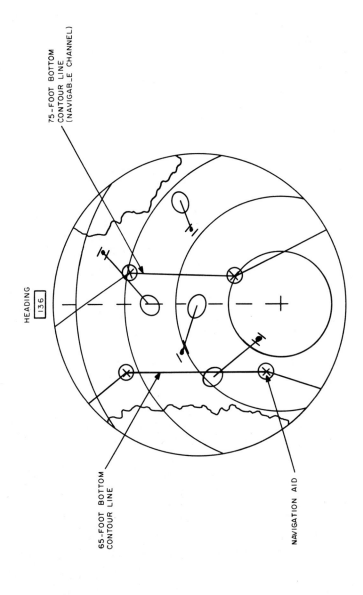

75-FOOT BOTTOM
CONTOUR LINE
(NAVIGAB_E CHANNEL)

HEADING

136

65-FOOT BOTTOM
CONTOUR LINE

NAVIGATION AID

Figure 3. Sperry Collision Avoidance System
With Navigation (Anti-Grounding) Capability

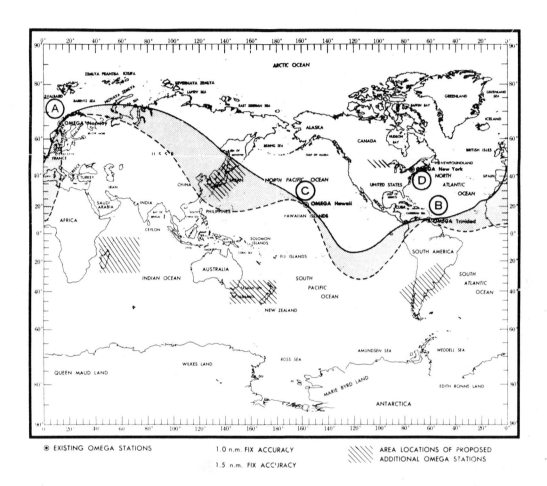

NOTE: Station D has been moved to North Dakota, U.S.A. since this map was prepared.

Figure 4. Omega Coverage Diagram
With Existing Stations

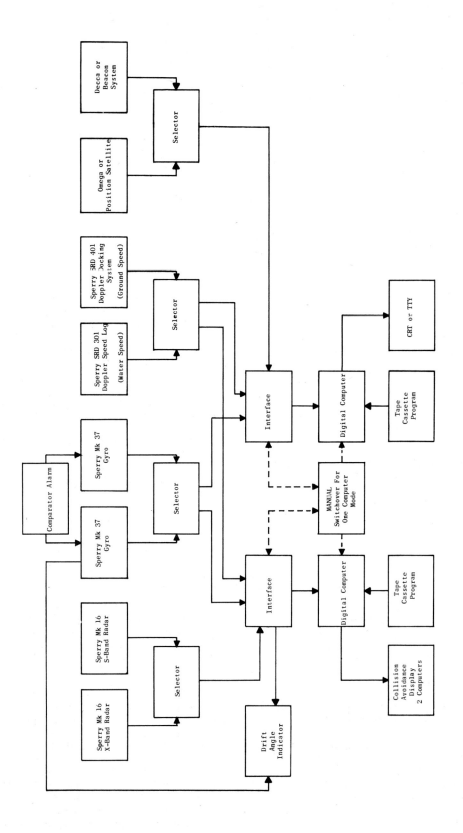

Figure 5. Sperry Integrated Conning System Schematic Diagram

NAVIGATION IN FAIRWAYS

Jan-Erik Öhrström
M. El. Eng.
Kockums Shipyard Inc
Malmoe   Sweden

BACKGROUND

In 1970 Kockums Shipyard Inc started a project
with bridge computer system together with Salén
Shipping Companies. The basic system is now
installed on 4 supertankers and the first system
is sailing since November 1971. The whole scope
of the system is shown on picture 1.

The reasons for projecting this system was

1 Safety and environment protection

   Anti-grounding by a) accurate position find-
                         ing system
                      b) navigation in fairways
                      c) doppler sonar system

   Anti-collision by computer assisted radar
                      system

2 Economy

   Shorter distance by a) accurate position
                          finding system
                       b) automatic great circle
                          navigation
                       c) automatic drift com-
                          pensation

   Higher speed by optimal rudder steering

   Saving of labour by high degree of automation
                         on the bridge

In this paper the project for navigation in
fairways is discussed. This system requires the
function of accurate position finding and of
anticollision and therefore these systems are
described first.

INTEGRATED NAVIGATION

Dead Reckoning

Navigation between the satellite positions is
done with information from doppler log, gyro
compass and calculated drift. With a Kalman
filter an optimal estimation of the position and
its accuracy is obtained. The best information
is automatically used e g owing to the fact that
the computer uses different filter constants,
when the doppler log makes measurements on the
bottom and when it makes measurements on the
mass of water. Furthermore the filter constants
will be changed, when the ship turns.

Satellite Navigation

Signal from "The Navy Navigation Satellite
System" are decoded in a receiver and the computer calculates with this information position
in latitude and longitude. Also the error of the
satellite position fix is computed.

Position Finding by Radar

This feature is described in the chapter navigation in fairways.

It is also possible to find the position by
optical bearings.

Position Filter

When a position fix is obtained, the Kalman
filter weighs the result with the result from
dead reckoning in an optimal way. The new
position is calculated in regard to earlier
measurements and error variances. See picture 2.

Drift Calculations

The drift is estimated from the results of
position filter and dead reckoning. The computer
also automatically corrects for calibration
errors of compass and speed log.

The computed drift is continuously corrected by
the information from the doppler docking system.
Different filter constants are used for bottom
and water track. The computed drift is used by
the dead reckoning program and by the autopilot
program for automatic course correction.

Great Circle Navigation

The great circle to the destination is computed
continuously and is given as set course to the
autopilot program. Maximum 10 destinations may
by fed into the computer via the typewriter.
When a destination is reached, alarm is given and

after the operator's acknowledge a change of course to next destination is performed.

ANTICOLLISION SYSTEM

A separate anticollision system, using its own computer has the following features:

Automatic tracking of 40 targets
Automatic detection of new targets at open sea
Manual tracking
Calculation of closest point of approach, CPA and time to CPA
Presentation on PPI-display of targets future position
Simulation of manoeuvres

The presentation on the PPI-display is shown on picture 3.

NAVIGATION IN FAIRWAYS

The system described up to now is quite sufficient when navigating at open sea. However, it is possible to utilise the computer system also at narrow waters when navigating optically or by means of radar.

Establishing a Fairway

Prior to entering the fairway the boundaires within which the ship must be navigated are taken from appropriate charts.

These boundaries are assumed to be a number of straight lines, see picture 4. The points of intersection of the lines are entered into the computer by means of the typewriter or the tape-reader. Normally these quantities can be determined once and for all and hence a punched tape can be made up for future use.

Position Finding by Radar

A pre-requisitive for the proper functioning of the fairway navigation system is that own ship's position can be obtained accurately and that the accuracy can be kept by repeated measurements or by accurate dead reckoning. See also chapter integrated navigation.

By entering the geographical coordinates for a number of suitably fixed radar targets, the system is intended to be capable of calculating the position by means of measuring range and bearing to such targets. If the targets are sufficiently well defined, the equipment will perform these measurements automatically. If not, the operator has to carry out these measurements manually by placing a special sumbol over the target on the PPI display by means of the joy-stick after which the values are automatically fed into the computer.

PPI Display

On entering the fairways the boundaries are shown on the PPI display, superposed the normal radar picture, thus producing a clear cut picture of the position of own ship in the fairway. A speed vector derived from ship's present speed and course can also be displayed enabling the position after a certain time to be predicted. For estimating the effect of manoeuvres course changes can be simulated by manually entering new courses in which case the displayed speed vector corresponds to this new course.

In addition to providing a graphic and instantaneous picture of the position of the ship, this picture can also be used as a basis for deciding when to start a turn, how to avoid a collision, etc.

The method can be regarded as a form of automatic plotting on the PPI display where the boundaries are intended as lines of reference relative to which the position of the ship is determined.

On the PPI display will be displayed a symbol over one of the entered radar targets. If there is a difference between the actual echo and the displayed symbol the calculated position is wrong and may be corrected by moving the symbol with the joystick until coincidence with the echo.

FURTHER DEVELOPMENT OF NAVIGATION IN FAIRWAYS

Predictor

A predictor can be programmed into the computer. At every sample the differential equations for the ship's motion are solved. The result can be used as information to the helmsman for steering. On a PPI display the future track of the ship is shown as a curve, after which the ship will sail with the actual rudder-angle and propeller rpm. This will give the helmsman information about the ship's dynamics and help him to steer free from the boundaries and other ships.

The predictor can also be used like this. A desired track can be fed into the computer. Alternatively the computer calculates an optimal track according to the actual traffic situation and own ship's position in the fairway. At every point along the track the predictor program solves the differential equations of the ship's motion and calculates the rudder order and propeller rpm so that the ship will follow the track. These values are used by the autopilot and the turbine control program which carry out the order. Also in this case the ordered track is shown as a curve on a PPI display.

Supervision

Alarm can be given e g in the following cases:

The computer is not capable to follow the ordered track accurately enough

Own ship comes too close to the boundaries of the fairway

Simulation

As the computer has information about the limits
of the fairway the voyage through it can be
simulated in advance. The boundaries can be
played up on a PPI display and be up-dated
according to simulated course and speed of own
ship. The operator is then able to make a trial
with manoeuvres along the fairway and check the
consequences.

ARRANGEMENT

To obtain the facilities of navigation in fairways the two computers have been interconnected.
See picture 5.

Distribution of the Functions in the System for
Navigation in Fairways

The A/C computer calculates:

Passing ships' range, bearing, course and speed
Fixed targets   "   "
Collision risk in form of CPA and TCPA
Result of simulation of manoeuvres
Speed vectors of own and other ships

The navigation computer calculates:

Own ship's position via the integrated navigation
system
The placing of lines on the PPI display corresponding to the boundaries of the fairway

Communication

Every 10 seconds the A/C computer sends information about range, bearing, course and speed for
up to 41 targets. This includes also own ship
and fixed targets for position finding. The
reason for chosing 10 seconds' interval is that
the transfer is synchronized to the dead reckoning program which up-dates the position at the
same rate.

With the same frequence the navigation computer
calculates the new placing of the boundaries of
the fairway and transfer the information to the
A/C computer.

The A/C computer has direct memory access for
this transfer while the navigation computer
uses program controlled input/output.

In closing, it is the author's opinion that with
increasing size of ship and higher demand of
safety of environment, the type of systems
described here will be necessary on board.

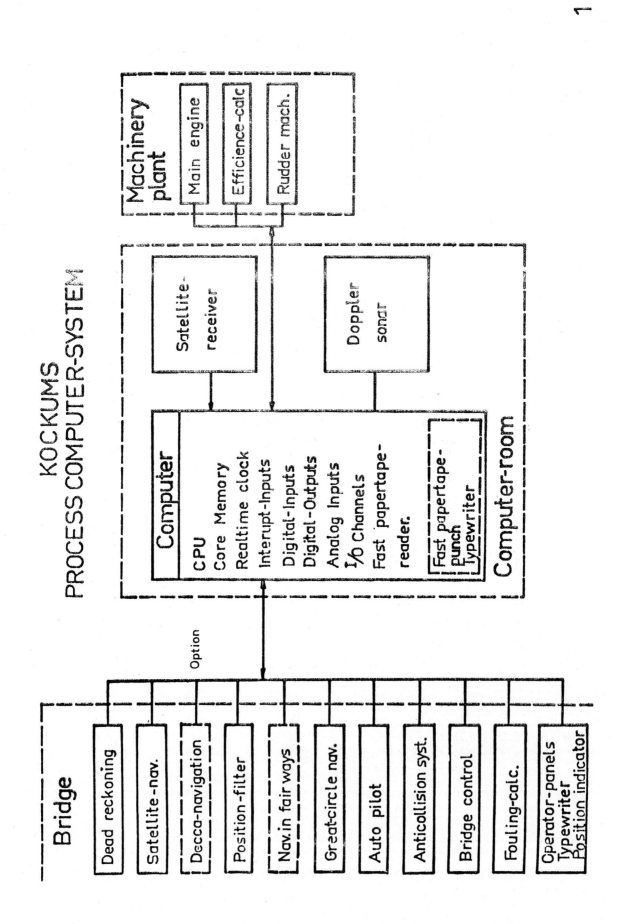

KOCKUMS
PROCESS COMPUTER-SYSTEM

Machinery plant
- Main engine
- Efficience-calc.
- Rudder mach.

Computer-room

Computer
- CPU
- Core Memory
- Realtime clock
- Interupt-Inputs
- Digital-Inputs
- Digital-Outputs
- Analog Inputs
- I/O Channels
- Fast papertape-reader.

Fast papertape-punch
Typewriter

Satellite-receiver

Doppler sonar

Option

Bridge
- Dead reckoning
- Satellite-nav.
- Decca-navigation
- Position-filter
- Nav.in fair ways
- Great-circle nav.
- Auto pilot
- Anticollision syst.
- Bridge control
- Fouling-calc.
- Operator-panels
  Typewriter
  Position indicator

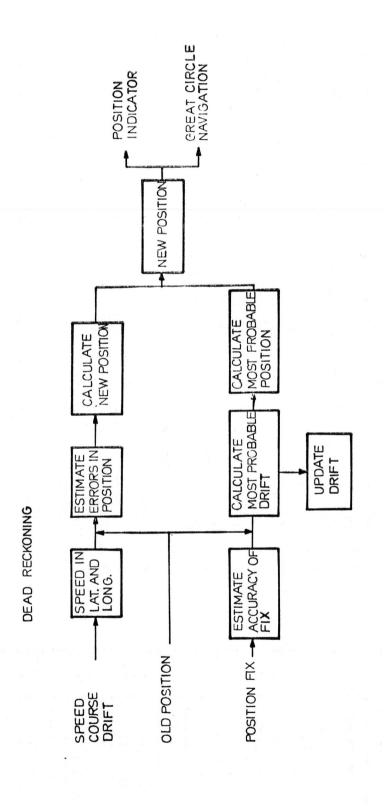

DEAD RECKONING

SPEED
COURSE
DRIFT

SPEED IN
LAT. AND
LONG.

ESTIMATE
ERRORS IN
POSITION

CALCULATE
NEW POSITION

NEW POSITION

POSITION
INDICATOR

GREAT CIRCLE
NAVIGATION

OLD POSITION

POSITION FIX

ESTIMATE
ACCURACY OF
FIX

CALCULATE
MOST PROBABLE
DRIFT

UPDATE
DRIFT

CALCULATE
MOST PROBABLE
POSITION

BLOCK DIAGRAM OF INTERGRATED NAVIGATION

22

3

PPI PRESENTATION: TRUE MOTION
VEKTOR PRESENTATION: TRUE MOTION

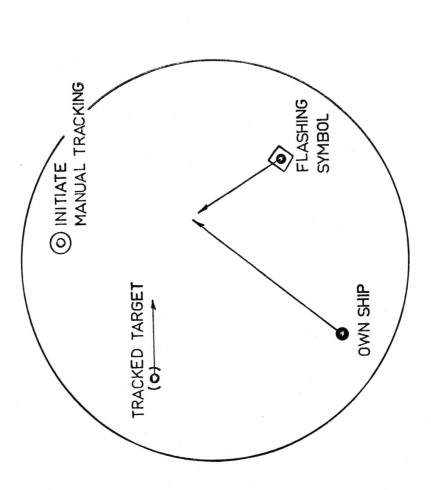

INITIATE
MANUAL TRACKING

FLASHING
SYMBOL

TRACKED TARGET
(o)

OWN SHIP

ANTI COLLISION SYSTEM , VEKTOR PRESENTATION

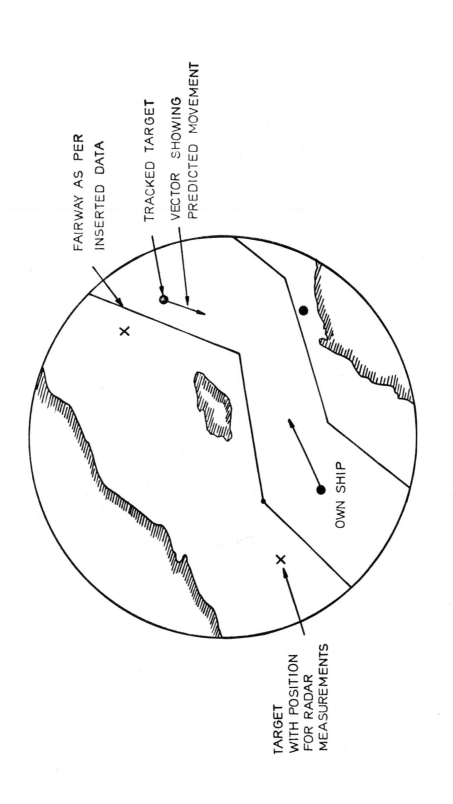

FAIRWAY AS PER
INSERTED DATA

TRACKED TARGET

VECTOR SHOWING
PREDICTED MOVEMENT

OWN SHIP

TARGET
WITH POSITION
FOR RADAR
MEASUREMENTS

NAVIGATION IN FAIRWAYS

ANTI COLLISION
SYSTEM COMPOSITION

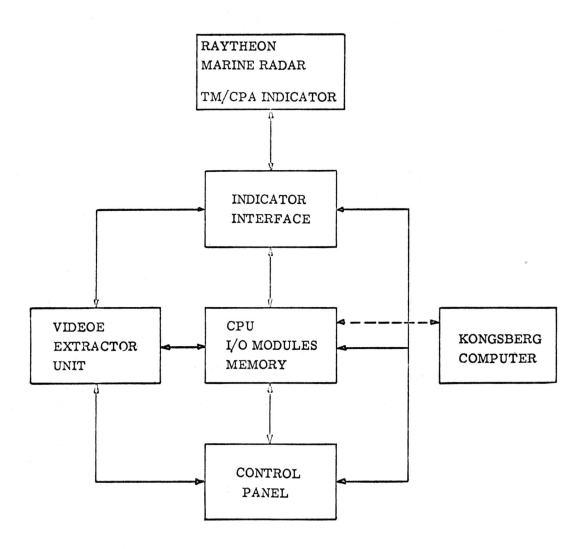

COST BENEFITS ANALYSIS

OF COMPUTER NAVIGATION AND SHIPHANDLING SYSTEMS

Joseph Chernof
Director of International Operations
Automated Marine International
Santa Ana, California, U.S.A.

INTRODUCTION

A commercial shipping fleet is a very large business and therefore quite properly addresses itself to the maximization of investment dollars in automation equipments, considering potential savings in operation, increased operating efficiency, reduced total voyage times, and improved safety factors. National Maritime Administrations, as well as private ship operators, have participated in studies and actual operational evaluations to determine quantitative measures of economic cost benefits of use of advanced bridge automation systems, including complete integrated bridges.

These advanced systems are relatively more costly and/or sophisticated than the present generation of navigation aids and radars, yet appear to offer improved accuracy, geographical coverage, automatic features and other new capabilities as inducements. The problem has been to determine, in a meaningful way, what are the economic benefits of these technological advances traded off against the offsetting cost and complexity factors.

This report and its accompanying slide presentation summarize a number of these evaluations and how the findings can be related to individual shipowner requirements for advanced navigation, docking, collision avoidance radar, and shipboard business systems.

ECONOMIC BENEFITS ANALYSIS

A. Navigation and Shiphandling Systems

A number of studies and actual shipboard trials have been undertaken to accurately determine the present and potential economic benefits to the commercial user of the worldwide, all-weather precision navigation capability available from advanced satellite-dead reckoning navigation equipments, such as the AUTONAV 50, and from integrated satellite-doppler sonar navigation and docking systems such as the AUTONAV 350. As a result of these efforts, three distinct areas of reduction in ship operating costs (and hence increase in profitability) have been identified and separately investigated.

These are:

a) Time and sailing distance saved enroute through accurate navigation to preselected waypoints, and accurate following of a preplanned track (great circle or loxodromic) to the desired destination.

b) Fuel savings, and related reduction in engine wear through the ability to operate at no greater than the speed needed to make the scheduled arrival time. Because the ship has available at all times exact information as to both its present position, and its projected ETA, the ocean passage can be made at a more realistic and economic speed, since no higher speeds are needed to compensate for lack of accurate navigational data.

c) Increased safety, both in the open sea, and during coastal operations, since the satellite-dead reckoning navigation provides a very reliable and accurate independent check on radar or similar navigation aids.

The paragraphs following, taken in conjunction with the technical references cited provide additional data on the probable savings achieveable from the factors listed above.

Time and Sailing Distance Saved

The AUTONAV 50 satellite-dead reckoning navigation system automatically computes the course to steer for great circle navigation to up to 16 preselected waypoints, including the time and distance to each and every waypoint. Further, it provides exact data on the great circle track following performance of the ship, by continuously computing and displaying speed and distance to go both along the desired track, as well as the cross track components. Even taking into account necessary course changes to avoid bad weather, automatic track following great circle navigation provides a significant saving in time/distance sailed. The U.S. Maritime Administration sponsored a year long program to evaluate the savings achieved in recorded tests on the C.V. AMERICAN ARGOSY through the use of satellite navigation. The results [1] exceeded expectations with the time saved estimated as amounting to approximately 10 days per year. Even more interesting is that these savings were achieved with a relatively early type of satellite navigation equipment, which only provided ship's position at the time of satellite passage and did not (as the AUTONAV 50 does) automatically and continuously compute the great circle track (provides course-to-steer to the helmsman) and as a result only improved the deviation from precise great circle navigation from 10 percent to 6 percent. In other words, the vessel still covered 6 percent more distance than required in the correct great circle track. Accordingly, the savings achieved on the AMERICAN ARGOSY were less than half that available from the AUTONAV system, which precisely follows the designated great circle track, and provides optimal steering commands to the ships autopilot.

Related savings, not easily measured except in specific cases, follow from the accurate knowledge of ship's position in coastal areas where ships normally are required to stay well offshore to be absolutely sure of avoiding potential hazards to navigation. Again, this knowledge can be used to steer a shorter track, without risk of grounding.

In the case of vessels which operate on time charter, the savings due to accurate navigation can be recovered from the charterer in the form of higher rates for a better than specified speed made good in exactly the same manner that a charter can presently be assessed for failing to make a contracted speed. The reference 2 paper gives an analysis of the cost benefits, achieved by improving the actual speed made good by a typical tankship. This analysis shows that a net improvement of only 0.20 knots over a nominal 16 knots in speed made good for a 250,000 DWT VLCC operating a 90% utilization factor, chartered at Worldscale 150, generates an annual profit of $220,000 - neglecting savings in fuel consumption.

It should be emphasized that the hard economic justification for the installation and subsequent dependence on these relatively sophisticated navigation systems ultimately relates back to operating costs saved on a per-day basis through reduction in time spent enroute. Data derived to date from all available sources indicates a range of from 1% to 3% for this parameter which, assuming a very conservative 70% yearly vessel at-sea utilization factor (excludes both time in port and time out of operation for maintenance), equates to a range of roughly 2.5 to 7.5 days saved per year.

Finally, what does this sort of saving mean in terms of justifying the purchase of $25,000 - $35,000 worth of complex equipment? The answer, of course, lies in relating operating days saved to individual vessel/fleet per day operation costs. These latter data are unfortunately not readily available, however, a very recent paper, reference 3, gives the figure of $18,500 per day for a typical tankship, which is very close to owner-private data recently made available to the writer. It can therefore be concluded that computer navigation aids, providing that they are reliable and inexpensive to maintain, can easily achieve payoff within one year of ownership.

Fuel Savings

Several types of ship operations normally require making landfall, entering a tidal estuary, or reaching dockside at a prearranged time. Passenger ships, for example, must make connections with other transportation facilities, while container-ships must make connections with available unloading equipment and dockside manpower. Timeliness is frequently not as critical for tanker operators, however, the failure to make the tide when approaching port can cause undesirable delay and increased operating costs. Typically, ships required to meet fixed schedules have been operated at higher than required speeds during most of the voyage, to guarantee prompt arrival. Then, frequently, the speed was reduced during the last day or so, whenever an accurate estimate of ship's position could be obtained. A graphic example of this amount of the fuel savings realized on the QUEEN ELIZABETH 2, as a result of exploiting the accuracy and reliability of satellite navigation to work out the optimum speed of the ship, allowing for the expected weather conditions, at all times. In the case of the QUEEN ELIZABETH 2 [4], the savings during its first North Atlantic season (1969) were worked out to be £ 4000, even at approximately one-half of current fuel costs. Again, these savings were achieved using an earlier type of satellite navigation equipment, and would be significantly increased by the automatic continuous route following capabilities of the AUTONAV system. Another form of fuel savings available from the AUTONAV 50 and AUTONAV 350 is the ability to sense and measure the effects of water currents, permitting the navigator to change routing to take advantage of favorable currents, or to avoid unfavorable currents. The latter is particularly important in areas such as the Malacca Straits, where actual currents vary significantly from predicted values.

The AUTONAV 50 and AUTONAV 350 automatically compute and display Set and Drift for use in this matter, in addition to correcting the dead reckoned track.

B. Collision Avoidance Systems

Savings through the successful introduction of equipments which improve the operational safety of the ship, particularly in the sense of avoiding collision or stranding, are difficult to evaluate in a purely deterministic, as contrasted with statistical, financial sense. This is similar to analyzing the economic benefits of carrying insurance, which are not apparent, until an actual accident occurs. One major oil company approached this problem by totaling all the losses from collision and stranding for tankers during a given year and prorating these losses by number and type of ship to its own fleet.

In this analysis, the fleet totalling 86 ships averaged 12 substantial collisions each year, which is a 14 percent rate. The average cost of repair was $136,000 for each collision. The ships were out of service an average of 23 days. Using this fleet's average operating loss of $7,500 per day, the total loss was $172,000 per accident. If the losses are amortized over 86 ships, the net loss per ship is approximately $43,000 per year. If we estimate that COMAN would very conservatively result in a 50 percent reduction in probability of collision, then the potential savings per ship are $21,500 annually. These losses per accident do not reflect the complete picture if one considers the tanker and supertanker fleets, for the costs in penalties and cleanup of cargo spillage, and related ecological damages can overshadow operating and repair losses. Also, the $7,500 per day loss factor is based on relatively small existing vessels and as previously noted, is not appropriate to the VLCC class of vessel.

Another graphic example was the recent case of the grounding of a supertanker in fairly good weather, due to the incorrect interpretation of a radar fix by the officer on watch. This would have been avoided, had a satellite position fix been available as an independent check on ship's position. In this case, the damage to the ship exceeded several million dollars, and the ship was out of operation for approximately six months due to the unavailability of repair facilities.

Reference 5 defines some of the existing problems and findings of previous research as to necessary information and display presentation to increase the effectiveness of conning operations. This study, which simulated total bridge operation for a Dover Strait to Rotterdam situation, determined that personnel could handle no more than one new potential threat every 10 minutes, with a maximum of 8 - 10 targets under observation on the eight mile radar scale.

Quantitative tests to evaluate savings resulting from improved conning operations are difficult to implement, since it is practically impossible to set up a control situation. In other words, tests of collision avoidance aids on the basis of extracting a measure of reduction of risk of collision cannot be implemented in a direct way, since by definition a collision had better not occur with or without the aid.

For this reason, evaluation of the efficacy of radar collision avoidance aids has proceeded along the lines of

a) determining reduction in operator work load and

b) determining improvement in operator performance relative to manual reflection plotting of radar targets.

In a typical series of quantitative tests performed using the MDS COMAN system on a handy-size tanker (see reference 6 for complete details) it was determined that in 30 seconds to two minutes time from target acquisition, the computer-aided collision avoidance system could automatically display all significant target parameters. In comparison, manual plotting to derive the same target parameters to the same degree of accuracy, when performed at all, was found to take from six to twelve minutes.

C. Other Computer Applications

The historical development of computers has had the business community as one of its leaders. Computers are used for the many accounting, payroll, inventory control, etc., functions of a modern business. In today's economics, a ship also represents a business plant, capitalized at from $10,000,000 to $90,000,000, which is also part of a larger organization, under control of the fleet operations offices and related port offices.

There are many applications for shipboard business programming systems for which fleet operators are able to economically justify a dedicated mini-computer on board each ship. The general purpose computer used in the navigation or collision avoidance system can be used for these other tasks with minimal additional capital investment, namely, software and an input/output terminal (usually provided with the basic system). AMI is under contract to develop a loading/unloading stress analysis program for use on board a fleet of tank-ships which are already outfitted with AUTONAV 350 Integrated Docking and Navigation systems. Providing this additional capability does not interfere with the primary navigation and docking functions of the system, as these tasks are being performed during port time. As the capabilities and computational power of these small computers are made known to operating personnel, + applications will increase and the system computer will be utilized for varying functions during all of the four phases of the voyage, open sea, confluence area or coastal waters, harbor entry and dockside time.

The addition of the doppler sonar docking and ship-handling capability, which permits precise accurate maneuvering of supertankers, thus avoiding damage during docking and berthing operations, can be similarly justified.

SUMMARY

Data has been gathered from existing cost-benefit studies, and independent operational tests which substantiates the economic returns from individual computerized navigation, shipbuilding and collision avoidance systems. The MDS Division of AMI has developed a complete Integrated Conning System, under the sponsorship of the U.S. Maritime Administration, which integrates all bridge navigation, control, safety, and monitory functions through dual redundant computers. This Integrated Conning System has been installed aboard the American Export Lines' containership EXPORT FREEDOM and is currently undergoing test and evaluation to determine the resulting improvement in operational capability, safety, reliability, and ship manning characteristics. The results of this test and evaluation can be expected to further extend our knowledge in this area.

REFERENCES

(1). Kolbe, Capt. W. (U.S. Lines) and Seelinger, J.
     (U.S. Maritime Administration), "Evaluation
     of the Economic Benefits of Satellite Naviga-
     tion on a Fast Containership," Institute of
     Navigation, September 1971.

(2) Johansson, L., ASEA (Now with Salen Shipping
     Company), "Computer Systems On Board Ships,"
     FCKS, 1.3.71.

(3) "Clean Hulls Means Increased Profit,"
     Marine Engineering Log, 3 May 1973,
     PP. 40-41.

(4) Smith, H. L. (Cunard Lines), "Operational
     Experience with Satellite Navigation Systems,"
     British Institute of Navigation, 1971.

(5) "Definition of Collision Avoidance Require-
     ments," Safety at Sea International, June,
     1971, PP. 14-19.

(6) Mara, T. D., MDS (Now with Sperry Gyroscope
     Co.), "Operational Specification for Marine
     Collision Avoidance Systems," RTCM, April 1972,
     Proceedings.

STANDARDIZATION OF NAVIGATIONAL AIDS
AND BRIDGE SYSTEMS (NAV)

Odd J. Tveit, Svein Bjørnebekk and Gunnar Verlo

Det norske Veritas

Oslo, Norway

ABSTRACT

This paper deals in general with standardization and of navigational aids and bridge systems in particular. Examples of factors involved in standardization are given. A specification (NAV) for navigational aids is developed. It discusses important properties and aims of the NAV-specification. A description of the minimum standard and additional systems or standards is given. Particulars of the NAV-concept are discussed and illustrated by examples.

INTRODUCTION

The need to lay down standards can be found at all levels of social activities, beginning with the individual who formulates his own particular requirements.

Within shipping, the following typical levels are found:

- Standardization within one ship, one object for instance being to reduce the number of spare parts.

- Standardization within one shipping company, one reason being to simplify education and training of personnel.

- Standardization within a shipyard, one important object being design and production rationalization.

- Standardization within each equipment manufacturer, much with the same motivation as for instance the shipyard.

- National standards.

- International standards, such as IMCO, ISO, IEC etc.

- The requirements of the classification societies.

STANDARDIZATION AND BRIDGE SYSTEMS

Standardization may be applied to a product at different levels of an installation:

- at the part level (like a connector or a resistor)
- at he component or unit level (like an amplifier or a printed circuit),
- at the subsystem level (like a collision avoidance system),
- at the system level (like a bridge system).

An owner's specification or standard typically deals with problems on the system and subsystem level and scarcely on the part or component level.

Time for standardization

Some people say it is always too early to fix a standard and always too late. Too early because subsequent experience or technological advances may make a decision of today obsolescent, too late because existing practice already has diverged from the standard about to be set up.
However, the time aspect will manifest itself very different in a "local" standard like a yard standard compared to an international standard; the latter being comparatively much more time-consuming to establish and to change.

Implications of standardization

Standardization of course has its merits and demerits. The disadvantages are most apparent when a certain standard is forced or requested upon a party whose own standard is different.

A standard for bridge systems should to some degree be of benefit to:

- the shipowner,
- the navigating staff (ship's mates, pilots etc.),
- the shipbuilder,
- the equipment manufacturer.

To what extent a given specification or standard will be beneficial, depends mainly on:

- the way the specification is written, - the details of the requirements or recommendations,
- the way these recommendations are introduced and applied in practice.

Evidently it is possible, and indeed an easy task, to write a specification which is disadvantageous to all parties.

THE NAV SPECIFICATION

The NAV-proposal defines a basic part or minimum standard which is set approximately at the level of a modern, well equipped merchant ship of today. However, a collision avoidance system, a harbour manoeuvring system and a navigation system (special parts) are defined in order to cover ships equipped at a higher level.

Important features of the specification:

- Reliability and availability analyses on the system and subsystem level.
- Specification of environmental strains, and testing of performance under specified environmental conditions.
- Monitoring of performance during operation with alarm when the system has failed.
- Performance testing of the completed NAV system.

The NAV-concept mainly aims at filling a need of the shipowner and could replace or supplement the shipowner's specification. Along with the standard follows of course a staff of specialists within the technical and navigational diciplines which apply. The average shipping company will normally not keep a staff to cover these fields.

Other noteworthy properties of the NAV concept are:

- NAV is not in opposition to existing IMCO-resolutions and recommendations. In most areas where they overlap, they are either in accordance or NAV is more specific.
- Other standards are applied as far as practicable, for instance IEC-standards for environmental testing.
- To a very small extent NAV goes into constructional details, however, without limiting the freedom of the designer. This is obtained by mostly formulating functional oriented criteria. Exceptions are mainly in the field of ergonomics or man-system relations.

Drawings, reliability and environmental conditions

The drawings specified should give information about the NAV-system and parts thereof. It usually pays well at this stage as far as possible to see if the NAV-system concerned meets the requirements set by the NAV-specifications.

The proposal emphasizes reliability and availability of the systems. Evaluation of failure modes and effect analyses (FMEA) is used to state the reliability of a NAV-system. The FMEA gives a description of the failure modes of the main components regarding the functional objects and a description of the corresponding failure effects. In an extended NAV-system (fig. 2) the analyses are more comprehensive than the basic NAV-system (fig. 1).

It is implied that navigational aids are designed to stand up to the severe environmental conditions onboard. The criteria in NAV are mainly the same as those for the engine room except vibration criteria.

Bridge arrangement

Thought is given to the part which a proper layout of bridge instrumentation can play in safety improvements. However, there is little evidence available to show how much or how little poor bridge layout is responsible with respect to collision and foundering. No doubt the bridge should command a good field of vision day and night.

In order to meet the specification one may slope the windows in the wheel house forward and install equipment such as window wipers, rotating windows, window washing arrangement and defrosting equipment. As regards bridge layout the arrangement of equipment in functional groups is emphasized, for instance manoeuvring, navigation and monitoring in separate groups.

Basic NAV equipment/systems

The basic part of NAV comprises the following systems and equipment:

- position - fixing system,
- autopilot,
- gyro compass,
- 2 radars,
- echo sounder,
- speed log,
- internal communication system,
- alarm system.

An example of the basic NAV equipment and their interconnections is shown in fig. 1.
The Decca system is considered to satisfy the requirement to position fixing in certain congested waters, e.g. the English Channel. In choosing an autopilot emphasis is put on reliability and operational aspects. Adaption to the ship's steering characteristica is an important feature as the autopilot is one of several parts in a control loop. Other parts are the steering gear and the ship itself. Because it is important to have one radar operational at all times, at least two radar sets are included in the basic NAV-system.

With regard to radar and echo sounder the specification is considered to cover at least the requirements set by IMCO.

The extent of monitoring of the NAV-system is decided from the failure mode and effect analysis and monitoring specified in the respective sections.

All units and systems in a NAV-system are preferably monitored by a centralized alarm system, fig. 3. Alarm is given for an abnormal condition such as one of the following:

- power failure,
- high temperature,
- deviation between two compasses,
- deviation between set course and sailed course,

Additional systems.

In addition to the basic NAV equipment the NAV-system may include some specialized systems as:

- collision avoidance system,
- harbour manoeuvring system,
- navigation system.

Example of a NAV-system including the collision avoidance system, the navigation system and their interconnection is shown on fig. 2.

The object of the collision avoidance system is to provide the officer on watch with information on the traffic situation in a manner which aids him in the navigation and the prevention of collisions. The collision avoidance system defined in NAV, predicts the future traffic situation. Many mathematical computations are involved in prediction

process, and usually one will find a digital computer in existing collision avoidance systems.

Ships which dock frequently like container ships and VLCC's and which are very difficult to manoeuvre, may require additional equipment for the docking operation. In the NAV-system this equipment, or harbour manoeuvring system, mainly comprises a log which measures the athwartship's velocity and fore- and aft velocity in relation to the sea bottom.

Presently, there is only one global navigation system in operation, and that is a satellite system. In the future, one may expect that the Omega system will be operational on a world wide basis. The navigation system defined in the NAV-specification is a global system which determines the position of the ship in terms of latitude and longitude. Additionally, it is an aid in computing great circle course and distance. Features such as estimated time of arrival, turnpoint and input to autopilot may be added to the system.

Manoeuvrability

The NAV specification include extensive manoeuvring tests. The purpose of the manoeuvring tests is to give the officer on watch all necessary information concerning the manoeuvrability of the ship, and to obtain the greatest possible value from the collision avoidance system and the autopilot.

The following tests are included in NAV:

- Turning tests to port and starboard.
- Spiral tests.
- Z-manoeuvre test.
- Stopping tests.
- Speed trials.

Testing

The testing of the total NAV-system onboard is given considerable significanse. During the building period the installation and assembly should be followed up in order to ensure the necessary quality of work. Before being put into operation, each unit or system is subject to a complete functional test.

The individual criteria for functional accuracy should be checked as well as the monitoring annunciating facilities for the respective units.

DISCUSSION OF SELECTED TOPICS

Collision avoidance systems

The proposed specification of a collision avoidance system can be taken as an example of a "frame specification" with a specified system purpose. One limit is the performance criterion defining the the function for predicting the motion of objects being tracked.

In principle different configurations can be accepted such as:

- manual acquisition and automatic acquisition;
- possibilities for display of simulated future situations and continuously display of possible collision areas;
- raw video presentation and synthetic generated situation picture.

It seems likely that the reliability criteria will be stronger for collision avoidance systems displaying only synthetic generated information than for system configurations presenting raw video as basic information.
Regarding presentation modes the navigator must not be mislead in mixing real situation with simulated situation and true vectors with relative vectors. The effect of such misinterpretations could cause hazardous situations. Consequently, there will be criteria for unambigous indication of which mode is in use.

Radars and gyros

From studies of reliability and availability of bridge systems, two complete radar sets are specified - a practice which is followed by a lot of shipowners today.

The principle of redundancy is also applied to obtain sufficient availability with regard to gyrocompasses in connection with extended NAV systems. The sub-systems using the ship's course as input information may in such a case be:

- collision avoidance system,
- navigation system,
- radars,
- autopilot.

In most cases a gyro failure has to be repaired by a shore specialist which means that down-time for the heading information source can be of long duration. The effect of such a failure will be partial or total loss of important functions which operational routines are based on.

Monitoring

The overall monitoring functions of the NAV-systems are considered to be an essential feature of the specification.

One principle in the monitoring concept is to compare information taken from independent sources. An example is alarm given for course deviation between two gyro compasses. Another example is deviation in determining the position of the ship which can be:

- calculated by means of course and speed
- determined by a satellite position fixing system.

When the principle of comparison can be applied the total chain of system functions will be monitored. This can also be achieved by monitoring the performance of a system.

To apply this principle in its full extent may be prohibitively costly in some cases. An example of this is radar performance monitoring. A "total-chain" monitoring should include for instance a fore-mast installed transponder which is an investment few shipowners would find reasonable compared to the benefits achieved. A compromise solution will be monitoring relevant parameters within the radar, a solution which is selected in the NAV-specification.

Computers

The most comprehensive, complex single unit used in the NAV-systems will normally be a computer or a similar unit.

The failure mode and effect analysis on this unit will determine the extent of the monitoring of the computer itself. The effect of a failure, e.g. internal power failure can be extensive with a large number of tasks connected to the computer.

Consequently, special measures have been taken in the specification to reduce the failure effects.

As an example autopilot tasks on a computer for several functions will have to have a back-up autopilot functionally independent of the computer.

CONCLUDING REMARKS

In the preceding text we have tried to outline some of the basic philosophy behind the NAV-principles as well as to give closer description of the NAV-concepts.

NAV is a proposed technical specification of navigational aids and bridge systems. The basic NAV "package" comprises those minimum requirements a standard for any modern, well equipped merchant ship ought to contain. However, the basic principles can be extended, if one wishes to do so, and the specifications are written to cover additional specialized systems.

Some new consepts have been introduced in the NAV-principles as compared to the traditional rules, namely reliability and availability of the systems. It is felt that requirements based on these important properties, together with system specifications, thorough testing and survey during building and operation, makes the NAV-principles fill the need for standardization and quality assurance of bridge systems aboard.

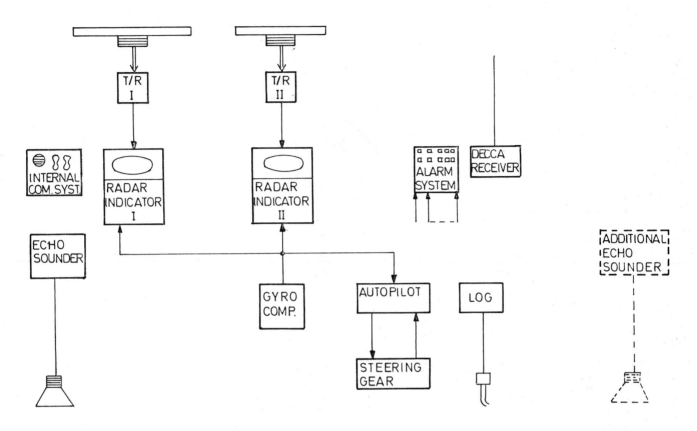

FIG. 1. EXAMPLE OF EQUIPMENT AND SYSTEMS IN A BASIC NAV-SYSTEM

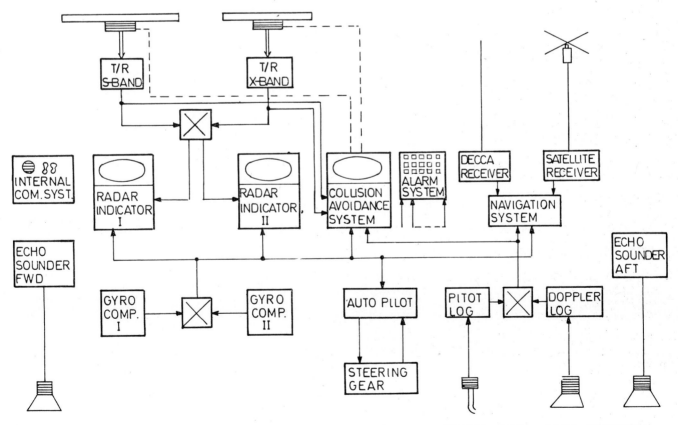

FIG. 2. EXAMPLE OF EQUIPMENT AND SYSTEMS IN AN EXTENDED NAV-SYSTEM

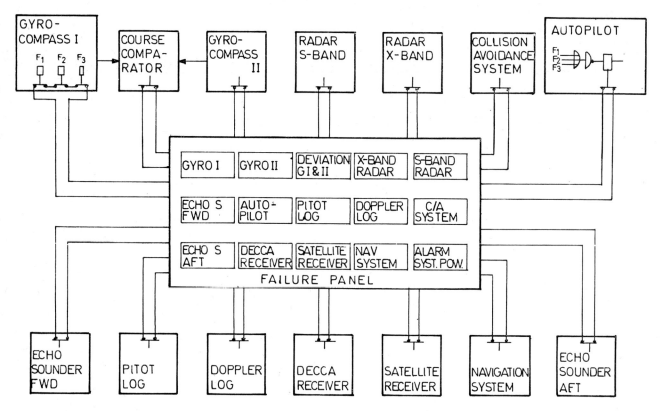

FIG. 3. EXAMPLE OF A CENTRALIZED NAV-ALARM SYSTEM

OPERATIONAL AND ORGANIZATIONAL PROBLEMS REGARDING

CENTRALIZED CONTROL OF A HIGHLY AUTOMATED SHIP

Per-Olov Bjurström

Captain B.A.

The Swedish Shipowners' Association

ABSTRACT

Smaller crews will mean greater automation and more complex technology on board ship.
Sophisticated control engineering is a precondition for the use of this technology. Such systems also provide increased safety for the ship and crew, as well as improved operating economy.

Control engineering systems and computers, used as controlling agents in various processes, constitute that part of technical development which most tangibly influences the work situation of the individual.

The automation of operations at a place of work very often means a reduced labour requirement - but it also means the elimination of monotonous, noisy and dirty jobs. For the individual, automation means a new working situation, a new environment, new and different training requirements and, possibly, also an opportunity for a new freedom at work. Well-developed automation also influences a variety of factors such as safety, economy, laws and regulations, organization development, etc.

The development of automation affects the majority of man-machine relationships wherever an automated operation has a direct significance for the individual's psychological or social situation on board.

INTRODUCTION

Control engineering systems can generally be divided into systems of a completely closed type, systems which are activated by an operator, passive information systems and systems which inform an operator when certain incidents occur.

These classifications are intended to indicate the degree of autonomy of different systems, i.e. their degree of inde-pendence from the operator, or vice versa.

When such control engineering systems are discussed, two questions are of primary interest:
- the need for and benefits of various functions
- technical feasibility of solving various functional problems

For a broad documentation of the first aspect it is necessary to co-operate with specialists in other disciplines, such as navigators, machine manufacturers, hydro-dynamics engineers. The second aspect will be discussed in this context.

Technical aims for the control engineering system should be based on factors such as the desired function of the ship, the human being as a control component, available technical knowledge and apparatus, costs, and legally regulated aspects such as environment and safety.

The technical aids, in the form of automation and information processing systems, which have been put into service hitherto aim primarily at relieving humans of routine supervision and other duties which could be handled as well, or better and more dependably, by machines and instrumentation. The task of the individual is then restricted to ensuring that the existing situation is normal, and that the aids which are available are operating in a proper manner. One of the advantages is that the human factor can be eliminated as a source of error, at the same time as the individual can act as a "re-insurance" for the automation.

The simplification of the operation of a ship presupposes a common control centre for machinery and navigation. This leads in turn to requirements for the uniform construction of automatic controls for all purposes on board. In other words, various systems which hitherto have been regarded as completely separate should in the future be integrated. Integration should comprise both performance and user aspects, as well as apparatus and component construction aspects. These latter aspects should be included to simplify care, maintenance and fault finding.

SYSTEMS DEVELOPMENT

Development of new systems is at present generally based on the willingness of individual companies to invest in a new product, or the availability of development funds from government or semi-government organs. These methods involve a number of weaknesses. First and foremost, the result is a variety of different systems which stipulate differing requirements as regards installation, commissioning servicing and maintenance, as well as giving poor adaption with regard to the meshing of the different apparatus in the functioning of the ship. In the future, it will be necessary to carry out development under uniform organization and control. The aim should be to integrate all controlling, regulating and monitoring equipment on board, so that the functioning of this equipment will be uniform from both ecological and service aspects. This requires a comprehensive effort and a great deal of work, which cannot be undertaken by any individual company.

MAN-MACHINE RELATIONS

Developments should be based on the rational feedback of experience. By this is meant that methods, problems and working methods which have applied hitherto in ships, should be analyzed and systematically employed as a basis for the new system. The aims adopted in the solution of problems should also be based on the anticipated level of knowledge of those who will look after the system.

The human factor plays a large role in the casualties which occur at sea. All too often, when a potential accident situation arises, the accident occurs despite the presence of the responsible operator. For various reasons, he enters a state of mental stress which affects his opportunities of acting rationally, a situation which could be avoided if he were able to evaluate the situation calmly as early as possible. One way of reducing this undesirable risk is to automate to a higher degree such functions as the navigation of the ship, to improve the flow and display of information for the operator, so that he may reach his decision at an earlier stage and on a better basis.

ECONOMIC ASPECTS

Cost-wise, it may be anticipated that the control engineering systems of tomorrow will be more expensive than is acceptable today. However, the ships of the 1980s will be considerably more cost-intensive than those of today, and for that reason they will also be able to bear a higher cost for control and monitoring equipment. For some years there has been a trend towards lower-priced electronics and other equipment, it is true. But the performance requirements stipulated for shipboard automatic controls will be sharpened at a faster rate, so that the total cost is nonetheless likely to rise.

AN INTEGRATED SYSTEMS APPROACH

A highly automated ship system could be constructed around six sub-systems:
- bridgesystem
- engine room system
- cargo handling system
- deck system (mooring etc.)
- security system and
- communications system.

These six systems are envisaged as being under the control of a central superior computer. In normal operation the central computer will have an administrative controlling role, but be able to act as replacement for the sub-systems in the event of breakdowns. However, just as the central computer should be capable of taking over the important functions of the specialized units, so must each of the six sub-systems be able to operate without the supervising computer. In this way, the necessary degree of redundance is secured, this being supplemented by the watchkeeping operator. The system should not be regarded as a separate working unit, but should be in contact with the shore organization via a communications link. The central computer must have access to a comprehensive library of programs, including programs for stand-by operation instead of the various sub-systems.

The core memory of the central computer will contain the operational system which must always be in effect.

Thus the central computer will comprise the following systems components:
- operational system
- supervisory program and
- mass memory with programs for stand-by procedure for other computers.

This brings us to the point where we can analyse in greater detail the principles which should form the basis of a cockpit organization.

PRINCIPAL ASPECTS OF A COCKPIT ORGANIZATION IN SHIPS OF TOMORROW

If one ignores costs, laws and statutes and, to a certain extent, safety, contemporary technology already permits automation to be carried to any stage. The problems associated with the operators' role in this context have attracted attention, particularly with regard to the need for training and for meaningful duties. On the other hand, the chances of the operator dependably interpreting information and taking the right action in various situations has seldom been placed in doubt. In consequence, the possibilities of, or need to, develop new principles for the actual control logics (interface between operator and technical system) have therefore not been sufficiently examined.

The concepts of control logics and control systems are of central importance in this connection. The starting point is found in the problems which the operator encounters when, under particularly variable conditions, he must efficiently and dependably employ a specific system comprising control devices and display equipment. The design of the system may easily become a compromise in which responsibility for the mutual adaption of operator and technical system is largely transferred from the design office to the people who happen to man the operations centre. The result can be that the operator must be required to have an alertness and an ability to remember and revise information which is in poor agreement with the intensity of his normal duties. Such a situation can give rise to a sequence of events created by the notorious human factor.

Specific control logics should be elaborated with a view to achieving adaption between the operator, in changing situations during the voyage, and the system he is expected to operate reliably. Only in this way can the requirements which the operations centre must satisfy with regard to the environment safety and varying technical complexity be satisfied. In order that the control logics shall be capable of adapting the working of the control devices and the display equipment to the actual situation of the operator and the ship, it must be programmable with parameters characteristic of the situation. A solution implies, popularly speaking, that the control logics system works somewhat like a telephone exchange which, after a certain situation has been identified and "dialled", transmits control signals and information between control devices suited to the operator on the one hand, and the technical systems which are to be influenced on the other hand.

The situation description used for programming of the control logics is arranged in steps, where each step comprises alternative states and is ranked relative to the others.

Ranking means that state A in stage 2 for instance, can have different situation implications, depending on the state obtaining in stage 1. The implication of the state in stage 3 will be similarly dependent upon the settings in stages 1 and 2.

The example of ranked, programmable control logics, given in the picture above comprises four stages, where the first three stages are manually connected by the operator, while the final stage allows for an automatic re-connection where required by sudden and unexpected changes in critical technical parameters for example. The practical implications of the different stages will be briefly dealt with in the following. It should be noted at the same time that a systemic step-by-step construction of the situation in which the operations centre must be able to function can be utilized for the evaluation of existing control systems, just as well as for the design of new ones.

The description of the different stages given below is meant as an example only, simply to demonstrate the principle under discussion. The final technical shape of the system could involve a different number of stages and perhaps also different sub-divisions.

Stage 1: Tactical Environment

During the voyage of a vessel from one port to another, and also during the stay in port, there is a sequence of occurences which all place different demands on the control system and the fuctioning and preparedness of the operator in the system. These stages can be said to constitute the ingredients in the tactical environment of the ship.

The following can be mentioned as examples of various states at this stage of the situation description:
- Ocean passage
- Navigation in congested areas
- Landfall
- Navigation in narrow channels
- Manoeuvering in port
- Mooring
- Loading - discharging
- Lying at anchor

The Stage 1 connection can be illustrated as a "changeover switch" controlled by one operator and with settings corresponding to states of the types indicated above. The setting in Stage 1 is a formal statement that a certain tactical situation should be considered to exist. As a result, suitable controls, displays, alarm and other signals are distributed through the control logics to the human or humans in the system. The operator is thus put by the control logics into the degree of contact with the technical systems which is necessary with regard to the situation - but neither more nor less. However, the exact implication of this depends upon, and is influenced by, the actual state in the following stages.

Stage II: Operator state

In other contexts it has been suggested

that, as part of the routine on board, the operations centre could be manned in a variety of ways and by people representing different combinations of competence. This means that various states will arise and these have been designated "Operator states" since they refer to the state of the operator system. The need for different operator states can, of course, also arise due to sudden changes in the ship's immediate vicinity or due to defects and disturbances which occur in the technical equipment.

Through the manual setting of the Stage II "changeover switch", a formal statement is made that a given operator state shall be considered to exist and that one is prepared to act in accordance therewith. With due regard to the tactical environment already set-up in Stage I, control organs, display equipment, level automation, etc., are now adjusted to the new situation through the agency of the control logics. The various states (="switch settings") which are distinguished may include:
- Manned/unmanned engine room
- Different manning alternatives in the operations centre
- Special conditions of competence in the operations centre
- Special states for training purposes
- External circumstances such as visibility.

It is important to note that the combined settings of Stage I and Stage II simultaneously define the allocation of responsibility and duties in the operations centre, as well as a state of readiness. This can be imagined as favourably influencing the opportunities of creating a good working environment in the ship, and facilitating the maintenance of the intended readiness.

Stage III: Technical state

To a certain extent the operator has access to information concerning the state of the ship and the comprised equipment. The data may refer to the operating parameters such as engine speed, to settings such as the automatic controls in service, or to special states such as the disengagement of a given item of equipment for maintenance purposes. In as far as such factors influence the requirements which it is desired to place on the functional control system in a certain Stage I-Stage II situation, there is a chance in a third stage of manually initiating adaption measures through the agency of the control logics.

Stage IV: Ship state

Ship state is defined as being a combination of the technical state and the state of the control system (linking of control logics and operator state). Certain changes in the technical state, such as defects and disturbances or the presentation by the radar of an echo which is a potential danger, may require immediate action or alterations to the control logics. This is particularly true of certain control states representing a low level of readiness. Stage IV in the control logics set-up has been reserved for such important and rapid changes.

An example: Suppose that with a view to safety in the future we wish to define permissible Stage I/Stage II/Stage III combinations and relate these to the state of the ship as above, then Stage IV can give an automatic alarm when preparedness is lower than prescribed. A combination of one man on the bridge plus unmanned engine room plus poor visibility plus navigation congested areas could be a situation (control state) which is unacceptable if one of the two radar sets were disabled or if a dangerous echo should be recorded.

To a certain extent, an automatic fourth stage can also be exploited to permit immediate action by the operator without his leaving his position or without the necessity for all display to be concentrated at one and the same place. Alarms, for example, may require immediate disengagement of certain equipment. Through a Stage IV reconnection, certain such measures can be automatically linked with a single easily accessible button, which then effects the right measures - or no measures at all, if that should be the right answer. In this way, the operator does not require immediate access to either an alarm diagnosis display or separate control devices for every feasible action.

A reconstruction of the Torrey Canyon catastrophe shows that limited automatic controls of such Stage IV type could be extremely significant as regards safety in critical situations. The principles for the design of a special control logics system here presented, could offer advantages from such aspects as safety, training, flexability in on board routines, and certain standardization of the operations centre regardless of the make of equipment and the degree of automation. Furthermore, it could mean that an extended systems philosophy is introduced with regard to the design of bridge functions, something which could smooth the way for new crew arrangements. In this context, it can again be pointed out that the principles indicated here also serve the purpose of facilitating the evaluation of alternative operations centres and the specification of the performance of the control system.

REFERENCES

Project of development; Manning of technically advanced ships of the future.
Jerk Oldenburg, Subreport no 1, "Control
engineering: feasible lines of development
in ships".
Hans Ebenfelt, Subreport no 2, "The operations centre".
The Swedish Shipowners´ Association 1972.

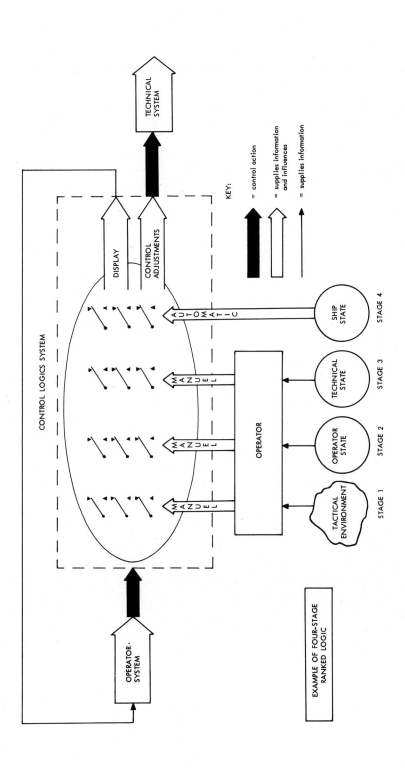

ONE-MAN NAVIGATION FOR SEAGOING VESSELS

Werner Hinsch
Kapitän
Gesellschaft für Kernenergieverwertung
in Schiffbau und Schiffahrt mbH.
Geesthacht, Germany

ABSTRACT

Spacious commanding-bridges of seagoing vessels hamper navigation. A vast supply of personnel (lookout, helmsman, officer of the watch and captain) does not ease the situation but brings up new risks.

The situation on the bridge of a number of seagoing vessels involved in collisions was examined. More than 40% of the analyzed collisions were caused by the fact that at least one of the vessels was navigated by a team or that the bridge installations were arranged for "team-navigation". This system of "team-navigation" hampers the passing and processing of information on the bridge of the vessel.

Except for the seagoing ship all other transport vehicles are controlled by the system of "one-man-control". One man has access to all navigational information, and this one man commands the vehicle controls directly.

Particularly towboats on the Rhine river serve as working examples of the principle of one-man bridge control of ships. Up to 11.000 tons of cargo are carried in a rigid array of barges pushed in front of the towboat. In the wheelhouse, which is perfectly equipped for "one-man-control", the navigator has access to all sources of information, such as optical view and radar, and in addition, he is in touch with the vessel's controls, such as helm and engine telegraph.

The system of "one-man-navigation" helped to keep the collision rate on the Rhine river on a constant level in spite of growing traffic density. "Continuous navigation" around the clock was introduced using shipboard radar. The reduced crew size is just an added benefit of this system of "one-man-navigation".

INTRODUCTION

Navigational information on the bridge of a seagoing vessel is normally processed the following way:

The officer on watch observes the traffic situation either by optical view or by radar. He gets the information and passes it on to the captain. The captain makes the decision to take actions. The helmsman gets orders to carry out the keep-clear-manoeuvre. The engine telegraph is rung and most frequently a receipt has to be given from the engine room before the order is executed.

Lookout or officer on watch	Captain	Helmsman
observation of traffic	→ making decisions	→ executing orders

Analyzed collisions show the disadvantage of this system. The man who made the decisions was not constantly in touch with his sources of information nor the vessel's controls.

- When navigating under reduced visibility the radar was not watched uninterruptedly.

- From the seat of the radar-navigator optical view was impossible to obtain.

- Entries in the chart made optical view impossible.

- Time was wasted by passing information from man to man.

- Errors arose by passing information from man to man.

ANALYZING FINDINGS OF THE MARITIME COURT

The findings of the German Maritime Court on collisions from 1968 to 1971 were evaluated to get information about the situation on the bridge of a seagoing vessel before a collision. This evaluation was made under the following conditions:

1. At least one of the vessels involved had a gross tonnage of more than 499 RT.

2. The situation on the bridge was not evaluated for ships with less than 499 RT.

3. Both vessels were underway on the river or on the open sea but not in ports or canals. These limitations restricted the evaluation to places and conditions where maximum damages could be expected.

4. The maritime court did find out how the collision originated.

45 collisions corresponded to these conditions. For 66 vessels involved information could be obtained about the situation on the bridge before the collision.

THE NAVIGATING-TEAM

According to statements before the maritime court there had been an average of 3.4 persons on the navigating bridge. There is roughly the following arrangement:

        1 officer on watch
        1 helmsman
        1 lookout
        the captain in 50% of the cases
        1 pilot when navigating on the
           river.

The navigating-team consists of 3.4 persons. The weakest link in this navigating team is the helmsman. On the river where he is mainly employed he directly caused every fifth collision (19%). It is stated in the findings of the maritime court that he did not understand his orders or acted unexperienced or on his own will.

Employing a lookout does not bring disadvantages to the ship's security, but the value of the lookout as source of information is dubious. On 49 vessels 54 lookouts had been employed either on the bridge or on the fo'c'sle. Only two of them who were placed on the bridge had at least a chance to detect or observe the opposing vessel. Indifferent to the decision-making on the bridge were all those lookout men placed on the ship's fo'c'sle and all 28 lookout men employed at a visibility of less than 2 nautical miles.

The presence of the captain on the bridge besides the officer on watch does not ne-

cessarily prevent the collision danger. At sea, at a visibility of less than two nautical miles, out of 22 vessels 15 were involved in a collision while the officer on watch and the captain were on the bridge together. Only 7 vessels collided when the watch-officer was alone.

The consideration of the present collisions leads to the conclusion that for safe navigation at sea o n e   m a n, and this has to be the one who makes the decisions, has to get access to all sources of information simultaneously while being in touch with the ship's controls. The most important sources of information are the sea-chart, radar, vhf-telephone and optical view. The controls are helm and engine-telegraph. This way all incoming information is immediately turned into manoeuvres of rudder and engine. All the delays and errors which originate in the communication from man to man are prevented.

BRIDGE LAYOUT

Most frequently the commanding bridges of larger seagoing vessels are laid out on an area of more than 100 square meters. Collisions frequently occur because of poor optical view from those bridges and their widespread arrangement of navigational aids. The man who has to make the decisions does not get all his information in one place. The radar for instance was only temporarily watched by the decision-making man. Defective radar observation could be demonstrated for 24% of all vessels navigating on rivers at a visibility of less than one nautical mile and for 55% of all vessels at sea at a visibility of less than two miles.

Five collisions occurred on the open sea at a visibility of more than two miles. Each time one of the opposing vessels kept it's course persistently, not obeying the rules of the road. Only in two cases could the maritime court show the reason for this behaviour. Each time the only man on the bridge did not detect the other vessel, because he had no optical view from the place where he made entries in the chart. It is after all not a large variety of navigational instruments which are actually in use on the bridge of a seagoing vessel and which, besides the sea-chart, have to be kept at the disposal of the navigator. In the analyzed findings of the German Maritime Court 26 occasions were mentioned where navigational methods or instruments were used to locate the position at sea:

    radar 18 times,
    radio direction finder 5 times,

terrestrical navigation 2 times,
Decca navigation 1 time.

On the rivers and approaches navigation
was exclusively carried out by optical
view or radar.

NAVIGATION OF SEAGOING AND OTHER TRANSPORT VEHICLES

The seagoing vessel has a spacious
bridge on which a navigating crew does
its duty preferably walking or standing.
This system is derived from the navigation of sailing vessels. It would be
very unusual to see any modern transport
vehicle guided by two or three men who
are observing the traffic situation,
making their decisions and shouting
their orders to another man who has nothing to do but handle the vehicle's controls. Except for the seagoing vessel
all other transport vehicles are controlled by the system of "one-man-control".

"One-man-control" does not necessarily
mean that there is only one man at the
vehicle's controls as it can be seen
for instance in the railway locomotive,
the bus, and in small aircraft. In
bigger aircraft the system "pilot and
pilot in command" is applied. Two e-
qually instrumented panels for "one-man-
control" guarantee that no dangerous
situation arises when one man or one
instrument fails.

Living examples for one-man bridges on
larger vessels are the towboats on the
Rhine river.

THE TOWBOATS ON THE RHINE RIVER

In the recent years Rhine river navigation was submitted to extensive changes.
Tugboats with towed barges where almost
totally replaced by pusher-type towboats.

A long-distance towboat displaces up to
500 tons. The length over all is 30 to
35 meters, the breadth is 10 to 15 meters. It is propelled by at least two
diesel engines, 1000 to 2000 hp each.
The navigator's concern is not only the
towboat alone but also the whole tow.
In front of the towboat four barges are
pushed, two side by side. This array is
manoeuvered like a rigid unit. It acts
like a ship with hatches forward, bridge
and engine aft. Such a tow carries up
to 11.000 tons of cargo. It is 183 meters long and 23 meters wide. It is expected that in the near future the
length of the tows will be extended to
265 meters, their cargo capacity to
16.000 tons.

Since 1966 towboats are equipped with

bridges for "one-man-control". Governmental regulations followed soon after.
The navigational regulations for the
Rhine river (Rheinschiffahrts-Polizei-
verordnung von 1970) allow one-man-control even in dense fog, if the navigational bridge is equipped accordingly.
Vessels under radar-navigation are free
from the necessity of employing a lookout. The one-man-bridge arrangement has
been scientifically researched. Models
in natural scale helped to solve ergo-
nomical problems as: optimal dimensions,
optical view of the navigator, arrangement of navigational instruments.

Expert opinions on medical problems were
gathered. The installations and their
arrangements on the one-man-bridge were
submitted to standardization.

WATCHKEEPING ON THE ONE-MAN-BRIDGE

Together with the river tows another new
system was introduced on the Rhine river:
watchkeeping and navigation around the
clock under all conditions of visibility.
There are two captains aboard each towboat. Each captain has equal rights and
is only responsible for the tow during
his hours of watch.

The captain occupies the navigator's
seat on the bridge. On less dangerous
sections of the river he is sometimes
relieved by an assisting sailor. Normally only one man navigates 11.000 tons
of cargo on the Rhine river, in good visibility as well as in dense fog. Even
when the tow is in the process of anchoring, docking, or when it is being
assembled, there is only one man on the
bridge. Only every 6 hours, when the
watches are shifted, are the two captains on the bridge at the same time.

Government regulations do not require a
lookout on the one-man-bridge. The
helmsman who is commonly employed on seagoing vessels is traditionally unknown
on Rhine river boats. The captain tends
the wheel. If a pilot boards the river
boat, he will take the wheel from the
captain.

BRIDGE INSTALLATIONS ON THE TOWBOAT

The outer dimensions of this wheelhouse
or cockpit are 4 by 4 meters. From his
seat the navigator has perfect optical
view in all directions. This cockpit is
situated on top of all superstructures.
It is even placed above the ship's funnel. Wheelhouse and accommodations are
put on elastic bearings to ward off all
noises caused by the engine and propeller. The navigator sits in a comfortable chair with arms and back. This
chair can be adjusted for and backward.

It is mounted on a platform which can be elevated at will. The radar screen is mounted in an inclined position in front of the navigator's seat. The whole radar set can be adjusted in its vertical position and, on modern boats, it can be automatically exchanged for a spare set. Main and spare radar sets are always simultaneously switched on at night and during reduced visibility. The radar which has an especially good discrimination for the use on rivers shows a relativ head-up display.

During any uncertain situation radar navigation is preferred over optical view. When navigating during twilight, the windows are shut with roller blinds so that the lights from the near banks cannot disturb the navigator.

In contrast to the seagoing captain, the river captain has the advantage of carrying out all his navigational tasks in fromt of the radar screen. There is nothing that diverts his attention from the radar.

The boats on the Rhine river do not have a compass. All ships equipped for radar navigation have rate-of-turn indicators. Two of them, one as spare set, are placed on top of the radar screen. On their scale, which is divided in degrees for port and starboard, the rate of turn in degrees per minute around the vertical axis of the vessel is indicated.

The rate-of-turn indicator informs the captain with great precision about the effects of his helm actions. Only the use of the rate-of-turn indicator, not the compass, enables clear decisions about the correct passage of a river bend. Manoeuvring at a certain speed in a certain bend a definite rate-of-turn has to be kept by the vessel. On seagoing ships the helmsman gets nothing else but course or helm orders, although his actual task is to get his vessel in a certain rate-of-turn or prevent any rate-of-turn on a steady course.

To the left and right sides of the radar set the divided control-panel is arranged. The nautical instruments and controls are placed on the right side, the engine controls on the left side.

The engine room telegraph is within reach of the navigator's left hand. Most commonly there are two levers for two engines. There is no fixed classification for the positions of the telegraph. It is moved without scales in accordance with the navigator's experience and the ship's actions.

There is a panel of about eleven lamps which indicate troubles from the engine room. These lamps are arranged in groups of three different colours:
  "white" - minor or beginning trouble,
  "yellow"- reduce engine,
  "red"   - engine stopped.
Right below the lamps there is a button for the alarm-bell to ring up the engineer if necessary.

The navigator's right hand can reach the rudder control. The traditional wheels to operate the rudder are abolished totally from the bridge of the Rhine river towboats. The navigator who is fulfilling his duties in a sitting position operates the rudder more conveniently with a tiller. The tiller functions according to the principle of "follow-up-control". From touch of his hand the operator knows exactly the position of the ship's rudder so that a rudder-position-indicator is not necessary.

There are two different vhf-sets at the navigator's disposal. One of them is for ship-shore, the other for ship-ship traffic exclusively. Governmental regulations require the ship-ship vhf-installation for all vessels equipped with radar. Ship-ship communication is commonly practiced in good visibility. Navigating in dense fog it is indispensable for all craft. On the river it is very simple to identify the vhf-partner by his position.

The navigator sitting in a chair has his feet available for the following activities. There are four different pedals, two for soundsignals, one as talk-listen button for ship-ship communication, and one for acceleration of the steering machines.

The towboat captain knows the river thoroughly. He has no need to use charts or nautical books. There are not even governmental regulations which require river boats to be equipped with charts.

RIVER AND DEEP-SEA NAVIGATION

The towboat captain does not have to track his position on a chart. There is transverse traffic only if a vessel is turning around on the river or in definite places such as bifurcations of the river, tributaries or harbour entrances.

Transverse traffic is not the problem of deep-sea navigation either. At sea, collisions occurred during poor visibility, and 79% of all analyzed collisions occurred at a visibility of less than 2 nm and between vessels with opposite courses which differed by not more than 45 degrees.

The speed of the vessels on the Rhine river is relatively low. On an average

it is 5 and 8 knots for up- and downstream traffic, respectively. The analysis of collision at sea showed that the
speed was 12 knots on the average in the
moment when the opposing vessel was detected for the first time. But the traffic density is incomparably higher on the
Rhine river than at sea. The international Rhine river fleet, which does not
include smaller craft in the national
trade, pleasure boats and ferries, comprises 12.593 motor vessels which share
460 nautical miles of the navigable
river.

The narrowness of the river and the traffic density can get the tow into collision danger immediately and at any moment. The captain counts on about two
minutes time from the moment he dis-
coveres an upcoming vessel until the
moment it safely passes. For him it is
absolutely essential to be in constant
touch with his sources of information,
such as radar and optical view, as well
as with the ship's controls, such as
rudder and engine telegraph. All incoming information is processed directly.
This is only possible in a wheelhouse
which is equipped for "one-man-navigation". No mistakes and no delays originate in the passing of information
from man to man.

At sea the opposing vessel was detected
on the average 16 minutes before the collision. From this fact it can be assumed that the difference between river
navigation and deep-sea navigation is
this: in contrast to conditions on the
river, preparations for a collision at
sea can take, on the average, as much
time as a quarter of an hour. This fact
does not require such a high standard in
bridge installations and bridge arrangements for the seagoing vessel.

CONCLUSION

Governmental regulations for continuous
navigation and radar navigation on the
Rhine river were issued for the first
time in Germany in 1966. From 1966 to
1971 the number of towboats on the river
has doubled. In 1971 tows shipped 19.2%
of all cargo which passed the Netherland-
German border at Emmerich. The total
number of ships passing the Durch border
increased by 26% since 1965.

Collisions at sea occur in areas of dense
traffic and when ships navigate by radar.
It could be assumed that growing traffic
density and the introduction of radar navigation on the Rhine river lead to a
growing collision rate.

There is no shore-based surveillance radar system on the Rhine river. In 1971

the river police registered 247 collisions between Bonn and the Dutch border
(Nordrheinwestfalen). Only in 6% of
these collisions were vessels navigating
with radar. This collision rate has
been nearly constant in the latest years.

	Ships passing Dutch border (1000)	Colli- sions Bonn- Dutch border	Colli- sions radar- vessels involved
1965	189	270	4
1966	201	261	2
1967	213	236	12
1968	225	266	17
1969	233	275	9
1970	223	299	15
1971	240	247	14

In the recent years, the power of propulsion of the vessels increased. Aids
to navigation were improved. The vessels
have grown in size.

Since 1966 regulations require all ra-
dar-navigating vessels on the river to
be equipped with a separate vhf-installation for ship-ship communication.

Since 1966 towboats and modern cargo
vessels are equipped with bridge installations for "one-man-navigation" where
the only navigator does his duties sitting in front of the radar screen. He
observes and acts accordingly.

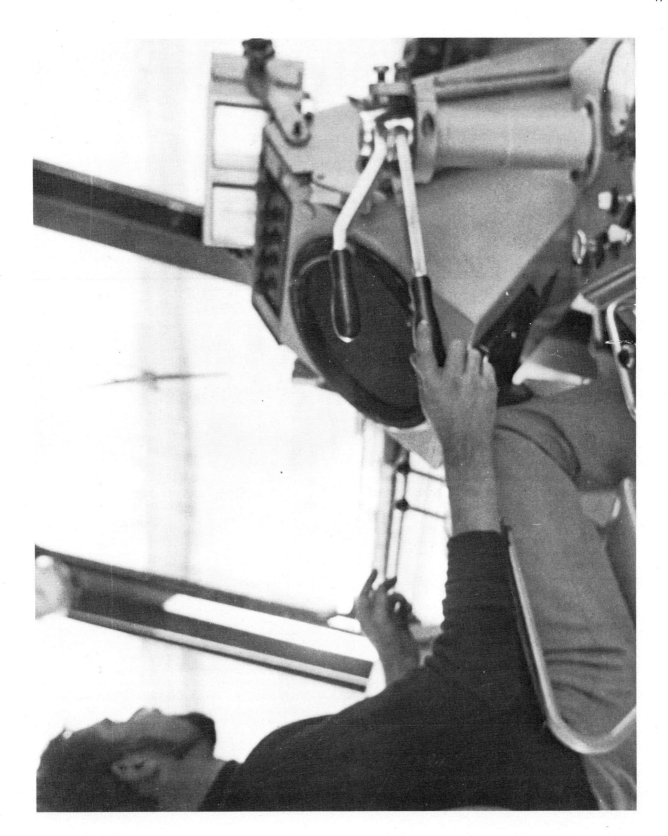

ERGONOMIC BRIDGE

Captain I S S Mackay RN

INTRODUCTION

In considering the present and future ships'
bridges, first we must look at the history of
the bridge itself. In the days of sail it was
necessary for the helmsman, and master, to
stand on the poop in order that they could watch
the trim of the sails. Therefore the
equivalent position of the bridge was right aft:
for the helmsman to get sufficient purchase on
the wheel he had to stand up. With the
introduction of steam propulsion it was necessary
to stand as near as possible to the machinery so
that orders could be passed by voice pipe; and,
therefore, initially "a bridge" was placed
between the two paddle boxes. From here the
quartermaster steered the ship and the master
either passed orders to the engine room by voice
pipe or mechanical telegraph. In the first half
of the century, as mechanical controls became
more reliable, the bridge was either moved
for'ard to the pivoting point of the ship or,
in bulk carriers or tankers, right aft to make
full use of the carrying capacity of the hull.
In both cases the original concept of the
"bridge" for power driven ships was retained, one
of the advantages being that by walking to the
side of the bridge it was possible to look over
the ship's side for berthing. However, with
this comparatively large promenade bridge,
instruments and controls were widely spaced and
of a sufficient size so that dials could be read
from most parts of the bridge.

THE USE OF THE BRIDGE

Since the days of sail verbal orders have been
necessary to control the propulsion and the
course of the ship mainly because the power
source, be it men in the rigging or machinery
spaces between decks, were physically divorced
from the command. Because of this slow transition and strong traditional outlook of the
mariner we now find that, apart from some old
fashioned electric road trams, a ship is the
last remaining platform which requires its
operator to remain standing. In this day of
rapidly changing technology this archaic approach
to the control of maritime platforms is no longer
acceptable, because any moving platform requires

its operator to be a part of the platform and
have all information and controls readily at
hand. If this philosophy is true then a
considerable change is required in the layout
and use of future ships' bridges.

Once the need for the command to cease moving
about the bridge is overcome, it is possible to
tailor the bridge requirements from the start to
the needs of the operator. Already ships are at
sea with only one officer on the bridge. In
these ships auto pilots are in use and direct
engine controls are sited on the bridge. However,
because of the wide bridge, other fittings such
as PPIs and chart tables are well dispersed and
the numerous bridge windows, invariably formed
into a gentle curve, produce many blank arcs
from the midships for'ard position where the
officer of the watch or helmsman invariably stand.
Furthermore, after 4 hours on watch the personnel
are naturally more fatigued than if they had been
sitting with their equipment within easy reach.

THE ERGONOMIC BRIDGE

The word "ergonomic" means "man's relationship
with his working environment". The future
bridge, if it is based on ergonomics, immediately
makes the form of a cockpit, train driver's cab
or car driving seat. There are naturally many
individual views on the layout of such a position.
However, the system I am about to describe is the
one that has been tried in the Royal Navy. The
primary requirement is the best possible all
round view from the officer of the watch's
position. The optimum size bridge to achieve
this is between 9' and 12' square or 10' in
diameter. By doing away with the binnicle or
pelorus round which the officer of the watch is
required to move, space is immediately saved by
putting a bearing taking device above the officer
of the watch which he could pull down when taking
a bearing. In front of him is the auto pilot's
controls and to the right the engine controls.
Directly in front of the officer of the watch
are the compass repeater, rudder angle indicator,
speed indicator and echo sounder repeater. To
the left of the auto pilot is the radar PPI which

can be linked with the ship's computer to give auto tracking of targets and navigational computation, or it can be a straightforward PPI with a reflection plotter. To the left of the PPI is the chart table with Navaids which can be reached by the officer of the watch from his swivel chair. This layout affords a natural flow of activity from visual and radar sources to the chart and thence to the ship control panel. In future it will be quite feasible to tie in the navigational chart to the radar and computer system. Similarly a visual bearing could be injected into the navigational system via the computer. With this layout there are a number of questions which immediately come to mind caused by our traditional way of using the present bridge. Such questions are:-

a. The officer of the watch will be restricted to one position on the bridge and will be unable to move around and keep an eye on the upper deck.

b. Because he is sitting down the officer of the watch will become drowsy and may well fall asleep.

c. The officer of the watch should not be tied down to operating equipment but should be free to keep a good lookout.

Against these questions are the results of a sea trial done last year with such a layout and the reactions, especially from the young officers, were quite illuminating. Experience confirms the original reasons for an ergonomic bridge because the officer of the watch

a. is facing for'ard for longer periods and thus keeps a better lookout

b. does not have to move about to look at the PPI and chart table and is therefore not so physically tired.

c. can stretch his legs and go to the bridge wings if he wishes when relieved by his assistant.

d. feels much more part of the ship which he is controlling and is more likely to monitor the actions that he takes. It is the detached feeling one gets from a conventional bridge which is often mentioned by Commanding Officers who are qualified aviators and therefore have considerable experience in other ergonomic control positions.

e. can very easily co-relate information visually and from the radar and chart.

f. the lack of all round visibility, although desirable, can be overcome by insistence on correct procedures between the officer of the watch and his assistant.

It is of interest that this bridge layout described with the chart table on the one side

and the PPI for'ard of the pelorus has already proved its worth when it was typical of bridges designed in the 1940s and 1950s. You will see from the slides the actual layout which was used in HMS EXMOUTH, the Royal Navy's first gas turbine driven frigate.

BRIDGE OPERATIONS

Bridge operations take the form of four phases:-

a. Ocean passage
b. Coastal
c. Pilotage
d. Berthing

During the ocean passage phase the rate of activities is low. The main requirement of the officer of the watch is to cover the lookout and surveillance task with the minimum of effort whilst working on a secondary task such as position fixing and routine bridge work. The main problem during this phase is prevention of boredom and fatigue. With the conventional bridge this is overcome by ensuring that the officer of the watch can walk up and down, even so during silent hours there is a tendency for the officer of the watch to use the captain's bridge chair. However, when using an ergonomic layout the officer of the watch has all the information in front of him and can take a continual interest in the visual and radar watch and in the ship's control.

During the coastal phase the main task for the officer of the watch comprises a mixture of collision avoidance and coastal navigation; these two tasks are virtually combined and are certainly inter-related. This phase is a most active period for the officer of the watch where much will be happening requiring his constant attention with easy and frequent reference to his chart, PPI, position fixing aid such as Decca, course and speed repeaters and his visual lookout. When using CPAs or parallel index runs on points of land, he will require rapid appreciation of his PPI, co-relation with the chart and almost subconscious control of the ship; this is the normal thought process and reaction required in handling any moving platform. The situation is similar although the sensors are different.

When considering the pilotage stage, at first sight the naval and merchant ship requirements appear to be different. However, they are fundamentally the same because the naval navigating officer assumes the duties of ship's pilot. The only difference being that the commercial pilot knows the geographical situation by heart, whereas the naval navigating officer, who may well be a stranger to the port, must refer to the chart and PPI as well as using a pelorus. With an ergonomic bridge, by standing behind the officer of the watch the pilot can monitor all actions taken from the control console repeaters, see the PPI and also the chart.

In narrow beam ships, or aircraft carriers with an offset bridge, it is perfectly feasible to berth the ship while standing by the pelorus by using known cutoff points along the ship's side to give the distance from the stem or from the dockside. It is naturally preferable to go to the bridge wing for the final berthing operation. With the ergonomic bridge it has been found best for the navigating officer to retain the con, as in the conventional bridge, until the final approach to the berth when the captain takes over. Throughout this phase the officer of the watch from his seated position is ideally situated to monitor all orders and to watch the approach to the berth without getting in the way of the navigating officer or captain.

MISCELLANEOUS POINTS

a. In order to save additional equipment, the conning intercom is available in the bridge wings in lieu of rudder and engine controls.

b. A system similar to captain and co-pilot in aircraft appears to work well. In the ocean passage phase, if the officer of the watch is alone on the bridge he sits in front of the console, leaving the other chair, situated to the right of the console, available for the captain. If an assistant, either an officer or seaman, is also on watch then he sits in front of the console and the officer of the watch moves to the captain's chair. For all other phases the captain's chair is available for the captain or navigating officer.

c. Many merchant ship bridges are at times wooded from for'ard due to masts, derricks, etc. This could be an argument against a fixed position for the officer of the watch. Either a higher bridge position should be possible or greater care must be taken to keep an unobstructed view especially ahead.

There are many other minor questions and doubts concerning such a layout, but once it has been used they fade into the background when the full benefits are experienced.

You will now see a film taken on board HMS EXMOUTH showing the prototype ergonomic bridge in use.

CONCLUSION

A more ergonomically designed bridge is clearly a requirement with the present state of technology in order that the information obtained can be used more effectively through remote control of the ship's rudder and engines. This is not so unusual as first appears and with very little practice can enhance the officer of the watch's job satisfaction and thus his standard of work; in ships which still require a helmsman manpower is saved. The ergonomic bridge is with us, let us now ensure that we can obtain maximum benefit from it.

SATELLITE NAVIGATION

Thomas A. Stansell, Jr.
Manager, Advanced Products
Magnavox Research Laboratories
2829 Maricopa Street
Torrance, California USA

INTRODUCTION

Navigation by satellite has been commercially available since 1967. Although there has been growth in its application to such functions as offshore oil exploration, only within the last two years has there been much application to merchant shipping. The reasons for this time lag have been the relatively high cost of early equipment, the lack of worldwide sales and service availability, and natural reticence to accept a new technique.

The situation appears to be changing rapidly. Manufacturers, such as Magnavox, have been successful in reducing total ownership costs by equipment simplification, improved reliability, and simplified maintenance techniques. The equipment now is being sold by agents in most major shipping countries, and service is available in Europe, Japan, and the United States. Perhaps most important, early users around the world are reporting success, and many are ordering additional equipment, which is the ultimate measure of acceptance.

The positive reinforcement of greater industry experience and acceptance, increasing volume of sales, further product improvements, and wider availability of sales and service should result in an exponential growth of satellite navigation for merchant shipping. All indications are that for reasons of safety, convenience, and economy, the accurate, automatic, worldwide, all-weather navigation provided by satellites is both welcome and needed by the modern merchant fleet.

THE TRANSIT SYSTEM

General

The U.S. Navy Navigation Satellite System, often called Transit, was developed to guide the Navy's Polaris submarine fleet, and Transit satellites have been in service constantly since January of 1964. In 1967, the U.S. Government decided to release details of the system in order to permit commercial use, which has been expanding rapidly since that time.

Today there are five operational Transit satellites. All are in polar orbits, which means they move in a north-south direction, down one side of the earth, across the south pole, and back up and over the north pole. They circle the earth every 107 minutes at a height of about 1075 kilometers. This constellation of orbits forms a "birdcage" within which the earth rotates, carrying us past each orbit in turn. Whenever a satellite passes above the horizon of a user, he has the opportunity to obtain a position fix. In general, at least 16 good position fixes will occur in every 24-hour day, and automatic dead reckoning between each fix provides continuous navigational information.

Many people are familiar with the concept of obtaining a position fix from shore-based radio navigation systems, such as Decca, Loran, Omega, etc. In each case, a shipboard receiver measures range differences between signals arriving from three or more shore-based stations. Signals from all stations arrive within 10 seconds or less of each other, so that a nearly "instantaneous" position fix may be computed. Furthermore, the shore stations are at known, fixed locations, so that navigational charts relating the radio measurements to fixed lines of position on the map may be prepared.

In the case of Transit, a shipboard receiver obtains signals from only one satellite at a time. Instead of measuring range differences from several stations simultaneously, Transit measurements are between sequential positions of the satellite as it passes. This process requires from ten to fifteen minutes, during which the satellite travels 4400 to 6600 kilometers, providing an excellent baseline.

Because Transit measurements are not instantaneous, motion of the ship during the satellite pass must be considered in the fix calculation. Also, because the satellites are in constant motion relative to the earth, simple charts with lines of position are impossible to generate. Instead, each satellite transmits a set of orbital parameters, permitting its position to be calculated quite accurately as a function of time. By combining the calculated satellite positions, the range difference measurements between these positions, and information regarding motion of the ship, an accurate position fix can be obtained. Because the calculations are both complex and extensive, a small digital computer is always employed.

Transit is the only navigational aid with worldwide availability at this time. It is not affected by weather conditions, including local thunderstorms, and it provides fixes with an accuracy matched only by short range radio navigation systems.

Accuracy

When Transit signals penetrate the earth's ionosphere, an error is caused by ionospheric refraction. To eliminate this error, Transit satellites transmit two signals, one at 150 MHz and the other at 400 MHz. By receiving both frequencies and combining them properly, the refraction error is eliminated. This capability is included in dual-channel Transit receivers such as the Magnavox MX 702 A. On the other hand, both cost and complexity can be reduced by using only the 400 MHz signals and suffering a small decrease in accuracy. The Magnavox MX 902 is such a single channel receiver.

There are two principal components of error in a Transit position fix. First is the inherent system error, and second is error introduced by unknown ship's motion.

The inherent system error can be measured by operating a Transit set at a fixed location and observing the scatter of the fix results. Figure 1 is a plot of position fixes obtained during system test of an MX902 single channel receiver. With respect to the surveyed antenna position, the maximum error was 242.3 meters, and the root mean square (RMS) radial error for the entire group was 87.8 meters. During the same period of time, a dual channel MX702A receiver yielded an RMS radial error of 34.3 meters with satellite passes between 10 and 70 degrees maximum elevation angle. These results are quite typical and have been repeated many times and many places around the world. Magnavox will not ship an MX902 unless it achieves an RMS error less than 92 meters, and the MX702A must achieve an RMS error less than 46 meters before acceptance.

One could ask whether there might be a large bias in the position fix results, regardless of the tight grouping of the individual fixes. This subject has received much scientific consideration, and measurements have been made many places around the world to detect system bias. The results indicate that if a bias does exist, it will not exceed about 20 meters. Far more important are considerations of datum difference and local survey error, which can appear as a relatively large bias between the Transit fix and the charted position. These, however, are not satellite position fix errors, and they are discussed later in this paper.

The second source of position fix error is introduced by unknown ship's motion during a satellite pass. Although the exact error is a complex function of satellite pass geometry and direction of ship's velocity error, a reasonable rule is that 0.2 nautical mile of fix error will result from each knot of unknown ship's velocity. This error has been combined (root sum square) with the inherent system error to give the fix error curves shown in Figure 2.

Transit System Future

We are hopeful of a policy statement from the U.S. Navy within the next several months guaranteeing future availability of the Transit system. Until then, we must draw conclusions from the available evidence. The five operational satellites are showing excellent reliability. The oldest was launched in April of 1967, and the most recent in August of 1970. In addition to these, the Navy has more than 10 additional spacecraft ready to launch whenever a replacement is needed. Therefore, the Navy has the equipment to operate the system for many years to come.

More important, however, is that the Navy needs the Transit system for its original purpose of guiding Polaris submarines, plus a greatly expanding fleet of

other Navy ships. Magnavox is just completing development of a new generation of Transit equipment, the AN/WRN-5, and deliveries to the Navy will begin this year. The trend is definitely toward expanded Navy use of the Transit system.

For several years, the U.S. Defense Department has studied alternate approaches to navigation by satellite, and the most likely candidate is the Air Force 621 B System. Assuming the most optimistic development schedule, and assuming a U.S. commitment to invest many billions of dollars in such a development, it would be at least 1990 before the Transit system could be discontinued for Navy use. It is also clear that user equipment would be more expensive for the proposed system. With these facts in mind, the U.S. Navy has begun to consider improvements to Transit, which must serve for at least another two decades. Already an experimental satellite called TIPS I (Transit Improvement Program Satellite I) has been launched and is being evaluated.

Although final plans have not been announced, it appears likely that the Navy will install an expanded network of satellites, providing more frequent position fixes to all users, and a stated objective is strict compatibility with existing Transit equipment. Based on all available information, it is abundantly clear that the Transit system will be available for many years to come, and the chances are excellent that both fix accuracy and fix availability will be improved.

DATUM SHIFT

When a survey is conducted and a map is drawn, the earth is assumed to be an oblate spheroid. A number of different spheroids are in use around the world, and a few of these are listed in Table I.

TABLE I - Sample of World Spheroids

Spheroid	Semi-major Axis (meters)	Reciprocal of Flattening
Bessel	6 377 397	299.15
Clarke 1866	6 378 206	294.98
International	6 378 388	297.0
Satellite (NWL-8D)	6 378 145	298.25

To make matters more confusing, each portion of the world has adopted a local mapping grid called a datum. Each datum is referenced to an "origin", defined to be at a specific known location. For example, maps of the United States employ the North American 1927 Datum with origin at Meades Ranch, Kansas. The Clarke 1866 Spheroid is the earth shape assumed for these maps. In Europe, the International Spheroid and the European Datum with origin at Helmert Tower are generally used. In Japan, it is the Tokyo Datum with origin at the old Tokyo Observatory and using the Bessel Spheroid.

Because the earth now can be "tied together" through accurate observations of artificial earth satellites, a consistent, Worldwide Datum has become possible. Several such worldwide datums have been developed as satellite geodesy has matured, such as the one used with the Transit system.

It is possible to transform coordinates from one datum to another. In a limited area, such as a port, the transformation can take the form of a simple shift in values of latitude and longitude. Table II gives two examples of datum shift, from local to satellite datum.

<u>TABLE II - Datum Shift Examples</u>

Local Coordinates	Local Datum	Shift (Satellite-local)
52°22!8575 N 13°03!979 E	European	0!043 S 0!069 W
35°39!2918 N 139°44!675 E	Tokyo	0!188 N 0!205 W

The total shift at the origin of the European Datum is about 112 meters and at the origin of the Tokyo Datum it is about 465 meters. Because the amount and direction of datum shift changes from one place to another, these values should be used only as single examples. Furthermore, local charts all too often are incorrect due to local survey error.

A navigator who uses the Transit system should be aware of the local datum shift in order to take maximum advantage of system accuracy. The local shift may be obtained in two ways. First is to measure the datum shift during each port call by comparing the average of several satellite fixes at dockside with the charted position. This technique automatically eliminates local survey error, which becomes part of the datum shift calibration. The second technique is to calculate the shift from published data. Magnavox is considering release of a computer program for this calculation, with the serious concern that local survey errors can defeat the intent of the datum shift calculation.

Several opportunities are created by the preceding considerations. First is that navigators can begin to interchange datum shift data. This process should be formalized into an international publication. Second, agencies which prepare navigational charts should consider adding datum shift information based on local calibration with Transit equipment. Finally, the opportunity now exists for slowly converting the world's charts to a common and consistent datum based on satellite tracking results.

GROWTH OF COMMERCIAL USE

Transit user equipment had been designed originally for military applications where ultimate accuracy, reliability at any price, and repairability aboard ship were firm requirements. Therefore, the equipment tended to be expensive and was designed for technical experts to operate and to maintain. These characteristics were not conducive to use aboard merchant ships, but there was a strong commercial interest in the equipment for applications such as oceanography, offshore oil exploration, and cable laying. Here, maximum accuracy was mandatory and operation by technical experts was feasible.

Producers of Transit equipment vied with each other to improve system accuracy and to add features, often through improved computer programs. These efforts resulted in such products as the Magnavox Model 200 Integrated Navigation System for offshore oil exploration. This system employs a four-beam Doppler sonar and an excellent gyrocompass for accurate dead reckoning between satellite position fix updates. The system computer drives several types of display, including a track plotter. Magnetic tape equipment is used for logging of

navigational and gravity data. Perhaps most impressive is that the ship is steered automatically by the computer along preset survey lines and from one survey line to the next. Attention was diverted from merchant ship applications by concentration on highly accurate, relatively expensive equipment.

MERCHANT SHIP APPLICATION

Over the last two years, producers of Transit equipment have focused increasing attention on the needs of the merchant fleet. For this application, requirements shift from ultimate accuracy toward those of:
a) Dependable performance without maintenance aboard ship
b) Simplicity of operation
c) Repairability during minimum port turnaround time
d) Minimum cost consistent with the above.

One could ask, "Why use satellite navigation for merchant ships?" Attempts to justify its use through calculated savings of time and fuel have been made, with savings up to 0.5-percent claimed by some. One oceanographic ship reported making port consistently on time or ahead of time, which was very unusual before installation of satellite navigation equipment. However, such advantages are difficult to prove except by careful monitoring of performance with and without satellite navigation over extended periods of equivalent operation.

The most compelling reasons are safety and convenience. When accurate position is available instantly, at any time of the day or night, during any weather condition, and without need for cumbersome plotting and calculation, safety is enhanced. Having accurate latitude and longitude without the need for manual calculation is certainly a convenience, but eliminating human error is also an important safety factor.

Two experiences during the 1964 Project Sea Orbit, when three U.S. Navy ships circled the globe, illustrate these points. A prototype satellite navigation set was first operated off the west coast of Africa. The navigation officer immediately contended that the equipment was faulty because of a 50 mile error. A careful check of his calculations showed the error to be human. After several such experiences, most navigators begin to trust satellite navigation implicitly. Later, between Australia and South America, there was a period of 10 days with constant overcast skies. Only satellite navigation provided position fix information during this long period, when dead reckoning error could have grown to hundreds of kilometers.

When both safety and convenience clearly can be enhanced by satellite navigation, perhaps the proper question should be, "Why isn't Transit equipment being installed on every multi-million dollar merchant ship?"

Equipment Configuration

The basic Transit navigation set consists of three items: (a) the receiver, (b) the computer, and (c) the input/output unit. Figure 3 shows these components in a single rack configuration. Position fix results are printed by the ASR-33 Teletype mounted on top of the rack. The computer program tape is loaded by means of the Teletype paper tape reader. Most Magnavox systems have had this configuration.

Automatic Dead Reckoning

The computer dead reckons between each satellite position fix update in order to provide continuous navigational information. Manual values of speed and heading are used if no other data are available. Naturally it is difficult to guarantee that these values of speed and heading are always correct, but even a manual dead reckoning function is better than none at all. The accuracy of the satellite position fix also is dependent on the accuracy of the manual speed and heading inputs.

It is preferable to use automatic speed and heading signals to describe ship's motion during each satellite pass and for dead reckoning between. For this purpose, Magnavox provides an optional speed and heading interface consisting of a card which plugs into the computer and a small junction box. This option accepts a wide variety of standard speed and heading signals. For example, the interface is compatible with Anschutz, Brown, Hokoshin, Microtecnica, Plath, Sperry, and other gyrocompasses, because it accepts 360 speed repeater drive signals in either stepper format (35 to 70 volt) or in synchro format (50 to 400 Hz, 50 to 125 volt exciter). Speed is obtained from signals like those used to drive true motion radars, e.g., 200 contact closures per nautical mile. Either contact closures or electrical pulses may be accepted, with scaling from 200 to 720,000 impulses per nautical mile. In fact, the scale factor is entered through the terminal keyboard when the computer program is first loaded, so that it is easy to change if a speed calibration error is detected. The operator also has the option of accepting the automatic speed and heading inputs or of substituting a manual value for either or both if necessary.

The automatic interface permits the computer to dead reckon with values of speed and heading which are updated once per second. Such constant attention to ship's motion insures much improved dead reckoning accuracy compared with manual methods.

Because heading is provided from the gyrocompass in 360-speed format, it is necessary initially to set every repeater compass to the correct value within one degree. The same is true for the satellite navigation set, which acts as a compass repeater when equipped with the automatic heading option. The preset is accomplished with a simple keyboard entry. One difference is that normal compass repeaters are powered by the gyrocompass, whereas the computer may have a separate source of power. Therefore, if power to the computer fails, upon return of power the video display will remind the operator to check heading alignment with the gyrocompass. Brief power interruptions normally will introduce no heading error, but it would seem advisable to connect both the computer and the gyrocompass to the same power source whenever possible.

Speed information may be obtained from a variety of sources. Some of these include: (1) propeller shaft revolution counter, (2) Pitot-static log, (3) EM log, and (4) Doppler sonar speed log or docking system. Accuracy will depend on the quality and type of instrument. As stated before, calibration error may be compensated by keyboard entry of a modified scale factor.

Satellite Position Update

When a Transit satellite passes above the horizon, the MX 902 receiver automatically acquires the signal and sends data to the computer. There, the satellite orbit information and range difference measurements (Doppler counts) are combined with ship's motion from the dead reckoning process. After the satellite sets below the horizon, the computer calculates latitude and longitude corrections to the dead reckoned position.

Before an update is applied, however, the position fix must pass a series of quality tests. The maximum elevation of the satellite pass must lie within the range of 10 to 70 degrees. There must have been at least 10 Doppler count measurements, and they must have been reasonably symmetric about the center of the satellite pass. The number of calculation iterations must have been five or less, and the difference between the satellite fix and the dead reckoned position must be reasonable. If any of the tests are failed, the dead reckoned position will not be affected, thus assuring that only the best quality navigation information is used.

The operator has the option of forcing an update if he wishes to override an automatic rejection by the computer. This may be required, for example, if a manually input value of speed or heading had been wrong for some time, causing a large dead reckoning error. The fix quality indicators can be displayed by keyboard request if the operator wishes to know the reason for the automatic rejection.

Great Circle Calculation

In addition to automatic dead reckoning and computing satellite position fixes, the latest Magnavox 4096-word program also computes and displays the great circle range and bearing to any designated spot on the earth. These values are updated frequently to take account of own ship's motion. By entering the latitude and longitude of a destination, the terminal and all remote video monitors will constantly show the course required to reach the destination by great circle sailing. In addition, the distance to destination also is displayed. This feature will be of value when setting a commanded heading into the ship's autopilot and for determining time of arrival.

Another use for this feature is in location or identification of features on a radar display when approaching land. For example, the location of a prominent coastal feature can be entered into the computer, and the terminal will show at what range and bearing the feature should appear on the radar display.

Automatic Steering

As mentioned earlier, Magnavox has developed techniques for automatic steering of geophysical exploration vessels in which the ship's rudder is under direct computer control. It has been suggested that the same concept would be desirable for control of merchant ships. The advantages would include (a) accurate great circle sailing without manual adjustment, (b) automatic compensation for drift with each satellite fix, and (c) possibly a reduction in drag through more efficient use of rudder commands, thus saving both time and fuel.

Because the Teletype is used only to record position fixes, it receives little wear and has shown excellent reliability. However, in response to complaints about Teletype noise and because it is an electro-mechanical device subject to wear and alignment problems, Magnavox has developed a Video Terminal as an alternate input/output device. The terminal encourages packaging the receiver and computer in a much smaller enclosure, which then can be mounted out of the way, as shown in Figure 4. System operation is controlled from the small terminal, Figure 5, which can be mounted for convenient access by the navigator. With either configuration, extra video displays can be added to distribute navigation information to any part of the ship.

MX 902 Receiver

The MX 902 satellite navigation receiver has been designed with emphasis on:
a) Reliability
b) Simplicity of operation
c) Ease of maintenance.
Reliability is enhanced by rugged physical construction, all solid state electronics using the latest integrated circuit technology, no requirement for field alignment, and a rigorous testing program before delivery, including extended operation at 50°C.

Because there are only two controls on the receiver front panel, operational simplicity is self evident. One control is the power switch. The other is a pushbutton which initiates an automatic self-test cycle. When the built-in test signal generator is actuated, the receiver searches for and acquires the test signal, as indicated by the signal lock lamp. After about two minutes of automatic testing, the test circuitry will indicate acceptable performance by lighting the test lamp for about a minute. If a fault is detected, the test lamp will flash for a minute. After the test, the receiver returns to normal operation searching for the next satellite signal. Manual control or tuning of the receiver is never required.

The MX 902 is designed for ease of maintenance. Large, functional circuit modules with accessible test points are employed to aid in rapid fault location. Repair is by replacement of plug-in circuit modules. If required, service personnel are available in Europe, the United States, and in Japan.

Digital Computer

Selection of a digital computer for merchant ship application requires evaluation of many factors, including:
a) Availability of service around the world
b) Modular construction for ease of maintenance
c) Inherent ruggedness and reliability
d) Computing power
e) Low cost consistent with the above.

Only a very limited number of computer manufacturers have adequate service capabilities around the world. After evaluating computers from all such firms, Magnavox has selected the Hewlett Packard 2100A. In our opinion, based on comparative environmental tests in some cases, the Hewlett Packard computer is the most rugged and dependable machine in its class. It is manufactured not only in the United States, but also in France, Scotland, and Japan. Adequate service is

available in many other parts of the world, and modular construction is employed for ease of maintenance.

Because of its superior computing power, Magnavox is able to provide very sophisticated program features while using only 4096 words of computer memory. Thus, maximum capability is provided with minimum investment in memory.

A computer is powerless until provided with specific instructions, i.e., the computer program. Satellite navigation programs are prepared on punched paper tape or on magnetic tape cassettes for loading into the Hewlett Packard computer. After loading, the program instructions reside in magnetic core memory. The computer is equipped with a "power fail-auto restart" feature which assures that the program will not be lost during power fluctuations. In fact, as soon as power is restored, the computer immediately begins to function again, and it notifies the operator that a power failure has occurred.

Video Terminal

The video terminal, shown in Figure 5, consists of three components: (1) the video display, (2) the keyboard, and (3) the magnetic tape cassette reader. The door with operating instructions attached provides access to the cassette tape reader.

The video display is driven directly by the computer and provides an eight line message of up to 16 characters each. The actual video signal is created by a special Magnavox card plugged into the computer chassis. The signal is sent to the terminal over standard 75-ohm coaxial cable. The cable also may be routed to any number of video monitors, thus repeating the terminal display at other locations around the ship. A red filter is placed over the video display, making it suitable for night viewing in dark-adapted areas.

A Phillips-type magnetic tape cassette reader is provided for loading computer programs. Although it is seldom necessary to load the program, it is much faster and more convenient with a tape cassette than with a roll of paper tape through the ASR-33 Teletype reader. It requires only one minute to load a 4096-word program from magnetic tape versus 13.5 minutes by paper tape through the Teletype.

The 16-key keyboard allows the operator to send both command instructions and data to the computer. In addition to the ten numeric keys, the six function keys are:
a) CLEAR
b) BACKSPACE
c) CHANGE SIGN
d) ENTER
e) SPACE
f) DECIMAL POINT
The basic instructions for operating the navigation system are printed to the left of the keyboard, so that an absolute minimum of training is required for a new operator. In general, the system functions automatically without human intervention, and the keyboard is used primarily to request additional information from the computer.

There are several arguments against direct computer control of steering. One is the increased cost of a larger computer memory and the steering control interface. Because a standard autopilot also must be installed, there would be no offsetting cost reduction. Finally, initial reports of computerized steering experience indicate little or no performance improvement compared to that provided by modern autopilots.

It would be relatively inexpensive to add automatic steering to the MX 902-hp satellite navigation system, although extensive testing would be required on initial installations. Magnavox is maintaining an open mind toward the subject and will await comments or requests by the shipping industry.

System Operation

After system installation, which normally requires only a few hours if workers are available to string cables and mount the antenna, the cassette program tape is loaded into the computer. When the program is started, the computer sequentially asks the operator to enter all necessary information, e.g., present latitude and longitude, Greenwich time, compass heading alignment, etc. After this, assuming the automatic speed and heading interface is used, the operator is not required to enter any other information.

All basic system operating instructions are printed to the left of the keyboard. There are three general functions: (1) enter command, (2) enter data, and (3) request data, and within these general categories, each individual function is identified by a code number. For example, to request display of the last satellite position fix, the operator types the number "50", which is displayed on the bottom line of the video monitor, and then he presses the ENTER button. Immediately the last position fix is displayed, as indicated by the label LFIX on the bottom line. Whenever the CLEAR button is pressed, the bottom line is cleared, and the display returns to the normal mode, which provides the following information:
a) DRT - dead reckoning time since last satellite position fix update.
b) LAT - present latitude.
c) LON - present longitude.
d) GMT - Greenwich mean time.
e) R and B - great circle range and bearing.
f) SM or SA - manual or automatic value of speed.
g) HM or HA - manual or automatic value of heading.

The great circle range and bearing is from present ship's position to any designated "point" latitude and longitude entered through the keyboard. The range and bearing information may be deleted from the display by keyboard command if not required.

One interesting feature is the LOCK command code. After its entry, the computer will refuse to accept data from the keyboard until a specific UNLOCK code is entered. This feature prevents accidental or "playful" entry of data not desired by the navigator.

The objective of this simplified data entry and display concept is to permit new operator training in a minimum of time. Basic operation can be mastered in 10 minutes and complete training, including how to load and start the computer program, can be accomplished in from one to three hours.

CONCLUSION

Satellite navigation for merchant ships is practical and advantageous. Today's equipment is less expensive, more rugged and reliable, and very simple to operate as compared with older equipment designed for military and survey applications. Pioneers of the shipping industry have begun to use satellite navigation, and their acceptance is reflected in sharply increasing sales. Most encouraging are additional sales to owners who have used the equipment and found it desirable for more of their ships.

Reciting all the advantages of satellite navigation, such as worldwide coverage, all weather operation, and excellent accuracy, does not convey the true benefits of this space-age instrument. Perhaps only the experienced but skeptical navigator who uses the equipment at sea can properly evaluate its advantages. At first, any of these men have distrusted the new instrument, believed it to be wrong at times, only to find that the error was their own. Later, they have discovered the secure feeling of knowing their exact position even during long periods of foul weather with no other navigational reference available. Many once skeptical navigators now are strong proponents of satellite navigation. They value the added safety, they appreciate the automatic convenience, and there is evidence that the improved accuracy leads to more economical ship's operation.

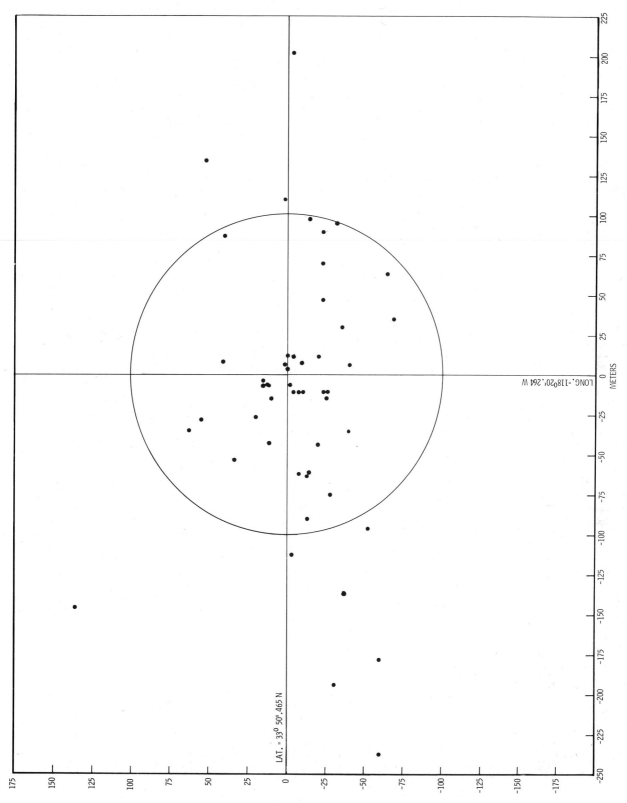

Figure 1. Scatter Plot of MX-902/hp Satellite Navigation Fix Results

58

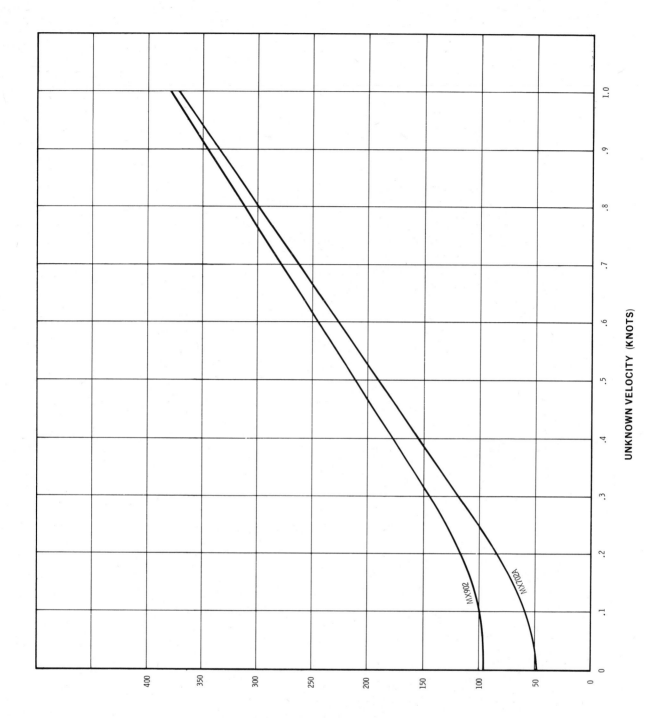

RMS SATELLITE FIX ERROR (METERS)

UNKNOWN VELOCITY (KNOTS)

Figure 2. Satellite Fix Error Versus Unknown Ship's Velocity

Figure 3. Standard Configuration of MX-902/hp Satellite Navigation Set

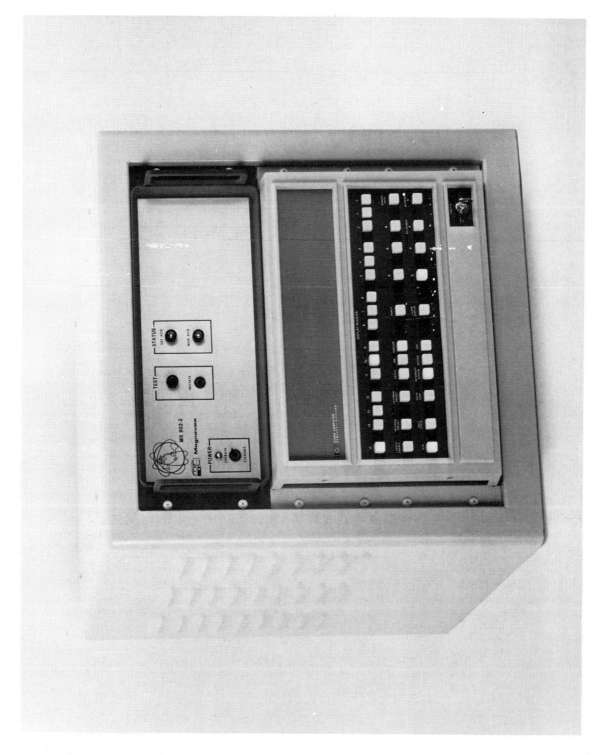

figure 4. MX-902 Receiver and HP 2100A Computer in
Compact Rack Configuration

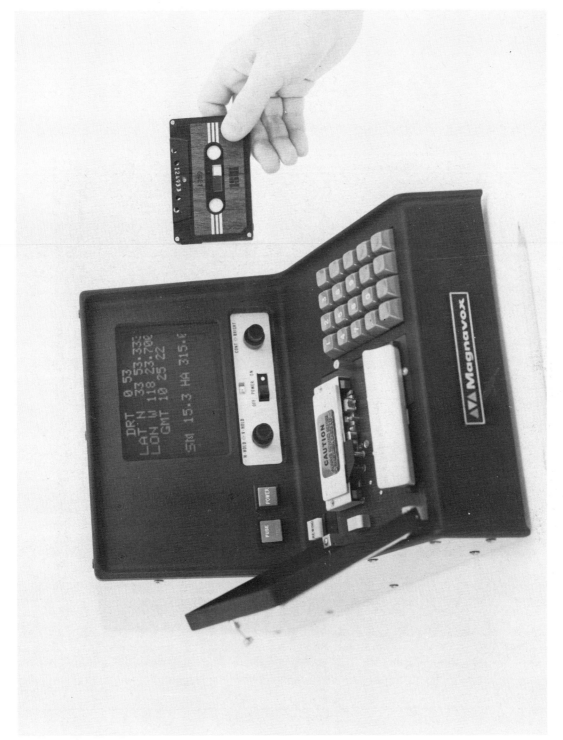

Figure 5. The MX-750 Navigation Display Terminal

Figure 6. Control and Display Provided by the MX-750 Terminal

ADVANTAGES OF MARITIME SATELLITES
FOR SHIP OPERATION AUTOMATION

Dr. H.C. Freiesleben
Standard Elektrik Lorenz AG
Stuttgart, Germany

ABSTRACT

A main advantage of the use of maritime satellites for civil shipping could be the automation of some navigational duties. The automatic warning of ships in the case of dangers will increase safety. Also meteorological, hydrographic and oceanographic messages could be received automatically, and observations in the same field, executed in ships, could be collected in this way. The watch for distress alerting could be automated. Finally position determination could be automated and executed without the crews participation and in the future traffic control including collision warning could be envisaged if todays techniques could be improved.

PRESENT STATE OF IMCO PLANNING

There are different views on the use of satellites for maritime purposes. As it is well-known IMCO discusses the problem of a maritime satellite system for some years. At the present state at least one geostationary satellite is provided for one area, probably the Atlantic, but with provisions for extension into a system with two or more satellites per area. As a minimum, the first phase should meet general communication requirements, in particular, public correspondence. In view of the improved communications through the establishment of a maritime mobile satellite service, allocated frequencies for distress and search and rescue, as now in the existing service, may not be required. The design of the first phase should not preclude the eventual addition of radio position determination facilities.

SHIP-OWNER'S INTERESTS

At present MF and HF is used for communication. It is expected that the use of satellites via L-band frequencies will be much more reliable. Naturally, ship-owners ask for benefits resulting by satellites. Although the International Chamber of Shipping did participate in all the important IMCO work of discussions and resolutions, the single ship-owner will weigh cost against benefit. Thus the designer of ship terminals for satellites must solve this problem and convince the ship-owner of the importance of the new aid. Formerly IMCO discussions gave priority to safety of life and consequently to search and rescue. Obviously the ship-owner is interested herein. It is expected that by the use of satellites search and rescue will be initiated faster and with higher reliability. However, fortunately distresses at sea implicate loss of lifes in less cases, compared with other kinds of traffic. A statistic of messages proves that distress cases make up only a very small percentage of the whole communications activity which serves mostly economic purposes. Economy therefore is an important factor.

AUTOMATION OF GENERAL INFORMATION

For communication between ship and land the projects, now under discussion, provide to call ships using a satellite as relay. There will be an individual selective call by a code, triggering only the receiver of the called ship, if an individual message will be sent or a telephone connection will be initiated. General information will be given to all ships, participating in the satellite system. Mostly, communication of this class belongs to safety traffic messages, consisting of data transmission for a particular area and comprising obstacle warning as drilling or production platforms, storms or icebergs etc. Other data are meteorological, hydrographic and oceanographic information including its transmission by facsimile. Such information does not need a man handling the receiver, but could be received automatically and stored by a tape to be used at given time. Now, by this the activity of the radio officer could be reduced considerably. The same applies for the collection of meteorological, hydrographic and oceanographic observations, effectuated by ships automatically and called off also automatically without the crews participation. The watch for distress cases could be automated too. Now, discussions with ship-owners taught that such saving work load from the radio officer would be highly appreciated.

AUTOMATION OF POSITION DETERMINATION

Presently position fixing by conventional aids satisfies all demands. At high sea celestial navigation is used very much when possible. For approach and coastal navigation radio aids as Decca or radio bearings and radar are available. In the near future OMEGA is expected to give a worldwide coverage and to yield as accurate fixes as by astronomical observations. However, discussions with ship-owners show, that there is also some interest, to get position fixes automatically by means of satellites, and that the demand for it may increase in the near future.

Shipping authorities would like to have a surveillance of ocean traffic to generalize the AMVER system. They point to the growth of the number of ships, especially of sea-going recreation craft, that indeed could make such a surveillance desirable in the near future. A traffic surveillance in confluence areas is wanted already today, but this may be performed by land radar stations.

A surveillance system by means of satellites would be effective only, if all craft participate. This requires a cheap ship board equipment, to be interrogated regularly by the surveillance organization, enabling it to fix the position of all participating craft without any aid of the crew. As there exist already beacons, interrogated automatically in this manner for several purposes, technically this could be realized. But the cost may be high, especially because of the allocation of sufficient frequencies for mobile services in the L-band only. Probably this will require directional antennas with high gain, to be directed towards a satellite. This is the reason, why there are allocated some very narrow bands near 157, 162 and 4o6 MHz for experiments with emergency position indicating radio beacons (EPIRB), working automatically. A U.S. contribution, submitted to IMCO, proposes to extend such experiments to 1.6 GHz too. It would be favourable to incorporate such an equipment to ship terminals needed for other purposes, and to fit all craft with it to increase safety. At all events such an equipment should work automatically. As a unit of an expensive ship terminal it could serve

for navigation, by transmitting automatically the result of position fixing to the ship, where it will be also indicated automatically. By a regular sequence of such measures navigation could be fully automated during an ocean voyage.

CONTINUOUS TRACKING, COLLISION WARNING

The land organization could track continuously ships by satellites and alert them, if equipped with communication units, via satellites in cases of danger, threatening a single ship only. As techniques improves the accuracy of position fixing could be sufficient to aid a ship by this way, also for navigation near coasts or in narrow passages. Some papers also propose collision warning. At present the interest of ship-owners in such use of satellites does not exist, but the more it could be automated, the more an interest will rise.

Automated Marine International
Maritime Services Satellite System
Definition Study
Newport Beach/Cal., Aug. 1971   (356 p.)

EUROSPACE Memorandum No. 8
The Use of Satellites for
Maritime Purposes
Paris, July 1971   (86 p.)

EUROSPACE
The Use of Satellites for
Maritime Purposes
The Results of a Survey Based on
Discussions with Some European
Shipping Companies
Paris, April 1973   (24 p.)

Intergovernmental Maritime
Consultative Organization
Panel of Experts on Maritime Satellites
1 Extraordinary Session Report
Nov. 1972   (42 p.)

National Academy of Sciences
Useful Applications of Earth-
Oriented Satellites
Panel 11: Navigation and Traffic Control
Washington, 1969   (85 p.)

AN INTEGRATED SYSTEM FOR NAVIGATION AND
ANTICOLLISION FOR SHIPS

F. Fjellheim   E. Gjeruldsen

N O R C O N T R O L
division of NORATOM-NORCONTROL A/S

1. SUMMARY

This paper describes the DataBridge integrated navigation system. The system comprises the following features:

- Anticollision computation

- Navigation and deadreckoning

- Position fixing (Satellite, Decca, Omega)

- Automatic steering (Autopilot)

The ever increasing demands made upon todays navigators due to larger, faster and more expensive ships is creating a need for better navigational aids. The DataBridge system performance is described discussing some problems concerning radar tracking and some aspects related to automatic steering of ships.

2. INTRODUCTION

There has recently been an explosive development in the traffic at sea. The trend is towards larger, faster and more expensive ships, and the demands on the navigators increase accordingly. As a consequence the education of the navigators lags the technological development. Ships are also in many cases poorly equipped with modern navigational aids.

This is not only due to lack of such equipment. Actually numerous ingenious devices have been developed, but some have proved of limited value, and others are rather expensive.

Radar is of course the first that comes to mind. This special instrument was introduced into the merchant marine after world war II. Radar was considered to be just what man required in order to navigate safely on the high seas. In the beginning this appeared to be so, but then collisions took place between ships both equipped with Radar.

Many collisions could soon be traced back to the Radar, and the notion: "Radar assisted collisions" came into existence, the most widely known being the collision between "ANDREA DORIA" and the "STOCKHOLM". Incorrectly extracted data from the Radar led the navigators to perform avoiding manoeuvres which resulted in collision between the two ships. This happened in dense fog. Study of collision records shows a close relation between the number of collisions and days with fog.

The Radar-assisted collisions, which all seem to appear during extremely poor visibility, has led to the conclusion that Radar is a rather poor anticollision device. Indeed, during the last years it has been developed a number of more or less manual methods to make the navigators analysis of information more easy, but they are all relatively timedemanding and/or inaccurate.

An inquiry among English navigators concluded that sufficient information about the traffic situation can only be obtained by graphical registration, i.e. presentation of target movements superimposed the radar's raw video. This ideal Radar presentation should include:

a) Detection of all detectional targets

b) Choice of targets with decreasing range and consequently possible danger of collision

c) Graphical registration of the apparent movement of selected targets in order to decide an approximate CPA (Closest Point of Approach)

d) Complete reproduction of all information regarding the movements of all targets which represent the greatest danger, and at the same time approximate information conserning all other targets so that sufficient information about the traffic-situation is available.

e)   Estimation of alternative manoeuvres
      to avoid collision with possibilities
      for evaluation of the effect of the
      manoevure on the traffic situation.

f)   Accurate prediction of the influence
      of the manoeuvre on the most dangerous
      target.

g)   Continuous plotting to detect evt.
      manoeuvres of surrounding ships.

h)   Continuous computation of CPA in order
      to turn back to original course as
      soon as possible.

i)   Continuous computation of the total
      situation

      The above points can not be achieved
by manual plotting. The modern computer is
however, well suited to deal with problems
of the above mentioned types. In the preceeding the DataBridge system is described
explaining how the system takes well care
of all the outlined functions in a simple
way.

3.   SYSTEM DESCRIPTION

Great care was taken in the design stages
to make DataBridge as modular as possible,
enabling the customer to acquire the system configuration most beneficial for
his purpose. A modular system also allows
the addition of sub-systems, at some later
date, if desired. The use of a general
purpose computer in DataBridge permits
a continuous updating of the sub-system
programs in use onboard. Fig. 1 shows
the system lay-out.

3.1 Anticollision

The DataRadar is a computerized anticollision system based upon signals from
ship's radar, gyro and log.

The system makes use of the ship's main
radar without interfering with the function
of the latter. Thus the operation of the
main radar is completely independent of the
DataRadar system operation.

The PPI included in DataRadar serves as
a slave to the main radar, showing the
same picture as the main radar. In
addition the slave indicator may display
a number of lines (vectors), squares and
a circle. The positions of the symbols
are always controlled from the computer.

The vector gives complete information about
speed and course of any tracked target.

The square indicates targets causing an
alarm.

The circle is used to pin point desired

targets to be tracked and may be moved on
the PPI by means of a joystick.

When tracking of a selected target is
initiated, the computer collects information about the target from the main radar
via an interface unit. The target speed
and course are calculated, and the result
is presented on the PPI in terms of a
velocity vector. The vector is a prediction
of the target motion during the next 30
minutes, and markers divide the vector into
5 minute intervals. It is possible to
track 15 targets simultaneously.

The operator may alternatively select 15
minutes vector length with 2.5 minute
intervals.

The target CPA is calculated as the length
of the perpendicular from own ship to the
direction of the relative target vector.
Collision warning will be given whenever
CPA becomes less than the specified limit
within the next 30 minutes.

This limit is set by the navigator.
The target on collision course will be
marked with a flashing square on the PPI
and the "Collision Warning" lamp will be
flashing. When the alarm is acknowledged,
the lamp as well as the square will change
to steady on-state, whilst the acoustic
warning is turned off. The square will
mark the target until the alarm situation
ceases to exsist.

When tracking a selected target, the
following data will also be available on
the numerical display:

-    True course and speed

-    Closest point of approach (CPA)

-    Time to CPA

-    Range and bearing

The range and bearing of the pointer
circle may be displayed at any time.
The operator may also simulate a proposed
maneuver. The simulation makes possible
a study of the future traffic situation
prior to the actual maneuver execution.

A simulation may either be performed to
give a continuously updating of the PPI
picture as long as the simulation is executed, or to give a result in terms of a
CPA Limit Course. In case of the former,
the operator may insert a time to execution of the proposed maneuver.

Next a lever is operated either to give
a starboard or port simulation. As long
as the lever is operated, the maneuver
course is updated at a rate of 2° per
second. The picture on the PPI is updated
accordingly.

In case of the latter, the operator pin point one tracked target which he wants to avoid. The computer calculates the least change in course needed to make the pointed target CPA become equal to the defined CPA limit. The corresponding traffic situation will be updated on the PPI.

If during simulation "COLLISION WARNING" start flashing, this means that a target not previously being on collision course, now is.

Up to twelve different presentation modes are available through the combination of the following facilities:

- North up/Head up

- True vectors/Relative vectors

- True motion/Relative motion

- OFF-CENTRED

3.2 Radar tracking strategy

Experimentally we have made use of two different strategies. One is automatic acquisition of targets where the extractor detects all targets within a range of 20 n.miles. The other is manual acquisition of targets where radar data is recorded from a window surrounding the target. Some of the result from the latter mentioned strategy is covered in this paper. Fig. 2. shows the necessary parameters for the data recording. A target (hatched area) is surrounded by a window W.

```
W    = BG x RG
BG   = Bearing gate
RG   = Range gate
CRSE = Own ship's gyro course
AP   = Antenna position ref. north
ØP   = Target true bearing
RP   = Target range
T    = Video threshold
VS   = Angle between antenna and start of
       recording area
```

The tracking is of the track-while-scan type and the following parameters are fed to the extractor during the target sample:

VS = controlling distance between the antenna and the target bearing gate edge

$RP-\frac{1}{2}RG$ - distance from own ship to range gate edge (start of video recording)

RG - recording interval (range)

At the end of the range recording interval the video pattern for the actual sweep is fed to the computer for future processing.

During the video recording the computer is interrupted every sweep in the bearing gate The extractor is rather simple and its only task is to record and quantize each sweep in the gate.

The resolution of the extractor is:

```
Range:    25 m
Bearing:  360 /(PRF x Antenna RPM)
          (degrees)
          Typical 0.15 degrees.
```

Fig. 3 - 6 show what the computer reads from the extractor. The video is recorded as a pattern consisting of ones and zeros. Ones indicate video exceeding the video threshold. The pattern show the quantized raw video before correlation. Four different patterns are shown.

Fig. 3. Showing a target in normal tracking phase. It has been sampled 144 times. The target is surrounded by sea clutter and the threshold is accordingly adjusted to 3.4 volts.

Fig. 4. Initial phase shows the first sample after acquisition. The gate is large to ensure lock on the target. The envelope of the target compared with the actual radar parameters indicate a ship with video returns from more or less the centre line.

Fig. 5. Acquisition of target in sea clutter. The pattern shows seven groups of video. In this case the target is far larger than the sea clutter.

This is not always true when the target is for instance a small fishing boat.

Fig. 6. Two succeeding samples of the same target in normal tracking phase.

By sweep to sweep correlation it is possible to eliminate noise-like interference. The criteria for video is a certain number of succeeding sweep having video at the same range. Equipment operating on radar signals normally are fitted with a video threshold. To be recorded as a video the strength of this must exceed the threshold. The threshold makes possible a discrimination of video of different strength. The threshold could be a function of range, the average noise level and strength of the actual target video. The threshold may be controlled only by hardware or there may be a feedback from software calculation.

In a tracking system using this target gate strategy the size of the gate should be controlled by the computer. The size should be time dependent and fig. 5 indicates that it would be wise to narrow the gate to isolate the target of interest.

In case of inaccurate positioning of the pointer circle at the acquisition of a target the gate may be positioned outside the target. The computer should in this case enlarge the gate to lock on the target.

Thus the gate size could be a function of:

- time
- range
- number of targets in the gate
- actual target size
- number of succeeding lost target samples.

The first step in the processing of the video pattern is to isolate the target of interest. The video data from the correlator is subjected to various kind of noise-like

- sea clutter (which only to a certain extent is eliminated by the correlator and threshold strategy)
- rain clutter
- variable size of the same target caused by pitch and roll in heavy sea

This makes it necessary to do some filtering before the calculation of the target centre of gravity.

The centre of gravity is then used as the measured position of the target in the tracking algorithmes.

Conclusion

The performance of a radar tracking system depends on the quality of the radar signals. Two other important parameters are

the antenna position and
own ships gyro course

The two latter may both introduce bearing errors which then will cause fluctuations in the target parameters. However, it is our experience that with today's electronics and filtering techniques it is possible to produce an anticollision system with sufficient accuracy, resolution and reliability.

3.3 Navigation and position fixing

Meeting the time schedule is a major factor in shipping economy and a very important part of today's navigation.

A properly selected and planned track for a voyage is also a safe route, and by taking into account the expected currents it will also be the most economical one.

DataSailing is a set of programs which perform navigational calculations when given information about the operators desired voyage. The calculations performed result in a loxodrome or Great Circle course, dead-reckoning position, drift angle and magnitude based upon automatically fixed positions as well as distance and time to any of 10 turnpoints.

Based upon basic navigational formulae the Loxodrome - or Great Circle - course is calculated between current position and the next turn-point on the desired route. The calculated course will be continously updated and transferred to DataPilot when the latter is operating. The course may be displayed whenever desired.

When required a Drift vector may be inserted manually. DataSailing will then compute the corrected course in order to compensate for the drift. The navigator can tell the system to steer uncorrected or corrected course. The correction angle is displayed together with the computer (uncorrected) course.

DataSailing includes the facility of accepting up to a maximum of 10 positions along a desired route. At each of these positions the DataSailing program will alter the course upon demand, such that the computed course at any time will be calculated along the path between the current position and the next turnpoint.

Based upon the logged speed, the program will also calculate the Distance To Turnpoint (DTP) and the Time To Turnpoint (TTP). Both calculations depend upon the operators choise of Loxodrome or Great Circle course calculation.

The communication with the system is very simple and the computer is guided through the operating procedure by lighting up of pushbutton switches which indicate the next step in the procedure. All communication with the system is through the DataSailing, the manual dataentry, and the datadisplay sub-panels.

In addition to the dead-reckoning based upon inputs from gyro and log, DataSailing may use inputs from automatic position fixing systems for correction of dead-reckoned position as well as for computation of drift.

The following position fixing systems may be interfaced:

- Satellite
- Omega
- Decca Navigator
- Doppler Sonar

The extended version of DataSailing is a completely automatic navigation system for continuous position fixing, computation of drift and corrected course demands to the DataPilot system.

In order to make the system as reliable as possible, various types of monitoring routines and self-checking steps are incorporated in the system.

In addition to the self-evident advantages arising from the use of an accurate navigational aid such as the satellite navigational system for instance, there are additional advantages arising from using such a system in an integrated navigational system such as DataBridge. These advantages arise from the close interaction between automatic dead-reckoning (DataSailing) the automatic position fixing, and the advanced autopilot (DataPilot) system.

Quantitative comparisons between use of separate navigational aid and integrated navigational system are as yet not available. On a qualitative basis, however, it is evident that an integrated navigational system will be able to make corrections earlier and thereby give rise to more accurate navigation. This is due to the fact that an integrated system will detect effects like drift and set and corrective measures can be implemented before the effects are serious thereby keeping navigational inaccuracies to a minimum.

The size of the computer memory prohibits integration of more than one of the navigation receivers. Nevertheless, provisions have been made for a special combination of The Satellite navigation and Decca. The two cannot be operated simultaneously, but one can choose which of the two one requires at any time. The advantages of both systems are thus available at a low price.

3.4 Automatic steering of ships

Based on optimal rudder movement it is the task of the DataPilot system to keep the demanded course. The aim is to increase the ship's overall speed, and this is made possible by using advanced control theories in the design.

Signals from the gyro compass and a rudder angle transmitter are used, and the DataPilot's subpanel on the DataBridge console will have the same controls as normally found in a regular autopilot system. However, the DataPilot is quite a lot more than a computerized autopilot, and includes features not found in convential system. All tuning parameters are accessible via the central data input function, and the operator is free to change these parameters

within predefined limits. The DataPilot also includes a self-checking facility and whenever a fault is detected, an alarm and a system failure is given.

Three modes of operation are possible:

- Rudder Control
- Manual Course
- DataSailing Course

In the first mode the rudder is operated directly from the "Course/Rudder angle" lever and the actual angle used is indicated through a small window situated above the lever. The indicator meter shows the actual telemotor position.

In Manual Course mode the DataPilot operates according to a reference course selected by the operator. The actual course to steer (setpoint) is shown on the display above the "Course/Rudder angle" lever, which is used for altering the desired course to steer.

In DataSailing Course the DataPilot operates according to a reference course calculated and updated by DataSailing. The calculated course to steer is shown on the display above the lever.

When a change in course is activated either by means of MANUAL COURSE of DATASAIL COURSE reference change, the DataPilot will not change the course instantaneously. A smooth change from the gyro course towards the reference course will be generated. The turning rate will depend upon the operator's choise between slow or high turning rate.

By operating the "LOADED SHIP" push button, the operator may choose between two sets of preselected tuning constants, i.d. loaded condition and ballast.

The "WEATHER ADJUSTMENT" factor will determine the sensitivity of the DataPilot. This is adjusted as a number between 0 and 8, where 0 gives maximum sensitivity and 8 gives minimum sensitivity.

Whenever the difference between the gyro-course and the reference course becomes greater than a predetermined limit value, a flashing "COURSE ERROR" alarm will be given.

Alarms are also given in case of faults in the DataPilot or in parts of the ship's steering system connected to the DataPilot. These warnings are presented as an acoustic alarm along with a coded definition of the failure.

A number of ships are now fitted with this type of autopilot, and the reports are very encouraging especially as far as abilities in rough weather are conserned.

SYSTEM GENERAL VIEW

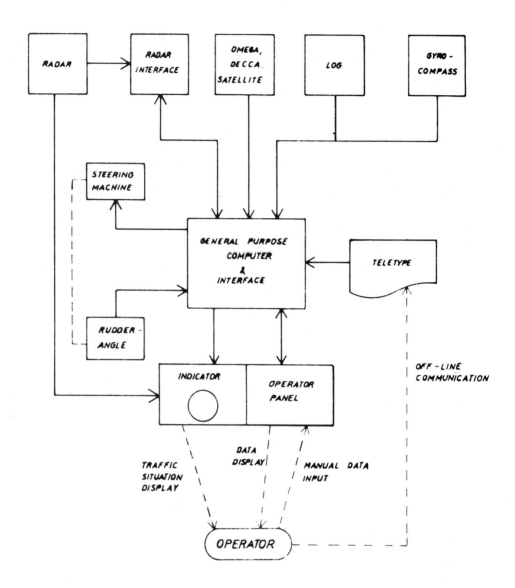

Fig. 1

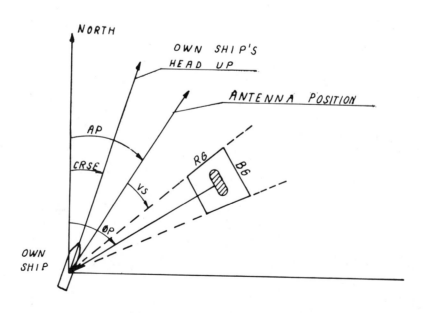

FIG. 2

Sample no	Course	Target no	Video thres-hold	Range	Bearing	Bearing gate	Range gate
000162	011175	000004	000330	001727	020331	000047	000014

Sample no	Course
000330	*0000000000000
000330	·000000000000
000330	··000000000000
000330	*0000000000000
000330	-0000000000000
000330	:·0000000000000
000330	*0000000000000
000330	*0000000000000
000330	*0000111000000
000330	··0000111000000
000330	*0000111100000
000330	·0000111100000
000330	*0000111100000
000330	*0000111100000
000330	*0001111100000
000330	*0001111100000
000330	·0001111100000
000330	·0001111100000
000330	*0001111100000
000330	*0001111100000
000330	*0001111100000
000330	*0000111100000
000330	·0001111000000
000330	*0001111000000
000330	*0001111000000
000330	*0001111000000
000330	*0001111000000
000330	*0001111000000
000330	*0001111000000
000330	*0001111000000
000330	*0001111000000
000330	*0000111000000
000330	*0000100000000
000330	+0000000000000
000330	*0000000000000
000330	*0000000000000
000330	·0000000000000
000330	*0000000000000
000330	·0000000000000
000330	*0000000000000

Fig.3

Target: 3000 tons ship
Range :   1727 = 1.6 n.miles
Cond: Sea clutter, normal phase

```
000001   052466   000002   000210   013242   056423   000043   000060

000210   000000000000000000000000000000000000000000000000000000
000210   000000000000000000000000000000000000000000000000000000
000210   000000000000000000000000000000000000000000000000000000
000210   000000000000000000000000010000000000000000000000000000
000210   000000000000000000000000111001110000000000000000000000
000210   000000000000000000000001111111100000000000000000000000
000210   000000000000000000000001111111110000000000000000000000
000210   000000000000000000000001111111100000000000000000000000
000210   000000000000000000000001111111100000000000000000000000
000210   000000000000000000000011111111100000000000000000000000
000210   000000000000000000000001111111110000000000000000000000
000210   000000000000000000000001111111110000000000000000000000
000210   000000000000000000000001111111110000000000000000000000
000210   000000000000000000000001111111110000000000000000000000
000210   000000000000000000000001111111100000000000000000000000
000210   000000000000000000000001111111110000000000000000000000
000210   000000000000000000000001111101100000000000000000000000
000210   000000000000000000000001111000000000000000000000000000
000210   000000000000000000000001110000000000000000000000000000
000200   000000000000000000000000000000000000000000000000000000
000170   000000000000000000000000000000000000000000000000000000
000160   000000000000000000000000000000000000000000000000000000
000150   000000000000000000000000000000000000000000000000000000
000140   000000000000000000000000000000000000000000000000000000
000130   000000000000000000000000000000000000000000000000000000
000120   000000000000000000000000000000000000000000000000000000
000110   000000000000000000000000000000000000000000000000000000
000104   000000000000000000000000000000000000000000000000000000
000104   000000000000000000000000000000000000000000000000000000
000104   000000000000000000000000000000000000000000000000000000
000104   000000000000000000000000000000000000000000000000000000
000104   000000000000000000000000000000000000000000000000000000
000104   000000000000000000000000000000000000000000000000000000
000104   000000000000000000000000000000000000000000000000000000
000104   000000000000000000000000000000000000000000000000000000
000104   000000000000000000000000000000000000000000000000000000
```

Fig. 4

Target: Unknown size

Range: 13242 = 9.8 n.miles

Cond.:   Target acquisition (first sample)

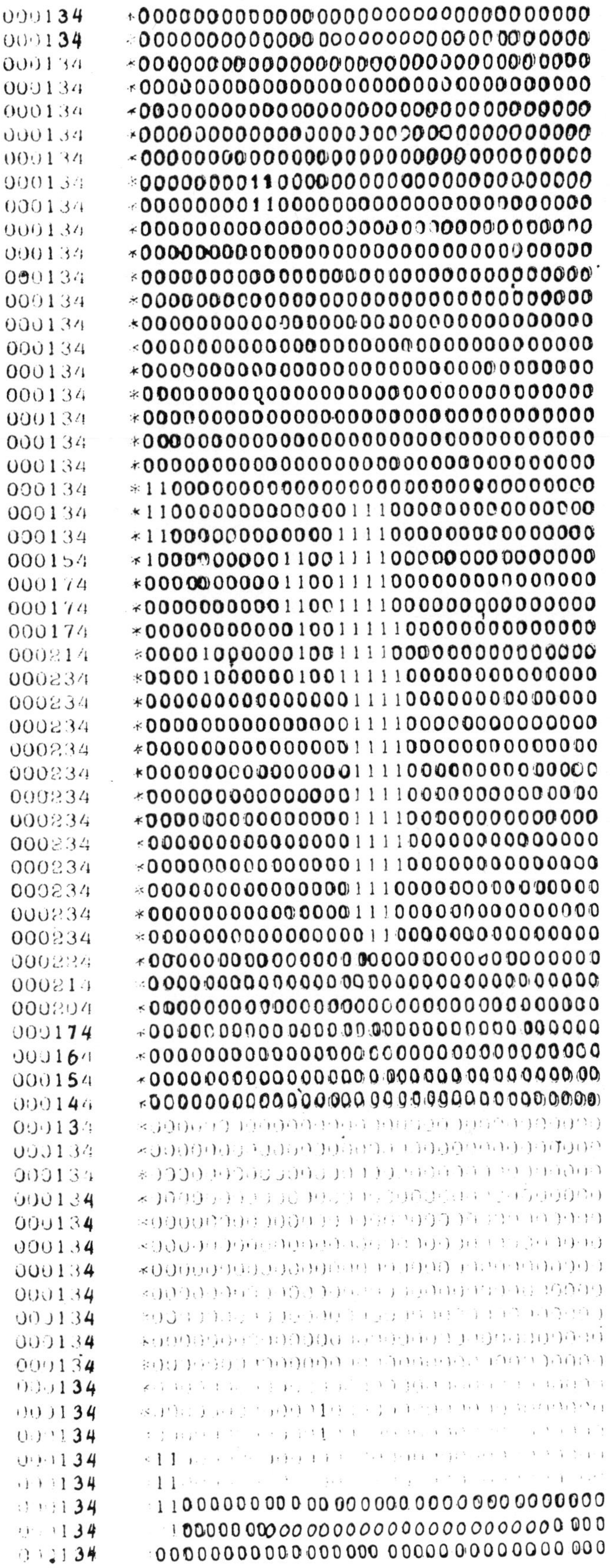

Fig.5

Target: 5-600 t
Range : 2106 = 1.8n.m
Cond.: target aquisi-
tion in sea
clutter

```
000110    011175    000004    000230    005323    016306    000021    000014

000230    .0000000000000
000230    .0000000000000
000230    .0000000000000
000230    .0000000100000
000230    .0000001110000
000230    .0000001110000
000230    .0000001110000
000230    .0000001110000
000230    .0000001110000
000230     0000001110000
000230    .0000001110000
000230    .0000001110000
000230    .0000001100000
000230    .0000000000000
000230    .0000000000000
000230    .0000000000000
000230     0000000000000
000230    .0000000000000


000111    011136    000004    000230    005274    016360    000024    000014

000230    .0000000000000
000230    .0000000000000
000230     0000000000000
000230    .0000001000000
000230    .0000011100000
000230    .0000011100000
000230    .0000111100000
000230    .0000111100000
000230    .0000111100000
000230    .0000111100000
000230    .0000111100000
000230    .0000111100000
000230    .0000111100000
000230    .0000111100000
000230    .0000011100000
000230    .0000001100000
000230    .0000000000000
000230    .0000000000000
000230     0000000000000
000230    .0000000000000
000230    .0000000000000
```

Fig.6

Target: Unknown size

Range: 4.7 n. miles

Cond.:   Normal phase
           Two succeeding samples of same target

SHIP'S INTEGRATED NAVIGATION SYSTEMS

J. B. Carr
Sperry Marine Systems Division
Sperry Rand Limited
Bracknell
Berkshire
England

Among the standard dictionary terms to describe the word Integrate we find: 'To make into a whole by adding or putting together constituent parts; to complete, to make entire'.

This description of 'Integrate' leaves us with the feeling that the constituent parts are of greater value when integrated than when separated, and indeed a major part of the concept of Integrated Navigation is to achieve this enhanced value of separate pieces of information or data when combined in an optimum manner.

An example of this advantage of integration is the computation of a long-term continuous position fix which is more accurate than any of the individual pieces of positional data being fed into the system. A further advantage of integration is that the data can be processed and displayed with a speed and accuracy beyond the capacity of the human brain, and be based on advanced mathematical concepts beyond the capability of most Navigating Officers.

Ships' Integrated Navigation Systems vary greatly in first cost and complexity, from missile carrying atomic submarines downwards and many systems are designed to do more than purely navigational functions. For the purpose of this paper, however, descriptions will be restricted to navigational systems of the type which will be of interest to operators of modern merchant vessels.

Before describing integration in any depth it will be useful to look at the general development of marine navigational instruments over the last few years, and the reasoning behind some of the latest equipment such as docking and collision avoidance aids. Nearly all standard nav-aids and instruments form part of the complete integrated system and integration cannot be discussed in isolation from the equipment which provides the raw data.

Brief History

Not so many years ago the standard navigation fit of ocean-going merchant vessels comprised: one radar, one gyro compass with bearing and steering repeaters, one standard magnetic compass, automatic pilot, speed log, echo sounder and one receiver for either the Decca or Loran position fix systems. Shipowners wishing to protect ever-increasing investments in expensive new tonnage, improved equipment availability by fitting twin radars and gyro compasses, dual channel steering controls etc. but essentially no really new concepts in navigational instruments or equipment were introduced between the years 1945 and 1970.

By 1970 new types of merchant ships were entering service in increasing numbers, and it was realised more and more by both equipment manufacturers and ship operators that the existing equipment could no longer cope adequately with the navigational problems raised by large, fast vessels operating in increasing traffic densities.

A frightening aspect of some of the new problems is that they frequently defy solution by even the most skilled officers as the data available to the officer is in some cases changing with a speed and complexity that taxes the human mind beyond its limits, or alternatively the critical motions are too small to be appreciated by human sensory perception.

The new problems confronting the navigator can be divided into two distinct areas, as follows:

1. Docking and anchoring of large displacement vessels

2. The handling of large and/or fast vessels at full sea speed through heavy traffic in restricted waters

The Docking Problem arises from the extremely large displacement of modern V.L.C.C.s, Bulk Carriers and O.B.O.s. Jetties and piers are designed to absorb a certain momentum when first contacted by the docking vessel. In order to achieve a constant limiting momentum the speed of say, a vessel displacing 250,000 tons must be only 10% of the speed allowed a 25,000 tonner and only 1% of the speed allowed a 2,500 tonner. The problem is aggravated by the fact that these values are speeds over the ground, not speed through the water.

The Master or Pilot of a V.L.C.C. during final docking manoeuvres must try to estimate velocity towards the jetty, fore and aft motion along the vessel's longitudinal axis, swing at bow and/or stern and the rate of change of all these motions. This is problem enough in still water but becomes infinitely more so when the vessel is under the influence of current, tide, wind and the pushing or pulling of several tugs.

With such large vessels the rate of change of any given motion is extremely small due to the large inertias involved, indeed the changing motion can become a significant factor before it has reached the value at which it can be perceived by the operator. Taking swinging of the bow as an example, it has been shown by simulation that humans cannot sense a swing or yaw rate of less than 0.05 degrees/ sec. An appreciation of the angular momentum generated by a yaw rate of this low value on a 250,000 dwt vessel is illustrated by the fact that at full sea speed a rudder angle of approximately three degrees is required to kill the swing.

The second problem: that of handling large vessels at normal sea speed, is the opposite in many ways to the docking problem. In the place of the lack of perceivable data, the officer can now be in the position of having more relevant data than can be handled efficiently. Because of their high momentum and extreme length, large vessels have long stopping distances and large turning circles. Ideally therefore, they should have more sea room in which to manoeuvre, but unfortunately the opposite is frequently the case, due to deep draughts restricting the useable width of channels etc.

Collision avoidance in restricted waters becomes a prime problem to be solved by the ship's officer; avoiding action must be taken much earlier in a possible encounter situation to allow for the reduced manoeuvrability. This in turn increases the number of targets which have to be plotted as plotting must be initiated on targets at a greater distance from own ship than in the past.

The situation is further complicated by the entry into service of Container Ships steaming at speeds of up to and even exceeding 30 knots. Although such vessels have a higher power to weight ratio than V.L.C.C.s, stopping distances are still longer than with more traditional hull forms and dimensions. This is due to the combination of high speed, fine underwater lines and loss of astern power resulting from propellor cavitation when rotating astern whilst the vessel still has a high forward velocity. Practical sea experience has validated model tank tests which showed that container ships with low values of G.M. cannot safely apply large rudder angles at full sea speed without risking cargo damage, by virtue of the high angles of heel generated. So great is this inherent danger of excessive heel that some modern automatic pilots are designed to restrict applied rudder angle as a function of speed. The container ship officer is therefore faced with manoeuvring problems similar in nature to the large V.L.C.C.s. Collision avoidance decisions must, however, be made even earlier in an encounter situation as a high cruising speed of say, 30 knots gives time to point of possible collision as low as half those times experienced by a V.L.C.C. at 15 knots.

Once again, the solution is to start plotting targets at a greater distance than normal from own ship with the resulting increase in the number of targets plotted.

The development of new devices to help solve problems in these two areas have led to the introduction into service of the first really new navigation equipments since the advent of radar and Decca/Loran systems.

Docking

Docking systems based on the Doppler Sonar techniques are now available from several manufacturers. Detail designs differ and as yet no standardisation has been reached on frequency, pulse or continuous wave signals, digital or analogue display, etc. and all designs are a compromise between several desirable features. All systems do, however, provide the required data for movement over the ground down to extremely small values and in all horizontal axes of motion.

An additional feature is that for the first time information is available on the actual speed of the vessel over the ground at normal sea speed when navigating in 'Continental Shelf' waters. As speed is measured in both the fore and aft and athwartship directions, the two values of speed can be resolved into a drift angle with the result that a vessel can now be steered on a true ground track in place of the normal compass heading. A well designed doppler sonar system can therefore provide important data to an integrated system in addition to its prime function of assisting in docking manoeuvres.

Collision Avoidance

Several types of collision avoidance systems have been designed in recent years to speed up radar plotting and to give the operator the ability to handle a greater number of targets. These systems can be divided into three major categories:

1. Collision Threat Assessment

   This allows the operator to quickly assess which targets are potentially dangerous. Plotting of the targets is then carried out manually by the traditional methods. Time is saved as only potentially dangerous targets take up the operator's time and attention.

2. Time Based Automatic Plotting Systems

   Such systems can be based on dedicated fixed programme computers, general purpose digital computers or composite systems using electrical, mechanical and optical devices. Whatever method of processing the data is chosen, the end result is very similar, producing automatically the same kind of plot as the operator would generate by using a grease pencil. Different time and heading trials are displayed by the computer on the PPI to assist the operator in arriving at a decision.

3. Graphic Situation Display

   This is the most advanced system currently available. Based on a general purpose digital computer, the display is independent of time and shows the position of the possible point of collision of every target entered into the computer. All target PPCs lying on own ship's heading marker are collision dangers and any heading change which does not intersect a target PPC is a safe heading. Time and heading trials are not required and the total situation is displayed continuously.

This paper is not the place to discuss Collision Avoidance Systems in detail, the important point is that any well designed system is based upon a general purpose digital computer and this piece of equipment is the key in turning many diverse pieces of navigational equipment into an integrated system.

General Comments on Integration

In describing any computer based system the term 'hardware' covers actual equipment used to generate raw data, transform the data into a form acceptable to the computer, the computer itself and the various devices to display or record the processed data.

The other term frequently used is 'software' which describes the instructions or programme held within the computer memory. Any system, regardless of the quality of its hardware, is only as good as its software programme and the writing of the programme can only be successfully undertaken by a team who thoroughly understand the problems to be solved. This understanding must include detailed knowledge of the data producing hardware, with its errors, variations and other limitations as well as the ergonomics or man/machine interface problems, so that the processed data is displayed in a form quickly, accurately and unambiguously absorbed by the operator.

For an integrated system of any kind to be a success, the overall concept, choice of hardware, writing of software, design of the interface or data conditioning electronics, etc. must be under the control of one central authority, known as the Systems Management Team.

Where Ships' Integrated Systems are concerned, the choice of individual pieces of hardware cannot be left to the shipowner or shipbuilder. Equally the overall system design and therefore the total responsibility for reliability and accuracy, must be placed in the hands of one prime contractor. Responsibility cannot be shared among several suppliers of appropriate hardware.

Available Data

Fig.1 is a block diagram showing the navigational equipment fitted to a modern V.L.C.C. The data available to the Ship's Officer from the associated instruments is as follows:

True Heading
Water Speed
Ground speed in two axes
X Band (3cm) radar, video and synchro-
    nising signals
S Band (10cm) radar, video and synchro-
    nising signals
Transit satellite raw data
Omega and corrected data
Collision Avoidance graphic display

Integration

The Collision Avoidance System provides
the central computer with input interface from the radars, gyro compass and
speed log. To achieve the simplest form
of integration we require in addition a
tele typewriter or CRT (TV) type display
and keyboard so that the operator and the
computer can communicate with each other,
a magnetic tape reader, 4,000 extra words
of memory and a software programme to
instruct and control the computer in the
solving of a particular problem.

Fig. 2 shows this basic system in block
diagram form and in this form the system
can calculate a continuous position fix
in latitude and longitude with extra update information from Decca, manual
sightings, etc. entered by the operator
via the keyboard.

Very few shipowners will feel that
expenditure on such a simple integrated
system is worthwhile and Fig.3 therefore
shows in block diagram form the type of
system which is becoming increasingly
accepted as a good standard design. The
prime task of the system is still the
calculation of the continuous position
fix but it will be seen that both transit
satellite and Omega signals are being
processed so that the system has a worldwide capability.

Satellite up-date of position is automatic and the computer carries out all
necessary data reduction so that the
satellite receiver and antenna are the
only additional hardware needed. The
software programme is able to automatically correct the Omega raw data and
the Omega Receiver can feed into the
computer automatically or the O.O.W.
can operate the receiver and enter the
uncorrected data into the computer by
the keyboard. This manual entry method
saves money and gives the O.O.W. a
routine duty to perform at say half
hourly intervals, to keep him interested
and alert. From the psychological point
of view it is important that the officer
feels that he is part of the system, with
an important function to carry out and,
at the same time, retain manual dexterity
in operating position-fix instruments.
Manual inputs of Decca, Sextant and Radar

or manual bearing fixes can of course also
be entered into the system through the
keyboard. It is a fact that the more data
from diverse sources that is available the
more accurate will be the computed
position.

With the amount and variety of data now
available to the computer, the position
fix accuracy becomes considerably better
than that achieved by manual position fix
calculations and more accurate even than
the best available single piece of data.
This desirable state of affairs is
achieved by using a mathematical concept
in the software known as a Kalman Filter.

Kalman Filtering

The Kalman Filter concept was developed
in the USA by that part of the space
programme concerned with precise navigation of manned space vehicles.
Basically, it is a repeat sequence of
mathematical expressions which remember
past data, receive present data, calculate
present position and calculate probable
future positions based upon the combination of past and present information.
New incoming data is firstly corrected for
known errors where errors are not random
but can be expressed in mathematical terms
i.e. north, south acceleration errors in
gyro compasses and Diurnal variations in
Omega data etc. The actual corrected data
is then compared with the synthetic data
calculated from past or historic information and from the comparison a Weighting
Factor is applied to the new data. A
Weighting Factor is a statement of credibility expressed as a percentage i.e. 90%
to 100% being excellent data while 10% is
poor data.

After the Weighting Factors have been
applied any position which still does not
agree with the forecast calculated
position is probably an error due to say
changing strength of current, small
perminent or slowly changing error in
gyro compass etc. and this now known
error is used to improve the next set of
future data. Fig.4 shows in simple
block diagram form the close loop taken by
data in the Kalman Filter process. As one
circuit of this loop takes only milli-
seconds and the existing data is constantly
rotating, any new piece of incoming information is absorbed, weighted, compared and
applied very quickly.

Fig.4a shows a plot of four position fixes,
three of which are good and lie where
expected whilst the fourth contains errors
not compensated for in the system. As a
Weighting Factor of only 10% has been
given to this data its disturbing effect
on the calculated position is small. The
error will, however, be held by the

computer and the future Weighting Factor increased or decreased depending upon how future incoming data changes.

From this simple explanation two things are apparent:

1. Where data is received constantly i.e. heading, water speed, ground speed, drift angle, etc. Weighting Factor corrections become very accurate.

2. Where only two pieces of data are available and one is in error, it is not possible to state which is the bad data, therefore the more data available the better, particularly if different pieces of data are subject to different types of error pattern.

Ship operators frequently ask: 'Which is better, transit satellite or Omega?', the answer being that the best results are achievable when both types of data are used in such a way that each enhances the other.

Fig.4b shows graphically the positional accuracy of four types of fix over a six hour period. In addition, the continuous position fix calculated by an integrated system based on the Kalman Filter technique is shown. Also shown are the Root Mean Square (RMS) values for each type of fix over the six hours. It will be seen that the integrated system fix is much superior to any of the other individual fixes.

Several additional types of information can be made available to the Navigating Officer, either through the CRT display or by separate analogue or digital read-outs. These include:

1. Heading of actual track made good over the ground, speed along track made good, and drift angle.
   Note: This information is only available while Doppler Sonar system is holding bottom lock.

2. Calculation and display of headings required to maintain Great Circle tracks.

3. Calculation and display of headings and speeds required to maintain or regain position on a pre-planned route, the details of which have been entered into the computer via the keyboard.

4. Issue of warning to O.O.W. when vessel has reached critical points in a route programme calling for change of heading, etc.

5. Interface with autopilot to allow continuous and automatic corrections for drift angle, Great Circle track, etc.

It is possible to think of more real time problems which could be solved. The restraining influence is not the capacity or ability of the computer but rather the costs involved in writing special software, designing clear, unambiguous data displays, etc. and finally facing up to the psychological problem posed by a Navigating Officer who is bored and who feels that the system is about to make him redundant. Systems must remain as aids to the Ship's Officer, the servant but never the master. Computers only know what is told to them in their software programme. The human brain, on the other hand, contains experience gathered from years of knowledge of the sea and ships, has data inputs such as sight, hearing, smell and feel which are denied to the computer and has the gift of imagination which allows the human brain to re-write its own software programme to suit unexpected or entirely new situations.

One of the advantages of a well designed integrated system is its flexibility. It can be changed as the years pass to keep abreast of new operating problems or to take advantage of new techniques. It is simple to expand its capacity and, when not being used for real time tasks, such as collision avoidance, position fixing etc. can be quickly re-programmed to carry out stress and stability calculations, machinery performance analysing, ship's business etc.

Reliability

A fully integrated system with all its hardware is a sizeable investment and this investment could be at least partially wasted if the system is unavailable due to breakdown when needed. Several systems are now being installed by the author's company where total systems availability is guaranteed to be not less than 98%, and at least partial availability guaranteed to be not less than 99%. To achieve such high values of availability many major components have been duplicated and interswitched (See Fig.3). Most of the hardware contains failure warnings and built-in test equipment. A certain level of spares is carried aboard ship and at least one member of the crew is given training in fault finding and component changing. Last but by no means least, the systems are backed by trained engineers and spare parts in major Ports on the vessels' trading routes.

Finally, it must again be stressed that, to be able to guarantee both performance, accuracy and reliability one prime contractor must be responsible for the whole system and preferably be in a position to design and manufacture the

80

majority of the required hardware in
addition to writing the software programmes.

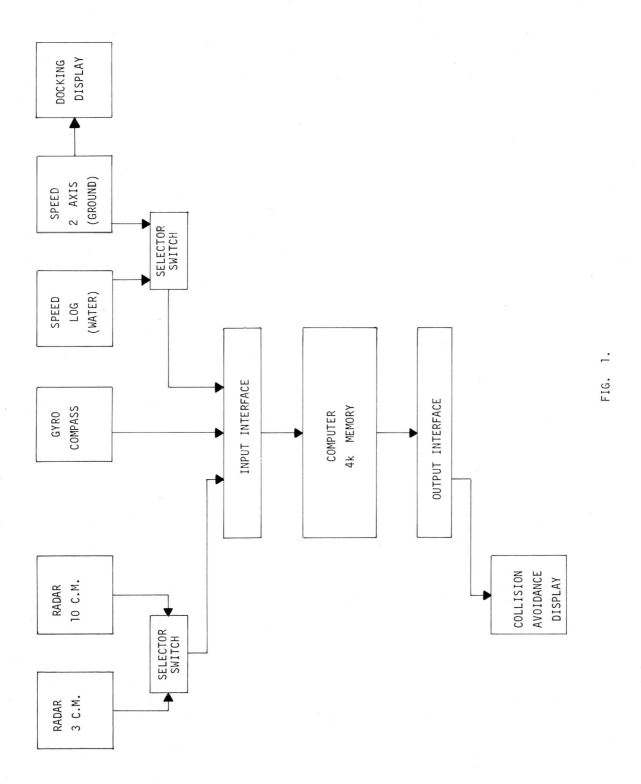

FIG. 1.

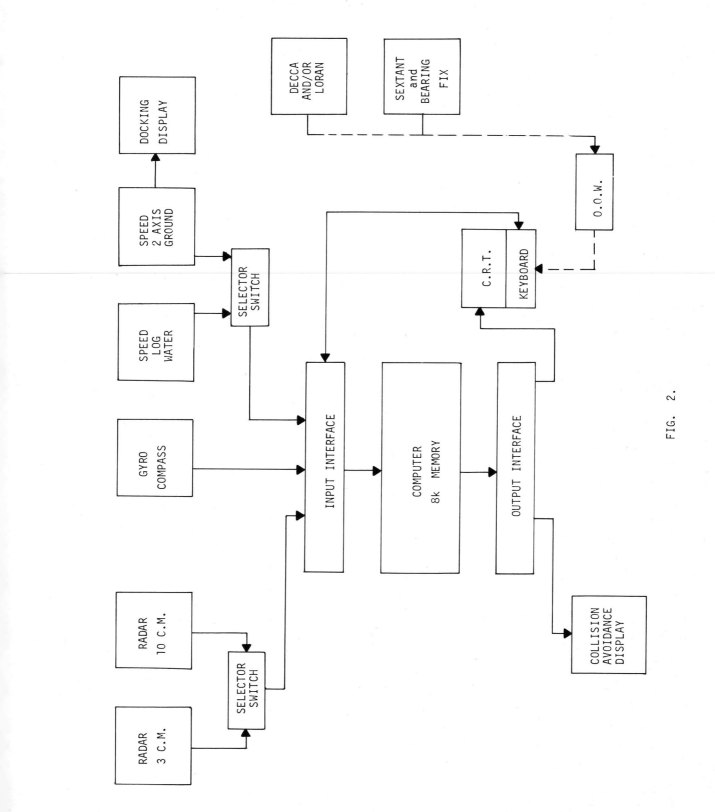

FIG. 2.

82

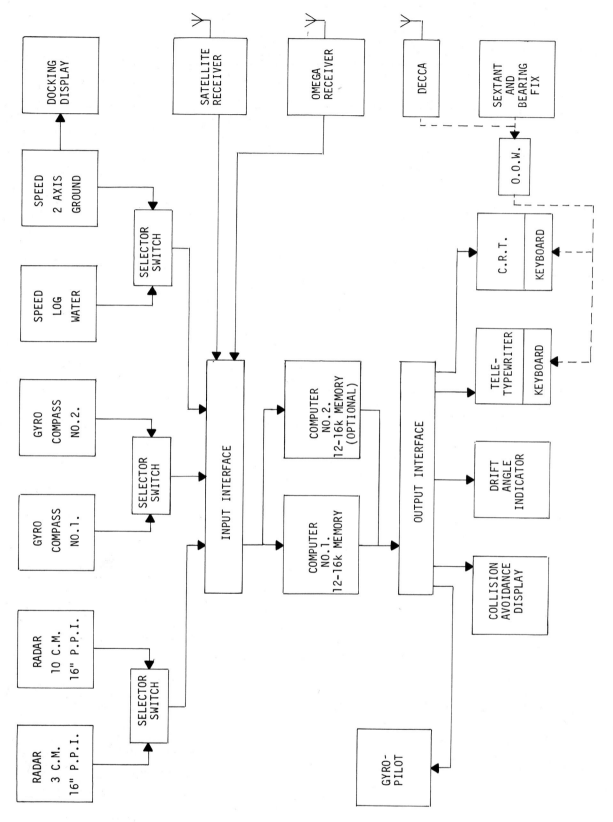

FIG. 3.

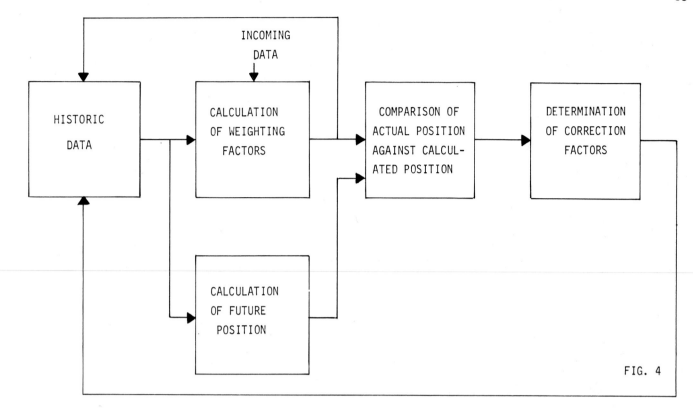

INCOMING
DATA

| HISTORIC DATA | CALCULATION OF WEIGHTING FACTORS | COMPARISON OF ACTUAL POSITION AGAINST CALCUL- ATED POSITION | DETERMINATION OF CORRECTION FACTORS |

CALCULATION OF FUTURE POSITION

FIG. 4

D

POSITION CALCULATED BY SIMPLE AVERAGING

A   B   C

= POSITION CALCULATED BY SIMPLE AVERAGING

= RESULTING POSITION AFTER
  WEIGHTING FACTORS APPLIED

WEIGHTING FACTORS
POSITION A = 90%
POSITION B = 95%
POSITION C = 85%
POSITION D = 10%

FIG. 4a

84

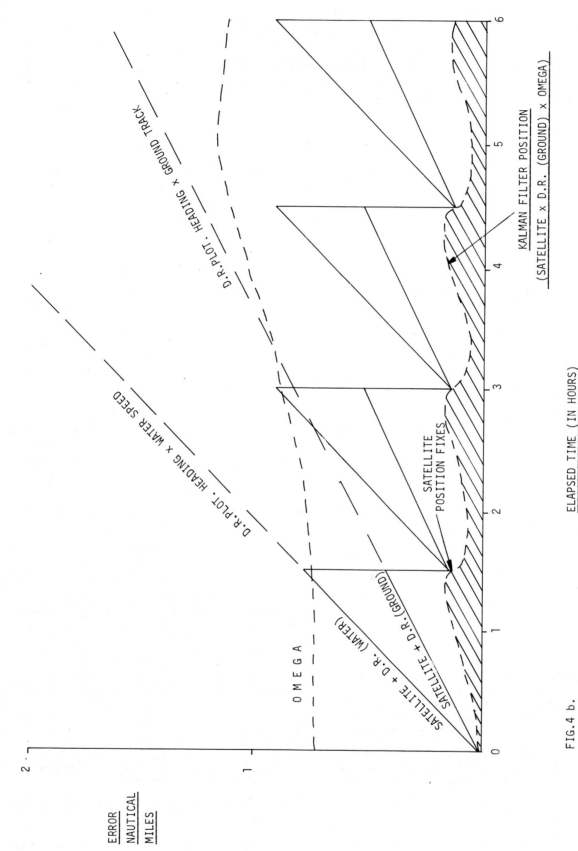

ERROR
NAUTICAL
MILES

FIG. 4 b.

ELAPSED TIME (IN HOURS)

OMEGA

D.R.PLOT. HEADING x WATER SPEED

D.R.PLOT. HEADING x GROUND TRACK

SATELLITE + D.R. (WATER)

SATELLITE + D.R. (GROUND)

SATELLITE
POSITION FIXES

KALMAN FILTER POSITION
(SATELLITE x D.R. (GROUND) x OMEGA)

INTEGRATED NAVIGATION SYSTEM

WITH OMEGA AS PRIMARY SOURCE OF POSITION INFORMATION

Per Bergstad
NORSK A/S PHILIPS
Oslo, Norway

ABSTRACT

An integrated navigation system relieves the officer on watch from much of his routine work. Safety is enhanced by better watchkeeping as well as the better position knowledge resulting from continuous Omega recordings being fed automatically to the central navigation computer. Other advantages are reduced sailing time and better prediction of arrivals. The navigation system is built around one central computer receiving inputs from speed log and gyro compass as well as a special Omega receiver.

The technology of navigational aids has evolved rather slowly through the centuries. The most drastic steps in this evolution are probably the events of radar and electronic navigation systems during World War II, which considerably reduced the seafarer's dependence upon visibility.

The present introduction of the computer on the bridge is in many ways less conspicuous, but while being an aid in the navigators' decision process, its impact may be of even greater importance to navigation than the other equipment.

The computer does not give the navigator any more information, but it enables him to utilize the available data in better ways and in much shorter time. In addition, the officer on watch will be relieved of much routine tasks. From time to time you hear an argument against rationalization at sea saying that "the duty officer must be on watch anyway, and he has nothing else to do". This is not so in a properly run company. Firstly, the duty officer should concentrate exclusively on his watch duty and not be disturbed by time consuming and boring, but nevertheless necessary routines. If he does have time available, however, for instance during ocean crossings in fair weather, his time should be filled with work that requires his particular skill.

The employment of the computer naturally leads to an extensive integration of the different navigation functions, since efficient use of the computer requires that the same data, once fed in, are used for many different applications. The degree of integration depends upon how far the automation is carried. One obvious extreme is that the robot with 100% automation and full integration of all systems. On board ships today, however, major decisions are all taken by man. Consequently our system is designed to give him the best possible advice while leaving him with a manual system whenever this is advantageous for the understanding of the overall picture.

The most important single item in all navigation systems is knowledge of own position at any place in the world at any time. However, the required position accuracy may vary depending upon the surroundings. Normally it is sufficient to know the position within 2-3 miles in the open sea, while in narrow waters it hardly can be known accurately enough during poor visibility conditions. The requirement for perpetual position knowledge can of course also be relaxed. Today measurement intervals of less than 5 minutes hardly appears necessary while the orbit interval of the present system of navigation satellites may at times be somewhat too long.

No available systems fulfil these requirements. We have settled on Omega because:

- It will cover all areas of the globe of interest to merchant ships,

- It gives practically continuous coverage in time, and

- The accuracy is satisfactory for ocean use.

In narrow waters normal Omega is definitely not good enough, but there most captains would use radar anyway. Besides, if differential Omega was to be installed in critical areas, that system probably will have the desired accuracy.

THE SYSTEM

The complete navigation system should take care of all functions from the planning of the trip through the sailing phase and finally give up control when the ship is berthed. Such a system belongs in the future and may never be implemented with manned ships. In our system are included those parts of the general system which we think will assist the navigator without infringing on his rights and duties to take the decision.

An example is the collision avoidance system, which is a part of our general ship automation system and shares the computer with the other applications in our trial system on board M/T "BERGE FISTER". It is installed next to the navigator's data teletype on the bridge giving him the necessary information, but not automatically partaking in his work.

The integrated navigation system comprises the following applications:

Route Planning where the different route alternatives are analyzed and forms the basis for the selection of route.

Weather Routing which is used in conjuction with the above route planning taking the forecast information about sea conditions into consideration.

Navigation Programme doing dead-reckoning based upon continuous and automatic data from log and gyro with automatic position updating from Omega and/or manual updating from celestial observations.

Great Circle Sailing which in conjunction with the navigation programme keeps track of course changes for the chosen great circle route and supplies course correctives. It may also be coupled to the auto-pilot, keeping the ship automatically on the great circle course.

The system is built up around an executive programme calling upon a number of sub-programmes. This system gives large flexibility for sharing the use of repeated routines or data, as well as for changes in the programme system.

ROUTE PLANNING

For most planners of sailing routes the main objective is the shortest time between ports. External factors such as strong currents/foul waters often causes this route to be not necessarily the shortest one. The different routes are entered into the computer in the following way:

From a chart the navigator selects the sailing routes which may be used while sailing from A to D, Fig. 1. The position of each turning point is entered into the computer. Thereafter the different routes are defined, each consisting of a start point, a finish point and a number of straight legs characterized by their end points and the expected speed on that particular leg, taking currents and sailing conditions into consideration. The computer may now be given an order to process the data, that means calculating the distances and required course settings both for great circles and loxodromes as well as the estimated time for each leg and for the whole trip. An example of such a computation is given in Fig. 2.
Checking routines, such as listing of all the entered positions, are also included in the programme system.

The great circle calculation programmes are also used for the Omega position determinations. They therefore have to be very accurate and require the use of an ellipsoidal model for the shape of the earth. The results from this have puzzled the users because the "computer's great circles" turned out to be longer, and accordingly less attractive, than those which they calculated themselves when trying the system near the equator.

During these experiments the navigators also suggested including a programme for loxodrome calculations. (A loxodrome is the track being followed when sailing at constant course between two points on earth, and it is therefore the most used sailing route at short distances). The solutions for the loxodrome are printed next to those for the great circle for easy comparison.

Based upon the expected sailing times for the different routes, the navigator now has to make his choice, and for each leg he can decide whether he wants to go by great circle or loxodrome. If the computer is governing the auto-pilot, he might as well go by great circles at all times, otherwise he might choose the loxodrome in order to simplify the steering, unless this is forbidden by the prolonged sailing time.

WEATHER ROUTING

During the route planning the speed on each leg was estimated by considering currents and safe speed in the particular waters. The speed may, however, be hampered by foul weather and subsequent rough sea. The purpose of the weather routing programme is to select the route between two positions which takes the shortest time under the forecast weather conditions. The system was described in a paper at the International Symposium on Maritime Navigation in 1969 [1] The problem solution is based upon a network model developed by U.S. Navy Research Facilities [2], where the straight line between origin and destination (Fig. 3) represents the shortest route, i.e. great circle, while the other branches in the network represent alternative routes, each branch being associated with a characteristic speed which is the maximum safe speed for the particular ship in the weather forecast for the day the ship will be in that area. The solution to the problem is now to find the least-time path along the branches in the network.

The required input data are the positions, the wave heights along the different branches which are forecast for the time the ship expects to be there, as well as safe speed as a function of wave height and direction. A further requirement to the wave data is that they must be in a format which is suited for being entered into a digital computer.

None of these data are easily obtained today. The relation between safe speed and wave condition is normally not known. It can be determined empirically, but without stress measurements of the ship it probably will be rather subjective. Wave data are available for the North Atlantic and parts of the Pacific Ocean. They are transmitted to the ships as a facsimile chart. The computer input will therefore require being preceded by a manual reading off the chart, which is quite a roundabout way since the charts already have been transmitted in a digital form, though not in a format that with reasonable recoding can be utilized by the computer.

Obviously meteorological and oceanographic data will never be broadcast for only one limited group of users, but with the growing employment of automatic data processing equipment on board ships, it should be possible to agree upon a standard format by which data could be recorded on paper tape or magnetic tape for later processing by the different application programmes. One further requirement for effective weather routing is sufficiently longtime wave forecasts. They are not available today, but will come as a

result of the increased ocean and weather watch programmes and the use of computers in meteorology.

By examining the network of Fig. 3 we notice that even a relatively small net requires large numbers of data and very quickly leads to an impressive number of possible paths to be examined. The former requires large memory capacity in the computer while the latter demands long computing time or very fast computers. Since a large net obviously may lead to a more efficient sailing route, this is what the navigator asks for. However, there is no point in making the branches shorter than the spatial resolution of the wave forecasts, since the large network may overload a shipborn computer. The answer to the last objection is to move the whole weather routing business ashore and thereby also save the wave forecast transmissions. However, in that case we are met with the arguments that the large nets cannot be handled efficiently, not because of the computer, but due to the administrative difficulties in attending a reasonable amount of ships with frequent changes of course.

All experience up to now has been with shore based weather routing. We are going to try it on board, but till now we have not had the opportunity since our test ship has been running in areas with poor meteorological coverage. If I am going to venture any prophecies, I see future weather routing being performed on board the ship by the navigator on the navigation mini computer. This computer will via satellite communication be tied to a computing center ashore where all the meteorological data are being processed.

COMPUTER ASSISTED SAILING

When the best route has been selected, the navigator may call the Great Circle Sailing programme. He now should give the computer the starting point at the exact time, thereby obtaining a reference and the correct Omega lane count. A dead reckoning programme will now run continuously with input data from the log and the gyro compass. It will assist the Omega lane count and mutually update dead reckoning positions from Omega or from manually introduced positions from celestial observations.

Omega updating is done automatically every minute. If the computer is coupled to the auto-pilot, the course set point will be continuously updated with the latest great circle course. In the case where there is no connection between the computer and the rudder, the course changes for great circle sailing may either be presented for pre-set increments, for instance $1°$, or at pre-set time, for instance at the beginning of every watch.

Computerized position calculation from sextant observations has not been attempted. We have considered it, but found that the work load, either by storing huge data tables or replacing the tables with complicated astronomical calculations would demand too much of the computer in comparison with the relatively simple hand calculations from tables. Some parts of the observation work, for instance time keeping, might be somewhat simplified by computer automation, but we have not looked into that.

The dead reckoning position will at any time be presented to the navigator on command, or may, if desired, be written out on the bridge teletypewriter at any chosen interval. Further, the teletype may well in advance inform about the course changes to come when the ship approaches the next turning point.

When the auto-pilot is not governed by the computer, the navigator may choose to sail loxodromes rather than great circles whenever the time difference between the two routes is reasonable. He may, of course, use the dead reckoning and the Omega programmes also in this case.

OMEGA

According to the latest schedules all eight Omega transmitters will be fully operational during 1974. The system will then offer world-wide coverage at VLF frequencies with a hyperbolic navigation system.

The different stations will be time multiplexed during a total cycle of 10 seconds as shown in Fig. 4. It is sufficient to receive only one of the three frequencies but correlation of data at two or three frequencies serves to increase the ambiguity interval between lanes, which for only the lowest frequency is about 8 NM.

Similar to other well known hyperbolic systems, Omega works on the phase difference principle. The transmissions from each station is controlled by a cosium-beam time standard with an accuracy of 10^{-12}. By intercomparison of signals from other stations good stability is maintained. The ship at sea receives these signals, each of approximately one second duration. The ship's receiver normally locks itself to the best, and records the phase differences between them. After corrections for phase errors in the radio wave propagation, the geographic position is worked out from the positions of the stations and the hyperbolic coordinates given by the phase differences.

Summarizing, the receiver has to perform the following functions:

- Detection of signals
- Station identification
- Phase comparison
- Skywave correction
- Coordinate transformation

Of these, all but the first, are well suited for processing by a digital computer. The last two may, however, in simple systems also be taken care of manually with tables and charts, thereby saving memory space in the computer.

The Philips Omega receiving system consists of a receiver head doing the detection part, and which is interfaced to a general purpose digital computer. The different users then has a choice whether they want to use tables and charts or to invest in a larger computer system doing all the functions, and thereby having the possibility of integrating Omega in a general navigation system.

The receiver is shown schematically in Fig. 5. It consists of a whip antenna (which may be replaced by a wire) with a preamplifier tuned to accept the entire Omega band 10-14 kHz, in the base. The signal is then fed to a similar amplifier stage in the main receiver before being separated by the narrow band channel filters feeding each of the three frequencies to mixer and detector stages. The frequencies are 10.2 kHz, 11 1/3 kHz and 13.6 kHz. The local oscillator frequency is near 2.6 MHz. It has a short time stability of about 0.2 ppm and is phase locked to the best station. A divider chain reduces this frequency to the correct reference frequencies and timing pulses. These are combined with signals from the different frequency channels in the phase computation circuits which are interfaced with the computer. The amplitude detector is fed from both the 10.2 kHz and the 13.6 kHz channels and its output is entered into the computer through an analogue to digital converter. The signal is used for station identification through the amplitude correlation programme. The receiver software comprises about 1500 words of machine language programmes and it performs the second and third functions on the list.

The station identification is carried out by a programme which correlates the received signal with the transmitter signal pattern of Fig. 4. The lengths of the pulses vary between 0.9 and 1.2 seconds for the different stations, and their puls pattern provides an unambiguous key to recognition of the reference point (start point) of the pulse train. The correlation programme places a heavy demand on CPU (Central Processing Unit) time and is only executed at the system start up.

Via the computer the local oscillator in the receiver is phase locked to a selected transmitting station. The phase differences between the local oscillator and the different transmitters are measured, and the phase differences for each combination of station pairs are calculated and stored in a table, which is the input to the coordinate transformation programmes.

However, before being transformed to geographic coordinates the phase information which actually is the coordinates in the hyperbolic system, has to be corrected for propagation anomalies. These corrections have been separated into two parts. One is a function of the geographic position with respect to each transmitter, and correction tables are published by the Omega Office[3]. They cover all relevant parts of the earth, and have been divided into areas corresponding to 4° by 4° at the equator. The other correction compensates for the diurnal effect caused by the sun on the reflecting layers in the atmosphere. Though correction factors also for that effect are given in the Omega Tables[3], a mathematical model for the correction[4] is more economic with computer memory space. But even without the diurnal correction, the total correction table for all stations is a formidable amount of fixed data. Our system therefore permits that correction tables for only a part of the world at the time is stored in the computer memory. Data for a new route may today be fed in from paper tape,for future systems probably from a magnetic tape cassette.

Finally the hyperbolic coordinates are transformed to latitude and longitude through an iterative computation programme where an ellipsoidal model for the earth has to be used in order to obtain sufficient accuracy.

The Omega position may be printed out on command, otherwise it will be used for automatic updating of the navigation programme.

EXPERIENCE AND ECONOMY

The Omega receiver was first tested in Oslo. To our surprise all four active stations were received well. We had been informed of previous test with ship-borne receivers where all stations except the Norwegian one were lost when entering the harbour of Oslo.

Our trial ship is, however, chartered in the trade between Japan and the Persian Gulf, which is an area with poor coverage by the four presently operating Omega stations. One occasional trip into the South Atlantic Ocean has proved that the receiver system performs well also on board the ship, but we did not have the opportunity to test out the entire system during the time we were within satisfactorily coverage.

The navigation system has therefore been tested without the Omega part. The tests have led to only minor corrections in the programmes and to the inclusion of the loxodrome programme which the navigators found useful, and it provided a good comparison with their old method. In the operators' communication sections we have put great emphasis upon simple operation codes and fault-checking procedures. Experience has shown this to be a necessity which we will always have to keep in mind. Until the computer becomes a part of everyone's life, we can hardly overemphasize the need for simple operation.

The price for this type of equipment depends largely upon the price of minicomputers, which in these days is on the way down. Furthermore, the cost of the navigation functions will be less if the computer can be shared with other applications, as for instance collision avoidance or cargo calculations, and the price will vary depending upon whether the different applications have to be simultaneously accessible. In order to arrive at any meaningful price, we therefore would have to discuss a specific system in detail.

Besides the price, any serious user would want to know what operational savings he can expect from his investment. In that case we also have to consider the specific type of ship and its trade. I have seen some authors, particularily in British publications, trying to affix numbers to the savings, but since they may add more confusion than help, I will limit myself to pointing out the areas of potential savings, and the user may himself evaluate his own savings.

The primary outputs of the integrated navigation systems are exact knowledge of the position at all times, and means for estimating future position at any time. Together with a knowledge of meteorological and oceanographic data these features contribute to minimizing the sailing time, and the importance of this is well known to everyone in the shipping industry.

But in addition the improved position determination assists in other ways. By a better estimate of expected times of arrival the ship can save time by advance reservations of berthing area, or it may do better planning for arrivals which are influenced by tide or limited by locks. Furthermore, accurate time estimates may improve the relationship with the customer.

The value of these features differs, as mentioned before, with ship and trade. They will for instance be very different for a Mediteranean dry cargo ship and a North Atlantic automobile carrier.

There is one area, however, where all ships benefit from accurate position knowledge: Ship's safety. Whether own ship is in distress, or if it may be of help to others, accurate position is of utmost importance. For this purpose alone any reasonable method for improving the navigation should be implemented.

REFERENCES

(1) Hustad, B., "Weather Routing of
     Ships", paper at the International
     Symposium on Maritime Navigation,
     Sandefjord, Norway, September 1969.

(2) U.S. Navy Weather Research Facili-
     ties, "Ships Routing by Numerical
     Means", Report NWRF 32-0351-042,
     March 1961

(3) U.S. Naval Oseanographic Office,
     H.O. Pub. No. 224, "Omega Skywave
     Correction Tables".

(4) E.R. Swanson, "VLF Phase Prediction",
     Proceedings from VLF Symposium,
     Sandefjord, Norway, October 1971.

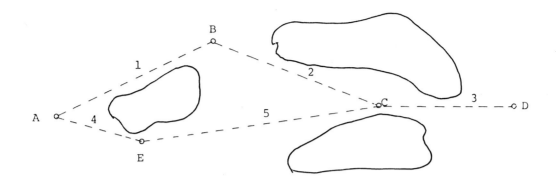

FIG.1   CHART FOR ROUTE SELECTION

ROUTE 1.

LEG	DIST	TIME	AZ	DISTL	TIMEL	AZL
1	600.0	35/17	128	600.5	35/19	130
2	600.3	35/18	171	600.8	35/20	173
3	450.0	26/28	153	450.2	26/29	154

TOTAL (GREAT CIRCLE)   TOTAL (LOXODROME)

DIST =   1650.8   DIST = 1651.5
TIME =   97/03   TIME =   97/08

ROUTE 2.

LEG	DIST	TIME	AZ	DISTL	TIMEL	AZL
4	306.0	18/00	169	306.2	18/01	171
5	820.0	48/14	141	823.5	48/26	144
3	450.0	26/28	153	450.2	26/29	154

TOTAL (GREAT CIRCLE)   TOTAL   (LOXODROME)

DIST =   1576.0   DIST = 1579.5
TIME =   92/42   TIME =   92/56

FIG.2   COMPUTATION OF ROUTE PLANNING.

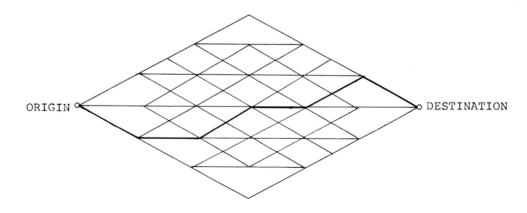

FIG.3 GRID NETWORK FOR LEAST TIME TRACKS.

92

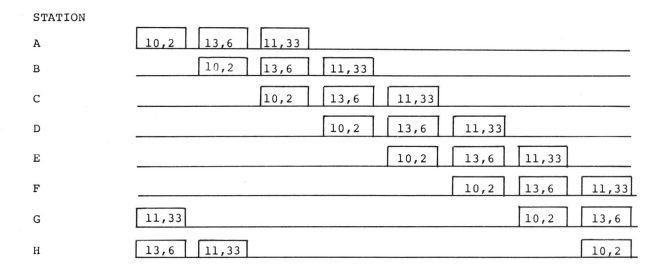

STATION

FIG. 4   OMEGA TRANSMITTED SIGNAL FORMAT

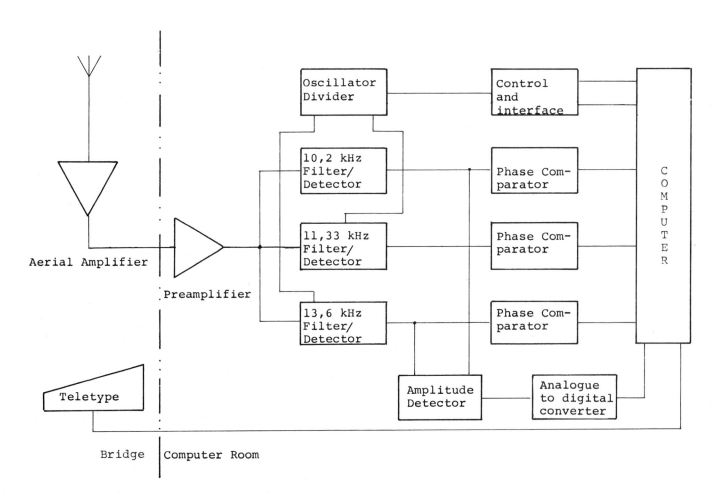

FIG. 5   SCHEMATIC DIAGRAM OF THE OMEGA RECEIVER

AUTOMATION OF COLLISION AVOIDANCE AT SEA
- WITH SPECIAL REFERENCE TO THE INTERNATIONAL REGULATIONS FOR PREVENTING COLLISIONS AT SEA

A. G. Corbet
Lecturer
Department of Maritime Studies
University of Wales Institute of Science and Technology,   Cardiff.

It is impossible to consider the prospect of automating the collision avoidance processes of vessels at sea without considering the International Regulations for Preventing Collisions at Sea (hereinafter referred to as the Regulations).

The Block Diagram in Fig. 1 gives an outline of the system of collision avoidance on a power-driven vessel. Many of the inputs shown in the diagram are required for attempting to comply with the Regulations as they are at present framed. It could be argued that not all of these inputs would be essential for the avoidance of collision with differently worded or constructed Regulations. In fact the requirements for the operation of both the present and the recently (October 1972) agreed future Regulations make total automation of anticollision actions virtually impossible. For example there is no sensor to replace man's eyes for determining whether vessels in the vicinity of the automated vessel are either in sight or not in sight. When vessels at risk are in sight the Regulations require the classes and aspects of the vessels to be identified in order to determine the responsibilities of each vessel for either giving way or standing-on (maintaining course and speed). This function of identifying class and aspect could be automated between highly sophisticated craft by utilizing radio interrogation methods but this co-operation could not be expected from the multitude of primitive craft such as junks, dhows, yachts and small fishing craft which will probably always exist.

On looking at the Regulations, present and future, for vessels out-of-sight it is perplexing to many to find that mariners are given virtually 'carte blanche' - they can do almost what they like provided that it is 'substantial' and taken in 'ample' or 'good' time. The interpretation of the words 'substantial' and 'ample' or 'good' is left entirely to those in charge. The real test of whether or not actions have been 'substantial' enough or early enough seems to be whether or not a collision occurs! The prime object of taking 'early' and 'significant' action is to enable such action to be recognised as quickly as possible by the other vessel on her radar, if she has one, in case she is taking, or is about to take, a cancelling action. In other words such alterations are a method of communicating intentions. Apart from a vague statement, in the present Regulations, about vessels normally altering course to starboard, and an even more vague statement, in the future Regulations, about vessels avoiding altering course to port, there is no real guidance to ensure that vessels will not take cancelling action[1]. Also, it can be shown, that in some cases, a starboard alteration can be highly hazardous.

It is well known that an electronic computer will only give sensible results if it is given a logical program and correct information. The human computer is not much different - because of the lack of precise instructions in the Regulations mariners and learned counsel have been arguing over their interpretation for decades. Many of the words and phrases used in the Regulations are so highly subjective that they are almost impossible to define. Such terms as positive (significant/effective?) action, substantial action, ample time, appreciable change, navigate with caution, ordinary practice of seamen, etc., seem only to suit the eloquence of barristers contesting collision cases in courts of law, are not very helpful to practising mariners attempting to avoid collision and are totally unhelpful to an electronic computer programmer.

It is little wonder that, despite two modifications to the Regulations since the second world war, collisions still occur with undiminished frequency. The recent, third, modification (1972) which has yet to be adopted, is unlikely to change the uncertain state of affairs. One can summarize the many worthless incantations of the Regulations with one worthless sentence "Do not have a collision or else ... "[2]. An astonishing revelation of the IMCO Collision Regulations Working Party deliberations is that a majority of its members 'voted' against adopting a mathematically sound method of directing vessels to avoid collision[3]. Such a method needs to be based on the natural law for avoiding collision which requires preferably that uncomplementary actions should not be taken or, at least, that any uncomplementary actions, which are allowed, should be controlled to ensure that they are non-cancelling. To adopt a man-made law which ignores natural law is simply asking for trouble.

In fairness to those who drafted the regulations, the framing of 'concrete' rules to ensure that just two vessels can avoid each other in all conditions of visibility, is far from simple, even in open waters. The problem stems from the fact that the equipment for determining collision risk and for communication between vessels is, on many vessels, either very poor or non-existent, - many are blind, deaf and dumb and, to cap it all, many craft have extreme difficulty in manoeuvring - they are either feeble or have very limited control (even a vessel regarded as being under command nearly always proceeds with little or no reserve of speed).

The essentials for avoidance of collision between two independently moving vessels are:

1. Recognition of collision risk

2. Specified or agreed manoeuvres by one or both vessels to give an acceptably safe passing distance.

3. Communication, either to agree upon, or to indicate, action.

At present collision risk is recognised visually by observation of aspect and bearing of an approaching vessel and/or with radar by observing principally the relative motion so as to predict the time of arrival at, and distance of, the closest point of approach.

Communication to indicate intentions is at present done mainly by adopting a conspicuous manoeuvring action either to be observed visually or to be detected by radar. Communication by radio-telephony is becoming more common and popular and allows the problem to be discussed and for complementary action to be agreed. Communicating either by flags, or by morse flashing lights is not normal and communication by sound signals is unreliable although it is required by present Rules 15 and 28 and might be the only method available and should therefore be used.

The advent of radar, of course, gave an enormous leap forward in the ability of vessels to detect risk of collision in all conditions of visibility, nevertheless, it is not a perfect instrument. The inherent instrumental bearing and range errors can lead to safety being indicated when there is real risk and vice-versa. There is also a real danger, when a near* negative passing is indicated, that one vessel will take action to increase the negative passing while the other vessel takes action in an attempt to change the small negative miss distance into a large* positive miss distance. In other words the vessels can easily take uncomplementary action. Again because of accepted instrumental and observational errors one vessel might predict a close negative passing while the other vessel predicts a close positive passing and each vessel takes action to increase the passing distances, negatively and positively respectively. Such uncomplementary actions and actions on inaccurate information or assessment have, together with lack of communication, been largely the cause of the many so-called radar-assisted collisions.

The only satisfactory way of resolving this difficulty is by reliable communication whereby the two vessels concerned can consult and agree on complementary action. The only acceptable form of communication for this purpose at present is V.H.F. radio telephony together with an international voice code in order to overcome any language difficulties. If other vessels are in the vicinity there can be difficulty in identification. This could be resolved by the use of racon for short periods, on request, in the same manner as an aircraft seeking advice is identified on radar by an air traffic controller. Alternatively, the approximate position of the observing vessel and the radar observed true bearing and range between the vessels could be given. Fitting of the necessary equipment and the training of personnel in its use is a reasonable proposition for vessels of more than, say 500 gross tonnes. In fact many such vessels are already in possession of radar and V.H.F. radio telephony and are putting them to use although an international voice procedure and a dialogue for dealing with the collision avoidance problem has not yet been developed.

Although the ultimate solution for collision avoidance between the more sophisticated vessels is foreseeable as outlined above, in the meantime for those vessels, and probably for all time for the primitive vessels and for encounters between primitive vessels and sophisticated vessels, some other reasonably practical and acceptable solution is required. There have been many suggestions in recent years all of which have virtues and, regrettably, weaknesses.

---

*(Negative and Positive passing distances are distances of closest points of approach (miss distances) associated with clockwise (negative) and anti-clockwise (positive) rotating 'sight lines' respectively.)

Now a fairly obvious and apparently simple solution to this problem is for each of any two vessels, which are approaching each other so as to involve risk of collision, to adopt a convention for taking only such action which will rotate the straight line joining them (hereinafter called the sight-line) in a specified direction, either anti-clockwise (positive) or clockwise (negative) with respect to the true meridian passing through each ship, if the other vessel maintained her course and speed (i.e. stood-on). It should be emphasized at this point that it is not being suggested that either vessel is expected to stand-on, only a condition for predicting the rotation of the sight-line by each vessel, is being stated.

To ensure a safe passing the sight-line should continue to rotate in the specified direction and never be allowed to become steady with decreasing range during the whole encounter. An encounter must be considered to last until both vessels are either on, or have returned to, their initial set courses and speeds towards their destinations and either the distance between them is increasing or the sight-line will continue to rotate in the specified direction until, at least, the distance between them starts increasing.

The above proposal to adopt a convention to avoid collision based purely on the rotation of the sight-line, has been considered by many seafarers for many years and has been propounded by Dr.E.S. Calvert, in his various contributions to the Journal of the (British) Royal Institute of Navigation.

In order to simplify further discussion two terms, positive action and negative action, require defining :

Positive Action is any manoeuvring action, i.e. change in velocity (course and/or speed), taken by a vessel which will rotate the sight-line positively (anti-clockwise), if the other vessel stood-on, i.e. maintains both course and speed). (N.B. In the present Regulations the word 'positive' presumably means 'effective', an extremely subjective term).

Negative Action is any change in velocity taken by a vessel which will rotate the sight-line negatively (clockwise) if the other vessel stood-on.

Thus a simply worded rule, which caters for cases where good communication exists and attempts to cater for cases where there is little or no communication, and based on a 'convention for rotating the sight-line' can be written as follows :

"If two vessels are approaching each other, so as to involve risk of collision, each vessel should take positive action only, except in such cases where :

either (1) agreement has been reached between the vessels either (a) for both of the vessels to take negative action, or (b) for one of them only to take either positive or negative action while the other maintains her course and speed.

or (2) a vessel, which is unable, because of existing circumstances and conditions, to take positive action, has to take emergency action to avoid a vessel which, for any reason, is not complying - in such case she must reduce the speed of approach by the best means available and she should signal, if possible, that a positive action has not been taken.

Any vessel which is unable to comply with this rule is to be regarded as a vessel not under command".

Such a rule could replace all the existing steering and sailing rules except Rules 25, 27 and 29, but a good deal of advice on the necessary tactics to produce obvious and adequate positive or negative manoeuvres, without dangerous increase in rates of approach, would be needed.

The virtues and difficulties of such a rule are now enumerated :

Virtues

1. It obeys the natural law of motion for avoiding collision and therefore it is a pure system because, except in emergencies, the positive (or agreed negative) actions are always additive and, provided that they are rapid enough and can be continued long enough to exceed any possible miss distance (of reverse sign to the sign of the manoeuvres) which might exist, then safe resumptions of velocity by either vessel, and a safe passing are ensured.

2. No 'yo-yos' will result (when vessels take uncomplementary action the initial result is not always dangerous, in fact, they can initially break clear of each other by increasing range, however when they have both resumed their initial velocities they might find that they have returned to the initial collision-course conditions - this going away and coming back is aptly described by the name of a child's toy, the 'yo-yo').

3. It allows the use of verbal communication so that when this is available both the initially close positive and initially close negative passings can be satisfactorily dealt with by agreement as can cases where one or both vessels are unable to take positive action. (It is a statistical fact that of all open sea

encounters, initially nearly 50% are positive and an equal number (nearly 50%) are negative - only the small remaining percentage are actual zero (collision) cases).

4. The wording is beautifully simple - the instructions, for all vessels, are both clear and concise.

Difficulties

1. In some cases it is <u>impossible</u> for a vessel to make a positive manoeuvre. For example if a vessel is going at her full speed she is unable to make a positive manoeuvre for a vessel on her port beam as this can only be achieved by increasing speed.(Thus, ideally, vessels ought to be required to proceed with a reserve of speed - this is probably the morally correct thing to do).

2. Some of the positive actions which can be undertaken are small and consequently difficult to be identified either by conventional radar or visually in clear weather.

3. It can be extremely difficult to establish satisfactory communication with the other vessel to reverse the convention (or to signal her in an emergency) especially during poor visibility.

4. * Justifiable negative manoeuvres by one vessel can cancel positive manoeuvres made by the other vessel - i.e. success can depend on the other vessel either standing-on or making a positive manoeuvre.

(* For example : a vessel without an operational radar, and ignorant of the presence of another vessel, would be justified in varying her speed to suit changing visibility conditions. Such a vessel would also be justified in making changes of course for navigational reasons and, if she were a sailing vessel, justified in changing tack).

5. There would be difficulty in training many seafarers of all seafaring nations to understand the differences between, and the meaning of, positive and negative rotations and passings and to know which manoeuvres either will or will not produce the desired positive (or negative) result.

6. Some positive actions dangerously increase the rate of approach without producing substantial changes in bearing. (For example, when acting positively, by altering course, to avoid a vessel approaching on the port quarter).

A working party of the (British) Royal Institute of Navigation has recently (1970/71) been considering the problem of collision avoidance and, because of the difficulties given above, many members of the working party felt that such a rule would not be found acceptable at present. However the working party has produced a diagram combined with some notes which together give a "Guidance on Manoeuvres to Avoid Collision". This is designed to prevent as far as possible, dangerous uncomplementary actions being taken by vessels wishing to avoid each other, particularly during conditions of poor visibility.

The Guidance, which is reproduced in Annex I, differs mainly from the suggested rule in the following ways :

1. It recommends various tactics in terms which, it is considered, will be easily understood by all seafarers, rather than states a general rule.

2. It places the onus of manoeuvre on the vessel which is more able, because of its relative bearing from the other, to take positive action.

3. The vessel less able to take positive action is generally recommended to stand-on. The object of this being to help to stabilize the situation in the event of several vessels being in the vicinity, i.e. to avoid a chain reaction of manoeuvres which can lead to utter confusion.

4. The negative actions which are permitted, i.e. the so-called escape-action when avoiding a vessel to port, and reductions of speed when avoiding a vessel to port, can easily be over-ridden by the positive action advocated for the other vessel and will not result in actual cancellation provided each vessel follows the advice on escape-action and on resuming course and/or speed, as appropriate.

5. Recommended ranges for taking action are given to avoid as far as possible, positive and negative actions occurring together and to ensure that there is normally adequate time for both assessment and action.

6. The terms positive and negative have been avoided.

7. There is a different emphasis of flexibility of manoeuvre, i.e. in the guidance not all positive manoeuvres are included and some negative manoeuvres are allowed.

8. No reliance whatsoever is placed on communication by radio-telephone - the only communication method considered being that of taking 'substantial' action, when possible, so that it will be obvious visually by day and by night, in clear weather, (by changing aspect) and by radar (by large changes of relative motion direction and/or rate).

Although the Guidance is envisaged as being of principal use in open waters for cases of two vessels only there is, nevertheless, reasonable flexibility to enable two vessels to avoid each other even when other vessels and obstructions, which are not of immediate risk, are in the vicinity. It is generally felt that for the more congested narrow waters the only real solution will be found in the use of separation zones and/or traffic control by a central authority.

The working party's "Guidance on Manoeuvres to Avoid Collision" can be considered as a rather crude set of tactics designed primarily for the avoidance of collision between partially blind deaf-mutes. Vessels which do not fall into that category, i.e. vessels which are able to establish verbal communication by means of V.H.F. radio-telephony really ought to be encouraged to exploit this ability to ensure that the degree of collision risk has been recognised by both parties and that complementary action is taken. This verbal communication will often allow more economical actions to be taken with adequate safety and justified confidence. The framework of the Regulations should not be dominated by the lowest common denominator of a low-powered, ill-equipped vessel of poor manoeuvrability.

Communication is one of the 'in-words' of this age and is in danger of becoming a bore, however the value of communication as an aid for avoiding collision and ensuring safety cannot be over emphasized. The use of radar has dominated papers and discussions on collision avoidance for many years whereas the use of V.H.F. radio-telephony has hardly received a mention, yet V.H.F. radio-telephony is in considerable use already and it is considered by many practitioners to be of greater value than radar, for example, many pilots have said that they would prefer the radar to break down rather than the V.H.F.! They have long realized that radar can only show the present positions and past motions of vessels whereas V.H.F. radio-telephony is better than a crystal-ball because it not only helps them to discover future movements of vessels it can also help them to modify future movements to suit their safety criteria. Radar for position finding is, of course, not so important for pilots because they often have nearby objects in view for referencing. Radar obviously has greater importance for identification etc., in wider waters.

I.M.C.O. could well look further into V.H.F. radio-telephony communication aspects - the use of V.H.F. should not be abruptly dismissed because of alleged language difficulties - where these exist the phonetic alphabet could be used with a specially devised brief code covering the dialogue required for collision avoidance. Such a code could easily be displayed adjacent to the communication equipment or, preferably, committed to memory.

The relative importance of radio-telephony viz-a-viz radar ought to be brought into proper perspective. It is regrettable that the 1972 Regulations make no mention of the use of radio-telephony. The only improvements in communications which have been introduced are some additional sound signals for dealing with overtaking cases and some flashing light signals to indicate alterations of course being executed. It is also regrettable that the new Regulations have failed to give precise instructions which could be understood by the moronic electronic computer - such Regulations would then be more likely to have equal meaning to all mariners in charge of vessels.

The "Guidance on Manoeuvres to Avoid Collision" in Annex I in no way infringe either the present or the 1972 agreed future Regulations for out-of-sight situations and could therefore be used as the basis of an anti-collision computer program but because the Guidance has not been internationally agreed and because other interpretations of the Regulations are possible, the time-consuming, although usually safe, escape-action described in the Guidance would probably have to be invoked more frequently than might have otherwise been the case.

Finally, it is the author's view that automating collision avoidance operations either partially or wholly would not allow for reduction in manpower on merchant vessels - the bridge watchkeeping manpower has already been reduced to the lowest limit. The development of such automated systems should nevertheless be encouraged in order to help the present bridge watchkeeping manpower to become more effective in avoiding collisions.

REFERENCES

(1) Royal Institute of Navigation "The Proposed Revision of the Collision Regulations - A Discussion" Journal of Navigation, V.25. (1972) p.433 and p.437.

(2) International Regulations for Preventing Collisions at Sea (1960) Rules 27 and 29 and (1972) Rule 2.

(3) Royal Institute of Navigation, ibid p.442.

ANNEX I

Guidance on Manoeuvres to Avoid Collision

COURSE ALTERATION DIAGRAM intended primarily for use in avoiding a vessel detected by radar and out-of-sight is shown in Fig.2.

RESUMPTION OF COURSE After turning to starboard for a vessel on the starboard side keep the vessel to port when resuming course.

ESCAPE ACTION A vessel approaching from the port side and rear sector can normally be expected to take early avoiding action. The suggested turns are recommended for use when such a vessel fails to keep out of the way. As an alteration to put the bearing astern may not complement subsequent

action by the other vessel it is recommended that
further turns be made to keep the vessel astern
until she is well clear.

SPEED CHANGES IN RESTRICTED VISIBILITY

REDUCTIONS OF SPEED A vessel can reduce
speed or stop at any time and such action is recommended when the compass bearing of a vessel
on the port bow is gradually changing in a clockwise direction (increasing). A reduction of speed
should be made as an alternative to, and not in
conjunction with, the suggested turn to starboard
for avoiding a vessel either on the port bow or
ahead. Normal speed should be resumed if it becomes apparent that a vessel on the port side has
either subsequently turned to starboard in order
to pass astern or stopped.

INCREASES OF SPEED It will sometimes be advantageous to increase speed if this is possible
within the limitations of the requirement to proceed
at a safe speed. An increase of speed may be appropriate when the vessel to be avoided is astern,
or on the port quarter, or near the port beam,
either initially or after taking the alter course
action indicated in the diagram.

LIMITATIONS The presence of other vessels
and/or lack of sea room may impose limitations
on the manoeuvres which can be made, but it
should be kept in mind that small changes of
course and/or speed are unlikely to be detected
by radar.

CAUTION IT IS ESSENTIAL TO ENSURE THAT
ANY ACTION TAKEN IS HAVING THE DESIRED
EFFECT . If not the recommended turns can
normally be applied successively for newly developed collision situations with the same vessel.

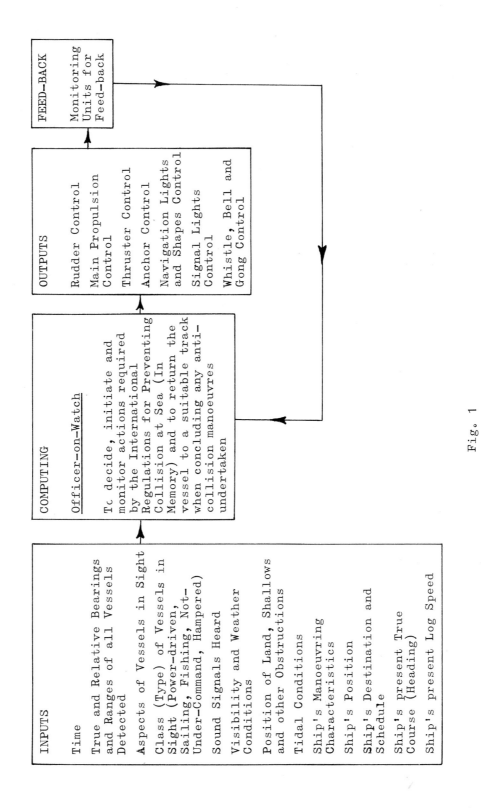

Fig. 1

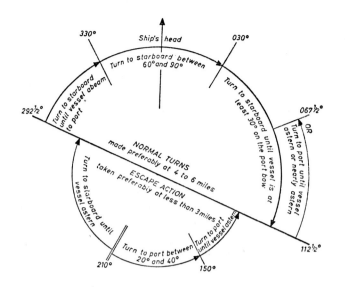

<u>COURSE ALTERATION DIAGRAM</u>

N.B. See the attached notes (Annex 1) on
RESUMPTION OF COURSE, ESCAPE ACTION
and CHANGES OF SPEED

Fig. 2

SOCIO-TECHNICAL ANALYSIS OF SHIP ORGANIZATIONS

Børre Nylehn
Institute for Industrial Social Research
Technical University of Norway
Trondheim

1. INTRODUCTION

A technical system may be described as a structure within which technical processes are taking place. An organization may in the same way be perceived as a social structure which will permit or restrict social processes. For both systems the processes will produce results that we evaluate against a set of goals. In case our results are poor in relation to our goals we may wish to alter the structure of our system in order to better the effectivity.

We will need theories concerning the type of system with which we are confronted, and we will want instruments or measures capable of changing our system. The important thing for us is that we need theories about our system. In connection with technical systems, this is a rather obvious and trivial statement. We all see the importance of having relevant theories before we construct a car or a ship. These theories will not all of them be excellent, but they will at least be based on a reasonable amount of research, and the possibility that they may be demonstrated to be invalid will always exist. Not so for theories concerning social systems - like organizations. There are different schools of thought, and each one will give a different picture of the organization, stressing some aspects of the system. The different theories will not necessarily exclude each other, but represent different ways of perceiving the system and they will be useful for different types of investigations. For he who wants to describe a social system, the first problem will be: Which one, of several equally "right" or "wrong" theories, should I use as a basis for my work ?

During the two last decades a school of organization thinking, working with socio-technical analysis has been fairly widely engaged in industrial organizations. I believe that ship organizations could be improved upon by implementing the ideas developed by this school, which I will try to present to you in the following. This represents a way of thinking about organizations. The important point to make seems to be that the question of obtaining effective ship organizations is dependent upon choices of theoretical structures.

Let us look briefly at the type of organizational thinking which I think has been predominant in our culture, and consequently also in shipping. I believe one has regarded organizing as a question of implementing a model organization. One has had ideas as to what is characteristic of effective organizations. Some, for instance, will say that desentralization is to the good, others will state that effective organizations are made by the leader, still others believe that emphasizing incentives is most important, some are convinced that rules and well defined work tasks are necessary, etc. Two points seem to be important:

a. People have a tendency to believe in measures or models. They state that this or that measure is important or effective. It is of course neither. It is never interesting to discuss whether some measure is good, but it is extremely important to analyse under what conditions it will lead to such and such results.

b. People have theories of organizations. When someone states that incentives are necessary to make people work hard, this is a theory. It is a theory of people, how they function and what values they have. And it is a theory of organizations, in the sense that the statement implies that incentives are something to be emphasized relative to other measures,

that might be preferred by
people with other theories.

I will proceed by outlining the theory
of organizations as social technical systems in contrast to the more traditional
way of thinking just mentioned. In the end
I will try to state the consequences of
adapting a socio-technical outlook.

2. SOCIO-TECHNICAL THEORY

The organization is viewed as a system
which is working in dependence on an
external world. The conditions outside
determine what characteristics will be
of importance to the organization. E.g. in
rapidly changing market the flexibility
of the organization will be of critical
importance. Another example: When the
average level of education is rising in
a country, the organizations must change
their job structure more or less in corre-
spondance with this development. At present
this is probably a situation that Norwegian ship owners will have to face.

Our system, the organization, is perceived
as consisting of two different sub systems.
There is a technical and a social system.
Each has its structure, its processes,
although they are of different kinds.
They are characterized by their own laws,
interdependencies and values or goals.
Corresponding to the lay-out of the technological system is the spatial distribution
of people. Transport of parts and raw
materials in the technical system may be
compared to communication in the social
system.

Between the two systems are strong interdependencies. A choice of technology
will impose distinct types of jobs and
qualifications needed, and an unchanging
and stable technology leads to a static
job structure and well defined departments.
A production system including a great number of machines and elements to be assembled will lead to a large administrative
structure, probably utilizing computers.

The social system will thus be confronted
with conditions in the outside world,
under which it will try to realize
specific goals, and it will influence and
itself be influenced by a technological
system. When we organize, we must therefore try to establish structures corresponding to these conditions. This is the
simple, central thought in socio-technical
theory. For organizing purposes we have
at our disposal several instruments, like
job structure, training programmes, wage
systems, information system, career
patterns. Having analysed the conditions
under which the organization will be
working, we apply our instruments to
obtain an organization suited for its

working conditions. This organization will
be characterized by being able to handle
the tasks that are to be performed and of
utilizing effectively the specific technology in the organization. It is also
characterized by being adjusted to the
people that work in it. The situation that
people are placed in will be such that
they can perform their tasks effectively,
while at the same time be able to behave
as individual human beings and also be
able to use some of their specific human
resources.

The basic thought may be said to be this:
We have certain tasks that are to be
performed by using known methods. We also
have a number of people with certain qualifications, values and characteristics. The
problem to be solved is to perform these
tasks in a way that utilizes the resources
and qualifications possessed by the individuals in a situation that allow them to
be and act as human beings. I believe it
is rather easy to find examples in industry
or in shipping of work situations that
are inappropriate in this respect. In
industry we can think of assembly line jobs,
where almost none of the specific human
qualities are utilized, and where the
worker is in a situation that is almost
completely alien to him.

This example illustrates an important
point: The social system will be changed
not only when we want and intend to.
When we change our technology, the working
conditions will be affected, the job
structure, the amount of training and
relations between people will be changed.
Implementing a technology will thus bring
about a new organization. In the assembly
line industry we could say that we have
got an organization which is modelled
around and created by a technology. The
choice of assembly line technology also
was a choice of an organization.

And this is the second main point in
socio-technical theory: We cannot pretend
that organizing is something done by the
personnel department. Technological and
organizational development will be interdependent functions. They must be considered simultaneously.

The effects of changing our organization
unintentionally or changing it without
a preceeding analysis of technology
and external conditions will be that we
end up with social systems that are poorly
adjusted to its working conditions. We may
get a division of work which is unsuitable
in securing a proper effectivity, or that
is alien to the people engaged in the
organization. This may be the case in
several industries where the division of
work has been carried too far. We may also
get low or wrong qualifications, as when
we try to fill our need for qualifications

by hiring highly trained experts, while we in fact need qualified workers in the concrete job situation. Or there may be too much, too little or irrelevant communication, as when the communication structure around an assembly line is vertical instead of horizontal. Lastly, we may get conflicts between groups and between individuals arising from strains in the work situation, as when automation eliminates interesting jobs from a machinery room on board a ship and induce the engineers to keep interesting jobs for themselves and leave the painting and washing to the rest of the crew.

In organizations where work is dependent upon the qualifications, loyalty and stability of employees and not only upon machines, it will be of prime importance to construct social systems that produce these types of employees. It is probably a fiction to believe that we can pay people to perform adequately. It is probably more realistic to accept that people function properly only when the work situation will make it possible for them to do so. This will mean that the work situation must be structured to allow a man to behave like a man and not like a machine. We cannot indefinitely continue to hire the type of people we need, we must shape them. And they are formed by the organization and the technology.

3. SOCIO-TECHNICAL ANALYSIS

Our theory implies that there are two subsystems that are interdependent of each other, and their combined functioning is understandable only in light of the external conditions.

The first step in an analysis must therefore be to describe our external world. We must ask what aspects of the outside world will be of importance to us. For the shipping industry it is easy to answer that market conditions, recruitment possibilities, seamen education are important, but also that political changes, like a greater participation in management on board being asked for, must be considered. Having established the external conditions for the working of the organization, we can proceed by developing and evaluating technological and social variables. These must be related to the external conditions and to each other.

Technological components will mainly be chosen after a techno-economical analysis, which will be based on market and financial considerations, but we must try to avoid carrying these analysis too far before considering the social aspects. To do this, we must regard the technological characteristics that have social signifi-

cance, and these will not always, of course, be those that are of techno-economical interest.

Fred Emery, an English theorist, considers the following technological variables as being of special significance (1):

Level of automation and mechanization.
Different product characteristics.
Physical environment.
Interdependencies between different work stations as to time sequence, quality, and methods.
Communication involved in operating the technology.
Differentiation in process requirements, i.e., variation in the work role.

These properties of the technological system will, according to Emery, influence the social system and this system will have to be constructed to comply with them. We must now seek to establish a list of those variables of the social system that are of relevance to the technological system, and that will permit evaluation of the organization as a social system.

The technological system will have to be evaluated by its techno/economic and social consequences. The same applies to the social system.

An example:

The size of tank ships must be analysed by economists and market analysts, and by mechanical engineers. But the size also has consequences for the size of the crew, the time at sea, and the task structure on board. Correspondingly, the size of the crew, apart from having economic consequences, must be related to the technologically determined tasks to be performed. The number of people is also of importance for the type of social relations that can be obtained on board.

We can from these simple examples see that technological solutions have social consequences, and that social systems must be related to technology.

The variables of the social system to be considered will be of two different types. First we have those having to do with the individuals, their needs and values, or in short: What is the nature of the people involved ?

Thorsrud & Emery have worked out a list of principles for job construction that implies a distinct conception of human nature (2):

1. the need for the content of a job to be reasonably demanding in terms of other than sheer endurance and yet provide a minimum of variety,

2. the need for being able to learn on the job and go on learning,

3. the need for some minimal area of decision-making that the individual can call his own,

4. the need for some minimal degree of social support and recognition in the workplace,

5. the need to be able to relate what he does and what he produces to his social life,

6. the need to feel that the job leads to some sort of desirable future.

To carry out a socio-technical analysis, it will not be necessary to accept this list, but something corresponding to it is imperative. We must, in order to organize, have a model of man as a basis for our decisions. To refuse to "speculate" on the nature of man, and claim to make decisions purely on the basis of practical observations of life, is no alternative to this. The practical experience will have to be perceived, organized and analysed. That is to say, made into a theory or fitted into a theoretical framework.

The other type of social variables have to do with the larger setting for jobs and for individuals. They will include groups and relations between people, distribution of competence of different kinds, communication patterns, behavioural rules and norms, goals and subgoals. These structuring elements of the social system represent the environment for the individual, to whom it will be more or less fitting. It will also be a setting for work processes, which will be more or less effective.

We could say that the larger social setting, which the mentioned variables describe, will to a certain extent be adjusted to needs of the individuals and the needs of the technological system. We must "construct" it with regard to both of these restrictions.

The socio-technical analysis will be carried out by drawing on theories on technological and social systems to make organizing decisions, which partially will aim at changing directly some social variables and partially may lead to a change in the technological components, methods and processes. The basis for this analysis is the list of variables that describe the sub-systems of the organization, and these lists will implicitly express models and theories.

4. IMPLICATIONS OF SOCIO-TECHNICAL THINKING

We are continuously making decisions that affect the social system. These changes are making the organization more or less adjusted to its working conditions. We must analyse the social consequences of our technological decisions. We cannot pretend to be just technicians, but are always also social engineers. Organizing is not as simple as to be left to the personnel department.

An organization will change continuously, and it will hardly be possible to work out the organizational solution to our present problems. The problems are changing, and so is the organization. Therefore the problem will be to do something about the direction of the organizational change. This means that the application of measures to bring about a change, whether technological or social, must be in accordance with each other, they must have an organizational theory as a basis.

Organizing is possible only on the basis of some fundamental premises that we have to choose by ourselves, - they are not to be regarded as given, or chosen because they are "self-evident":
- what traits of the organization are important in our situation, and what is our "situation".
- what values and dispositions are characteristic of man.
- what are the goals and values we are pursuing.

5. SOCIO-TECHNICAL ANALYSIS OF AUTOMATION

We are, at my institute, currently working on a project that aims at evaluating the consequences of implementing a computer in a steam-turbine machine-room on board a tanker.

There are as yet no results to be reported, but to illustrate what I have said so far it might be of interest to convey to you a few of the problems that we shall have to analyse:

1. the computer will change the information available and also the communication structure:
- In what way will this affect the education needed to do a good job as an engineer.
- In what way will relations between the ship and the office have to be changed.
- What will the new decision processes be, if they are to be patterned around the computer, and will it be possible to get

accept for this sort of change.

2. The computer will change the types of tasks to be performed.
- Will the new task structure be in accordance with seamen preferences. If not, what repercussions will this have, and will it be possible to utilize the computer without eliminating preferred tasks. Will new, attractive tasks arise, and for whom.

- Will a new job-structure be wanted, and will it be possible to make such changes. To what extent will the computer be utilized if no organizational changes are possible.

- Will we have to create new tasks to keep people engaged, or can we change the task force in such a way as to fit the available jobs. Will this bring about an organization with more or less conflict, stratification and isolation.

To sum up, the computer will represent a more sophisticated technological system on board, but:

- Will the organization be able to utilize it.
- Would the effectivity of the ship organization (which is what we are trying to do something about) be increased with lower costs if we had tried to solve some other problems (that might have been a lot simpler and less exciting to work with).

Purely technological or purely social problems do not exist in any organization. A research project should not be undertaken until the interdependencies have been clarified. To eliminate detrimental effects of a technological change afterwards is probably more difficult than trying to perceive possible consequences in beforehand, and react to these consequences by appropriate measures.

REFERENCES

(1) Emery, F.E.: Characteristics of Socio-technical Systems. Doc.No.527, TIHR, London 1959.

(2) Emery, F.E. & Thorsrud, E.: Industrial Democracy Project, No. IV. (In manuscript).

ON THE AUTOMATIC DETERMINATION OF AN OPTIMAL ANTICOLLISION STRATEGY

MAURO PIATTELLI   -   ANTONIO TIANO
Laboratorio per l'Automazione Navale
National Council of Researches
Genoa, Italy

ABSTRACT

A method is proposed for the marine collision
avoidance problem, which has been developed for
implementing anticollision systems on computeri -
zed radar units. Such method allows us to deter -
mine a solution of kinematic type for the colli -
sion avoidance problem, consisting of a sequence
of evasive optimal manoevres, each of which is
computed according to the rules, as in IMCO text
of the 1972 Conference.
The validity of each evasive manoevre in restricted
waters is extended to the navigation boundary
lines, in order to take our ship's draft into
account, while the dynamic characteristics of the
manoeuvres are derived from the data on the ship's
behaviour stored in the anticollision computer.
The optimum characteristics of the anticollision
strategy are obtained by requiring the minimization
of a suitable cost function, which is associated
to each evasive manoeuvre and whose form is specialized on dependence of both short range and long
range dangerous situations.
Furthermore, the optimal anticollision strategy,
off-line computed according to the C.A.I.R.O. method, is periodically checked and updated on the
basis of the radar information flow about the motion of the targets.

INTRODUCTION

A number of anticollision systems have been developed, in the last years, involving the use of a
computer interfaced with the radar. The computer
aids the radar operator, elaborating in real time
the kinematic characteristics of a certain number
of targets, which are auto-tracked by the system.
Such systems however still present a few limitations. First of all they supply the operator only
with an informative picture of the situation, but
do not give a tactical geometry or a strategy in
order to plan the anticollision manoeuvres. Thus
the operator must himself select a safe manoeuvre
experimentally and this imposes a remarkable mental
strain on him. Therefore in the worst situations
such a procedure may lead to the impossibility of
finding an evasion manoeuvre.
In order to obtain a collision avoidance strategy,
many theorètical approaches are possible. See for
example in[1] [2] an application of the dynamic programming algorithm.
But an optimal solution from the mathematical point
of view does not appear suitable today for the real
ships operation.
Several reasons warrant the above statement:
- the ship system cannot be exactly controlled,
  first of all because its non-linear mathematical
  model is not well known;
- the anticollision problem involves human factors,
  as the crew behaviour in the presence of danger
  and the legal background and its interpretation;
- today it is forbidden to control the ship in
  closed loop by a computer or others automatic
  devices for anticollision purposes;
- since the procedure involves a safety problem, it
  is more convenient an approach which increases
  the safety, than a high accurate mathematical
  method;
- a real time solution must be obtained by an
  onboard computer, which is necessarily a small
  size one, and so the use of too sophisticated
  procedures is not allowed.
In the future an optimal absolute solution of this
problem will be possible, when the ship identification methods and the reliability of the automatic
systems will be satisfactory. In this way it will
be possible in fact to reduce the weight of the
human operator.
That being stated, let us assume we use an anticollision computerized system, as the Rayscan of Selenia
Raytheon[3], for example, which at least performs
the following operations:
- auto-tracking of the targets by manual or automatic initialization;
- periodical computation of the targets position,
  speed and course;
- prediction of collision danger, derived from the
  above information.

Thus, a method is proposed, C.A.I.R.O., which implements such system in order to determine a complete A/C strategy. The method is supported by a program stored on the anticollision computer memory and presents to the operator a plan of manoeuvres, when a risk of collision occurs, from the actual point until the danger is over.

The anticollision problem is approached for open sea, where there is unlimited manoeuvring space, then it is extended to narrow waters.

STATEMENT OF THE PROBLEM

Let us consider our ship as a controlled dynamic system, whose state vector at time t, $\underline{\xi}(t)$, is described for every $t \in [t_o, +\infty)$ by the differential equation

$$\frac{d\underline{\xi}}{dt} = \underline{f}(\underline{\xi}, \underline{u}, t) \qquad (1)$$

where the state vector $\underline{\xi} = (\varphi, \lambda)$, constituted by the ship's position coordinates, latitude and longitude, belongs to a given sea region $X \subset R^2$. Owing to the narrowness of the area involved in the problem, this is assumed as a plain.

The control vector $\underline{u} = (\nu, \psi)$, constituted by the ship speed and course, belongs to a suitable control set $U \subset R^2$, which takes the ship's characteristics into account.

Let us suppose that this system is sailing, according to a reference control vector $\underline{u}_o = \underline{u}(t_o)$, through the above region X from an initial point $\underline{\xi}_o = \underline{\xi}(t_o)$. The terminal point may belong to the region X: $\underline{\xi}_f = \underline{\xi}(t_f)$, or not. In the latter case, the terminal point is not determined, but at time t_f, the original control $\underline{u}_o = \underline{u}(t_o)$ must be re-assumed. Within the same region X, there are r moving targets, the motion of which is described by equations analogous to (1)

$$\frac{d\underline{\eta}^k}{dt} = \underline{g}^k(\underline{\eta}^k, \underline{q}^k, t) \qquad (2)$$
$$k = 1, \dots r$$

where the control vector $\underline{q}^k = (\nu^k, \psi^k)$, at the k-th target's disposal, is supposed to belong to a given control set $Q^k \subset R^2$.

The state and control vectors of the targets are periodically observed by the anticollision system onboard our ship. According to this assumption, we may consider the control vectors as stepwise functions, i.e. they remain constant between two observations.

Let us define COLLISION the situation at which for some $t > t_o$ it occurs

$$d(\underline{\xi}(t), \underline{\eta}^k(t)) < \varepsilon \qquad (3)$$

i.e., when the euclidean distance d between our ship and one target at least results less than a preset safe value ε.

The minimum distance from the k-th target is the closest point of approach CPA^k.

$$CPA^k = \min_{t \in [t_o, +\infty)} [d(\underline{\xi}(t), \underline{\eta}^k(t)] \qquad (4)$$

Let us define COLLISION DANGER the situation at which we expect the collision between our ship and the target, if both maintain the actual controls. The COLLISION TIME is the time delay between the actual instant and that in which the collision is expected. The initial time t_o is that in which the collision danger occurs.

Analogously, CTA^k is the time after which the closest point of approach is expected with respect to the k-th target.

The collision is avoided by altering the control vector of our ship. Therefore the A/C (avoidance or anticollision or evasion) manoeuvre may be defined as an alteration of the controls, which allows us to avoid the collision, i.e., to obtain a CPA not less than the safe value ε.

The RESUMING POINT is the point at which the A/C manoeuvre is over and the ship can resume, under safety conditions, the original controls.

Let us assume that the original control vector determines an optimal routing for our ship. The optimality is obtained by a cost function, which is to be minimized.

The cost may be the time [4], the risk, the fuel consumption or a suitable combination of them [5]. Thus, among the possible avoidance manoeuvres, which satisfy the constraints imposed by the international rules, a solution is obtained by minimizing a suitable cost functional. The proposed method implies a kinematic treatment of the problem, however some dynamic characteristics are taken into account in order to obtain the path of our ship manoeuvre.

IMCO INTERNATIONAL RULES

In the IMCO Conference of London, 1972, the collision regulations were discussed. The new rules are expected to come into effect on 1st January 1976. We have taken these rules into account, in order to determine the constraints on the avoidance actions of the proposed method, even if the Rules do not appear favourable to the automatic systems which use radar information.

According to the Rules, when a collision risk occurs, the operating situation is recognized: long or short range.

The discrimination is based on the collision time; which expresses the approaching speed directly. The method C.A.I.R.O. uses the above discrimination to choose the safe distance ε and the cost functional J for the evasion action. According to the spirit of the Rules, the method requires an action as soon as a collision danger occurs in order to avoid close quarters approaches.

In this way the anticollision problem should be

solved normally in a long range situation while
short range cases should occur only during complex
evasion sequences, when some targets also change
their controls.

Therefore we have assumed for the long range actions
a safe distance which is longer than that of the
short range situations. If a close quarters situation
cannot be avoided, the shorter safe distance allows
us to find, however, a solution to the problem.
The cost functional associated to the avoidance
actions must be different for the two situations.
For the long range, it appears suitable to minimize
the shifting from the original track, which is
assumed as optimal. For the short range case, we
have an emergency situation and it seems necessary
to take the distance or the time, after which the
risk is over, also into account. Furthermore, the
rules recommend that the manoeuvre must be evident
and both such criteria implicate avoiding actions
larger than that of minimum shifting,(6)(7).

Owing to the above considerations, a sidestep manoeuvre appears suitable, but its mathematical definition is not easy.

After the range discrimination, the operating case
is recognized. Six cases may occur: overtaking of
the target from port-side or starboard, crossing
with the target from portside or starboard, head-on
with the target from portside or starboard.

The recognition is derived from the comparison between our ship's course and the observed dangerous
target's course, as shown in Fig. 1. Each case
imposes suitable constraints on the alteration of
the control vector $\underline{u}$ for our ship, according to the
basic rule of the sea, which requires an anti-clockwise rotation of the sight-line,(8).

The control vector alteration may consist of turn
only or of turn and speed change. The Rules constraints concern the rotation direction only, while a
speed reduction is ever recommended in restricted
visibility and also in order to allow more time to
assess the risk of collision. The method C.A.I.R.O.
proposes a speed increase, if possible, for crossing
with the target from port beam.

THE LONG RANGE PROBLEM

Let us assume that our ship and the targets move
according to a stepwise rectilinear uniform motion.
Therefore, eq.(1), which describes the motion of
our ship, can be written component wise in explicit
form for the i-th step, as follows:

$$\begin{cases} \varphi_i\,(\tau_{i-1}+t) = \varphi_{i-1}+\nu_i\cdot t\cos\psi_i \\ \lambda_i\,(\tau_{i-1}+t)=\lambda_{i-1}+\nu_i\cdot t\sin\psi_i \end{cases} \tag{5}$$

$$i=1,2,\ldots$$

where $\underline{\xi}_{i-1}=(\varphi_{i-1},\lambda_{i-1})$ is the initial point of
the step, $\underline{u}_i=(\nu_i,\psi_i)$ is the control vector, assumed constant during the step, and $(\tau_i-\tau_{i-1})$ is the

duration of the i-th step.

Therefore we pass from one step to the subsequent
one, only when an alteration of the control vector
occurs.

The first step begins at point $\underline{\xi}_0$, at time $t_0=0$,
when a collision danger is recognized with respect
to some target and finishes at the point $\underline{\xi}_1=\underline{\xi}(\tau_1)$,
when the evasion action begins.

According to the spirit of the rules and to the
operating reality, let us control our ship only by
means of a track angle alteration, i.e., in the
long range manoeuvres, the ship speed is constant.
The relative lenghtening of the ship's route is
assumed as the cost of the manoeuvre in the long
range situations. Thus, the cost depends only on
the track angle alteration and on the point at
which it occurs. However, this point $\underline{\xi}_{i-1}$ is determined by dynamic considerations, treated in the
following section, and the cost may be written

$$J_i\,(\underline{\xi}_{i-1},\underline{u}_{i-1},\underline{\eta}^p_{i-1},\underline{q}^p_{i-1}) = \sec\,(\psi_i-\psi_{i-1}) \tag{6}$$

where $\underline{\eta}^p_{i-1}$ and $\underline{q}^p_{i-1}$ are the last observed state and
control vectors of the dangerous p-th target, and
$\Delta\psi_i=(\psi_i-\psi_{i-1})$ is the track angle alteration
from step i-1 to step i, required for avoiding the
collision.

The optimum problem consists of determining the
angle alteration $\Delta\psi_i$, which minimizes the cost
(6) and takes the safety constraints $CPA^k\geq\varepsilon$, for
every k=1,2,...r, into account.

Such optimization concerns the single manoeuvre
only and not the whole evasion sequence with respect
to all the targets which may be dangerous, since
this is the operating reality.

For a given point $\underline{\xi}_{i-1}$, and with respect to the
dangerous target only, such minimization is very
easily performed by kinematic or geometrical procedures.

As shown in Fig. 2, let us consider a suitable
reference system, whose origine is placed in the
initial point $\underline{\xi}_{i-1}$, the X axis of which has the
same direction of the actual course ψ_{i-1} of our
ship. The dangerous target p has the actual position
$\underline{\eta}^p_{i-1}$ and the control vector $\underline{q}^p_{i-1}=(\nu^p_{i-1},\psi^p_{i-1})$.
Thus the parametric equations of the motion of our
ship, for a given altered course $\Delta\psi_i$, result:

$$\begin{cases} x\,(t)=\nu_{i-1}t\cos\Delta\psi_i \\ y\,(t)=\nu_{i-1}t\sin\Delta\psi_i \end{cases} \quad t\in[\tau_{i-1},+\infty) \tag{7}$$

and analogously, for the dangerous target

$$\begin{cases} x^p(t)= (\lambda^p_{i-1}-\lambda_{i-1})\cos\,(\psi_{i-1}+\Delta\psi_i)+(\varphi^p_{i-1}-\varphi_{i-1})\cdot \\ \qquad \sin(\psi_{i-1}+\Delta\psi_i)+\nu^p_{i-1}t\cos(\psi^p_{i-1}-\psi_{i-1}) \\ y^p(t)= -(\lambda^p_{i-1}-\lambda_{i-1})\sin\,(\psi_{i-1}+\Delta\psi_i)+(\varphi^p_{i-1}-\varphi_{i-1})\cdot \\ \qquad \cos(\psi_{i-1}+\Delta\psi_i)+\nu^p_{i-1}t\cos(\psi^p_{i-1}-\psi_{i-1}) \end{cases} \tag{8}$$

Now, we determine the minimum value of $\Delta\psi_i$, which
exists under the initial condition d $(\underline{\xi}(\tau_{i-1}),\underline{\eta}(\tau_{i-1}))\geq\varepsilon$

This minimum value is obtained by imposing that, for every $t > \tau_{i-1}$, the above inequality is satisfied, and then by solving the associated equation. Among the four solutions, the required value is obtained by imposing the Rules constraints.

The same solution may also be obtained from merely geometrical considerations. As shown in Fig. 3, the resulting solution becomes:

$$\Delta\psi = \alpha - \beta - \arcsin\left(\frac{\nu^p}{\nu}\sin\alpha\right) \qquad (9)$$

where $\beta = \psi^p - \psi \leq 180°$ and $\alpha = \beta + \gamma + \delta$, while

$\gamma = \arcsin \varepsilon/\delta$ and δ is the observed bearing.

We note that the above equation must be changed for a head-on situation with target from portside as follows:

$$\Delta\psi = \alpha + \delta - \arcsin\left(\frac{\nu^p}{\nu}\sin\alpha\right) \qquad (9')$$

After the determination of $\Delta\psi_i$, the corresponding new course between ξ_{i-1} and ξ_i is tested with respect to the other targets. If the safety constraints are not satisfied for at least another target, the method suggests a new solution which is obtained by altering stepwise the track of a quantized value according to the maximum admissible course alteration. This procedure gives the final solution $\Delta\psi_i$. If there are not solutions, the procedure is repeated using a reduced or increased speed according to the constraints imposed by the Rules.

The final evasion manoeuvre can now be tested with respect to the navigation boundary lines, if the navigation occurs in narrow waters.

The CPA^p is assumed as resuming point, i.e. from this point, own ship can re-assume the original course with respect to the dangerous target P. Thus the above test procedure is repeated for the track from the resuming point with the original course. If the resuming course results dangerous, a new course alteration is computed with respect to the actual course ψ_i.

ON THE DYNAMIC FEASIBILITY OF THE A/C MANOEUVRE

The point ξ_{i-1}, at which a new course is assumed during a long range action, depends on the dynamic characteristic of the ship.

Let us suppose we know the ship's response to the rudder action, consisting of a matrix, the rows of which are identified by quantized speed values and the columns of which are identified by quantized value of the track alteration. Corresponding to each pair of speed and turn values, we obtain the total time T requested for the manoeuvre in the actual conditions. The rudder angle also can be associated to each manoeuvre time.

Owing to the little requested turns and the great safe range, we can neglect the safety reduction caused by the delay by which the manoeuvre is really completed in the long range actions. Thus, we

compute the optimum $\Delta\psi_1$ for the first A/C Course alteration with respect to the point $\xi(T_f)$, i.e., after T_f from the initial time, where $T_f = 20$ seconds is a fixed delay taking into account the time requested by the operator for the manoeuvre acceptance and the computation time also, which is however very short.

Entering the above matrix with $\Delta\psi_1$ and ν, we can so obtain the total time T_1 required to the A/C turn.

Thus, the point ξ_1, at which in theory the turn istantaneously occurs, is determined by computing the covered distance in the direction ψ_1 with the actual speed during the time $T_f + T_1/2$; while the turn must begin in reality after T_f and is completed after $T_f + T_1$.

In this way, the proposed manoeuvre presents a little forward shifting with respect to the optimum, but the safety check in regard to the other targets takes this shift into account.

Then, the CPA^p is assumed as resuming point ξ_2. Obviously, if the resumed course is safe from danger, the time of the resuming action is still T_1 and the resuming manoeuvre must begin at time $CTA^p - T_1/2$ and it will be over at time CTA^p Fig. 4 shows a short range overtaking case as example of this procedure.

If the other targets or the navigation boundary lines do not allow our ship resumes the course, another evasion action is computed from the CPA^p by means of the above procedure and so forth. In this way, we obtain a step sequence from the actual point to the point when all dangers are over. The sequence may be recomputed every time a new collision risk occurs.

Finally we note that the above turn model compensates, at least partially, the real speed reduction by means of a longer theoretical path (see Fig.4).

THE SHORT RANGE PROBLEM

For the short range actions, the criterion of minimum path lenghtening does not appear suitable, first of all owing to the emergency situation to which the manoeuvre is required to obviate.

In this case the distance or the time, after which the collision danger is over, seems to be more convenient, but, on the other hand, this only criterion implies too remarkable track alterations, which are not allowed by the dynamic behaviour of the ship.

In conclusion, a suitable combination of the two cost terms appears the most convenient solution. Thus the cost functional may be written

$$J_i(\xi_{i-1}, u_{i-1}, \eta_{i-1}^p, q_{i-1}^p) = \sec\Delta\psi_i + \mu\cosec\Delta\psi_i$$

where $\cosec\Delta\psi_i$ takes the distance or the time before the CPA^p into account and μ is a suitable weighting factor. Obviously, the value of $\Delta\psi_i$, which minimizes the above cost, depends only on the factor μ.

This factor is preset, according to the operating case and the observed bearing, between 0,05 in the head-on situation with the target from starboard and the minimum bearing and 1 in the crossing situation with the target from starboard and the maximum bearing. The corresponding turn $\Delta\psi_i$ change from about 20 to 45 degrees.

The obtained value of $\Delta\psi_i$ must satisfy the safety constraint $CPA^P \geq \varepsilon$ imposed in the short range actions.

Then, the determination of the A/C sequence is analogous to the one of the long range situation, but the dynamic considerations assume much more importance, owing to the larger actions required in this case.

At the first track angle alteration, the delay T_f does not involve in this case a safety reduction,but a delay at the resuming point only. In fact, the approach results closer, but ever under safety conditions. See for example in Fig. 4.

Furthermore in the short range actions, a speed change may be suggested if the turn only is not sufficient and the speed decrease may be obtained by crash arrest too.

COMPUTER PROGRAMS

The C.A.I.R.O. program requires as input data the kinematic parameters of our ship and of the auto-tracked targets. This information is usually supplied by the computerized A/C radar system.

The operator must choose the following variables:
- safe range   for the l.r.avoidance actions
- safe range   for the s.r.avoidance actions
- discrimination time between short and long range
- interval time between two subsequent observations of the targets
- maximum and minimum speed values of own ship

Furthermore, the data concerning the dynamic response of the ship to the rudder actions, her draft, and the preset values of the weighting factor μ ,for the s.r. case, must be stored in the computer.

The program starts when the first collision danger is recognized and indicates if a long or a short range situation occurs with respect to the most dangerous target.

Then, the operating case, according to the Rules, is recognized and the optimum avoidance manoeuvre is computed together with the resuming point and the corresponding time , as described in the previous sections.

The optimum manoeuvre is tested with respect to the other targets and to the navigation boundary lines. If the tests do not result satisfactory, the action is corrected by increasing the turn and /or by changing the speed.

After computing the resuming point and the resuming time, the same program re-starts by assuming

this point as the initial one and so forth as long as to reach a point where the collision danger is over. Fig. 5 shows a simplified flow diagram of the program.

In order to minimize the computation time the program is shared in one main program and some subroutines. This distribution takes into account the necessity of employing some of these for other navigation functions too.

The outputs of the program consist of:
- course and speed suggested for each step of the evasive manoeuvre
- time instant when each step begins
- CPA and CTA of the dangerous target

The output data may be presented by introducing suitable signals in the radar, in order to display on the PPI the geometrical sequence of the avoidance manoeuvre, or by a video display for alphanumerical presentation, or by typewriter.

Let us clarify the procedure for testing the manoeuvre with respect to the navigation boundary lines. A conversion program has been carried out,which couverts a given geographical line into a broken line, with a preset accuracy. By means of this program, we obtain a table of the vertx coordinates of the navigation boundary lines.

Then the onboard computer may be supplied with these data for the usual landings of the ships and her usual drafts.

The test subroutines, stored in the seagoing computer, verifies if there are intersections between the ship evasive path and the navigation boundary lines. Obviously, the safety conditions require no intersections.

However, this test gives other information also: if the final point belongs to a navigable sea region (even numbers of intersection) or not (odd numbers of intersections). In fact, this subroutine is utilizable also for anti-grounding purpose and for the manoeuvre in narrow waters.

In order to take these aspects into account, the anticollision problem is solved in true motion. In this way the real position of the ship allows us to locate the navigation boundary lines correctly.

CONCLUSIONS

The anticollision procedure supported by an onboard computer, presented in this paper, does not employ sophisticated control techniques, because it seems today that heuristic algorithms of very simply form are preferable from the operating point of view.

In fact, more advanced approaches can result interesting from a theoretical point of view but have not a real possibility to be used in the ships operation and automation today.

By the C.A.I.R.O. Method, we have attempted an heuristic approach in order to supply the human operator with a complete optimal anticollision strategy.

The computer programs are today tested in the Computer Center of the Genoa University by simulation of all the possible cases. The obtained results are very satisfactory, but not still conclusive.

Contemporarily, some programs are tested, by means of the computer system installed onboard M/s"Esquilino" for research purposes. These programs concern only the long range situations with a few numbers of targets and the human response to this automatic procedure.

Finally, if the above tests will give satisfactory results a complete computerized radar system will be installed onboard a research ship of the National Council of Research and subsequently, another program will begin in order to test the validity of the method, when all the ships travelling in the same sea region use it.

For this purpose, the computer S/7 IBM installed in our Laboratory will be equipped with some input devices, hand controlled, simulating the ship controls. The computer will give to each operator, by means of suitable output displays, the evasive sequence and will verify the total safety implementation of the whole traffic system.

REFERENCES

1- TIANO A.,DAGNINO P.,PIATTELLI M.,"Determination of an optimal trajectory in the presence of risk" AGARD Conference on Automation in manned aerospace systems - CPP-114 Preprint No.114,October 1972, U.S.A.

2- PIATTELLI M.,"Anticollisione e teoria dei giochi" L'automazione Navale - Anno II-N.2, 1971

3- MASTROPIETRO G.-"Sistema radar automatico di navigazione e anticollisione" Symposium Selenia-Raytheon-Socorama- Genova, February 1971

4-ZOPPOLI R., "Minimum-time routing as N-Stage Decision process" Journal of Applied Meteorology, Vol. 11 n° 3 April 1972.

5- PIATTELLI M.,PULIAFITO P.,ZOPPOLI R.,"Optimum ship routing as an N-Stages decision process" Accepted to IFAC Symposium on "Automatic Control in Space", Genoa, June 1973

6- CALVERT E.,"Collision Avoidance by Manoeuvre" The Journal of Navigation, Vol. 24, N° 3, 1971

7- GARCIA FRIAS J., "The Turn Criterion and the Collision Rules" The Journal of Navigation, Vol. 24 N° 1, 1971

8- JONES K.D., "Practical Manoeuvres to Avoid Collision at Sea" ibidem

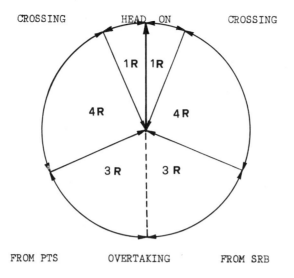

CROSSING   HEAD ON   CROSSING

1R   1R

4R   4R

3R   3R

FROM PTS   OVERTAKING   FROM SRB

Fig. 1 DISCRIMINATION OF THE OPERATING CASE

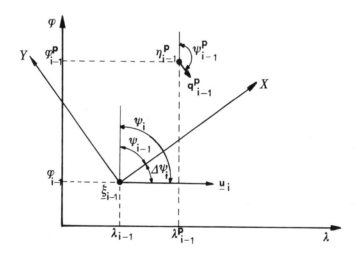

Fig. 2 CHANGE OF REFERENCE SYSTEM TO OBTAIN $\Delta \psi_i$
IN THE LONG RANGE SITUATIONS.

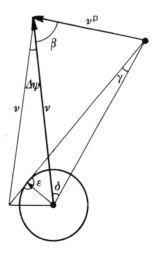

Fig. 3 GEOMETRICAL DETERMINATION OF $\Delta \psi$ IN THE

113

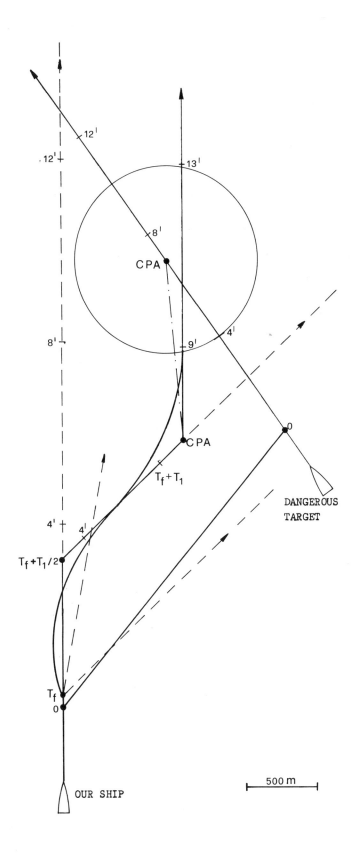

Fig. 4   SHORT RANGE OVERTAKING CASE

114

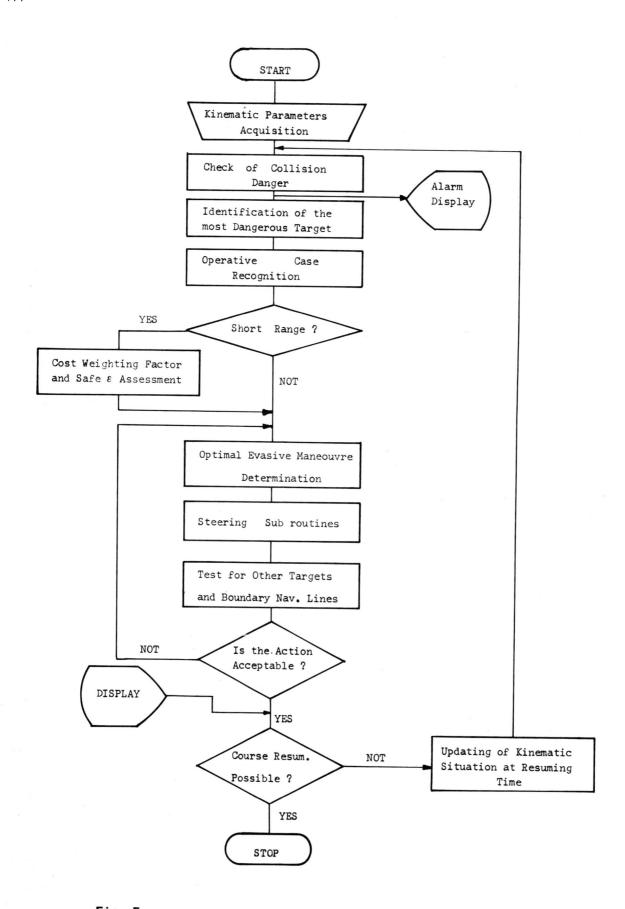

Fig.5 SIMPLIFIED FLOW CHART OF THE COMPUTER PROGRAM

AUTOMATIC PATH GUIDANCE

W.H.P. Canner
M.R.I.N., C.ENG., M.I.E.R.E.
Department of Maritime Studies,
University of Wales Institute of Science and Technology,
Cardiff, CF1 3NU.

ABSTRACT

The Decca Navigator is an electronic aid to navigation which provides information of the observer's position at any instant of time. An automatic pilot is an aid which assists the pilot to maintain a selected course. The coupling of these two aids together has been achieved by the Decca Navigator Company using an Omnitrac Computer. The method used is highly complicated and expensive to manufacture. This paper is a feasibility study of the possibility of solving the problem in a more economical fashion for marine applications.

The proposals outlined employ a line following technique and could be adapted to suit any positional finding system using an x, y, t plotter as a sensing device to derive a path error signal.

1 INTRODUCTION

Rapid advances in recent years have led to the development of several electronic aids to navigation which may, in principle, be fitted to any type of moving vehicle. The most advanced systems have appeared in aircraft and ships, and in more recent years, hovercraft have received a specialized approach resulting in the development of reliable aids designed specifically to suit the peculiarities inherent in these vehicles. Some use is also made of electronic aids in the navigation of land vehicles over desert country.

Broadly speaking, it would be fair to regard electronic navigational aids as falling into one of two categories. The first deals with locating craft position, whilst in the second category we have automatic steering, and it would be reasonable to regard these aids as being pilot aids. In the first category, any system which provides information of heading, speed, and more specifically position may be regarded as being a navigator's aid.

Considerable research has been carried out in coupling positional information to automatic pilots, with varied success in application. Probably, the most noteworthy has been in the automatic approach and landing of aircraft where precise positional information in both height and locality has been geared to the automatic pilot to enable accuracies greater than those achieved in manual pilotage to be flown – coupled with reliability figures certainly comparable and often claimed to be better than those achieved in manual flying. Path guidance in level flight may also be carried out (e.g. the Smith's Flight System coupled to the Electric Pilot).

It will be appreciated that much of the labour of navigation can be removed both in the air and at sea when positional information is fed into an automatic steering device to provide path guidance. This will allow more time for the navigator to pursue his responsibilities of collision avoidance, weather observation, fuel calculations, and the general work associated with navigation. Today, as the density of traffic increases, collision avoidance is becoming more paramount.

In the marine field, the Decca Navigator has been coupled to the automatic pilot by the addition of an interface unit known as an Omnitrac computer. Unfortunately, due to its cost, many shipowners have proved reluctant to install this system.

Finally, a word about Hovercraft. These vehicles have inherited the worst features of both sea and air navigation. They are susceptible to tide when waterborne in the terminal areas, and since this involves inshore navigation, there are added hazards from land promontories. Once airborne they are affected by wind to such an extent that the angular difference between course and track can be as much as 45°. This is due to the slow speed of operation compared to a normal aircraft flying in excess of 200 knots. They are also heavily involved in collision avoidance, since the route may lie at right angles to the shipping traffic when operating a ferry service. Economical coupling of a navigational aid and an automatic pilot could well prove particularly useful in the solution of this problem.

The author wishes to make it clear that the paper has been based on a Decca Navigator Marine System and detailed investigations were originally carried out with this aid. Where references are made in the text to aircraft application they are intended in general terms only, and do not imply that the specific design is necessarily suited for in-flight control.

2 UNDERLYING PRINCIPLES

2.1 The Decca Navigator

The Decca Navigator is a hyperbolic system which provides three single position lines on a three-dial read-out display. Each position line represents a line along which the observer may lie and since at least two of these position lines are provided continuously and simultaneously, the equipment provides a continuous method of fixing the observer's position. The method used to obtain each position line is essentially by phase comparison of two coherent sources of radiation of unmodulated continuous radio frequency energy in the frequency range of 70-130kHz. The general principles of this system are well known* and will not be described here, but the author would like to lay emphasis on the visual present-ation of position provided by the automatic plotting devices - namely the Flight Log and the Marine Plotter.

In both of these devices, Decca information is translated into related movements of a roller-mounted chart, and a plotting pen, along axes lying at right angles to one another. The pen indicates the position of the craft in relation to the lattice and traces a record of craft move-ment. In the case of aircraft, the display head is designed for cockpit mounting and may if desired be fitted flush into the instrument panel. In ships, the display head is larger and free standing and would appear to be adaptable to the suggested application in this paper more readily than the Flight Log.

2.2 Automatic Pilots

In automatic pilots for ships or aircraft, a disturbance of craft equilibrium creates a signal which is used to initiate a chain of events that results in a control surface being displaced at a rate compatible with stability. This change in position of the control surface drives the craft back to the original attitude from which it has been disturbed. Craft dynamics alone will provide a degree of stability, but only if there is suff-icient feedback of the right type will it be possible to create a perfectly stable craft able to maintain its state of equilibrium regardless of the disturbances applied to it. Apart from distur-bances of this nature, however, a positive demand in certain circumstances is also required to initiate a positive change in attitude. In order to achieve this overall requirement, more than one loop will be required. Figure 1 illustrates the general case.

Consider the action starting with a positive demand signal (left of diagram) fed in to change the attitude of the craft. The demand signal passes through a suitable shaping network and thence to the amplifier. The amplifier drives the servo mechanism which is coupled to the control surface. The control surface moves, and in doing so generates a feedback signal produced by the control surface translator. (Simply, the translator could be a potentiometer with its wiper arm connected to the control surface or, a tacho-generator giving an output voltage proportional to the rate of change of position of the control surface). The feedback signal is used to back off - or damp down - the positive demand at the amplifier. The effect of this is to reduce the rate of displacement of the control surface so that the craft gradually, rather than suddenly, changes its position. It is some-times an advantage to provide manual control over the degree of feedback in order to cope with variation in craft loading. The value of feedback should however be such as to ensure stability. The concept of $A' = \frac{A}{1-B(A)}$ for the gain of the loop will be familiar from feedback amplifier design. Here A is the feedforward path of the amplifier, servo, and control surface, whilst B is the feedback path of the control surface translator. Since B is negative, the overall gain A' will be $A/1 + B(A)$, or, the ratio of output torque to input signal will be $F_F/1 + F_F.F_B$. Clearly, the more feedback in the system the smaller this ratio becomes.

The new position taken up by the control surface creates a torque which causes the craft to move at a rate governed by craft dynamics. As the attitude changes, it approaches the desired atti-tude set in by the demand signal, and feedback is continuously provided by the attitude translator in the demand loop. This effectively reduces the demand as the desired attitude is approached, until the input to the shaping network becomes zero when the attitude translator signal is equal to the attitude demand signal. Such feedback can be over-ridden if the operator simply wishes to change the attitude continuously (i.e. in the case of a heading change he may wish to move in a circular path), but in many systems where the demand is provided by a sensor pre-set to some desired value the relationship between the desired attitude and the indicated attitude will be readily available, and will be used to govern craft motion.

Consider now the effect of an external disturbance attempting to upset the equilibrium of the craft. The torque so produced is again resisted by the craft dynamics, but any change in attitude which may result feeds a signal from the attitude translator to the input of the amplifier as a negative going demand. This moves the control surface in such a direction as to oppose the torque producing it. The control surface loop, and the demand loop together in a well-designed system should ensure a stable craft which will ultimately take up an attitude able to counteract the disturbing force applied to it.

3 PROPOSED METHOD OF COUPLING

3.1 Deriving the Path Error Signal

The heading demand signal to an automatic pilot is derived from a gyro compass repeater. The relative position of the heading indicator and a manually adjusted pointer on the face of the repeater is used to derive d.c. voltage of some value related linearly to the angular difference between them. This signal is amplified and follows the process of feedback autopilots in general as described in Sect. 2.2.
Basically, to provide path guidance, a similiar signal derived from a sensor which compares the

craft's true position with a desired route, could be used to give a heading demand signal capable of bringing the craft onto the desired route and allowing it to take up a heading to maintain that route. The problem lies in relating the position of the craft to the desired route and using this signal in the correct sense as the path error signal.

The true position of the craft is frequently given by the Decca Navigator, and in aircraft the flight log is generally carried. The Decca Marine Automatic Plotter, as the marine counterpart to the flight log, is sometimes used in ships. These devices indicate the position of the craft by the movement of a pen over the surface of a roll of paper which is overprinted with the Decca lattice.

It is proposed to use the automatic plotter as the path sensor, and to achieve this the required route should be laid down over the paper in the form of a narrow conducting strip of zero resistance accurately inserted for specific routes. The conducting surface so presented on the paper can then be used as the I-bar of an E- and I-signal generator. The E-transformer should be small and light in weight and should be mounted on the arm which carries the pen. It could be an addition to the pen if, at the same time, it is required to use the automatic plotter in its prime use, or in place of the pen, if it is felt that the E-transformer would obscure vision.

The idea behind the derivation of the path error signal is shown in Fig. 2.

With the pen, and/or its attached E-transformer, over the centre of the conducting strip forming the I-bar, the output from the secondary coils of the E-transformer will be zero. The secondary coils are wound on the outer limb of the E-piece and are in series opposition (Fig. 2(a)), so that equal amplitude signals are taken from both sides in antiphase. The net output is therefore zero and the flux linkages on both sides are equal.

Any deviation of the I-bar from the E-transformer, or vice versa, results in a fall in the amplitude of the output from the secondary coil with the weaker flux linkage. Should the E-transformer move to the left of the I-strip, the flux deteriorates in the left-hand magnetic circuit since the air gap has now widened on that side. The net output signal will be of a particular phase and amplitude dependent on the direction (governing the phase), and the distance (governing the amplitude) of the movement. It will be appreciated that the maximum amplitude is reached when the I-strip is completely displaced from one of the secondary coils (Fig. 2(b)). Should there be a deviation of the I-bar (path) wholly to one side of both secondary coils then the output will again fall to zero. This is important, since it will govern the maximum permissible change in the direction of the route. It will not be possible in this case to alter course by 90°.

A large deviation of the E-transformer from the I-strip could be caused by two factors. The first is a change in the environmental conditions surrounding the vehicle which may cause a change at a rate which cannot be compensated in time by the autopilot amplifier to prevent the E-transformer from moving completely away from the I-strip. Experimentation would reveal whether or not this is likely to occur, but if it should do so, it is suggested that it may be overcome either by widening the I-strip (within the limits of an accompanying loss of accuracy), or by using a tacho-generator attached to the shaft of the heading repeater. Such a generator will produce an output in proportion to the rate of change taking place. If this is fed to the autopilot amplifier only when its value rises above a predetermined level, then it should compensate for the fall in output voltage of the E-transformer.

The second, and more likely cause, is a change in the projected direction of the track as laid down by the I-strip which is too large to cope with. (See Fig. 3.)

The output from the E-transformer will deteriorate for changes in direction of the I-strip from 'head up' greater than 45°, so that the ideal solution is to ensure that this angular change is never exceeded. This is not to say that changes in track should not exceed 45° - a straight line projection within these limits for all conditions could be achieved by a 90° swing of the hyperbolae on the chart to ensure a plus or minus 45° head-up presentation at all times. This will necessitate switching the Decca input signals from the chart roller to the pen carriage and from the pen carriage to the chart roller as the demarcation point is reached. A pulsed output signal, used as a trigger automatically to initiate the change over, could be obtained from a second pick-up on the edge of the chart as discussed later in Sect. 3.5.

In general, whenever changes in route of angles less than 45° are involved, the I-strip should be laid down with rounded alterations to act within the limits of the vehicle's manoeuverability. This will reduce the possibility of complete displacement of the E-transformer from the I-strip.

The output signal derived from the E-transformer may now be referred to as the path error signal. This should be amplified and subsequently fed to a phase-conscious rectifier (p.c.r.) where it would be converted to a d.c. output of polarity dependent on the direction of movement of the I-strip from the E-transformer. The amplitude of the d.c. signal will vary and will depend on the degree of displacement subject to the limitations mentioned. The width of the I-strip would be governed by the accuracy required.

For an aircraft flight system - or indeed a maritime system - a transducer which recognizes the relationship between the track made good and a desired track on an automatic plotter could be effectively designed which is not necessarily based on the E- and I-transformer proposed in this paper. The author has in fact been lately advised that the Decca Navigator Company now hold a patent for doing this in a maritime application which is based on an optical method. Another possibility would be to investigate the use of a capacitance bridge.

The d.c. signal produced by the p.c.r. provides

the heading demand to reach the desired path, and can be switched into the autopilot amplifier directly in place of the signal which might otherwise be derived from the gyro or magnetic heading sensor.

To ensure stability, reference should also be continuously made to the rate of change of heading, and this can be achieved by a rate of turn gyro and integrator. The gyro rate signal is then used to back-off the heading demand created by the path error signal. The integrator feeding directly into the servo amplifier can be given a requisite amount of gain which will result in the craft gradually aligning with the track and ultimately allowing it to take up a suitable drift angle to compensate for the environmental conditions with zero tracking error as shown in Sect. 3.4.

3.2 The Overall System

Figure 4 illustrates the underlying principle of the complete system. Two modes of operation are envisaged, the first is the gyro mode and the second the path mode. (Switch at centre of diagram.)

An analysis of the action in the gyro mode follows closely on that given under Sect. 2.2 for a control surface in general. In this particular case however, the input signal is a heading demand (top of diagram). The heading translator gives the indicated heading so that the heading error, being a combination of these two, could be derived from the relative setting of the desired heading and an indicated heading on a gyro compass repeater as is normal. The heading error signal passes to the shaping network, and after amplification, feeds the rudder servo system. (In the case of aircraft, the required control over heading is also by the aileron servo mechanisms.) Two closed loops are used in the general system - the rudder loop providing feedback via the rudder angle translator, and the heading loop providing feedback via the heading translator to back-off the input demand. In the event of an external disturbance of equilibrium (above right of diagram), craft dynamics provides a natural degree of feedback, but a negative heading error signal is given by the heading translator to drive the rudder (or ailerons) in such a direction as to oppose the disturbance. The two loops should operate to ensure a stable craft under all normal conditions.

If the system is switched to the path mode, there will now be three closed loops. The rudder loop remains the same as in the gyro mode. This adjusts the change of rudder angle to be compatible with the demand as in the general case. The heading loop however is now taken from a rate-of-turn gyro. If the head swings too rapidly, the rate gyro produces a strong feedback signal to back off the heading demand provided by the p.c.r. It would be possible to use the same heading loop as that used in the gyro mode, provided the gyro compass repeater was set for the desired track and continuously monitored for track changes. The suggestion of using a rate gyro is probably more flexible, and better suited to the system.

It has been suggested that the heading demand signal provided by the p.c.r. may be derived from the Decca automatic plotter. This will then have two inputs - the desired path in the form of the I-strip running through the paper, and the pen (E-transformer) position provided by the Decca Navigator. The third loop is therefore the path loop with feedback provided via the Decca Navigator - i.e. a position translator - and regulated by craft kinematics. The output from the automatic plotter as a combination of these two is the path error signal which feeds the amplifier and p.c.r., whilst the output from the p.c.r. is a heading demand to make good the required route.

It is interesting to note that the Decca Navigator does not necessarily have to be the position translator. A Doppler system, or any navigational aid capable of giving accurate position continuously could be used to feed a plotter based on the more conventional x,y, t plotter. The key lies in relating the known position to a desired path, and using this in the right sense to give the path error signal.

3.3 Automatic Reorientation

The Decca marine automatic track plotter in ships has a manual pattern selector switch which enables a display with ship's heading upmost presented at all times. The operation of this switch changes the direction of rotation of the servo motors which drive the pen carriage and paper roller. Under normal operating conditions the pen moves from left to right for an increasing reading of the Decca lattice readings, and is referred to as a positive drive. The paper in the same condition is said to have a positive drive when readings increase from the bottom of the paper upwards.

The method of switching involves the use of a wafer switch which in itself would not be easy to reproduce directly for automatic operation, and since automatic re-orientation would be necessary to facilitate large changes of heading an alternative solution was looked for which would be less involved.

The diagram shown in Fig. 5 illustrates the general principle of operation of the track plotter.* In a particular case we may assume that the output from the receiver is from Master/Red to drive the pen, and from Master/Green to drive the roller. The principle of each is the same so in considering the operation of the plotter, only one input will be considered, i.e. the pen drive obtained from the Master/Red.

The signal arriving from the receiver is in the form of a sine and cosine value. This is fed to a d.c. reversal circuit in order to provide four output signals of sine, -sine, cosine and -cosine value. These are then fed to a ring resistor at four 90° displaced tapping points producing a rotating potential diagram having two null points. As the ship moves over the lattice the null points will rotate with the changing phase of the incoming signal. By using an appropriately graded track on the ring resistor a linear relationship between change of phase angle and displacement of the null positions will be obtained. Mounted on the ring resistor is a movable wiper arm which feeds the servo amplifier and motor driving the pen carriage.

The pen drive is also geared to the wiper arm so that as the motor is driven the wiper arm rotates until it is in the null position. Subsequent movement of the ship is then going to result in a movement of the null position and automatic follow-up results.

Before considering any suggestions for automatic re-orientation, let us first examine the movement of the servo motors for a craft moving on an imaginary track which follows a rectangular path as shown in Fig. 6. It can be seen from the Figure that the drive for each of the headings is considered positive simply because readings increase from left to right and from bottom to top. The servo motors will change direction naturally and not through any change brought about by switching at each corner.

In order, however, for the route to be presented as head up throughout, switching action would need to take place at each of the corners in the sequence A, B, C, and D. The turns are rounded to facilitate craft's manoeuverability.

On the Northerly run from A to B, the pen is driven by Master/Red feeding servo motor 1, whilst the paper is driven by Master/Green feeding servo motor 2. Positive drive is given to both servo motors.

At position B, the system should be switched so that the pen is driven by Master/Green and the roller by Master/Red. This means that the drive to the pen has to be interswitched with the drive to the roller. Secondly, the pen drive now has to be made negative since readings decrease from left to right. This means the servo motor of the pen drive has to be reversed in direction.

At position C, switching action is again required. Once more, interswitching needs to take place between pen and roller. Further, the pen drive has to be negative and so has to be the roller drive.

At position D, interswitching is again necessary, but in this case the pen drive is positive whilst the roller drive is negative.

At position A, the final interswitching is required with both drives back to positive. A tabled analysis of the switching necessary is shown in Table 1. It can be seen that for any situation only two actions are required. The first is interswitching, whilst the second is to reverse the phase of the requisite servo motor drive.

The process of achieving this automatically could be carried out by the use of bistable multivibrators. They would need to be triggered by pulses derived at the right instant from the edge of the chart and picked up by a stationary contact (or set of contacts) bearing against the surface of the paper.

3.4 Interswitching the Drive Signals

The feed to the servomotor is normally provided by the power coil of a magnetic amplifier which forms the basis of the servo amplifier. It would be possible to interswitch these connexions by using two bistable multivibrators in the manner shown in Fig. 7. The transistors have only two conditions under which they are operating in this type of circuit - either they are conducting fully, or they

are not conducting at all. Using a switch analogy it means that they are either 'open' or 'closed'. In the circuit diagram the inter-transistor coupling and steering diodes required, which would follow standard practice, have been omitted for simplicity.

Four transistors are involved. Assume that TR1 is closed, TR2 open, TR3 open, and TR4 closed with bistables in the quiescent condition. In this state, the 'paper drive voltage' taken from the magnetic amplifier has a closed path to the 'paper servo motor' via TR1. Similarly, the 'pen drive signal' voltage has a closed path to the 'pen servo motor' via TR4.

If a trigger, derived from the 'paper' at the requisite turning point is then fed via steering diodes to all four transistors then both bistables will flop into the opposite state resulting in TR1 opening, TR2 closing, TR3 closing, and TR4 opening. In this condition the 'paper (roller) drive signal' voltage is fed to the 'pen (carriage) servo motor' via TR2, and the 'pen (carriage) drive voltage' is fed to the 'paper servo motor' via TR3.

The transistors would need to be capable of carrying sufficient current, and should be biased sufficiently to prevent the a.c. input from changing the state of conduction.

3.5 Reversing the Motor Direction

A similar arrangement also using two bistable multi-vibrators could be used to reverse the phase of either the driving voltage to the servo, or the reference voltage required by the servo motor.

In Fig. 8, TR1 and TR2 belong to one bistable multi-vibrator, and TR3, TR4 belong to a second bistable multivibrator. The associated circuitry and trigger input has again been omitted for simplicity.

In the condition shown, TR1 is open, TR2 is closed, TR3 open, and TR4 closed. The supply voltage is fed to the base of the transistors, and can therefore reach the motor winding via the base-collector path of TR2 and TR4. On receiving a trigger pulse however, the state changes so that TR1 closes, TR2 opens, TR3 closes and TR4 opens. In this case the supply reaches the motor winding via TR1 and TR3 and is therefore in anti-phase to the original.

An alternative solution to the problem would be to interswitch the sine, cosine connexions at the input end of the plotter. This would have the advantage of low current operation, and the circuit design would be similar to that of the switching device described for the crossover of the servo motors. In any event the method chosen could be decided upon by experimentation.

4 APPLICATIONS

The method outlined of coupling the two aid together appears to be theoretically feasible.

It would seem on balance to be more readily suited to straight line operation, unless the operator is prepared to meet the cost of additional equipment required for the interswitching of the Decca drive signals to the automatic plotter. This, in itself, would probably not amount to a great deal extra,

but costs may rise with the design of suitable
Decca charts for individual 'one off' routes.
However, **straight** line operation is found in
hovercraft navigation, airways flying, airfield
approach paths, and on many standard sea routes
for shipping. The system may also have an
application in the navigation of land vehicles
over desert country.

The traditional presentation of the Flight Log
and the Marine Automatic Plotter need not be
interfered with at all, if it is felt that the
presence of an E-transformer would mar the
presentation. A separate plotter could be mounted
in some convenitent position in the vehicle and
used for this purpose only. An interesting
extension of this idea, and which would also help
to reduce the 'one-off' problem, would be to use
a marker in place of the pen to lay down a route
using a conducting fluid in place of ink. If the
route was first traversed accurately using conventional navigation procedures, the I-strip would
be laid out by the marker and thus provide a
memory run which could be used again. The route
would not necessarily have to be a long one, and
could perhaps be an approach to land for any
airfield in the country. It would then provide
an approach aid which would be completely independent of facilities at the airfield. A
similar application exists for the harbour control
of shipping, and the exact run to a marker buoy
or lock entrance with overall monitoring by shore-
based radar control could prove useful. Military
applications in providing precise runs to a target
or in the patrol of fixed borders also might be
considered.

Short of installing an elaborate simulation system
in the laboratory, an analysis of errors can only
be satisfactorily carried out by conducting extensive operational trials. A thorough knowledge of
craft steering and control dynamics would be needed
before any sensible attempts could be made. It is
appreciated that errors will arise from the pic-
torial presentation itself apart from inherent
errors in the transducer design employed. Such
trials will reveal limitations, some of which have
been indicated (Sect. 3.1).

5 ACKNOWLEDGEMENTS

The author would like to thank Professor D.R.
Towill for helpful suggestions, and Professor A.D.
Couper for his encouragement. Also, he wishes to
acknowledge the facilities provided by the
University of Wales Institute of Science and
Technology.

* References.

O'Brien, W.J. 'Radio navigational aids',
J. Brit. Instn Radio Engrs, 7, p.215, 1947.

'Handbook for Flight Log' Decca Navigator
Corp., New Malden, Surrey.

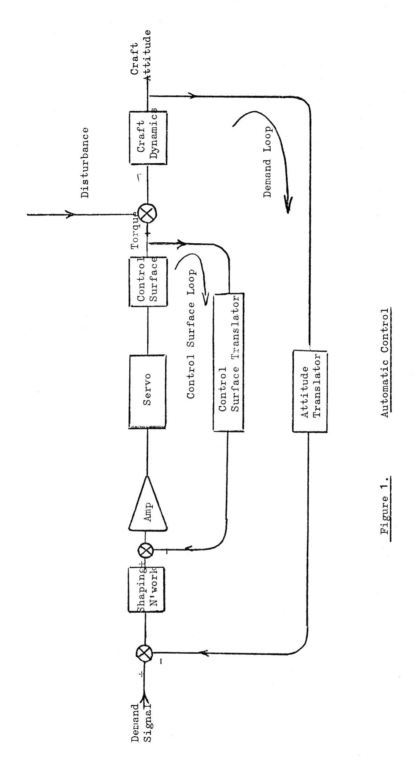

Figure 1.   Automatic Control

122

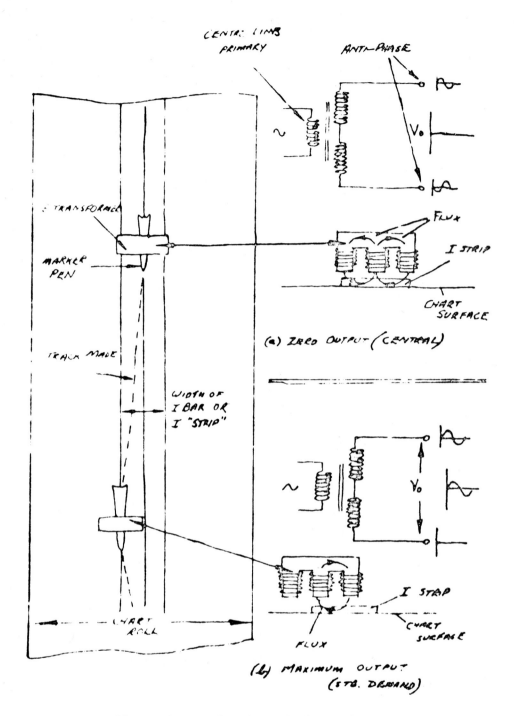

- Figure 2. Derivation of the Path Error signal.

123

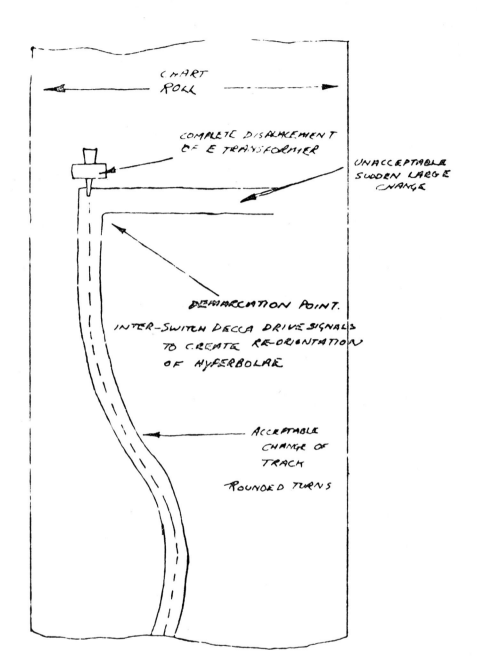

Figure 3. Unacceptabel changes of route.

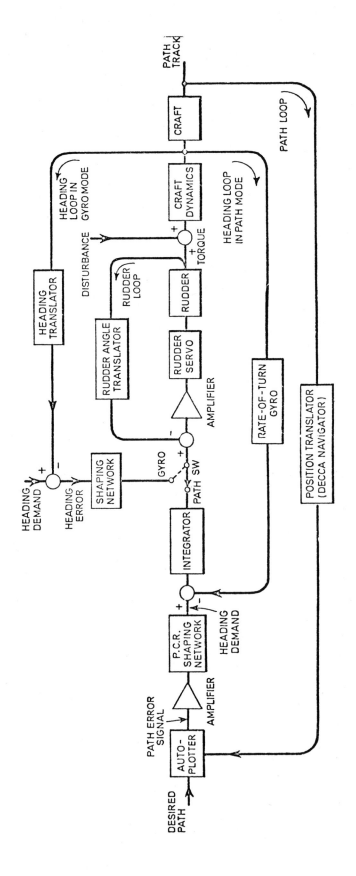

Figure 4.   Block diagram of the overall system.

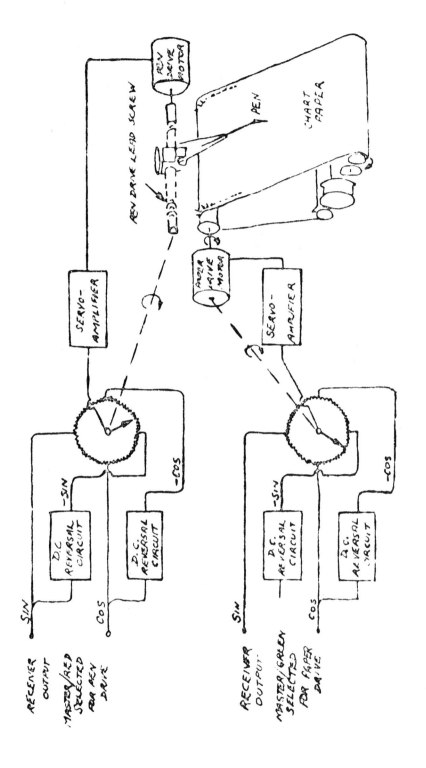

Figure 5. Principle of the automatic plotter.

126

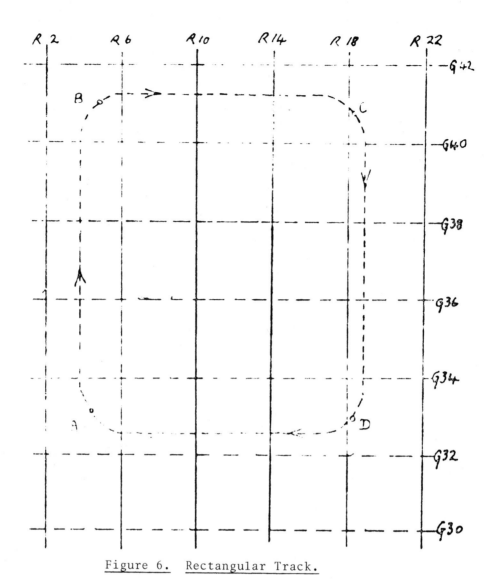

Figure 6. Rectangular Track.

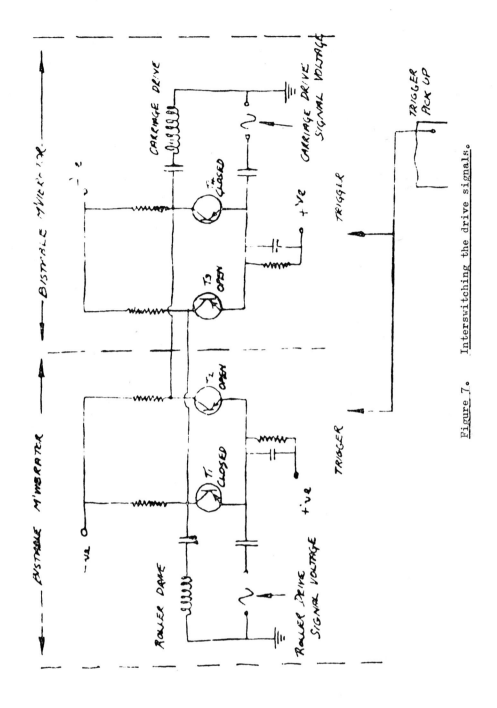

Figure 7.   Interswitching the drive signals.

128

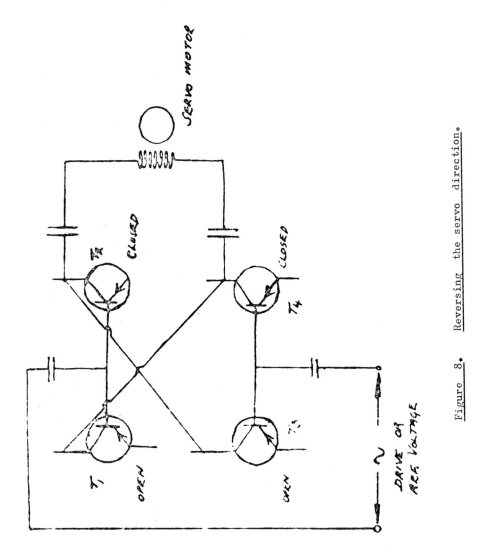

Figure 8. Reversing the servo direction.

Position	Pen Drive	Paper Drive	Requirement	Switching Action
A	Master/Red +	Master/Green +	Normal	+ Pen / + Paper
B	Master/Green −	Master/Red +	Interswitch Drives. Change direction of Servo 1	− Pen / + Paper
C	Master/Red −	Master/Green −	Interswitch Drives. Change direction of Servo 2	− Pen / − Paper
D	Master/Green +	Master/Red −	Interswitch Drives. Change direction of Servo 1	+ Pen / − Paper
A	Master/Red +	Master/Green +	Interswitch Drives. Change direction of Servo 2	+ Pen / + Paper

Table 1. Tabled Analysis of Switching Required.

"PROGETTO ESQUILINO": AN EXPERIMENT ABOUT AN OPTIMAL GYRO-PILOT

Dagnino P., Leccisi D.,Piattelli M., Tiano A.
Laboratorio per l'Automazione Navale
National Council of Research
Genoa, Italy

ABSTRACT

Among the researches performed on board M/s "Esquilino", an experiment has been planned in order to
study the optimization of the course holding process.
This paper deals with the criteria on which this
experiment is based, and illustrates the hardware
and the software, accomplished on board for this
purpose.

INTRODUCTION

Among the researches performed on board the M/s
"Esquilino" of "Lloyd Triestino" an experiment is
now current in order to determine the characteristics of an optimal auto-pilot.
This research is being carried out by the "Laboratorio per l'Automazione Navale" of C.N.R. in Genoa,
with the partecipation of Microtecnica, Selenia and
Owner Company.
A Decca Arkas 550 gyro-pilot, a Sirius MB 12 gyro
compass and a new remote control of the steering
gear, have been installed on board in May 1972,
only for research purposes. Indeed, the standard
equipment existing aboard could not give the requested high accuracy for the course measure and
the rudder angle control.
Precedently, a Selenia Computer, General Purpose 16,
was installed on board for the study of an integrated navigation system. In November 1972, the hardware was completed by a rate-gyro for the yaw rate
measure, supplied by Microtecnica.
The ship "Esquilino" is in currently in line on the
routes to the Far East and her usual voyage lasts
about four months.
During the voyage, which begun at December 20th
1972, a group of researchers has been embarked in
order to carry out the experimental programs.
These programs concern essentially:
- on-line identification of the linear model for the
  ship's response to the rudder;
- on-line evaluation of the cost for the automatic

steering process;
- on-line determination of the optimal gyro-pilot
  adjustments in order to minimize the cost at various sea conditions;
- on-line employement of the computer for the digital control of the steering process, its feasibility and convenience.
For this purpose, a few computer programs have
been carried out and tested at the Computer Center
of the Genoa University, before transferring them
to the onboard computer.

HARDWARE

The hardware installed on board concerns three
functions: measure, computation and control.

Measure equipment

To gauge the rudder angle, a high resolution, accuracy potentiometer is directly connected to the
rudderstock. It is supplied with 24 V d.c. and
therefore gives a signal, whose level is then to
be reduced for the computer analog input but it
has been chosen in order to limit the noise tras-
mission on the line. This potentiometer is, in fact,
the farthest transducer from the computer.
In order to gauge the heading, a gyro-compass Sirius
is connected with a Rotax encoder. The Sirius allows
us a $\pm$ 0,3 degrees static accuracy. For the other
technical data see the monography published by the
builders. The gyro-compass has also requested the
installation of the supply rotating set and the
usual accessories. The optical type Rotax encoder
Series VR 6000, is able to signal 3,600 different
positions in 360°, i.e., it shows a sharp 0,1 degrees resolution. The encoder output, Gray Coded,
is amplified and becomes a digital input word to
the computer, which then decodes the heading measure by a suitable program.
To gauge the turn rate, a rate-gyro is employed
having the following main data:
- resolution less than 0,02 degrees per second

- linearity within $\pm$ 2% or $\pm$ 10 mV
- maximum input velocity 3 degrees per second
- natural frequency about 4 Hz
- damping coefficient about 0,4
- electrical supply 115 V, 26 V 400 Hz
- maximum output level 9 V $\pm$ 10%.

The amplitude and the phase signals are demodulated and amplified according to the level of the analog input in the computer.

Furthermore a ship's speed signal, of analog type, is obtained by a Jungner SAL 24 log by a potentiometer and the excitation of the steering gear solenoid valves is recognized by suitable relais.

Computation equipment

With reference to Fig. 1, the computation equipment consists of

- computer Selenia GP16 with 16 bit word length, 16 K memory with 4 microsecond cycle time;
- processor unit with 8 analog inputs, 48 digital inputs, 16 process interrupts, 32 digital outputs;
- auxiliary memory Sykes Compu Corder 100 with magnetic cassettes, each of 360 K bits;
- card read punch IBM 1442;
- high speed tape reader TR 11, 300 characters per second;
- high speed tape punch TP 11;
- two typewriters TT 21, one of which installed on the bridge, with tape read punch 10 ch/sec;
- video display, alphanumerical type VDO 12".

The computer center is completed by a 029 IBM card punch. The lay-out of the experimental equipments aboard is shown in Fig. 2. The room chosen for the installation of the computer lies in the promenade deck, stern side.

The electrical supply for the experimental equipment is obtained by an independent rotating group, consisting of a 16 HP d.c. motor and a 12,5 kVA, 60 Hz, 3 phase synchronous generator equipped with an automatic frequency and voltage control.

In order to ensure the optimal environmental conditions, required during the computer operation, an auxiliary air conditioner has been fitted outside, abaft the computer room.

Ship's computer system operating satisfactorily aboard from Dec. 1971 suffered no failures ever since.

It is worth noting that, in order to expand the capability of the mini-computer GP16, a cassette system of very low cost has been employed. This solution appears very interesting for implementing the functions of these mini-computers used in the integrated navigation systems.

Control equipment

The control equipment consists of a Decca-Arkas gyro-pilot 550 of standard type. A modification concerns the use of the time position of the main function switch, to connect the solenoid valves control directly to the computer digital output. By this way a choice of manual or gyro-pilot or computer control can be accomplished for steering gear operation. The computer may also control the course alteration directly by an analog signal. However this function does not interest for the course holding problem.

A SHIP'S LINEAR MODEL

The very first problem we are faced with when studying an optimal ship steering control certainly is the identification of a suitable mathematical model of the ship and her environments dynamics. In this section, on the basis of a stochastic extension of the Nomoto [1] equation, which takes the external disturbances into account, we shall briefly discuss the identification technique, which has been used.

The ship is regarded as a rigid body with six degrees of freedom, subject to forces and moments, which are rather complicated function of the motion. If the equations of the motion are expressed in coordinates fixed to the ship's center of gravity, a certain semplification is obtained by assuming small perturbation around a given uniform rectilinear motion [2].

In particular it can be shown that the yawing and swaying motions can be decoupled from the other motions of the ship.

In such a way, with reference to Fig. 3, the yawing and swaying motions can be described, in the non-dimensional form by the linear differential equations

$$\begin{cases} (m_0 - \bar{Y}_{\dot\psi})\dot\psi - m\dot\vartheta - \bar{Y}_\vartheta\vartheta = \bar{Y}_\delta \cdot \delta \\ i\ddot\varphi - \bar{N}_{\dot\varphi}\dot\varphi - \bar{N}_\vartheta\vartheta = \bar{N}_\delta \cdot \delta \end{cases} \tag{1}$$

where ψ is the yaw angle, ϑ is the drift and δ the rudder angle; m_0 and m are the non-dimensional true and apparent masses of the ship, i is the n.d. moment of inertia, while the remaining are n.d. hydrodynamic derivatives.

Using Eqs. (1), we can obtain the yawing $\psi(t)$ and swaying (or drift) $\vartheta(t)$ in response to any movement of the rudder $\delta(t)$. By eliminating ϑ in the latter Eq. (1), we obtain

$$\frac{d^2\dot\varphi}{dt^2} + a_1\frac{d\dot\varphi}{dt} + a_2\dot\varphi = b_0\delta + b_1\frac{d\delta}{dt} \tag{2}$$

which describes the steering-to-yaw response directly in terms of the angular velocity $\dot\psi$. Eq.(2) is the well known Nomoto equation, which may be written also as transfer function in the form

$$\frac{\dot\varphi(s)}{\delta(s)} = \frac{k(1+sT_3)}{(1+sT_1)\cdot(1+sT_2)} \tag{3}$$

and also in the approximated first order form

$$\frac{\dot{\psi}(s)}{\delta(s)} = \frac{k}{1+sT} \qquad\qquad ;T=T_1+ T_2- T_3 \qquad\qquad (3')$$

where k is regarded as a gain, and T_1, T_2, T_3, T as time constants. These steering indexes result function of the ship's speed and draft [1], anyhow, for a given stationary navigation condition, such indexes may be assumed as constant.

We note that Eq. (2) does not take the effects of the external environments (sea condition, wind, currents) on the ship's steering dynamics into account. The description of such perturbed dynamics is rather complicated, essentially owing to the difficulty of representing the disturbances acting on the ship by a mathematically useful form.

If we consider only excitations applied by the sea waves, which are the most significant disturbances, we observe that they act as instantaneous swaying force and yawing moment, which must be added to the second parts of Eqs. (1).

In order to evaluate these perturbative terms, it is necessary to integrate the wave pressure over the immersed surface of the hull, according to the strip-theory, for example.

By means of a linear approximation, it can be shown [3] that the perturbed dynamics, in the presence of long-crested irregular waves, may be described by Eqs. (1), adding the terms $\bar{Y}_e e(t)$ and $\bar{N}_{\dot{e}}\dot{e}(t)$ to the exciting actions.

The disturbance term $e(t)$ is a band-limited white noise, the whiteness of which follows from the statistical properties of sea waves spectra; $\bar{Y}_e$ and $\bar{N}_{\dot{e}}$ are the n.d. coefficients of the amplitudes of the exciting force and moment, which depend on the behaviour of the irregular sea waves as well as on the geometrical characteristics of the ship.

Such equations have been derived by applying the principle of linear superposition to a result obtained by Rydill [4], in the case of sinusoidal regular waves.

The resulting steering-to-yaw response can be therefore modelled in terms of a stochastic differential equation driven by white noise of the type:

$$\frac{d^2\dot{\psi}}{dt^2} + a_1\frac{d\dot{\psi}}{dt} + a_2\dot{\psi} = b_0\delta + b_1\frac{d\delta}{dt} +c_1 e+ \qquad (4)$$
$$+c_2\frac{de}{dt} + c_3\frac{d^2e}{dt^2}$$

Though such equation has been deduced by means of a strong linear approximation – which might be questionable in the case of storm-generated short waves– we shall assume it as a mathematical model of the ship's dynamics in a seaway.

In fact, the introduction of non-linear terms into the equations of motion would so complicate the tratment as to destroy any hope of an analytical solution of the problem.

SHIP'S IDENTIFICATION

The identification of the ship's steering dynamics

consists in determining the indexes of Eq. (4), whenever they change their values. Since, for the optimal control problem, we are interested to determine only a_1, a_2, b_0, b_1, i.e. the Nomoto indexes which interview in the deterministic part of such equation, the identification concerns them only. We need to perform this identification whenever the ship's speed or draft change remarkably.

The same identification is utilized when the ship's speed and draft do not change, to test the validity of the above model at different sea conditions. From the operational point of view, the ship identification must be performed after every reaching of a steady speed.

The identification procedure is the Anström maximum likelihood method [5], which has been successfully applied to different dynamic systems and to the ship too [6].

Without going into the details of such method, we shall briefly discuss about the application to our problem.

Since a digital computer is used in this case, let us consider a discrete-time version of Eq. (4).

$$y(t)+a_1'\cdot y(t-1)+a'\cdot y(t-2)=b_0'\ \delta(t-1) +$$
$$+b_1'\ \delta(t-2)+ \mu\left[e(t)+c_1'e(t-1)+c_2' e(t-2)\right] \qquad (5)$$

where $y = \dot{\psi}$ for simplifying the scripture, $t=0,\pm1$, ..., is the discretized time; $e(t)$ is a sequence of indipendent random variables, which are assumed to be normal and equally distributed.

The sampling time interval is chosen in a such a way to be a submultiple of the delay between the rudder action and the ship response.

The identification problem is solved by determining the maximum likelihood extimate of all parameters, which appear in Eq. (5) and of the standard deviation of the prediction error μ of the model, on the basis of a sequence of input-output records of type $(\delta(t), y(t)$, t=1,2,..,N), [5]. This corresponds to minimizing a suitable loss function with respect to the unknown parameters.

Such minimization is very easy to be performed, even on a small size computer, involving only a matrix inversion and a gradient routine.

Under fairly general conditions the maximum likelihood estimate has nice asimptotic properties, i.e., it is consistent, asimptotic, normal, and efficient. One of these conditions concerns the rudder angle function, to be used as input of the ship system. This function must have a constant spectral density; therefore pseudo random bynary sequences may be used.

During the identification experiments, the rudder is changed manually or better by the computer directly, and the resulting variations in the angular velocity are measured by the rate-gyro at the sampling times. Using the computerized control, the pseudorandom sequence is applied, by a suitable program, to the solenoid valves of the steering gear. Therefore, the Eq. (5) must be changed, taking into account the steering gear too. The transfer function of the corresponding block is assumed of the form $K'/(1+sT')$ and the variables K' and T' are identified preliminarily by the same procedure. Of course, input signals magnitudes must be bounded so that the corresponding rudder angle values do not exceed the limits of the linear model.

THE PERFORMANCE INDEX

The purpose of auto-pilot, according to the most generale definition, is to navigate the ship from a given point to that of arrival with a minimum expenditure. The least expenditure is intended as the least loss, due to disturbances, to go forward, when the ship is sailing along the prescribed course. Regarding to disturbances of the course-keeping process, we may accept the approach proposed by Motora [8]. So, these two losses only, due to lenght increase of path and to rudder activity, will be considered in appraisement of autopilot's operation. All other losses, in fact, can be neglected as compared with those two.

Thus, we assume as performance index the cost:

$$J = \bar{\psi}^2 + \lambda \bar{\delta}^2$$

constituted by the weighted sum of the mean square deviations of path in a seaway $\bar{\psi}^2$ and of the rudder angle $\bar{\delta}^2$. The factor λ is a rational trade-off between course deviation and rudder action and is usually derived from model tank or full scale trials. The use of the above performance index strictly requires the stability of the whole system, consisting of the ship and her control equipment.

Thus, according to Motora, the explicit form of the cost results

$$J = \int_{-\infty}^{+\infty} (|\frac{\psi}{\dot{\psi}_d}|^2 + \lambda |\frac{\delta}{\dot{\psi}_d}|^2)\, S\dot{\psi}_d\, d\omega \qquad (6)$$

where $S\dot{\psi}_d$ is the spectrum of angular velocity of yawing due to external disturbances only, while $\dot{\psi}_d$ is the disturbance. This quantity $S\dot{\psi}_d$ cannot be directly obtained therefore we get it by subtracting the spectrum of the steering component $S\dot{\psi}_\delta$ from the measured spectrum of the yawing angle rate $S\dot{\psi}$.

The above spectra are derived from records of $\delta(t)$ and $\dot{\psi}(t)$, by using the fast fourier transform, directly to obtain $S\dot{\psi}$ and $S\delta$, thus by applying the ship's transfer function (3) or (3'), to $S\delta$, we obtain $S\dot{\psi}_\delta$ and finally $S\dot{\psi}_d = S\dot{\psi} - S\dot{\psi}_\delta$ The duration of the data acquisition for the records depends upon the sampling time interval and is the minimum time below which a remarkable amplitude alteration occurs at the smallest significative frequency.

The particular form of Eq.(6) allows us to express

the cost J as a function of the gyro-pilot adjustement parameters, by means of the transfer functions connecting the disturbance $\dot{\psi}_d$ to the controlled angle ψ and to the rudder angle δ. For this purpose, let us consider the block diagram of Fig. 4, where giro-compass, gyro-pilot, steering engine and ship are shown. The transfer function of the ship and the steering gear are obtained by the identification procedure as described in the previous sections, while the others are derived from the builder's technical data. Fig. 4 shows also the physical connections between the process and the computer, employed as on-line tester. If we denote $F(s)$ the transfer function of the subsystem constituted by gyro-compass, autopilot and steering engine, thus we obtain

$$\left|\frac{\psi}{\dot{\psi}_d}\right| = \left|\frac{F(s)}{1 + \frac{K\,F(s)}{1+sT}}\right|; \; \left|\frac{\delta}{\dot{\psi}_d}\right| = \left|\frac{1}{s + \frac{K\,F(s)}{1+sT}}\right| (7)$$

where the simple form of Eq. (3') is adopted for the ship.

The explicit form of $F(s)$ gives evidence of the adjustment parameters of the gyro-pilot. In order to minimize Eq. (6) cost, we have chosen the following variables:
- K6 weather sheering and 3 weather damping, jointly regulated
- K2 counter rudder
- K4 counter amount

OPTIMIZATION PROCEDURE

The minimization of the Eq. (6) cost must be performed every time the ship alterates her course or speed, every time sea conditions change. In the first case, ship's identification is also required. In both cases, the computer gauges the involved variables with a preset sampling, during a significative time interval. Thus the actual cost is computed according to the actual parameter adjustment and then the minimum cost is obtained by the optimization procedure, choosing a suitable set of the parameters values.

The computer does not control directly the new adjustment, but suggests it through the bridge typewriter to the officer on watch. After the manual adjustment, the computer verifies the cost value and, eventually, elaborates a new set of values.

The officer may compare the ship behaviour before and after the adjustment change, by looking at the course records and at the rudder angle records obtained by a Brush recorder.

If the ship identification is also required, the procedure involves the application of a pseudo-random sequence as input to the system. This sequence can be applied to the steering gear directly by the computer.

In this way, the computer may be used for another experiment, during which a digitalized control of ship's course _ keeping process will be tested.

We have assumed, in this case, the first order model (3') for the ship, connected with the first order representation of the steering engine.

The resulting model is a single input-single output system, driven by the control signal of the rudder remote control, and whose output is the angle ψ . Owing to the linearity assumed for the system, we represent all disturbances as a single disturbance acting on the output ψ . Therefore, the discrete-time input-output relation of such system is analogous to Eq.(5).

After the identification of all the equation parameters, a digitalized control strategy is computed imposing the minimization of the discrete-time version of the cost functional expressed by Eq.(6). Since our system is a complete state information one, it can be shown [7] that the optimal control strategy is easily obtained by means of dynamic programming procedure, according to linear stochastic control theory.

Testing this control law at different sea conditions, particular care will be devoted to determining a suitable value of the weighting factor λ in Eq.(6) in order to obtain the most convenient form of the cost for our ship.

CONCLUSIONS

This paper deals with the hardware and the software provided for a full scale experiment about the optimal control of the course-keeping process. Neither new hydrodynamic approaches, nor original control procedure are proposed, but only the adopted criteria were discussed in the previous sections. Similarly no practical results can be treated, because this first research project will be over at the end of May 1973.

However, as conclusion, we shall point out some of the difficulties, which stand out from this preliminary phase.

The necessity of employing particular input signals for ship's identification does not appear convenient from an operational point of view.

On the other hand the computerized control requires the presence onboard of a certain number of skilled electronic technicians. Furthermore, in both cases, the procedure causes a remarkable delay in the determination of the optimal control laws and requires a certain time interval, during which the ship is necessarily not controlled or unwell controlled. Therefore, this procedure is not appreciated by the crew. For the above mentioned reasons, some different approaches shall be tested to find ship's identification by records obtained during normal navigation.

The mathematical difficulty connected with this approach consists in the existing correlation between input and output, which can't be accepted in the standard identification techniques since it's biasing the extimation.

For the optimization of a gyro-pilot operation, we note the limitation of the parameters chosen for this purpose, which are three only indipendent. In fact, the described procedure requires that all other parameters incorporated in the gyro-pilot are perfectly adjusted for our ship and this cannot be secured because the adjustment is often approximate and some times its range does not contain the suitable values for our ship. However, the proposed procedure can be easily implemented to determine the optimal values of all the parameters, even if these values are not allowed by the system.

Finally, the approach for a computerized digital control of the process does not appear complete, because it neglects the two ship's outputs constituted by the angular velocity and the transversal speed. This first experiment should demonstrate the effective convenience of such a control, though not complete, in order to extend subsequently the treatment .

For this purpose, the main difficulty is the hard working with a not complete state information system, because generally the traversal speed is not measurable. Another serious task is the proper choosing of a suitable cost function, because the cost of Motora does not appear adequate for the three outputs approach.

As final aim of our research, we intend to determine the characteristics of an optimal control system for the course-keeping process.

REFERENCES

(1) NOMOTO,K. "60th Anniversary Series of the Society of Naval Architects of Japan",Vol.11 (Chap.2)

(2) ABKOVITZ,M.A. "Lectures on ship hydrodynamics steering and manoeuvrability", Report No Hy-5, Hydrodynamics Laboratory Lingby,Denmark,1964

(3) TIANO,A.,LECCISI,D."On the ship steering dynamics", L'Automazione Navale, n°1, 1973

(4) RYDILL,L.J. "A linear theory for the steered motion of ships in waves", transactions of I.N.A., London, 1959.

(5) ANSTRÖM, K.J., BOHLIN T."Numerical identification from normal operating records", I.F.A.C. Symposium Theory of self-adaptive control systems, Teddington (U.K.), 1965

(6) ANSTRÖM,K.J. "Recent advances in automatic control and some implications for ships control systems" Technical Report Jungner Instruments, 1971

(7) ANSTRÖM, K.J. "Introduction to stochastic control theory" Academic Press, 1970

(8) MOTORA,S.KOYAMA,T."Some aspects of Automatic

Steering of Ships", Japan Shipbuilding and Marine
engineering, n. 3, 1968.

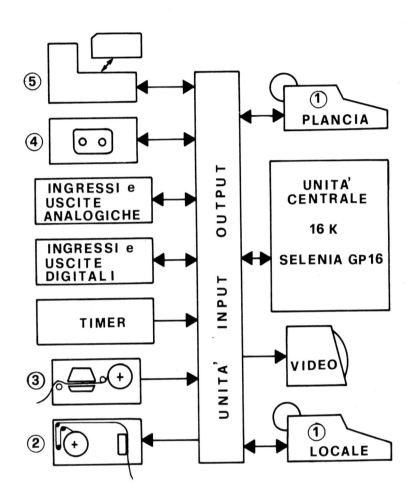

Fig. 1 COMPUTER SYSTEM INSTALLED ONBOARD M/S "ESQUILINO"
1) TYPEWRITER 2) TAPE READ 3) TAPE PUNCH 4) AUXI-
LIARY MEMORY CASSETTE TYPE 5) CARD READ PUNCH.

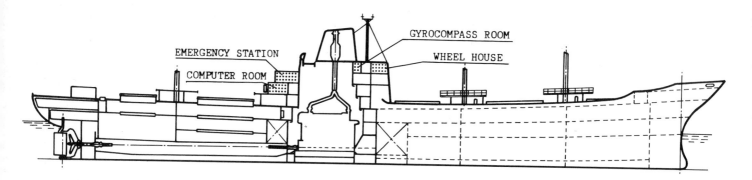

GYRO COMPASS ROOM

1. 400 Hz Power Supply
2. Standard Gyro Compass

WHEEL HOUSE

3. SIRIUS Gyro Compass
4. DECCA Arkas Gyro Pilot
5. Typewriter

EMERGENCY STATION

6. Computer power Supply
7. Air Conditioning Board

COMPUTER ROOM

8. GP 16 SELENIA Control Process Unit
9. Local Typewriter
10. IBM 1442 Card Read Punch
11. IBM 029 Card Punch
12. Tape Punch
13. Tape Reader
14. Auxiliary Memory Cassette Type
15. Rate Gyro
16. Analog Inputs Test Panel

17. Air Conditioner for Computer Room

18. Rudder Angle Transducer.

Fig. 2   LOCATION OF EXPERIMENTAL EQUIPMENTS ON BOARD M/S "ESQUILINO".

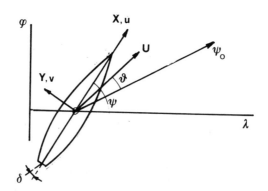

Fig. 3   REFERENCE SYSTEMS FOR THE SHIP.

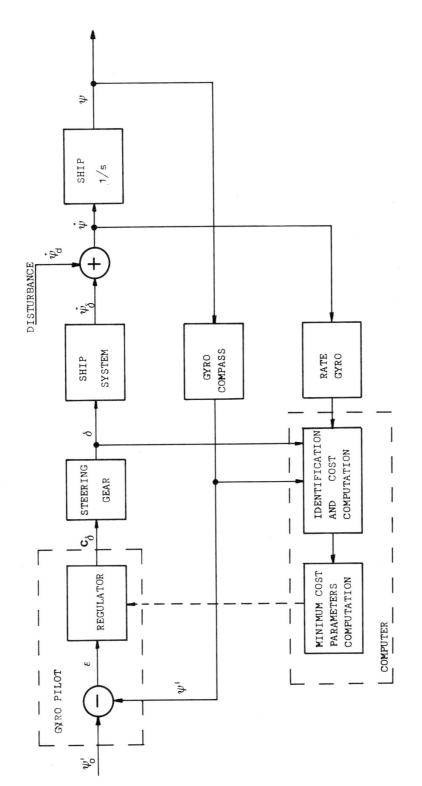

Fig.4 BLOCK DIAGRAM OF AUTOMATIC STEERING SYSTEM

AUTOMATION OF SHIP STEERING CONTROL
ON A DESIRED TRACK

Andrew A. Yakushenkov, D.Sc.
Navigation Department
Merchant Marine Central Research Institute
Leningrad, USSR

ABSTRACT

The advent of modern navigation techniques makes it possible to solve the problem of continuous automatic track-keeping control of a ship on a desired track. Thus the safety of navigation in congested areas may be significantly improved. One of the pioneering works in this field belongs to J.Goclowski and A.Gelb /I/. The authors discussed a control loop of a ship ensuring a desired quality of the transient performance. The matter discussed in the present paper is the synthesis of the ship's control system based upon the minimization of the mean-square estimate of the ship's deviation from the desired track. The information required may be obtained from radionavigation receiver, gyrocompass and log.

ROUTE COORDINATES ESTIMATION

The desired track of a ship may be interpreted as a sequence of loxodromic segments between prescribed turning points. To control the ship's movement on the track it is convenient to apply so-called route coordinates, i.e. distance travelled along the track and lateral displacement from the track. The most probable estimates of the route coordinates to determine the ship's position relative to the desired track may be calculated by shipborne computer. A different nature of errors in dead-reckoning and radionavigation measurements allows to get the best estimates of the coordinates by integrated processing of the data obtained from the mentioned aids. For the integrated processing the methods followed from the Wiener theory of optimal filtering and realized by the Wiener-Kalman filter may be applied/2/. Using the DR coordinates the range differences between the ship and the coast stations are calculated. Deviations of these values from the measured ones are used for corresponding corrections of the DR coordinates and their derivatives. The errors of dead-reckoning are mainly caused by low-frequency errors of the ship's velocity due to unknown currents, while the RNS errors are mostly resulted from the phase disturbances of the received signal due to sky-waves. The analysis has shown that the correlation function of the errors of the phase radionavigation systems (Decca and similar) may be satisfactorily approximated by

$$R(\tau) = \sigma^2 e^{-\mu|\tau|} \cos n\tau \qquad (I)$$

where $\mu = 0.052 \text{ min}^{-I}$
$n = 0.045 \text{ min}^{-I}$

and the dispersion σ^2 is nonlinearly

related to the distance to the transmitter. According to the Kalman theory the RNS errors should be included in a number of estimated parameters. Since (I) corresponds to the forming filter of second order, three position lines are to be measured and route coordinates with their derivatives are to be estimated, that results in state vector of tenth order. This will require a comparatively large write-read memory capacity and a high-speed operation of the computer, that is perhaps undesirable when using special-purpose computer. A simplification is seen to be attained by preselecting the dimension of the estimated state vector. It occured that a quasioptimal algorithm may be synthesized which involves the RNS errors correlation without including these errors in a number of estimated parameters. Then a sufficient accuracy appears to be obtained when the dimension of the state vector is taken equal to four /3/. A sampling interval for estimated route coordinates reception should not exceed some seconds to eliminate the sampler's affect in the closed-loop system.

SYSTEM SYNTHESIS

The obtained estimates of route coordinates may be used for forming the control signals. It is of interest to define an optimal linear continuous system based upon known dynamics of the ship that is in essence a further development of a conventional autopilot.

In fig.I

ψ - course angle (angle between track reference line and ship's centerline)

β - yaw angle (angle between relative velocity vector and centerline)

δ - rudder angle

y - position of ship's center of gravity perpendicular to track reference line (one of route coordinates).

The motion of the ship's center of gravity might be represented as a composition of two vectors - $\bar{v}$ (velocity relative to water) and $\bar{u}$ (transfer velocity relative to earth):

$$\bar{V} = \bar{v} + \bar{u}$$

Then the rate of the ship's lateral displacement from the desired track may be given in form

$$\frac{dy}{dt} = -v \sin(\beta - \psi) - u_y$$

where u_y - $\bar{u}$ -vector projected to normal to track line.

Let y be expressed in portions of the ship's length L. Then, introducing the dimensionless time $t_1 = t \frac{v}{L}$ and assuming angles β, ψ to be small, one obtains

$$\frac{dy}{dt_1} = \psi - \beta + \alpha \qquad (2)$$

where $\alpha = -\frac{u_y}{v}$ is the drift angle which may be regarded as an external disturbance with the known statistics.

A disturbed motion of the ship may be described as follows /4/:

$$\begin{aligned} \dot{\beta} + q_1\beta + r_1\Omega + h_1\beta|\beta| &= -l_1\delta \\ \dot{\Omega} + q_2\beta + r_2\Omega &= -l_2\delta \qquad (3) \\ \dot{\psi} &= \Omega \end{aligned}$$

where q, r, h, l - hydrodynamic coefficients.

The following assumptions are used in (3):

(a) The ship moves at a relatively constant speed V.

(b) The sea is calm enough so that both the nonstationary changes in q, r, h, l and the effect of roll and pitch motion into the ship's response to rudder deflection can be neglected.

As a performance index it is natural to adopt

$$\overline{[y(t_1)]^2} = min$$

provided that the steering device energetic constraints are involved in form

$$\left[\overline{\frac{d\delta}{dt_1}}\right]^2 < C$$

For a linearized model the optimal control may be obtained by state space methods in form of linear functions of state coordinates:

$$\delta = K(t_1)\hat{X} \qquad \hat{X} = \begin{vmatrix} \beta \\ \Omega \\ \psi \\ y \end{vmatrix}$$

The number of feedbacks in the optimal system corresponds to the number of state coordinates, the feedback coefficients being certain time functions /5/. To realize the optimal system the continuous measurements of the ship's yaw angle, course angle, angular velocity and lateral displacement are required. Of practical value is the system based upon two sets of data: measured course angle and calculated lateral displacement estimates. The classical approach allows to find a rather simple solution. The following simplified transfer functions of the open-loop system relating the deviation y to the rudder angle δ and drift angle α may be obtained from equations (2) and (3) after linearizing:

$$G_\delta(s) = \frac{k_\delta(1-\tau s)}{s^2(\pm 1 + Ts)}, \quad G_\alpha(s) = \frac{1}{s} \quad (4)$$

where k_δ, τ, T – positive dimensionless parameters defined through hydrodynamic coefficients.

The minus sign in denominator $G_\delta(s)$ corresponds to a ship unstable on a straight track. The adequacy of the linearized equations for the case of a ship moving without considerable course deviations has been proved experimentally by H.Eda and C.L.Crane /6/.

Simplification of the transfer function $G_\delta(s)$ follows from regarding the ship as a low-frequency filter with a limited bandwidth (up to 0.2 – 0.3 rad/sec for conventional ships).

The transfer function G_δ may be written

$$G_\delta = G_1 \cdot G_2, \quad G_1 = \frac{\psi(s)}{\delta(s)} = \frac{k_\delta}{s(\pm 1 + Ts)}, \quad G_2 = \frac{1-\tau s}{s}$$

where G_1 relates the heading to the rudder angle. It is obvious that G_1 has no zeroes while G_2 has no poles in the right half of the s-plane.

Fig.2 reproduces a block diagram of the closed-loop control system with feedbacks in the heading and drft channels. Let us introduce a closed-loop transfer function relating the heading to the drift angle

$$\frac{\psi(s)}{\alpha(s)} = F(s)$$

Consequently

$$\frac{y(s)}{\alpha(s)} = FG_2 + G_\alpha$$

$F(s)$ has no poles in the right half of the s-plane. As seen from the block diagram

$$\delta(s) = \frac{F\alpha}{G_1}$$

Thus

$$[\overline{y(t_1)}]^2 = \frac{1}{2\pi j}\int_{-j\infty}^{j\infty}(FG_2 + G_\alpha)(\bar{F}\bar{G}_2 + \bar{G}_\alpha)\Phi_{\alpha\alpha}\,ds$$

$$[\overline{\frac{d\delta}{dt_1}}]^2 = \frac{1}{2\pi j}\int_{-j\infty}^{j\infty}\frac{F\bar{F}}{G_1\bar{G}_1}s\bar{s}\,\Phi_{\alpha\alpha}\,ds$$

where $\Phi_{\alpha\alpha}(s)$ – spectral density of random function $\alpha(t_1)$.

A line over symbols means that in the corresponding functions $-s$ is taken instead of s, the argument being omitted.

In accordance with variance method the optimal transfer function $F_{opt}(s)$ may be defined from the condition

$$\overline{[y(t_1)]}^2 + \lambda^2 [\overline{\frac{d\delta}{dt_1}}]^2 = min$$

where λ^2 – the Lagrange multiplier. After substituting and rearranging one obtains /7/:

$$F_{opt} = -\frac{1}{QP}\left[\frac{\bar{G_2}G_\alpha P}{\bar{Q}}\right]^+ \qquad (5)$$

where

$$Q\bar{Q} = G_2\bar{G_2}\left(1 + \frac{\lambda^2}{G_\delta\bar{G_\epsilon}}S\bar{S}\right), \quad P\bar{P} = \Phi_{\alpha\alpha}$$

The sign $[\ ]^+$ means a separation of the function in which all zeroes and poles are located in the left half of the s-plane.

Relating to transfer functions G_1, G_2

$$Q = \frac{1}{S}\prod_{i=1}^{n}(1 + a_i S), \quad n = 4$$

where a_i^2 - roots of the fourth order algebraic equation

$$z^4 - \tau^2 z^3 - \frac{\lambda^2}{k_\epsilon^2}z + \frac{\lambda^2}{k_\epsilon^2}T^2 = 0 \qquad (6)$$

If the ship's drift from the track is caused by sea currents, $\alpha(t_1)$ may be represented as a stationary random function with the spectral density

$$\Phi_{\alpha\alpha}(s) = \frac{D\nu}{-S^2 + \nu^2}$$

where ν may constitute $1,0\cdot10^{-5} \text{sec}^{-1}$
Therefore

$$\left[\frac{\bar{G_2}G_\alpha P}{\bar{Q}}\right]^+ = \left[\frac{D\nu(1+\tau S)}{S(S+\nu)\prod(1-a_iS)}\right]^+ = \frac{D\nu[1+(a+\tau)S]}{S(S+\nu)}$$

Here the terms with ν in a more than first power are omitted. The last expression is quite true for random sequences of step functions with independent amplitudes.

Substituting into (5) yelds

$$F_{opt}(s) = -\frac{1+(a+\tau)s}{1+as+bs^2+cs^3+ds^4} \qquad (7)$$

where $a = \sum a_i$
$b = a_1 a_2 + \ldots + a_3 a_4$
$c = a_1 a_2 a_3 + \ldots + a_2 a_3 a_4$
$d = \prod a_i$

On the other hand, from the block diagram in Fig.2

$$\frac{\Psi(s)}{\alpha(s)} = \frac{-H_1(s)k_\epsilon}{S^2(\pm 1+Ts) + H_1(s)k_\epsilon(1-\tau s) + SH_2(s)k_\epsilon} \quad (8)$$

A comparison of (7) and (8) indicates that they are identical under the following conditions

$$H_1(s) = k_1 + \frac{k_2}{s}; \quad H_2(s) = k_3 + k_4 s$$

$$\frac{k_1}{k_2} = a + \tau; \quad \frac{k_3}{k_2} = b + (a+\tau)\tau \qquad (9)$$

$$\frac{k_4 k_\epsilon \pm 1}{k_2 k_\delta} = c; \quad \frac{T}{k_2 k_\delta} = d;$$

Note, that although the equation (6) has conjugate complex roots, $a \ldots \alpha$ in (7) are real positive values.

The Lagrange multiplier in (6) should satisfy inequality

$$\frac{1}{2\pi j}\int_{-j\infty}^{j\infty}\frac{F_{opt}\bar{F}_{opt}}{G_1\bar{G_1}}S\bar{S}\Phi_{\alpha\alpha}ds < C$$

In fact, taking into account a rather slow change of the transfer velocity the said inequality is always satisfied if the energetic constraints are adopted for the heading channel only, where the main role belongs to relatively high-frequency disturbances (for instance those due to sea waves). Since it is desirable to retain an appropriate performance of the system when this is used as a conventional autopilot, the λ-parameter should satisfy these additional requirements.

Thus in the optimal system the feedback in the drift channel includes proportional and integral elements whereas that in the heading channel - proportional and differential ones. The control law may be presented in form

$$\delta(t_1) = k_1 y(t_1) + k_2 \int y(t_1)dt_1 + k_3\Psi(t_1) + k_4\frac{d\Psi(t_1)}{dt_1}$$

or, in terms of dimensional time

$$\delta(t) = k_1 y(t) + k_2 \frac{v}{L} \int y(t)\, dt + k_3 \psi(t) + k_4 \frac{L}{v} \cdot \frac{d\psi(t)}{dt}$$

The derivative in the heading channel
ensures the closed loop stability if the
ship is unstable on straight tracks in
lack of control. Nonminimal phase ($\tau \neq 0$)
results in increasing the gains in both
channels of the optimal system. In lack
of the heading signal ($k_3 = 0$) the nonminimal phase leads to the closed loop being unstable. An integral element in the
drift channel appeared because of the
adopted restriction on the mean square
rate of rudder deflections, however the
same link eliminates the static errors
of the system. When no position fixes
are available the system may be applied
as a conventional autopilot.

To illustrate the matter let us consider
a ship (large tanker) with the following
simplified transfer function, all terms
being dimensionless

$$G_\delta = \frac{1.6 (1 - 0.32 \tau)}{s(-1 + 9.1\,s)} \; ; \; \frac{v}{L} = 0.029 \text{ sec}^{-1}$$

It is evident that the unsteered ship is
unstable.

Assuming $\lambda = 2.2$ the equation (6) has
roots

$$a_{1,2}^2 = 2.52 \pm j\, 2.45$$

$$a_{3,4}^2 = -2.47 \pm j\, 2.53$$

from which

$$a = 4.93 \; , \; b = 11.98 \; ; \; c = 17.40 \; ; \; d = 12.41$$

From (9)

$$k_1 = 2.42 \; ; \; k_2 = 0.00005 \; ; \; k_3 = 6.28 \; ; \; k_4 = 8.63$$

Fig.3 shows the computerized responses
of the ship to a step changing of the
drift angle up to 5°. The changes of
lateral displacement and course angle
are plotted. To examine the correctness
of the adopted assumptions a complete
nonlinear model of the ship subjected
to equations (3) was used.

A maximum deviation of the ship's center
of gravity from the desired track appeared to be not more than I/4 of the ship's
length, the time of the transient state
being less than ten minutes. The drift
of the ship in the steady state is compensated by a corresponding change of
the course angle. The results prove the
adequacy of the simplified model of the
ship adopted here for the optimal system
synthesis.

CONCLUSIONS

It is shown that a linear closed-loop
system for a track-keeping ship may be
synthesized as a further development of
the conventional autopilot concept provided that the ship's lateral displacement from the desired track may be continuously measured and estimated. To define an optimal system the minimum mean
square deviation of the ship from the
track with the steering device energetic
constraints being imposed was taken as
a performance index. The design and parameters of the regulator have been obtained relative to linearized model of
the ship. The results are illustrated by
computing the responses to a step alteration of the ship's transfer velocity,
the complete nonlinear model of an unstable ship being applied. The data required for the control system may be obtained by integrated processing of radionavigation measurements and dead-reckoning data. Other sources of information
to determine the ship's deviation from
the desired track may be also used.

REFERENCES

I   J.Goclowski and A.Gelb, "Dynamics of an Automatic Ship Steering System", IEEE Trans. of Aut. Control, vol. AC-II No 3, 1966.

2   R.E.Kalman, "A New Approach to Linear Filtering and Prediction Problems" Journ. of Basic Eng., March, 1960.

3   А.Каяндер, А.Якушенков "Некоторые вопросы автоматизации судовождения", Труды Центр.Научно-иссл.ин-та мор.флота, "Судовождение и связь", №167, Ленинград, 1973 г.

4   А.М.Басин "Ходкость и управляемость судов", изд.Транспорт,Москва, 1968 г.

5   A.E.Bryson, Jr., and Yu-Chi-Ho, "Applied Optimal Control", Blaisdel Publ. Co. Waltham, 1969.

6   H.Eda and C.L.Crane, Jr., "Steering Characteristics of Ships in Calm Water and Waves", presented at the 1965 Annual Meeting Soc. Naval Arch. and Marine Eng., N.Y.

7   Sheldon S.L.Chang, "Synthesis of Optimum Control Systems", Mc Graw Hill Book Co., inc. N.Y., 1961.

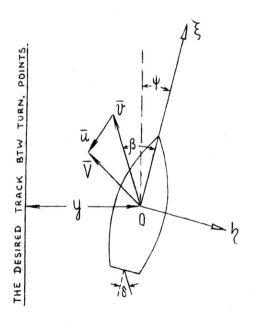

Fig. 1

144

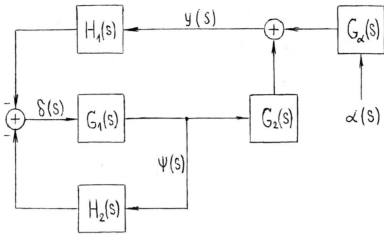

Fig. 2

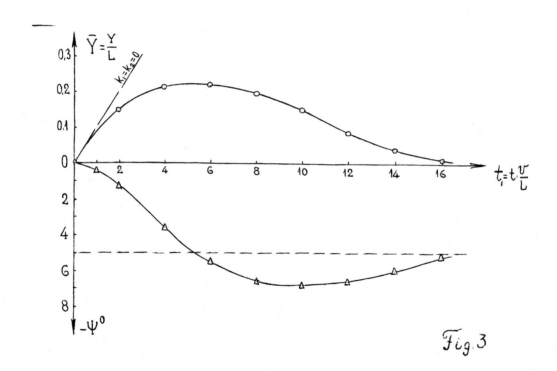

Fig. 3

MODERN CONTROL THEORY APPLIED TO SHIP STEERING

H-F Millers
SAAB-SCANIA AB
Missile and Electronics Section
Electronics Development
Gothenburg, Sweden

ABSTRACT

Modern control theory is applied to the problem of maneuvering a large tanker through a narrow passage when it is disturbed by stochastic current. The problem consists of two parts, estimation and control. Kalman theory is used to derive optimal estimates from measurements contaminated by measurement errors. The estimates are used in the control and the control law derived minimizes a quadratic performance index. The algorithms obtained are applied to a tanker of 210 000 tdw and the numerical results show that an accuracy of a few meters can be achieved.

INTRODUCTION

The size of tankers has during the last decade increased tremendously and introduces new demands on maneuvering and steering. In some cases new harbours have to be built and it often happens that the tanker has to pass through a narrow passage during its way to the harbour. That is e.g. the case at Brofjorden, Sweden, where a new harbour is being built for super tankers. The problem of maneuvering a super tanker through the narrow passage that exists at Brofjorden initiated this study and the purpose was to find out if modern control theory applied to ship steering could help solving the maneuvering problems. The study was carried out during the first part of 1970.

Fortunately the development of control theory and electronics have advanced rapidly during the same decade. The control theory has adopted the state space approach and great advances have been made in filter theory and optimal control.

Pioneering work has been made by Kalman and Bucy (1) (2), who replaced the old Wiener theory by a new estimation theory which makes it possible to calculate the optimal estimate of the state of a linear dynamic system, when it is influenced by stochastic disturbances, both during a transient period and in the steady state.

The theory for controlling a dynamic system has also changed during the same period. Previous work was carried out in the frequency domain but the new theory is using the time domain. The control laws are calculated by minimizing a performance index or loss function. Most frequently the transient time, the energy or the sum of squares of the states and the forcing functions are minimized.

The hardware implementation of the derived control is not discussed in this paper but would probably require a modern process computer of the mini-type.

In this paper the maneuvering problem has been solved using the so called "separation theorem" (3) (4) which implies that the problem can be divided up into two subproblems, of which one is a filter problem and the other one is a control problem.

The solution to the first subproblem is a Kalman-filter and the solution to the second subproblem is an optimal control law. In both cases we get a set of recursive matrix equations, which are well suited to be calculated on a digital computer.

LATERAL MOTION OF SHIP

The motion of a ship can be described by a set of linear differential equations (5) (6) (7) if small deviations from nominal values are assumed. Some of the notations to be used are shown in fig. 1, where the x, y-system is earth fixed, ψ the yaw angel, δ the rudder angle, V is the velocity of the ship, which is assumed to be constant, and v its component perpendicular to the ship axis.

It is also assumed in the following that the ship stays close to the x-axis. The departure from the x-axis can then be written approximately as

$$\frac{dy}{dt} = V\psi + v \qquad (1)$$

or in normalized form

$$\frac{dy'}{dt'} = \psi' + v' \qquad (2)$$

It is customary to express the equations of the

ship motion in normalized, dimensionless form using ship length L, velocity V and water density ρ as basis for the normalization. Under the heading Nomenclature the current notations and normalizations are listed. In the following only normalized values will be used and the primes ' will be dropped.

The linear differential (normalized) equations describing the motion of the ship in the lateral plane are

$$a_{11}\frac{d^2y}{dt^2} + a_{12}\frac{dy}{dt} - b_{11}\frac{d\psi}{dt} - a_{12}\psi =$$

$$\frac{2kc^2}{v^2}\delta + a_{12}\mu \qquad (3)$$

$$a_{22}\frac{dy}{dt} + b_{21}\frac{d^2\psi}{dt^2} + b_{22}\frac{d\psi}{dt} - a_{22}\psi =$$

$$-\frac{kc^2}{v^2}\delta + a_{22}\mu \qquad (4)$$

where μ now is normalized current perpendicular to V disturbing the desired motion of the ship. This disturbance is changing in a stochastic manner and can therefore not be compensated for by introducing corrective maneuvres in advance. The current perpendicular to the path of the ship can be up to 1 knot occasionally at Brofjorden and the speed of the tanker should be kept at about 8 knots to maintain good steering.

The rudder is controlled by a servo, which can be approximated by a first order differential equation. The reference signal to the servo is called δ_r, the time constant T_δ, and we get

$$\delta + T_\delta\dot{\delta} = \delta_r \qquad (5)$$

Substituting the numerical values for a tanker of 210 000 tdw given in Nomenclature into (3) (4) (5) and solving the characteristic equation yields the following eigenvalues

$$\lambda_1 = -10, \ \lambda_2 = \lambda_3 = 0, \ \lambda_4 = -2.66, \ \lambda_5 = 0.31 \qquad (6)$$

The ship by itself is thus unstable and will not return to its course if disturbed. It is necessary to utilize a good control system, in particular, if the ship has to go through a narrow passage.

STATE SPACE APPROACH

In modern control theory the state space approach is used almost exclusively. A description and formalization of the technique is given in Zadeh and Desoer (8).

In the state space approach the differential equation for a linear, continuous system with constant coefficients is given by

$$\dot{x}(t) = A\,x(t) + B\,u(t) + C\,w(t) \qquad (7)$$

where A, B, C are constant matrices, x, u, w column vectors and t time. The x-vector is the state vector and gives the necessary information of the state of a system, e.g. the elements of the vector might be position, velocity, acceleration. The other vectors u and w are forcing and disturbance functions resp.

In a discrete or sampled system the equation corresponding to (7) has the following form

$$x_k = D\,x_{k-1} + F\,u_{k-1} + G\,w_{k-1} \qquad (8)$$

where D, F, G are constant matrices and x_k, u_k, w_k vectors as before sampled at instance kT, T being sampling period.

Between A, B, C and D, F, G we have the relations

$$D = e^{AT} \qquad (9)$$

$$F = \int_0^T e^{A(T-\tau)}\,B\,d\tau \qquad (10)$$

$$G = \int_0^T e^{A(T-\tau)}\,C\,d\tau \qquad (11)$$

In the following we use the discrete discription to get equations in a form suitable for digital computation.

MEASUREMENTS

For the estimation of the state of the ship it is assumed that three different measurements are available

- yaw angle,
- rate of yaw angle,
- position,

The first two can be received from a gyrodevice and the last one from e.g. radar information.

The measurements are denoted by z and the measurement errors by b and v. We assume that

$$\begin{aligned}
z_1 &= \psi + b_1 + v_1 \\
z_2 &= \dot{\psi} + b_2 + v_2 \\
z_3 &= y + v_3
\end{aligned} \qquad (12)$$

The error b is a constant error which later can be included in the dynamic equations if we write

$$b_k = b_{k-1} \text{ where } b = \begin{bmatrix} b_1 \\ b_2 \end{bmatrix} \qquad (13)$$

The constant error is assumed to have normal distribution with the covariance

$$E\left[b_k \, b_j^T\right] = \begin{bmatrix} b_{11} & 0 \\ 0 & b_{22} \end{bmatrix} \qquad \forall \, k,j \qquad (14)$$

Thus b represents the low frequency error. The high frequency error is introduced through $v = \begin{bmatrix} v_1 & v_2 & v_3 \end{bmatrix}^T$ which is white noise with

$$E\left[v_k\right] = 0 \qquad \forall k \qquad (15)$$

$$E\left[v_k \, v_j^T\right] = R \, \delta_{kj} = \begin{bmatrix} r_{11} & 0 & 0 \\ 0 & r_{22} & 0 \\ 0 & 0 & r_{33} \end{bmatrix} \delta_{kj} \qquad (16)$$

where δ_{kj} is the Kronecker delta.

The numerical values of the errors are

$$\sigma_{b1}^2 = b_{11} = 3.04 \ 10^{-6} \ rad^2 \qquad \left[(0.1^\circ)^2\right]$$

$$\sigma_{b2}^2 = b_{22} = 1.74 \ 10^{-4} \ rad^2/normtime^2 \qquad \left[(0.01^\circ/sec)^2\right]$$

$$\sigma_{v1}^2 = r_{11} = 1.2 \ 10^{-5} \ rad^2 \qquad \left[(0.2^\circ)^2\right]$$

$$\sigma_{v2}^2 = r_{22} = 1.7 \ 10^{-4} \ rad^2/normtime^2 \qquad \left[(0.01^\circ/sec)^2\right]$$

$$\sigma_{v3}^2 = r_{33} = 10^{-3} \ normlength^2 \qquad \left[(10 \ m)^2\right]$$

$$(17)$$

where σ is the standard deviation

CURRENT

The current acts on the ship as a disturbance. If the current was constant and known a corrective maneuvre could be programmed. However, at Brofjorden the current is of stochastic nature. A way to approximate such a disturbance is to assume a first order Gauss-Markov function.

$$\mu_{k+1} = \alpha \mu_k + w_k \qquad (18)$$

$$E\left[w_k\right] = 0 \qquad \forall k$$

$$E\left[w_k, w_m\right] = \begin{cases} q & k=m \\ 0 & k \neq m \end{cases}$$

$$E\left[\mu_{k=0}\right] = 0$$

$$E\left[\mu_{k=0}^2\right] = M_o$$

Eqn. (18) may be derived from a continuous first order differential equation. In that case we get

$$\alpha = \exp\left(-\frac{T}{T_c}\right) \qquad (19)$$

where T is sampling period and T_c time constant of the continuous system. In the stationary case we get for the variance

$$E\left[\mu_k^2\right] = \frac{q}{1-\alpha^2} \qquad \text{if } k \to \infty \qquad (20)$$

Fig. 2 shows schematically what μ_k is like.

We notice that if $M_o = q/(1-\alpha^2)$ the sequence $E\left[\mu_k^2\right]$ would remain constant, that is the sequence would start in a statistically stationary state.

At rare occasions the current perpendicular to the path of the ship around the narrow passage becomes about 1 knot. The time constant T_c is estimated to 1/5 of the time the ship needs to travel 3 Nm. With these values we get

$$E\left[\mu_k^2\right] = \sigma_\mu^2 = \left(\frac{1}{3 \cdot 8}\right) ; \qquad (21)$$

$$E\left[w_k, w_k\right] = q = 2.2 \cdot 10^{-5}$$

where the standard deviation σ_μ is set to one third of the value given above.

COMPLETE MODEL

To get a complete model for the problem we combine equations (3) (4) (5) and apply (9) (10) (11) and add equations (13) (18). This results in an equation of the form (8)

$$x_k = D \, x_{k-1} + F\delta \, r_{k-1} + G \, w_{k-1} \qquad (22)$$

where the state vector has the form

$$x_k = \begin{bmatrix} \psi & \dot\psi & y & \dot y & \delta & \mu & b_1 & b_2 \end{bmatrix}^T_k \qquad (23)$$

The other variables are scalars

$$\delta r_{k-1} = (\delta_r)_{k-1} ; \qquad w_{k-1} = w_{k-1} \qquad (24)$$

The matrices are computed according to (9) (10) (11). Before integration the exponential is expanded into a series expansion. The matrices are constant matrices.

The measurements z are given by

$$x_k = H \, x_k + v_k \qquad (25)$$

where

$$H = \begin{bmatrix} 1 & 0 & 0 & 0 & 0 & 0 & 1 & 0 \\ 0 & 1 & 0 & 0 & 0 & 0 & 0 & 1 \\ 0 & 0 & 1 & 0 & 0 & 0 & 0 & 0 \end{bmatrix} \quad z_k = \begin{bmatrix} z_1 \\ z_2 \\ z_3 \end{bmatrix}_k \quad v_k = \begin{bmatrix} v_1 \\ v_2 \\ v_3 \end{bmatrix}_k$$

The equations (22) and (25) constitute the complete model of the system.

MANEUVERING PROBLEM

General

The maneuvering problem can be divided into two subproblems according to the separation theorem. The first subproblem is to measure and compute the state of the ship in an optimal way so that a good estimate $\hat{x}$ is obtained. The second subproblem is then knowing the state of the ship $\hat{x}$, to control or steer the ship in order to minimize a performance index. The situation is shown in fig. 3

Estimation Problem

The state of a linear, dynamic system is best obtained using Kalman theory. This theory gives a linear estimate of the state vector, calculated in such a way that the estimate has maximum likelihood. It may also be described as the estimate which minimizes every positiv definite quadratic form of the error of the state.

The linear filter can be shown to be absolute optimal, i.e. it is not possible to find a non-linear filter, which gives a smaller error variance, as long as the errors have normal distribution. If the disturbances are non-normal the linear filters are optimal up to the second order statistics, i.e. a non-linear filter would have to consider third order or higher distribution functions of the errors to be able to give a smaller error variance.

The estimate of x, based on equation (22) and the minimization of (28), is denoted $\hat{x}$, and is given by

$$\hat{x}_k = (D-F\Lambda_{k-1})\hat{x}_{k-1} + K_k \left[z_k - H(D-F\Lambda_{k-1})\hat{x}_{k-1} \right] \qquad (26)$$

In equation (26) we have introduced the control matrix Λ_{k-1}

$$\delta_{r_k} = -\Lambda_k \hat{x}_k \qquad (27)$$

which according to the separation theorem is the solution of the control subproblem.

The matrix K_k is determined so that the estimate $\hat{x}$ minimizes the positive, definite quadratic form

$$E\left[(\hat{x}_k - x_k)^T (\hat{x}_k - x_k) \right] = E\left[\tilde{x}_k^T \tilde{x}_k \right] = \text{Trace } E\left[\tilde{x}_k \tilde{x}_k^T \right] \qquad (28)$$

where

$$\tilde{x}_k = \hat{x}_k - x_k$$

The covariance matrix of the errors is denoted P_k

$$P_k = E\left[\tilde{x}_k \tilde{x}_k^T \right] \qquad (29)$$

The expressions for K_k and P_k are given under the heading Solution.

Control Problem

The arrival of a ship to a narrow passage is schematically shown in fig. 4. At time t=0 the approach of the passage begins and at this point it is off the ideal path. If it continues without any corrective maneuvres it will strike ground. The control must take the ship towards the ideal path and steer it through the narrow passage in the middle of the gap and as close to a zero state $y=\dot{y}=\psi=\dot{\psi}=0$ as possible. It is assumed that the coordinate system xy is positioned with the x-axis along the ideal path and that the approach starts at t=0 and that the ship passes the gap at $t=t_N$.

The solution of the control problem is given as the control strategy which minimizes the following performance index

$$J = E\left\{ \frac{1}{2} x_N^T S_N x_N + \frac{1}{2} \sum_{k=1}^{N-1} \left[x_k^T \delta_{r_k}^T \right] \begin{bmatrix} \phi_k & 0 \\ 0 & \Omega_k \end{bmatrix} \begin{bmatrix} x_k \\ \delta_{r_k} \end{bmatrix} \right\} \qquad (30)$$

where S_N, ϕ_k, Ω_k are coefficients and S_N, ϕ_k are positive semi-definite matrices and Ω_k positive definite matrices. The coefficients are given specific values depending on our objectives. A large ϕ_k suppresses x_k more than a small ϕ_k and a similar reasoning applies to S_N, x_N and Ω_k δ_{r_k}.

The solution of the control problem is a control function

$$\delta_{r_k} = -\Lambda_k \hat{x}_k \qquad (31)$$

The equations necessary for calculating Λ_k is given below.

The position and the yaw angle and their derivatives at time t=0 will vary from arrival to arrival. We assume that the elements of the arrival states are statistically distributed (normal) and cover in that way the different types of initial conditions that will occur. The control law (31) is independent of the initial state and hence the same control law can be used in every approach of the passage.

SOLUTION

The derivation of the solutions (26) (31) are rather lengthy and will not be given here. Instead we state the solutions of the two problems.

The solution of the filter problem (26) may be written in two steps

$$\hat{x}_k = \hat{x}_k' + K_k \left[z_k - H \hat{x}_k' \right] \qquad (32)$$

$$\hat{x}_k' = D \hat{x}_{k-1} + F(\delta_r)_{k-1} \qquad (33)$$

where $\hat{x}'$ is an intermediate estimate, the estimate before sampling.

The solution of the control problem is (31)

$$\delta_{r_k} = -\Lambda_k \hat{x}_k \tag{34}$$

The coefficients K_k and Λ_k can be calculated from

$$\Lambda_k = (F^T S_{k+1} F + \Omega_k)^{-1}(F^T S_{k+1} D) \tag{35}$$

$$K_k = P_k' H^T (H P_k' H^T + R)^{-1} = P_k H^T R^{-1} \tag{36}$$

where

$$S_k = DTS_{k+1}D - \Lambda_k^T(\Omega_k + F^T S_{k+1} F)\Lambda_k + \Phi_k \qquad S_N \text{ given} \tag{37}$$

$$P_{k+1}' = DP_k D^T + Q \qquad P_o' \text{ given} \tag{38}$$

$$Q = E[Gw_k(Gw_k)^T] = GqG^T \tag{39}$$

$$P_k = P_k' - K_k(H P_k' H^T + R)K_k^T \tag{40}$$

Equations (36) (38) and (40) solve the estimation problem and Eqns. (35) (37) the control problem. All equations are recursive and well suited for computation on a digital computer. The equations are solved forward in time with the exception of (37), which starts with S_N and is solved backwards in time.

The solution is shown in blockdiagram form in fig. 5.

The accuracy of the control is given by

$$X_k = E[x_k x_k^T] \tag{41}$$

and can be calculated from

$$X_k = X_k' + P_k' \tag{42}$$

where

$$P_k' = E[e_k e_k^T] \qquad e_k = \hat{x}_k' - x_k \tag{43}$$

$$X_k' = E[\hat{x}_k' \hat{x}_k'^T] \tag{44}$$

The matrix P_k' is (38) and derivation of X_k' yields

$$X_{k+1}' = (D - F\Lambda_k)(X_k' + P_k' - P_k)(D - F\Lambda_k)^T \tag{45}$$

The initial values of (45) are X_o and P_o', which are given values depending on the situation. Equations (41) - (45) solves the standard deviation of the state variables during the control.

Similarly we get for δ_{r_k}

$$E[\delta_{r_k} \delta_{r_k}^T] = \Lambda_k[X_k' + P_k' - P_k]\Lambda_k^T \tag{46}$$

To get initial values to start the recursive computations we assume that $\hat{x}_o' = 0$ with $X_o' = 0$ which makes $X_o = P_o'$.

NUMERICAL SOLUTION

The numerical computations were carried out on a digital computer. The filter and control equations were programmed in Algol-Genius on SAAB D22. All numerical values apply to a tanker of 210 000 tdw, length 310 m and width 50 m.

The covariance matrix of the ship states at time t=0, X_o, is assumed to have the following diagonal elements, other elements are zero. Values withing [] are corresponding non-normalized values.

$$\sigma_\psi^2 = 1.22 \cdot 10^{-3} \text{ rad}^2 \qquad [(2^o)^2] \tag{47}$$
$$\sigma_{\dot\psi}^2 = 6.95 \cdot 10^{-4} \text{ rad}^2/\text{norm time}^2 \qquad [(0.02^o/s)^2]$$
$$\sigma_y^2 = 1.04 \cdot 10^{-1} \text{ norm length}^2 \qquad [(100 \text{ m})^2]$$
$$\sigma_{\dot y}^2 = 1.22 \cdot 10^{-3} \text{ rad}^2 \qquad [(0.14 \text{ m/s})]$$
$$\sigma_\delta^2 = 1.22 \cdot 10^{-3} \text{ rad}^2 \qquad [(2^o)^2]$$
$$\sigma_\mu^2 = 1.55 \cdot 10^{-3} \text{ rad}^2 \qquad [(2.3^o)^2]$$
$$\sigma_{b1}^2 = 3.04 \cdot 10^{-6} \text{ rad}^2 \qquad [(0.1^o)^2]$$
$$\sigma_{b2}^2 = 1.74 \cdot 10^{-4} \text{ rad}^2/\text{norm length}^2 \qquad [(0.01^o/s)^2]$$

The first four values corresponds to the state of the ship (ψ, $\dot\psi$, y, $\dot y$) and at time t=0 the ship has one of several possible states defined by the standard deviations above. For instance the yaw angle has a σ-value of 2° which implies that at rare occasions the yaw angle may be about $\pm 6^o$. The same reasoning goes for the other elements of the state vector.

The controlled phase of the approach lasts for 300 sampling periods, each of T=0.02 norm time, and corresponds to 6 norm ship lengths. The current is given by (21) q=2.2·10^{-5}.

The optimal control minimizes the performance index (30). The cofficients S_N, ϕ_k, Ω_k are chosen with respect to the requirements on the control. The specific values chosen are given in Table 1 of Nomenclature and Numerical Values. In the first part of the approach the coefficients are smaller than in the last part in order to get a smooth transient to the ideal path.

The results of the computations are shown in fig. 6 - 10. The first two figures refers to the filtering and the other three describes the control.

In figs. 6 and 7 are outlined the diagonal elements of the covariance matrix P, equation (40). The diagonal elements, which are the variances of the estimation errors, are normalized with respect to the variances of the first sampling. After 6 ship lengths the errors are reduced to the following standard deviations of non-normalized form

$$\sigma_\psi = 0.11^\circ \tag{47}$$

$$\sigma_{\dot\psi} = 0.0046^\circ/s$$

$$\sigma_y = 1.1 \text{ m}$$

$$\sigma_{\dot y} = 0.006 \text{ m/s}$$

$$\sigma_\delta = 0.0$$

$$\sigma_\mu = 0.012$$

$$\sigma_{b1} = 0.10^\circ$$

$$\sigma_{b2} = 0.0006^\circ/s$$

Thus, the optimal filtering gives small errors in the estimation of the state variables. Only the constant error of ψ which is b_1, does not improve. The values of (47) should be compared with the accuracy of the sensors (17). The yaw angle is measured using a sensor, which has a constant error of 0.1° and a noise of 0.2°. The yaw rate measurement has a constant error of 0.01 °/s and a noise of 0.01 °/s. The position is measured with an error of 10 m. The other variables are estimated in an optimal way using these measurements.

The resulting control performance is described by the diagonal elements of the matrix X, equation (41), which are shown in figs. 8 - 10. A smooth transient to the x-axis, the ideal path, is experienced. The final point, at 6 norm ship lengths, is at the narrow passage. The curves show that an additional effort is exercised just before the critical passage. The final state of the ship in non-normalized form is

$$\sigma_\psi = 0.8^\circ \tag{48}$$

$$\sigma_{\dot\psi} = 0.015 \text{ °/s}$$

$$\sigma_y = 2.2 \text{ m}$$

$$\sigma_{\dot y} = 0.065 \text{ m/s}$$

The values show that it is possible to pass through a narrow passage. The position error is only 2.2 m and the other state variables have deviations of the same order. The results (48) should be compared with the narrow passage of Brofjorden which is 270 m and the width of the ship which is 50 m.

CONCLUSION

In this paper we have applied modern control theory to the problem of maneuvering a ship through a narrow passage in order to be able to compensate for stochastic current and measurement errors. The filtering and control strategy is given by a set of recursive formule, which are well suited for programming on a digital computer, e.g. a minicomputer. The standard deviations from the ideal path through the narrow passage are a

few meters and should be a satisfactory control. The optimal control strategy can be changed by giving the coefficients S_N, ϕ_k, Ω_k other values than in this paper to suit specific situations. Before implementing an optimal strategy the sensitivity due to parameter variations should be investigated. In the case of extreme sensitivity a suboptimal strategy with a flat optimum might be preferred to an optimal strategy. The optimal strategy derived in the paper demonstrates one way to attack a delicate problem and what can be achieved.

NOMENCLATURE AND NUMERICAL VALUES

L	= 310 m	= ship length
W	= 50 m	= ship width
V	= 4 m/s (8 knots)	= velocity of ship
$t' = \dfrac{V}{L}$		= dimensionless time
$\psi' = \psi$		= yaw angle
$y' = \dfrac{y}{L}$		= position
$\delta' = \delta$		= rudder angle
$\delta'_r = \delta_r$		= rudder angle reference
$T'_\delta = \dfrac{V}{L} T_\delta = 0.1$		= rudder time constant
$\dfrac{kc^2}{V^2} = 0.866$		= rudder coefficient
$\mu' = \dfrac{\mu}{V}$		= water current $\perp$ V
$T' = \dfrac{V}{L} T = 0.02$		= sampling period
T		= transpose of matrix
λ		= eigenvalue
α		= current coefficient
σ		= standard deviation
E		= statistical expectation
x		= earth fixed x-axis
$\hat{x}$		= state vector
		= estimate of state vector
$\hat{x}'$		= intermediate estimate of x
y		= earth fixed y-axis
z		= measurement vector
b		= bias error
v, w		= white noise
$q = 2.2 \cdot 10^{-5}$		= variance
A,B,C		= matrices, continuous case
D,F,G		= matrices, discrete case
H		= measurement matrix
K		= estimate coefficient matrix
S, ϕ, Ω		= control matrices
Λ		= control law
P,R,Q,X		= covariances matrices
$T'_c = \dfrac{V}{L} T_c = 3.1$		= line constant, current
J		= control perf. index
N = 300		= sampling index
k		= sampling index

For a tanker of 210 000 tdw, length 310 m and a depth of water of 70 m the dimensionless coefficients of (3) and (5) have the following values.

$a_{11} = 2.048$ $b_{11} = 1.432$

$a_{12} = 1.274$ $b_{21} = 0.1278$

$a_{13} = 4.142$ $b_{22} = 0.2207$

$a_{22} = 0.7990$ $b_{23} = 1.565$

$k = 0.192$ $T = 0.1$

Table 1. Values of S_N, ϕ_k and Ω_k

S_N		ϕ_k			Ω_k	
			$0 \leq k < 150$	$150 \leq k \leq 300$		
s_{11}	$1.64 \cdot 10^5$	φ_{11}	2.74	$2.74 \cdot 10^2$	ω_{11}	21.9
s_{22}	$6.94 \cdot 10^4$	φ_{22}	$1.30 \cdot 10^{-1}$	$1.30 \cdot 10$		
s_{33}	$3.05 \cdot 10^5$	φ_{33}	$2.08 \cdot 10$	$2.08 \cdot 10^3$		
s_{44}	$1.64 \cdot 10^5$	φ_{44}	2.74	$2.74 \cdot 10^2$		
s_{55}	0.463	φ_{55}	$6.94 \cdot 10^{-1}$	$6.94 \cdot 10^{-1}$		

$s_{ij} = 0$ if $i \neq j$ $\varphi_{ij} = 0$ if $i \neq j$

REFERENCES

1. R.E. Kalman: A New Approach to Linear Filtering and Prediction Problems. J. Basic Eng. Mars 1960.

2. R.E. Kalman, R.S. Bucy: New Results in Linear Filtering and Prediction Theory. J. Basic Eng. Mars 1961.

3. T.L. Gunckel, G.F. Franklin: A general solution for linear sampled data control. J. Basic Eng. 1963.

4. H.W. Sorensen: Kalman Filtering Techniques Advances in Control Systems, ed. Vol. 3, 1966.

5. P. Mandel: Ship Maneuvering and Control.

6. M.A. Abkowitz: "Lectures in Ship Hydrodynamics, Steering and Maneuverability", Hydro-Og Aerodynamisk Laboratorium, Reprot Hy-5, Denmark, May 1964.

7. B.J. Andersson: Om inseglingen till Brofjorden KTH, Stockholm.

8. L.A. Zadeh & C.A. Desoer: Linear System Theory. The State Space Approach. Mc Graw-Hill 1963.

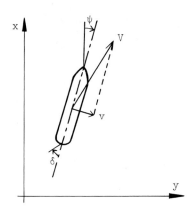

Figure 1.   Lateral ship motion

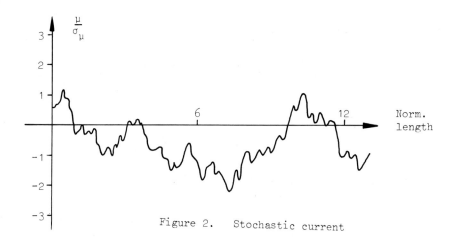

Figure 2.   Stochastic current

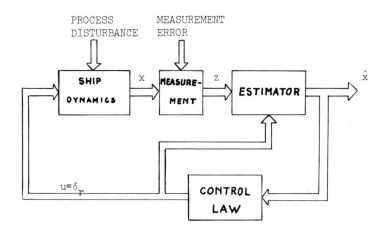

Figure 3.   Maneuvering of ship

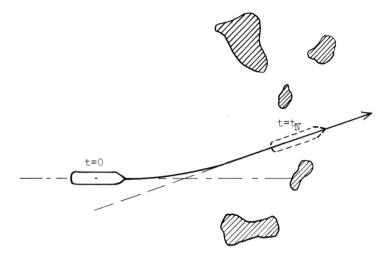

Figure 4.   Narrow passage

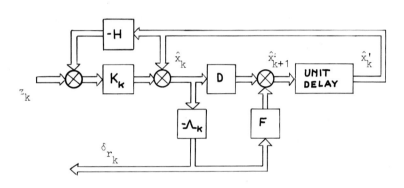

Figure 5.   Estimation and control

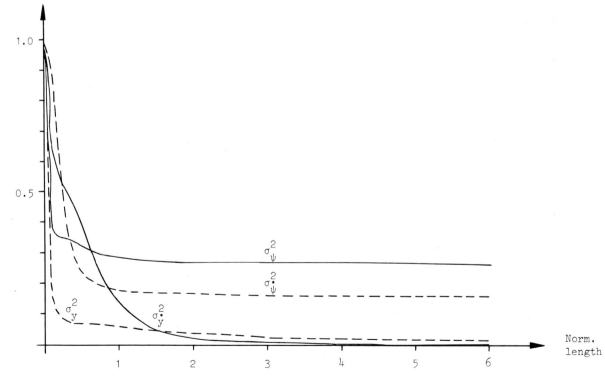

Figure 6.   Normalized estimation errors.

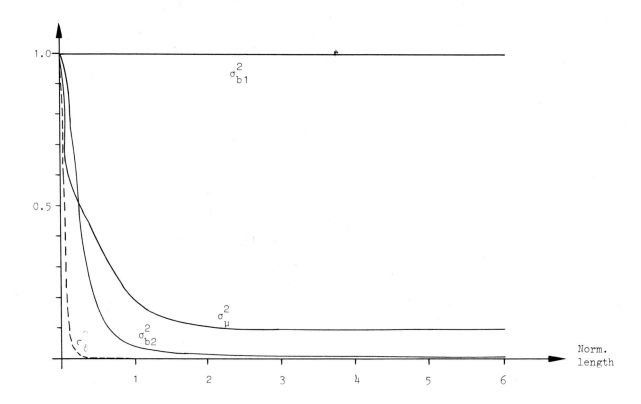

Figure 7. Normalized estimation errors

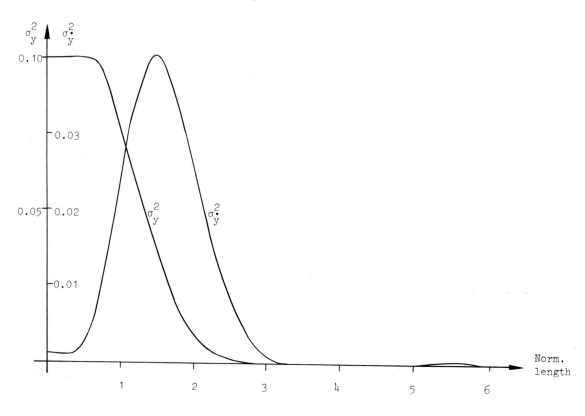

Figure 8. Control errors

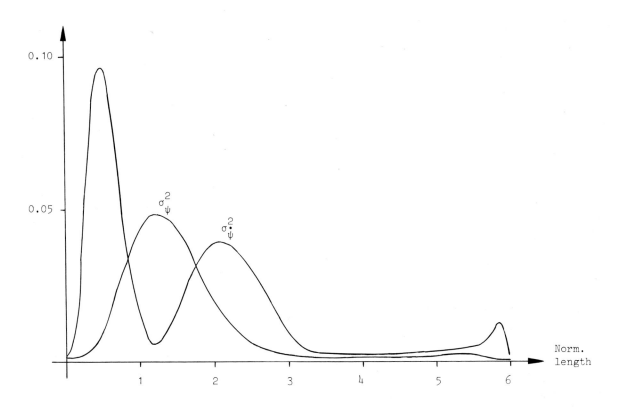

Figure 9.   Control errors

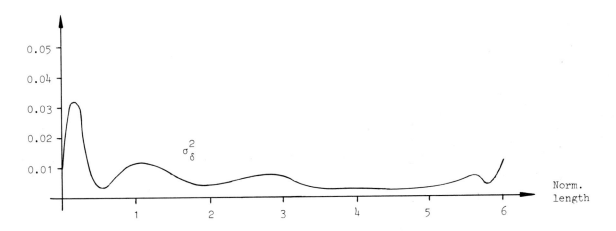

Figure 10.   Rudder angle

ADAPTIVE AUTOPILOTS FOR SHIPS

J. van Amerongen   A.J. Udink ten Cate

Control Laboratory
Department of Electrical Engineering
Delft University of Technology
Delft, Netherlands

Summary

For control purposes the steering characteristics
of a ship at constant thrustpower, can be described
by a relatively simple mathematical model.
The dynamic behaviour of the ship, and hence also
the parameters of this model are strongly dependent
on the external circumstances and the applied
thrustpower. When the ship is steered with an autopilot it is necessary to adjust the parameters of
the autopilot dependent on the change of the steering characteristics of the ship. The best way to
do this is to adapt automatically the parameters
of the autopilot.

In this paper two methods of adaptation are compared. First a description is given of an autopilot, synthesized according to the "sensitivity
model" approach, especially designed to meet the
course instability which can occur at very large
ships. Second a method of adaptation known as the
stability (Liapunov) approach is used. By simulation with the model of a ship of 2000 brt, a comparison is made between the two methods. The
results are tested in practice on this ship.
During the measurements at sea special attention
is paid to the problem of filtering the disturbances due to yawing.

1. Introduction

In the past several autopilots for ships have been
developed. Generally they are specially designed
for keeping a constant course; some of them can
also be used for a variable course. They are composed of rather simple controllers and should
correct the disturbances of the set course. They
must also give the desired response at course
changes. This can be achieved by adjusting the
parameters of the controller in accordance with the
steering characteristics of the ship. For small
variations in the steering characteristics the
feedback system corrects automatically the overall
behaviour. For large variations the parameter
settings of the autopilot must be adapted manually.

Especially for supertankers the variations can be
large and they can appear suddenly, for instance
when the depth of water changes. Due to their size
these ships are also manually difficult to handle.

Therefore autopilots that can be used to make
accurate course changes in narrow coastal waters,
will be of great importance. Commonly applied autopilots have many parameter settings but they must
be set manually. The introduction of an automatically adaptive autopilot permits the application of a
course feedback system in those situations where
varying conditions give rise to difficulties until
now.

It is known that variation of depth of water may
introduce even course instability. By application
of an appropriate rate feedback this phenomena can
be avoided. The gain of the rate feedback should
be adapted automatically to obtain the desired
behaviour of the system in all circumstances.
In this paper two alternative methods are described
and compared.

2. The mathematical model of a ship

Generally a ship can be described as a system with
two inputs, rudder-angle and thrustpower, and two
outputs, course-angle and speed. However, to design
an autopilot such a model is too complicated. Most
of the autopilots that are on the market at present
are specially designed for keeping a fixed course
with a course-stable ship. As in this case only
small rudder-angles occur, a simple linear transfer
function between the rudder-angle and the course
can be used to describe the behaviour of the ship.
This transfer function can be derived from the complicated, non-linear models that are used in shipbuilding technology. Such a model is described by
Nomoto [1].

$$\tau_1\tau_2\dddot{\psi} + (\tau_1+\tau_2)\ddot{\psi} + \dot{\psi} = K\delta + K\tau_3\dot{\delta} \qquad (1)$$

For the definition of symbols, see figure 1.
Using the Laplace transformation, (1) can be
written

$$\frac{\psi(s)}{\delta(s)} = \frac{K(s\tau_3+1)}{(s\tau_1+1)(s\tau_2+1)s} \qquad (2)$$

K, τ_1, τ_2 and τ_3 are parameters related to the
hydrodynamic coefficients, the mass and the speed
of the ship.
The rudder-angle should not exceed 5°. For our
aims this model is too simple. We want also to

describe course-unstable ships and course-stable ships, using rudder-angles larger than 5°. Therefore the transfer function has to be extended with a non-linearity as is done by Bech [2].
When the thrustpower is assumed to be constant during the manoeuvres, then $K/\tau_1\tau_2$, $(\tau_1+\tau_2)/\tau_1+\tau_2$ and τ_3 are approximately constant, whereas $1/\tau_1\tau_2$ is changing considerably. Dividing (1) by $\tau_1\tau_2$ and substituting $(1/K)\psi = H(\dot\psi)$, yields

$$\dddot\psi + (\frac{1}{\tau_1}+\frac{1}{\tau_2})\ddot\psi + \frac{K}{\tau_1\tau_2}H(\dot\psi) = \frac{K}{\tau_1\tau_2}(\tau_3\dot\delta+\delta) \qquad (3)$$

If the rudder-angular velocity is neglected [3] and if

$$a_1 = 1/\tau_1 + 1/\tau_2 \qquad \text{and} \qquad K = K/\tau_1\tau_2$$

equation (3) simplifies to

$$\dddot\psi + a_1\ddot\psi + K'H(\dot\psi) = K'\delta \qquad (4)$$

$H(\dot\psi)$ is a non-linear function of $\dot\psi$, the other coefficients in (4) are constant if the external conditions do not change.
$H(\dot\psi)$ can be found from the relationship between δ and $\dot\psi$ in the steady state ($\ddot\psi = \psi = \dot\delta = 0$). Experiments, known as the spiral test, give this relationship (For course-unstable ships the "reversed spiral test" must be used).
$H(\dot\psi)$ can be approximated by

$$H(\dot\psi) = a\dot\psi^3 + b\dot\psi \qquad (5)$$

a is always a positive in value while b can have positive and negative values. When b is negative the ship is course-unstable. $H(\dot\psi)$ is called the reversed spiral curve. The coefficients K' and a_1 can be found from zig-zag trials.

Two types of disturbances are acting upon the system.
a) Disturbances that cause deviations from the set course
b) Disturbances which affect the steering characteristics of the ship (i.e. the parameters of the model)

Wind and waves belong to the first category. They should be corrected as far as possible by means of a feedback. Generally the frequencies of the yawing motion are so high that they cannot be corrected by the rudder.
Therefore the rudder should not be activated by course deviations, caused by this fast motion, as this will only give loss of speed. Usually this problem is solved by applying a dead band in the steering gear, which can be set dependent on the sea conditions. The deviations of a lower frequency should be corrected totally, without any dead band. For this reason it is better to separate these two components with a low-pass filter, rather than using a dead band which not only damps the fast yawing motion, but also causes deviations from the desired course.
A frequency analysis of the wave disturbances is given in appendix C.

The small disturbances of the second category

(parameter variations) can be corrected with a feedback, but large parameter variations have to be compensated by means of adaptation.
The loading of the ship and the depth of water belong to this category. The loading of the ship influences $H(\dot\psi)$, K' and a_1. The depth of water influences primarily the function $H(\dot\psi)$, i.e. the form of the reversed spiral curve. In a certain range of depth of water, ships with a poor course-stability can even become unstable. The variations in K' and a_1 are much smaller. Details are given in [4].

3. Adaptation

Now we will point out how to meet the change of the steering characteristics of the ship by means of automatic adaptation.
Especially the influence of the depth of water, which changes the shape of the $H(\dot\psi)$-graph, will be compensated. Let us examine (5) again.

$$H_w(\dot\psi) = a_w\dot\psi^3 + b_w\dot\psi \qquad (6)$$

When the depth of water changes the changes in a_w are relatively small, while b_w changes over a wide range. A changing b_w can be compensated easily. Say, we want (6) to be

$$H_d(\dot\psi) = a_w\dot\psi^3 + b_d\dot\psi$$

This can be achieved by adding a factor $K_d\dot\psi$ in (6), which gives

$$H_d(\dot\psi) = a_w\dot\psi^3 + b_w\dot\psi + K_d\dot\psi$$

with

$$K_d = b_d - b_w$$

When the steering gear dynamics are neglected - which is allowed in comparison with the ship dynamics - the factor $K_d\dot\psi$ can be seen as a rate feedback (figure 2).

To get an appropriate rate feedback for a varying b_w, the value of K_d must be set automatically. This is implemented by a model reference adaptation technique.(figure 2). The course error signal $(\psi_g-\psi_w)$ is also used as input signal for a model which has a response as is desired for the ship. The difference of the responses is measured and the error signal is manipulated in such a way that K_d is found. In the following sections the two adaptation methods that are investigated are described and compared.

4. The sensitivity model

Adaptation with a sensitivity model is in fact an implementation of a continuous hill-climbing technique. The criterium that has to be minimized, is the difference between the responses of the ship and the model. A quadratic criterium as is chosen here, is mathematically easy to handle

$$C = \tfrac{1}{2}e^2 \qquad \text{with} \qquad e = \dot\psi_m - \dot\psi_w$$

The control equations of the adaptive system are derived in [5] and in appendix A.

It is found that the minimum of the criterium with respect to b_w is reached when

$$\frac{\partial}{\partial b_w}(\tfrac{1}{2}e^2) \approx e\frac{\partial\dot\psi_m}{\partial b_m} = 0$$

with $\overset{\circ}{K}_d$ given by the equation

$$\dot K_d = Ke\frac{\partial\dot\psi_m}{\partial b_m}$$

where

$$\frac{\partial\dot\psi_m}{\partial b_m} = u$$

is called the sensitivity coefficient.

This coefficient indicates the variation in $\dot\psi_m$, due to variations in b_m and can be computed easily from the model output $\dot\psi_m$ by the sensitivity model. The sensitivity model differs from the reference model only in the non-linearity. When u is multiplied with e and the product is integrated, K_d is found and is used to adapt the rate feedback gain automatically.

The implementation of this adaptive control system is drawn in figure 3.

5. Liapunov approach

In this section an alternative method will be introduced, which is based on the second method of Liapunov.

In the Liapunov approach the system and the reference model are assumed to be of the same order. If there is a difference between the state vectors of the model and the system, the parameters of the system are adjusted in order to minimize this difference. It should be noted that in the Liapunov approach the difference between the state vectors is minimized instead of the error signal (i.e. the difference between the response of the model and the system) which is minimized by using a sensitivity model.

It is assumed that the system parameters can be adjusted directly.

When $\underline{x}$ denotes the system state vector of dimension n, where n is the order of the system, and $\underline{y}$ is the model state vector, the system error of the adaptive system is defined

$$\underline{e} = \underline{y} - \underline{x}$$

where $\underline{e}^T = (e_1, e_2, \ldots, e_n)$. The superscript $.^T$ denotes the transpose of a vector.

Following the Liapunov approach, a Liapunov function V is formed of the system error, the plant inputs and the parameter difference of the model and the plant. Computing the time derivative $\dot V$ of the Liapunov function it can be shown that if certain adaptive laws are fullfilled, $\dot V$ will be negative

definite with respect to $\underline{e}$. The adaptive system will therefore be asymptotically stable in the sense of Liapunov for $\underline{e}$, which means that after an initial disturbance $||\underline{e}|| \to 0$ for $t \to \infty$, where the Euclidean norm $||\underline{e}|| = \sqrt{e_1^2 + e_2^2 + \ldots + e_n^2}$

When the plant is linear, the Liapunov method can be applied straightforward, but in the non-linear case no general design procedures can be given.

For the application in the adaptive autopilot the Liapunov approach is followed in appendix B, where one of the difficulties is the forming of a suitable Liapunov function for the non-linear ship dynamics (4). Using Ingwerson's method [6] a Liapunov function is formed and following the guidelines given by Winsor & Roy [7] for the feedback gain K_d an adaptive law is derived

$$\dot K_d = -\alpha(c_1 e + c_2\dot e)\dot\psi_w \qquad (7)$$

where the speed of adaptation $\alpha > 0$ is an arbitrary constant to be determined in simulation, $c_1 = a_{1m}$ the reference model parameter and $c_2 > 1$ gives the weighting of $\dot e$ in the adaptive law. The time derivative $\dot e$ can be formed with an derivative circuit

$$\frac{s\omega_d}{s + \omega_d}$$

with ω_d sufficiently large. The computation of K_d according to the adaptive law (7) is shown in the basic diagram of fig. 2

6. Results

The adaptive autopilots which are tested have been designed according to the coefficients of the ship dynamics, which were obtained from measurements at sea with the Dutch pilot ship "Capella" of 2000 Brt.

After laboratory simulations [5] a prototype of an autopilot using a sensitivity model was build and tested at sea on board the "Capella". Because this ship is course stable under all circumstances, the experiments were carried out by setting the initial value K_{do} of the rate feedback K_d on an incorrect value and measuring the time needed to reach the correct value.

The experiments were realized under several external circumstances, while the magnitude of changes of the desired course-angle ψ_g and the speed of adaptation were varied. A typical result is shown in fig. 4.

The influence of yawing can be translated in a noise signal added to the course-angular velocity $\dot\psi_w$. During the tests – and in simulation – it was found that in the presence of noise, and because of drift in the adaptive controller, it is necessary to have a course change occasionally, otherwise K_d is drifting to an incorrect value. It was also concluded that with noise a lower speed of adaptation has to be chosen and that the speed can be exchanged for sensitivity to noise.

During the experiments a yawing filter was used. The motivation for this filter, which is based on a frequency analysis of the disturbances measured at sea, is given in appendix C. It was shown that the movements of the rudder due to yawing disturbances can be suppressed (see fig. 6).

Next, in the laboratory a comparison was made between an autopilot designed following the Liapunov approach and one using a sensitivity model. The prototype which was tested at sea, was used with an analog simulation of the ship dynamics. A Liapunov autopilot was also implemented.

A course-unstable ship was simulated by setting the coefficient b_w of the function $H(\dot{\psi}_w)$ to a negative value. The time needed to adapt K_d was measured and was found to be 2-3 times the dominant time constant of the ship ($\pm$ 10 sec.). The performances of the two autopilots were similar, a typical response is shown in fig. 5.

When the disturbances on the course-angle were simulated by a white noise signal with zero mean added to $\dot{\psi}_w$, the performance of the Liapunov autopilot is quickly degrading. Because the noise is additive to both $\dot{\psi}_w$ and e and in the adaptive law (7) these signals are multiplied, the value of K_d is dependent on the RMS value of the noise. This difficulty is overcome when the filter described in appendix C is applied to filter the e-signal.

When in the Liapunov approach the filter is used, both autopilots are performing satisfactory, even at a low signal noise ratio. The performance of either of the autopilots was not demonstrated to be significantly better.

7. Conclusions

A prototype of an adaptive autopilot using a sensitivity model was tested on board a ship of 2000 Brt. and produced satisfactory results when used for manoeuvring.

Occasionally course changes are necessary, because otherwise in the presence of noise the adapted parameter will drift to an incorrect value. In the absence of course changes the parameter can be set in hold.

It was measured that the yawing frequencies are beyond the bandwidth of the ship dynamics. Therefore the high frequency rudder movements can be suppressed succesfully with a low-pass filter.

Simulation results of the autopilot using a sensitivity model and one designed following the Liapunov approach showed no significant difference. In the presence of noise a low-pass filter is essential in the adaptive loop of the Liapunov autopilot.

In the near future more experiments at sea are planned.

Appendix A

The control equations of the adaptive system with the sensitivity model.

In the adaptive system the transfer between δ_g and $\dot{\psi}_w$ is considered. The following approximations are made:

a) The function $H(\dot{\psi})$ can be approximated by a third order polynomial $a\dot{\psi}^3 + b\dot{\psi}$; the even factors of this polynomial can be neglected; for course-stable ships a and b are positive, for course-unstable ships a is positive and b is negative;

b) The coefficient a of this polynomial is assumed to be constant and known, whereas the coefficient b is varying;

c) The parameters K' and a_1 of the ship are constant and known;

d) The influence of the dynamics of the steering gear on the behaviour of the system can be neglected.

Approximation b) is not necessary, but if it is fullfilled the value of K_d is independent of δ_g. The differential equations of the model and the system are:

$$\text{model} \quad : \quad K'_m \delta_g = \dddot{\psi}_m + a_{1m}\ddot{\psi}_m + K'_m(a_m\dot{\psi}_m^3 + b_m\dot{\psi}_m) \quad \text{(A1)}$$

$$\text{system} \quad : \quad K'_w \delta_g = \dddot{\psi}_w + a_{1w}\ddot{\psi}_w + K'_w(a_w\dot{\psi}_w^3 + b_w\dot{\psi}_w) \quad \text{(A2)}$$

$$\text{the error:} \quad e \quad = \quad \dot{\psi}_m - \dot{\psi}_w \quad \text{(A3)}$$

$$H(\dot{\psi}) \quad = \quad a_w\dot{\psi}^3 + b_w\dot{\psi} \quad \text{(A4)}$$

In these equations:

$$
\begin{aligned}
a_m &= a_w \\
b_m &= b_{\text{deep water}} + K_{do} \\
K'_m &= K'_w \\
a_{1m} &= a_{1w}
\end{aligned}
\quad \text{(A5)}
$$

K_{do} is the amount of rate feedback necessary to obtain a satisfactory behaviour of the course control system in deep water. The adaptive controller minimizes the function f(e) by adjustment of K_d. The function f(e) is chosen here as

$$f(e) = \tfrac{1}{2}Ke^2 \quad . \quad \text{(A6)}$$

The adjustment of K_d is made using a steepest descent technique. Let the difference between b' and b_m be denoted by

$$\varepsilon = b' - b_m, \quad b' = b_w + K_d \quad \text{(A7)}$$

Incremental changes in ε are made according to the gradient method:

$$\Delta \epsilon = -K \frac{\partial f(e)}{\partial \epsilon}$$

b_m is fixed, changes in ϵ can only be made by changing b'. Therefore

$$\Delta \epsilon = -K \frac{\partial f(e)}{\partial b'} \quad .$$

Calculation of $\frac{\partial f}{\partial b'}$ requires prior knowledge about b', which is not available.
However, for small values of ϵ this can be approximated by

$$\Delta \epsilon = +K \frac{\partial f(e)}{\partial b_m} \quad .$$

Substituting (A6) and (A3) yields

$$\Delta \epsilon = Ke \frac{\partial \dot{\psi}_m}{\partial b_m} \quad .$$

According to (A7) ϵ is changed by changing K_d, thus

$$\Delta \epsilon = \Delta K_d = Ke \frac{\partial \dot{\psi}_m}{\partial b_m} \quad .$$

The incremental change $\Delta \epsilon$ is made in the time Δt; for an infinitesimal small amount of time Δt we get

$$\lim_{\Delta t \to 0} \frac{\Delta K_d}{\Delta t} = \dot{K}_d = Ke \frac{\partial \dot{\psi}_m}{\partial b_m} \quad .$$

It is assumed that variations in e due to the adaptation are much faster than variations in e due to changes in the input signal of the ship and the model δ_g.
Also b_w must be varying slowly compared with the rate of adaptation.
The gradient $\frac{\partial \dot{\psi}_m}{\partial b_m}$ can be determined as follows:

The model equation is

$$K'_m \delta_g = \dddot{\psi}_m + a_{1m} \ddot{\psi}_m + K'_m (a_m \dot{\psi}_m^3 + b_m \dot{\psi}_m)$$

Differentiate this equation with respect to b_m

$$0 = \ddot{u}_{b_m}^{\psi_m} + a_{1m} \dot{u}_{b_m}^{\psi_m} + K'_m (3a_m \dot{\psi}_m^2 + b_m) u_{b_m}^{\psi_m} + K'_m \dot{\psi}_m$$

$$u_{b_m}^{\psi_m} = \frac{\partial \dot{\psi}_m}{\partial b_m} \quad .$$

Rewriting this equation yields

$$-K'_m \dot{\psi}_m = \ddot{u}_{b_m}^{\psi_m} + a_{1m} \dot{u}_{b_m}^{\psi_m} + K'_m (3a_m \dot{\psi}_m^2 + b_m) u_{b_m}^{\psi_m} \quad .$$

Except for the non-linearity, this equation has the same form as the differential equation of the model.

The model which generated $u_{b_m}^{\dot{\psi}_m}$ is called the sensitivity model of the system. The sensitivity model has the same structure as the system, the input is different.

Appendix B

In this appendix an adaptive law will be derived by the second method of Liapunov. The Liapunov approach for the synthesis of a model reference adaptive system was already introduced in section 5 and therefore no attention will be paid to the general aspects.
The reader is supposed to be familiar with the second method of Liapunov for the investigation of the stability of a set of differential equations. For an introduction is referred to [8].

In the adaptive system the transfer between δ_g and $\dot{\psi}_w$ is considered under the same approximations (a-d) as in appendix A. A law will be derived for the adaptation of the feedback gain K_d following the guideline given in [7].

Therefore, the differential equation of the model (A1) is rewritten into state space representation, with $y_1 = \dot{\psi}_m$

$$\dot{y}_1 = y_2$$

$$\dot{y}_2 = -a_{1m} y_2 - K'_m (a_m y_1^3 + b_m y_1) + K'_m \delta_g \quad . \quad (B1)$$

Rewriting the ship dynamics equation (A2) with $x_1 = \dot{\psi}_w$ yields

$$\dot{x}_1 = x_2$$

$$\dot{x}_2 = -a_{1w} x_2 - K'_w (a_w x_1^3 + b_w x_1) + K'_w \delta_g \quad . \quad (B2)$$

The relation between the parameters of (B1) and (B2) is given in (A5).
The difference ϵ between the parameters b_w and b_m will be compensated by the rate feedback gain K_d,

$$\epsilon = b' - b_m \quad , \qquad b' = b_w + K_d \quad . \quad (B3)$$

The system error of the adaptive system is defined

$$\underline{e} = \underline{y} - \underline{x}$$

where $\underline{e}^T = (e_1, e_2)$, $\underline{y}^T = (y_1, y_2)$ and $\underline{x}^T = (x_1, x_2)$.

The superscript $\cdot^T$ denotes the transpose of a vector. Substracting eq. (B2) and (B1) yields the system error equation

$$\dot{e}_1 = e_2$$

$$\dot{e}_2 = -a_{1m}e_2 - K_m'(a_m e_1^3 + b_m e_1) + K_m'\varepsilon x_1 \quad . \quad (B4)$$

The design procedure begins by forming a Liapunov function V consisting of terms of $\underline{e}$ and ε. Because of the non-linearity in $(B4)$ the Liapunov function cannot be chosen straightforward, but special methods have to be used for the construction of V.

Application of Ingwerson's method [6] results in

$$V = \tfrac{1}{2}(a_{1m}^2 + cK_m'b_m)e_1^2 + \tfrac{1}{4}cK_m'a_m e_1^4 + a_{1m}e_1 e_2 +$$

$$+ \tfrac{1}{2}ce_2^2 + \tfrac{1}{2}\varepsilon^2/\alpha' \quad (B5)$$

where $\alpha' > 0$ is an arbitrary constant to be determined later.
V will be positive definite under the sufficient condition

$$a_{1m}, \; a_m, \; b_m, \; K_m' > 0 \quad \text{and} \quad c > 1 \quad . \quad (B6)$$

The time derivative $\dot{V}$ of $(B5)$ is

$$\dot{V} = (a_{1m}^2 + cK_m'b_m)e_1\dot{e}_1 + cK_m'a_m e_1^3\dot{e}_1 + a_{1m}\dot{e}_1 e_2 +$$

$$+ a_{1m}e_1\dot{e}_2 + ce_2\dot{e}_2 + \varepsilon\dot{\varepsilon}/\alpha' \quad .$$

Substituting of eq. $(B4)$ yields

$$\dot{V} = -a_{1m}K_m'a_m e_1^4 - a_{1m}K_m'b_m e_1^2 - a_{1m}(c-1)e_2^2 +$$

$$+ K_m'\varepsilon(a_{1m}e_1 + ce_2)x_1 + \varepsilon\dot{\varepsilon}/\alpha' \quad (B7)$$

under the conditions $(B6)$.

Now select $\dot{\varepsilon}$ as

$$\dot{\varepsilon} = -\alpha'K_m'(a_{1m}e_1 + ce_2)x_1 \quad . \quad (B8)$$

In that case $\dot{V}$ will be negative definite with respect to $\underline{e}$ so that asymptotic stability in the sense of Liapunov for $\underline{e}$ is assured, which means that after an initial disturbance $||\underline{e}|| \to 0$ for $t \to \infty$.

The Euclidean norm $||\underline{e}|| = \sqrt{e_1^2 + e_2^2}$. Because $\dot{V}$ is independent of ε, $\dot{V}$ is negative semi-definite with respect to ε, which means that after an initial disturbance ε may not converge to zero.

Under the assumption that the parameter b_w of $(B2)$ is varying slowly compared to the rate of adaptation, $\dot{\varepsilon} = \dot{K}_d$. Substituting in $(B8)$ with $e_1 = e$, $e_2 = \dot{e}$ and $x_1 = \psi_w$ results in

$$\dot{K}_d = -\alpha(a_{1m}e + c\dot{e})\psi_w \quad (B9)$$

where $\alpha = \alpha'K_m'$ is the speed of adaptation to be determined in simulation, and the constant $c > 1$ gives the weighting of $\dot{e}$ in $(B9)$.

With $(B9)$ the adaptive law for the adjustment of the feedback gain K_d is given.

Appendix C

Frequency analysis of the wave disturbances

In this paper the wave disturbances are mentioned in two different ways. At first as a noise signal disturbing the desired course and second as a signal which prevents a good functioning of the adaptative loop, especially with the Liapunov method.

Fast disturbances of the desired course due to yawing should not be corrected by the rudder. The rudder cannot correct these course deviations and it is not necessary too. Only when the mean value of the deviations is not equal to zero, there must be a correction occasionally.

It is already stated that a bad way to achieve this behaviour is the use of a dead band in the steering gear. Not only the desired components of the signal are suppressed, but also the components that should activate the rudder without limitations. A better solution is applying a low-pass filter before the steering gear, at least when it is possible to seperate the two components by means of their frequencies. Therefore, the frequencies of the yawing motion should be outside the bandwidth of the system.

Applying test signals of several frequencies and sailing with several angles between course and the direction of the sea motion, experiments at sea were carried out to analyze the frequency spectrum. Afterwards the signals were analyzed with the fast Fourier transformation at the digital computer of the laboratory. The results of this analysis are shown in figure 6. The frequencies of the yawing are clearly seperated from the frequency components caused by the rudder (figure 6a). In a closed loop system the high frequencies are activating the rudder too (figure 6b). To prevent this also trials are done with a linear second order filter, with a transfer function

$$\frac{1}{s^2/\omega_n^2 + 2z/\omega_n s + 1} \quad .$$

Repeating this trial under the same circumstances as in figure 6a, b gives the result that is shown in figure 6c, d.

The first problem - the noise on the course signal - is solved with the application of the filter. The second problem - a good functioning of the adaptive loop - can now be solved too. As the filter gives a good separation between signal and noise, the same filter can be applied in the adaptive loop. In that case the error signal between model and ship is filtered, so that differentiation and multiplication of this signal gives no more problems. In the sensitivity model the filter is not essential, with the Liapunov approach the adaptation will not work without a filter.

162

Acknowledgement

The authors wish to express their gratitude to the
Delft University of Technology, to the Royal
Netherlands Navy and to the Royal Educational Fund
of the Merchant service, for the opportunity to
carry out this research.
Especially the stimulating discussions in the
"steering comittee autopilots" and the support of
Ir. G. Honderd have been of great value to the
work.

References

[1] Nomoto, K., "Response Analysis of Manoeuvrabi-
    lity and its Application to Ship Design",
    6oth Anniversary series, Vol. 11, Soc. of Naval
    Arch. of Japan
[2] Bech, M. and Wagner Smitt, L., "Analogue
    Simulation of Ship Manoeuvres", Hydro-og Aero-
    dynamisk Laboratorium, Lyngby, Denmark, Report
    nr. Hy-14, September 1969
[3] Wonink, Ir. G., "Regeltechnische benadering van
    het scheepsgedrag bij manoeuvreren", Symposium
    "Modelvorming voor Scheepsbesturing", December
    1970, Delft University of Technology (in Dutch)
[4] Fujino, Dr. M., "Experimental Studies on Ship
    Manoeuvrability in Restricted Waters", part I,
    International Shipbuilding Progress, Vol. 15,
    Nr. 168, August 1968
[5] Honderd, G. and Winkelman, J.E.W., "An Adaptive
    Autopilot for Ships", Third Ship Control
    Systems Symposium, Ministry of Defence, Septem-
    ber 1972, Bath
[6] Ingwerson, D.R., "A Modified Liapunov Method for
    NonlLinear Stability Analysis", IRE Trans. on
    Aut. Control, Vol. AC-6, 1961
[7] Winsor, C.A. and Roy, R.J., "Design of Model
    Reference Adaptive Control Systems by Liapunov's
    Second Method", IEEE Trans. on Aut. Control,
    Vol AC-13, April 1968
[8] Barnett, S. and Storey, C., "Matrix Methods in
    Stability Theory", Nelson, London, 1970

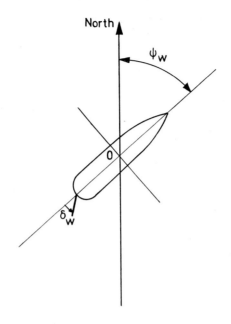

O $=$ ships center of gravity

δ_w $=$ rudder angle

δ_g $=$ desired rudder angle, input to steering gear

ψ_w $=$ course

ψ_g $=$ desired course

$\dot{\psi}_w$ $=$ course angular velocity

fig. 1

definition of symbols

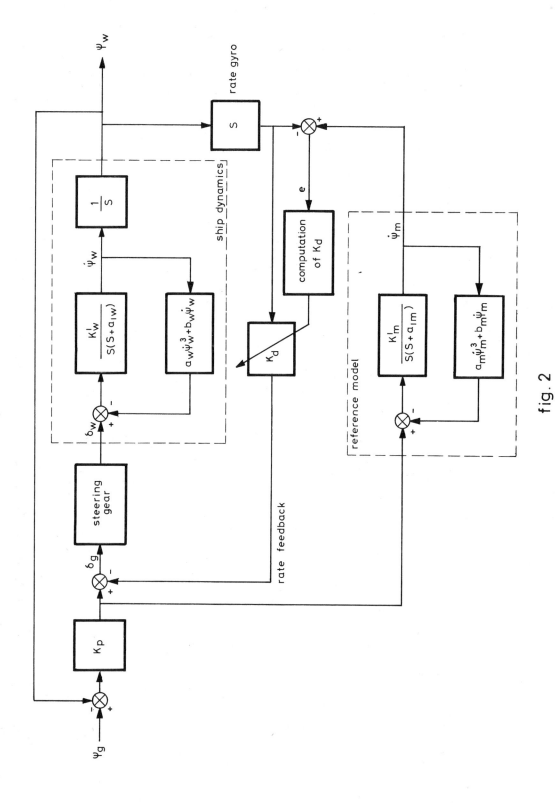

fig. 2

model reference adaptation

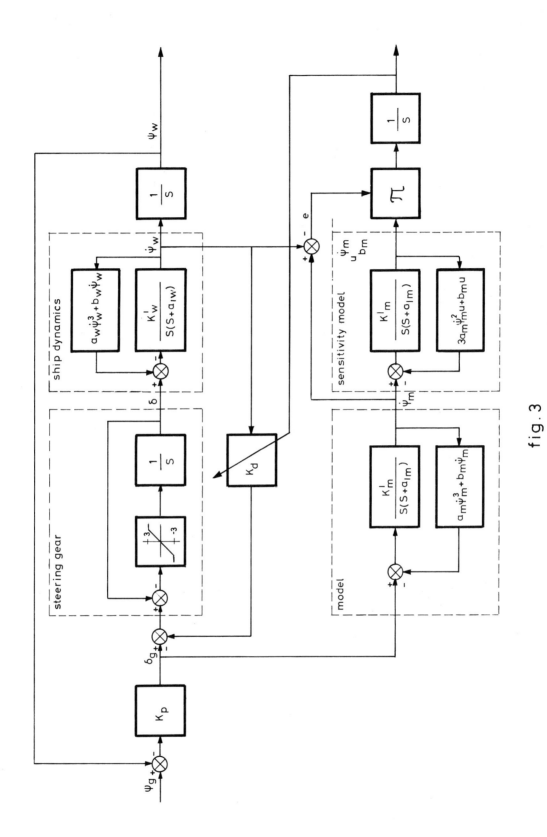

fig. 3

adaptive autopilot with a sensitivity model

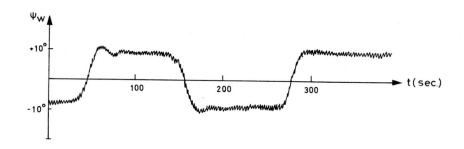

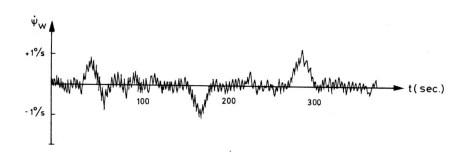

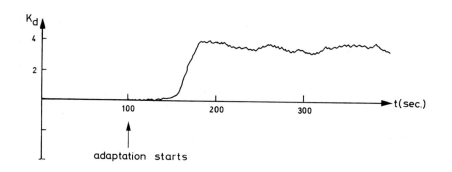

fig.4

result of experiment at sea

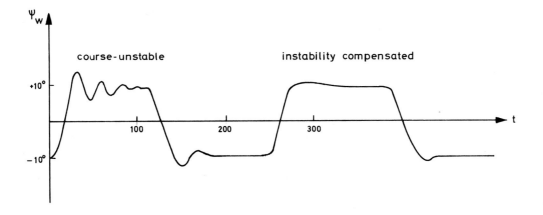

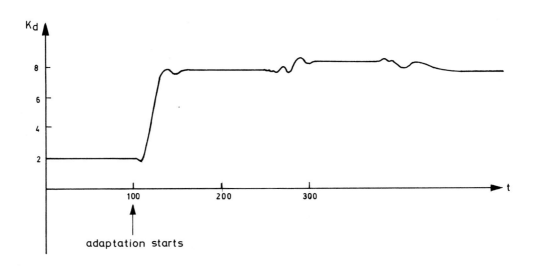

fig. 5

simulation results of the adaptation
with a course-unstable ship

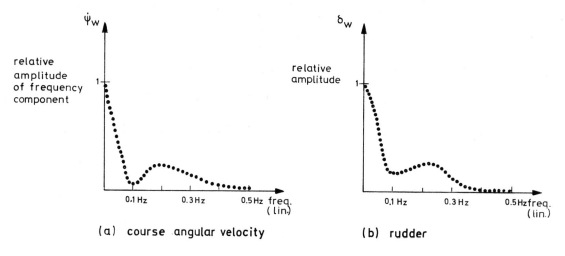

(a) course angular velocity (b) rudder

with out filter

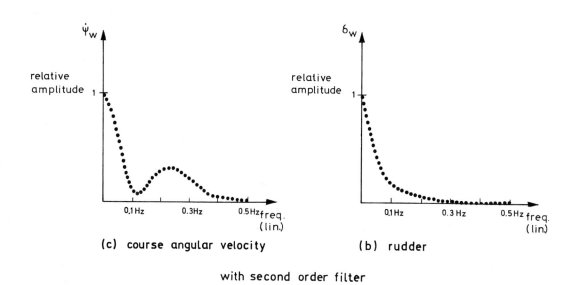

(c) course angular velocity (b) rudder

with second order filter

fig.6

frequency analysis

THE DESIGN OF A NEW AUTOMATIC PILOT FOR THE COMMERCIAL SHIP

Dr. D.L. Brook
Chief Engineer
S.G. Brown Limited
Watford, England

ABSTRACT

A new automatic pilot specifically designed for the needs of commercial shipping is discussed. In conceptual design, the auto-pilot represents a departure from previous practice in that an analogue rudder demand signal is fed to the steering compartment instead of the usual switching demand signal.

The characteristic equations governing the motion of a ship under the action of an auto-pilot are presented and the relevant parametric terms required for good course keeping are treated in some detail.

A feature of the equipment is that the operational controls have been simplified and the circuitry is designed so that individual parameters can be adjusted for sea state and vessel load conditions without the usual cross-coupling effects. The methods used to isolate the controlled functions and to ensure signal line integrity are described.

INTRODUCTION

Currently almost all commercially available ships' automatic pilots operate on a steering control algorithm formulated from parametric representation of:

(i)   Rudder position and

(ii)   error in ships heading.

The output of such an automatic pilot is controlled by the algorithm and is of the 'bang-bang' variety with a small 'dead zone' incorporated for operational stability. Thus, steering control information flow through the ship between the bridge and the after end takes two forms:

(i)   A rearward feed from the automatic pilot to the after end steering engine of a tertiary logic demand signal, and

(ii)   a forward feed from the steering compartment to the automatic pilot of an analogue signal representing either the applied rudder or the actual rudder position,

depending upon the type of steering engine used (Fig. la).

Over the past few years S.G. Brown Limited have been involved in the design, development, testing and, latterly, production of a new automatic pilot capable of being used for a wide range of vessels both commercial and military. Great attention has naturally been given to the algorithmic formulation within the automatic pilot but, in addition, it was decided at an early stage that the rudder positioning control servo should be completely self-contained within the steering flat and that the demand lines from the bridge should carry analogue signals representing rudder demanded (Fig. lb). This method has two distinct advantages; firstly, the number of critical lines running through the ship are reduced and, secondly, the improved performance of the more modern types of steering engine currently becoming available on the commercial market is more readily harnessed.

SHIP'S CHARACTERISTIC

If we make a number of simplifying assumptions regarding the hydrodynamics of a ship and its rudder actuator, it is easy to show that the equation governing the lateral motion of the ship is of the form:

$$\phi(s) = \frac{k(s+\alpha)}{s\left[(s+\alpha)(s+\beta)+\delta\right]} \cdot \delta(s) \qquad (1)$$

where $\phi(s)$, $\delta(s)$ are the Laplace transforms of the heading and rudder angle respectively, k, α, β, δ are design parameters, and s is the complex frequency operator. In a ship, the parameters α and β are positive and of the same order but δ is made negative in order to achieve an adequate rate of turn. Consequently, the characteristic equation has two poles on the real axis and can be re-expressed as:

$$\phi(s) = \frac{k(s+\alpha)}{s(s+b)(s+c)} \cdot \delta(s) \qquad (2)$$

Now, to the order of accuracy of immediate interest, the track of a ship for a given rudder angle is almost independent of speed and it therefore becomes convenient to re-write the transfer function in terms of a non-dimensional Laplace operator.

170

Thus:

$$\bar{\phi}(p) = \frac{K (p + A)}{p (p + B)(p + C)} \cdot \bar{\delta}(p) \qquad (3)$$

where $p = \frac{s\ell}{u}$, and the new unit of time is that taken by the ship to cover its own length; ℓ and u being the length and speed of the vessel respectively.

The poles at p = -B, -C straddle the zero at p = -A and since the ratio of C to B rarely exceeds 10 to 1, the response of the ship is very similar to that of simple time constant. However, the spread of the poles is important in that it influences the design of any automatic pilot since the phase change with frequency is also spread over a wider range.

In the design of an automatic pilot critical parameters are A, B and C since the requirements caused by the coefficient K can be suitably met by an inverse change in the automatic pilot gain. Initially, four ships from 1,000 tons upwards were studied and data was obtained from either turning trials results on the full scale vessel or from tank testing and calculation. Each ship's characteristic was assumed to be of the form (3) and least square error methods were used to deduce the parameters A, B, C in each case. In general, it was found that C > A > B and that A was just less than unity.

Figure 2 illustrates the spread in the results when plotted on a Bode diagram. In all cases, the co-efficient K has been suppressed and the 0 db point has been taken at p equal to unity. It can be seen that the characteristics are all contained within a fairly narrow band when plotted in this reduced form. It is not suggested that this band represents the extremes that are possible but the results do indicate that one control algorithm could well be applicable to all ships.

BASIC AUTOMATIC PILOT

One possible automatic pilot control algorithm that immediately suggests itself is shown super-imposed on Figure 2. Note that an inverse scale of gain is used so that the distance between the two plots gives the gain round the control loop.

For good control, this gain needs to be large in the range of frequencies used in manoeuvres, but small at high frequencies to avoid useless wear and tear on the steering mechanism. Further, it is necessary to make the control algorithm have a gain that rises with frequency in the vicinity of the crossover point, where the loop gain is unity, so that the rate of change of loop gain with frequency is small in this area and a well damped response results.

For a ship that operates at one speed a phase advance circuit with a relative gain of 3 between high and low frequencies would be adequate if the break points were properly chosen. If a wide speed range were envisaged, then best results would be obtained by alteration of the break frequencies automatically by control signals

routed from the log. This method is, in fact, adopted in military versions of this autopilot.

Commercial shipping tends to operate under automatic pilot control at speeds that are relatively constant for a given vessel. Even so, the automatic pilot may be in use when the vessel is operating off design so that initial studies were carried out with relative gains of 10 as shown in Figure 2. Fixed control parameters, designed around the full speed capability of the vessel in question, were used and hence the phase advance stage has a full speed characteristic of

$$\frac{10 (p + 1)}{(p + 10)} . \qquad (4)$$

INITIAL SIMULATION STUDIES

To test the validity of the heuristic deductions outlined above a study was made on an analogue computer of the response of the four vessels previously mentioned. Step changes in heading of 5° and 30° were used at each of four speeds - full, half, quarter and eighth.

Certain assumptions were made, the principal ones being:

(i)   The after power unit had a fixed parametric 'time' constant, and so acted as a low pass filter.

(ii)   At the steering engine itself, the rudder rate varied linearly with error demand, up to a maximum of ± 60° per length travelled at full speed, and then saturated at this rate.

(iii)   The rudder angle was limited to ± 30°, and a linear response law was assumed.

(iv)   The change of speed due to the turn was neglected.

Initially, neither an integral term to eliminate steady state errors nor a 'yaw gap' to improve stability under rough sea conditions was used and the nominal loop gain at p = 1 was chosen to be 4, it being assumed that any actual auto-pilot would have sufficient range of gain to achieve this figure.

Figures 3 show typical results from the simulation. In general, the form of the results is encouraging and the tendency to overshoot at the lowest speeds is less than would have been expected from the form of Figure 2.

It can be concluded that most ships should be controlled satisfactorily over a speed range of at least 4 to 1 by an automatic pilot having properly chosen fixed parameters.

Further, it is suggested that the basic 'rule of thumb' choice of the parameters should be such that:

(i)   The non-dimensional rate of turn per unit heading error is made approximately 4 : 1,

(ii)   the lower non-dimensional break frequency of the phase advance term within the automatic pilot should be equal to unity, calculated on the basis of ships' length and normal operational speed, and

(iii) the upper and lower break frequency ratio within the automatic pilot should be at least 5 : 1.

FURTHER SIMULATION

With the results obtained so far it is clear that a firm basis for automatic pilot design has been achieved. However, certain of the assumptions made in the simulation studies are open to some doubt and it now becomes necessary to study the effects of second order phenomena.

A number of variations on the theme were, therefore simulated, the automatic pilot equations being chosen in each case in accordance with the basic rules given above.

The unstable ship

Certain ships are unstable at small rates of turn. If we refer to equation (1), the instability arises because δ has been made more negative than the product $\alpha\beta$. However, the weathercock stiffness $\alpha\beta$ is non-linear and increases with rate of turn so that eventually the ship becomes stable at a finite turning rate with the rudder central. The effect can be simulated by reversing the signs of the lateral stability terms in the ships' characteristic equation, although this is a rather more drastic instability than that actually occuring in practice. The results of such simulation are also shown on Figures 3. Clearly, the overshoot to the step change in demanded heading has been increased but satisfactory behaviour is still implied.

Non-linear rudder 'effectiveness'

Since the weather-cock stiffness of an actual ship increases with rate of turn, the effectiveness of the rudder appears to be reduced at the larger angles, as is easily demonstrated by the results of spiral manoeuvre trials. A satisfactory form of simulation is to assume a non-linear system loop gain, dependent on rate of turn. Results indicate that such a non-linearity has little effect on stable ships but causes even greater overshoot on the unstable ship described above. It was concluded that a higher degree of phase advance was essential on such a ship and a reversion to a break frequency ratio of 10 : 1 proved satisfactory.

Weather helm integration

In order that steady state heading errors should not occur due to external torques acting on the vessel, an integral term becomes essential within the automatic pilot control algorithm. Such an integral term is always de-stabilising and it is important to use the longest practicable time constant to avoid instabilities in course keeping.

However, if the time constant is too long the settling time onto the new course is also unacceptable and an awkward compromise has to be made. Further, the integral term should ideally be inhibited during course changes to avoid the consequential overshoot.

After some experimentation, it was found that an integration 'time' constant equal to that taken by the ship to cover between 4 and 10 lengths at normal speed was satisfactory over the operational speed range, and that a reasonable condition was that the integral term should be set to zero whenever the heading error was greater than 10°.

It must be stressed that this conditional use of the integral term is not the ideal but is one satisfactory criteria that can be easily applied within the automatic pilot without costly complication.

Figure 4 demonstrates the effect of such a simulation for a 30° course change.

Yaw control

Under certain sea conditions, it becomes necessary to insert a yaw gap into the auto-pilot characteristic in order to overcome unnecessary wear on the after power unit and steering engine. In practice, the yaw dead zone can be arranged to operate either on the heading error signal itself, or on the final demand signal at the rudder. (In fact, if the final rudder control system is of the bang-bang type, there is always a small yaw gap at the rudder control for local stability reasons.) Such a yaw gap allows the ship to wander within a restricted range about the ideal heading and is naturally detrimental to good course keeping. Simulation studies showed that for acceptably low rudder operation frequency under rough sea conditions, the yaw gap was best located so that it operated on the actual heading error. Further, it is suggested that the following two features assist in maintaining an accurate mean course with lowest rudder operation frequency:

(i)   The weather helm integral control should be outside the loop containing the yaw dead space, and

(ii)   when the set yaw limit was exceeded, the automatic pilot should revert to normal operation with no yaw gap, and should reset the yaw gap only when the ships head next passed through the zero error position.

Criteria for automatically adjusting the yaw gap are being studied but such an adaptive automatic pilot would necessarily be more expensive and the choice of setting is currently left to the ships' staff.

AUTOMATIC PILOT

Figure 5 shows in block schematic form the final embodiment of the automatic pilot designed around the results of the simulation studies. It must be stressed that this diagram is schematic only and some licence has been used in the presentation as an aid to the reader.

The main signal flow from heading error, scaled at 0.25V d.c./° heading, to rudder demand, also scaled at 0.25V d.c./° rudder, follows the direct route through Selector 1. A parallel path through Selector 2 is employed for the weather helm integration and the two signals converge at Summing Amplifier 1.

All the user controls are designed and positioned in the circuit in such a manner that they are not interactive and suitable audible alarm circuitry is included. The equipment is all solid state and a mixture of integrated circuits and discrete components is used.

The following features should be noted:

Yaw control

The heading error signal is routed to the phase advance circuitry via Selector 1, which is operated by a control signal emitted by the Yaw Comparitor. The yaw setting is a facility available to the ships' staff and a six position switch allowing the yaw gap to be adjusted from $0°$ to $± 8°$ is provided.

In operation, the Yaw Comparitor examines the heading error and if this is less than the selected gap, emits a signal to Selector 1 causing the '0' volt input to be routed to the Phase Advance unit. When the heading error exceeds the yaw gap the form of the control signal to Selector 1 is changed and the heading error signal itself is now routed through. The new control signal is also fed back to the comparitor so that the yaw gap is automatically closed to zero until the heading error next passes through the zero. (Figure 6).

Off-Course Alarm

The off-course alarm setting is also tied to the yaw switch and is automatically adjusted with the yaw setting. If this is at $≤4°$, $≥6°$ the off-course alarm is energised when the heading error is $6°$, $10°$ respectively. The circuitry is arranged so that the audible alarm can be silenced by a push button for course changing purposes with automatic revertion to normal operation when the heading error next falls within the allowable limits.

Phase Advance Unit

This follows the general lines suggested by the simulation studies. An internal pre-set switch allows the lower break frequency to be adjusted in discrete steps to suit the type of vessel. The upper break frequency is naturally moved in sympathy, and operation of the switch does not affect the gain. Lower break frequency time constants in the range 8 sec to 40 sec are provided.

The following table compares the time taken by a number of ships to cover their own length at normal operational speed, with the best lower break frequency time constant found for the automatic pilot during setting to work trials. Five of the ships were those chosen for pre-marketing development purposes and the sixth is a military vessel equipped with a military version of the automatic pilot.

TABLE 1

Weight (tons)	Length/Cruising Speed (Secs)	Best Time Constant From Trials (Secs)
809	10	Position 4, 9.25
4,371	11.5	Position 6, 13.88
12,552	16 *	Position 7, 16.16
16,425	21.5	Position 7, 16.16
252,970	42	Position 8, 22.40
Military setting from log	Slow 27 Fast 7	27 7.8

* unstable ship

It will be noted that the super tanker is the only vessel for which the 'rule of thumb' settings on automatic pilot were not near the optimum. Here it was found on trials that slight improvement in course keeping, with no significant alteration in course changing, could be made by reducing the lower break frequency time constant and increasing the loop gain (rudder quantity). Reference to Figure 2 indicates that such a combined adjustment should make only a marginal difference to the overall response characteristic but it was just sufficient to be noticeable in practice.

Weather Helm Integrator

When the automatic pilot is in use the Weather Helm Integrator receives heading error signal via Selector 2. A time constant of 80 secs is used, although this can be changed if necessary. The comparitor examines the heading error signal and automatically discharges the integrator whenever the heading error is $>10°$. As a consequence, the integrator starts from null whenever large course changes are demanded and the overshoot caused by such a course change is kept within acceptable limits.

One further facility is worthy of mention: When the ship is being steered by hand the weather helm integrator prepares itself for the time when the automatic pilot will be called into play by monitoring its own output against that being used by the helmsman. Under these circumstances, Selector 2 brings the upper loop through Summing Amplifiers 1 and 2 into circuit.

Rudder Quantity (Gain) and Rudder Limits

The rudder quantity control is available to the ships' staff and takes the form of a six position

switch. The range of the control is 6 : 1;
equivalent to rudder angles of 3° down to 0.5°
per degree of heading error.

Similarly, rudder limiting is arranged as an
operator's control and is achieved by switching
diode conducting circuits into the local amplifier
feed-back. In this way, the gain is not effected
but the saturation level is controlled. Limiting
is provided in 5° steps up to 20° and then a
final position allows full rudder angle to be
used.

Line Integrity Alarm

The final rudder demand signal is passed through
a line integrity circuit before being routed out
of the automatic pilot and down to the steering
flat via the main demand lines running through
the ship. The integrity circuit senses the
presence of a small A.C. signal which is
superimposed onto the demand lines at the after
end; it being so arranged that an alarm is
sounded in the event of either a break or short
circuit on these lines.

This alarm is combined with the normal power
failure alarm and is powered by the usual trickle
charged dry cell.

CONCLUSION

A new commercial automatic pilot has been developed
as a result of simulation studies on an analogue
computer. Although there is no particular feature
of the control algorithm that is novel in itself,
the over-all approach and embodiment has advantages
over earlier models, especially with respect to
the need for fewer operator's controls.

The equipment is suitable for any commercially
viable vessel and can be tuned to a particular
ship by a simple pre-calculable internal switch
setting.

It is suggested that the reduction in the
number of critical control lines running through
the ship, together with the use of line integrity
monitoring is a significant contribution to ship
safety.

ACKNOWLEDGEMENT

The author wishes to acknowledge that he is only
acting as a reporter on the work described in
this paper. The equipment itself was designed
and developed by a team of people at S.G. Brown
Limited and much of the original thought and
computer simulation is due to the Department of
Control at the University of Bath under the
direction of Professor K.V. Diprose, whose
'company confidential' reports are the source of
much of the information presented here.

174

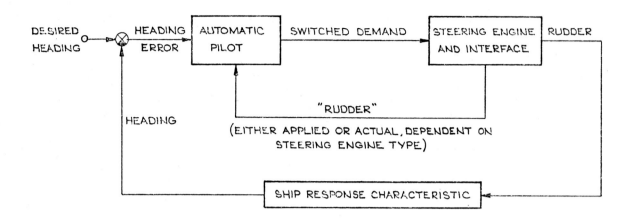

FIG. 1a   SCHEMATIC OF NORMAL STEERING CONTROL
SYSTEM IN AUTOMATIC PILOT MODE

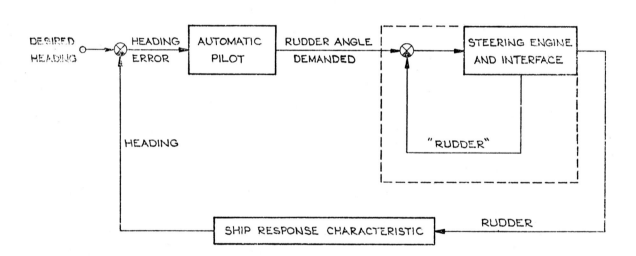

FIG. 1b   SCHEMATIC OF "OCEAN SERIES" CONTROL
SYSTEM IN AUTOMATIC PILOT MODE

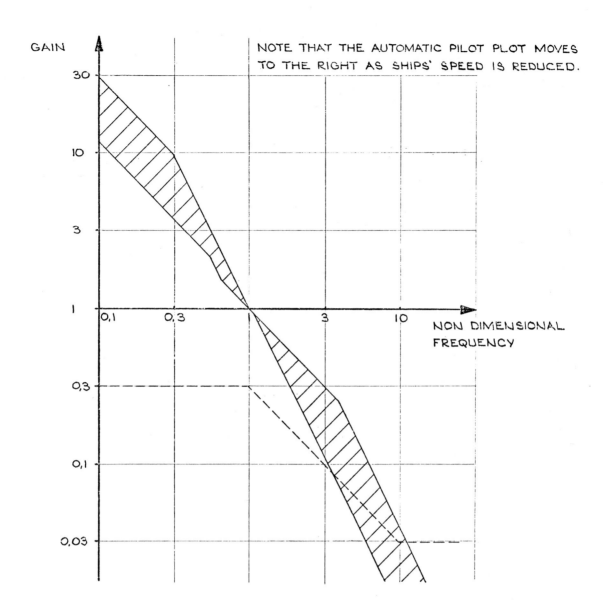

FIG 2   BODE DIAGRAM OF REDUCED SHIPS CHARACTERISTIC
AND INVERSE OF ONE POSSIBLE AUTOMATIC PILOT
CHARACTERISTIC.

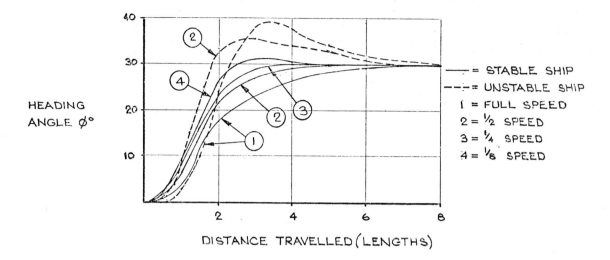

FIG 3a   30° HEADING CHANGE

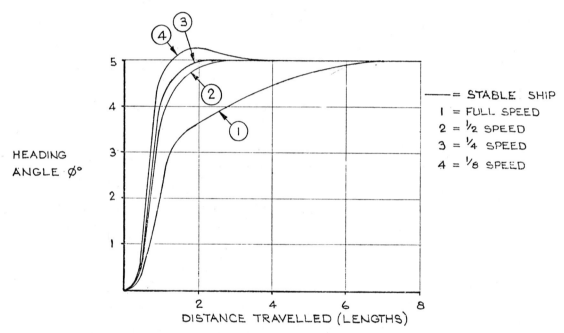

FIG 3b   5° HEADING CHANGE

FIG 3   RESPONSE OF TYPICAL SHIP AND CONTROL SYSTEM TO STEP CHANGE IN DEMAND HEADING

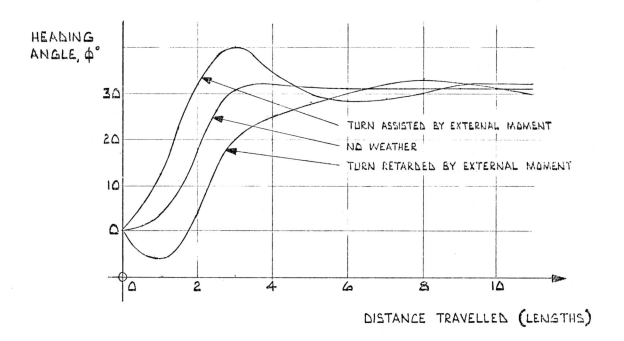

(INITIAL CONDITIONS TAKEN AS ZERO HEADING, ZERO RUDDER ANGLE)

FIG. 4   TYPICAL RESPONSE OF SHIP PLUS CONTROLLER TO STEP CHANGE IN HEADING DEMAND WITH WEATHER HELM INTEGRATER.

178

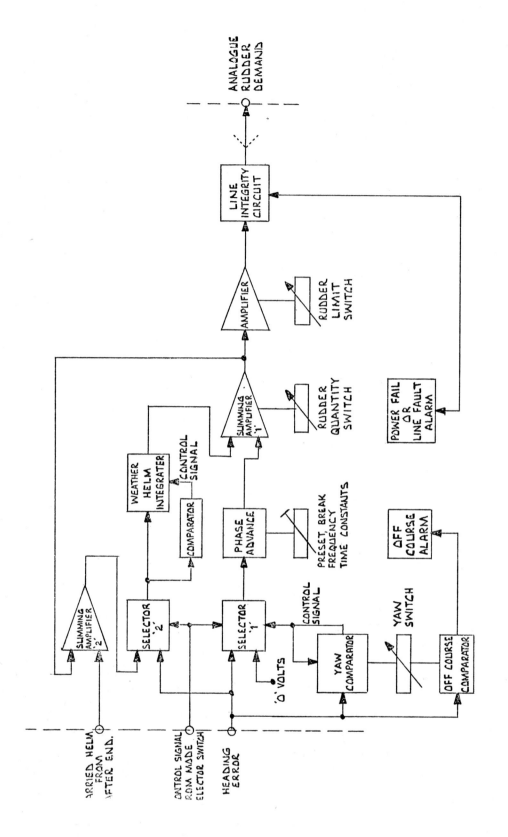

FIG. 5   SCHEMATIC DIAGRAM OF AUTOMATIC PILOT AT BRIDGE POSITION.

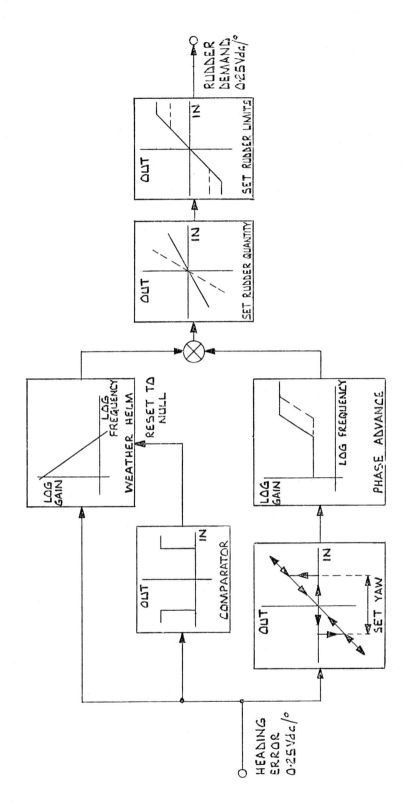

FIG 6.　FUNCTIONAL DIAGRAM OF AUTOMATIC PILOT, MAIN CHARACTERISTIC.

HULL UNDERWRITING

and the

CHANGING TECHNOLOGY

By:

A. E. Schumacher, Chairman, and
W. J. Pettersen, Jr., Underwriter
American Hull Insurance Syndicate

Together, we are involved in a period of change
in maritime technology not unlike that encountered by our predecessors a century and a half
ago when the sailing ship was first being challenged by the propeller driven vessel. The experience accumulated during generations of sail
could no longer fully serve shipowners, builders,
designers, or underwriters as they found themselves reaching out toward that relative unknown--
the concept of propulsion by steam.

Today, we have new challenges to face, with an
expanding need for large, high-speed, sophisticated, special purpose vessels such as our
forefathers could never have envisioned. Each
day sees contracts signed or deliveries made of
containerships, barge carriers, combination ore/
oil carriers, mammoth tankers and, most recently,
liquified natural gas carriers. There are new
cargoes to carry, new ports to serve and new
ocean routes to follow. There are new exposures,
and higher values than were dreamed of a few
years ago. With these changes coming so quickly,
there is little accumulated reliable experience
to serve as a guide.

It is precisely to fill this void that you are
gathered here to exchange information and seek
out answers to some of the problems which are
challenging you. Thank you for taking a little
time to hear how the underwriting members of
the maritime community face this uncertain
future.

THE NATURE AND PURPOSE OF INSURANCE

Before we discuss insurance and the role of the
underwriter in these times of change, it might
be useful to take a moment to review with you
the nature and purpose of insurance itself--
what it is and what it seeks to do--because this
is often not fully understood by the public, and
many misconceptions stem from this lack of
knowledge.

In the course of human endeavor, there are hazards which must be faced--some of them by reason
of the imperfect nature of man himself and
others by reason of forces acting outside his
control. Disruption or ruin may occur if these

hazards befall him. The function of insurance
is to eliminate this risk in the economic sense
by transferring it from the shoulders of the individual to the hands of a professional risk taker
who then amalgamates that risk with those of other
men in such a way that uncertainty gives way to
greater certainty by reason of the operation of
the law of large numbers.

The insurance buyer acquires his protection
against the elements of risk through the pay-
ment of a premium which, in essence, is nothing
more than the redistribution of losses over all
those who have sought protection from that type
of loss. The important point here is that while
the risks are eliminated through the process
described, the losses are not. They still exist
as an absolute economic waste to drain the financial resources of a society. It is essential
that we bear in mind that premiums paid are the
direct reflection of the aggregate of these
losses, and there is no way in the world for the
fair share paid by any policyholder to be reduced until means are found to reduce the losses
themselves. This is the plain and simple truth.
One cannot be disassociated from the other.

All of us are familiar from our own personal experiences with fire and automobile insurance.
Because there are so many millions of automo-
biles and homes, the broad statistical base permits the underwriter to predict his results with
great certainty. In the case of life insurance,
the actuarial sciences have almost completely
displaced the element of uncertainty so far as
the underwriter is concerned. With the insurance of ships, however, it is a different matter because there simply are not that many vessels in the world to develop a matching statistical base of equal credibility. In hull
insurance, then, the uncertainty is not eliminated, but merely lessened. For this reason,
the insuring of ships is recognized to be a
form of high-risk underwriting.

THE MARINE UNDERWRITER

Mention has already been made of the fact that
the marine underwriter considers himself part
of the maritime community. His mission, through

insurance, is to provide an atmosphere of security in which the shipowner can pursue his economic goals. In carrying out his financial support role, you will find the average underwriter far more often talking with shipowners and others in the field of international commerce than he will be talking with the fire and automobile people in his own company. Admittedly, however, there are times when the marine underwriter envies these other departments for the statistics which develop from the great numbers of homes and cars they have to cover. In addition to the relative certainty which can be predicted with all those units, no one of them is likely to be of such value that its loss can affect overall results greatly. Without the advantage such statistics provide, the marine insurer must rely more heavily on what we call "judgment underwriting," making his determinations on a selective, risk-by-risk evaluation basis against a variety of exposures, hazards and conditions.

Selecting the right kind of business and acquiring it in sufficient numbers and balance is one part of underwriting. The other part involves money. Do we obtain a balanced and sufficient amount of premium overall so that, when the day is done, the losses are paid, there is a reserve for the shock which will happen somewhere tomorrow, and something is left for the underwriter for his services in absorbing the risk. This brings us to the approach which is employed to determine the premium need.

Time does not permit a detailed discussion of this topic, but perhaps we can help you gain some appreciation of it. As mentioned, our normal approach is to apply so-called "judgment underwriting," which involves the application of the experiences of the past to the expectations of the future. The experience of the past receiving the greater emphasis is the experience of the individual operator.

There are really two parts to any premium equation. First there is that portion necessary to cover the costs of those losses which are not of exceptional magnitude and which an individual owner over a period of years ought to be able to amortize himself. When we refer to an owner "making his own record" or to "experience rating" of a fleet, this is what we have in mind, and the premium level of any given fleet reflects in large part this factor. The second part of the premium equation has to do with costs which must be met in responding for total losses and major partial losses which are of a magnitude too great for any one owner to absorb and which must, therefore, be shared by all fleets and vessels of common class. Each owner's share of these major casualty factors must also be included in the premium assessed against his fleet.

But the emphasis thus far has been on experience and normal approaches. If it were intended that things should remain normal, we would not be meeting here today.

THE UNDERWRITER'S REACTION TO CHANGE

At a meeting of the American Petroleum Institute in California last year, these comments were made:

"With the changing times hull underwriters are obliged to function for periods of time without the assistance of their most valuable ally, experience. The adverse claims pattern which so often accompanies changes in design and operation is complicated by the fact that at the early stages--during the period of growing pains--there are usually not enough of the new type of vessels operating to develop meaningful experience quickly. The sampling is small and the law of large numbers is simply not operable. With no more access to a reliable crystal ball than any other members of the maritime community at this critical stage, underwriters are obliged to set initial rates on the basis of assessment of potential exposures, utilizing a mixture of 'informed judgment' and 'educated guess.' In such circumstances it is generally necessary to 'class rate' the newly evolving vessel at inception. We have had to do this with the VLCCs, and undoubtedly it will be the pattern for the LNGs initially. More knowledge about the proper level for rating each class will be developed and refined as experience is gained and then, hopefully, in not too long a period of time, the class rating concept can be put aside in favor of the preferred method of rating on individual record. By that time we can again rely on experience to reveal the relative degrees of operating excellence between one fleet and another."

You will see from this that, stripped of the security which experience provides, the underwriter is exposed, along with all his colleagues in the community, to the pitfalls of change which accompany each new venture into the unknown.

Reference was made to the adverse claims pattern which is encountered initially in so many cases. In 1950, a cargo vessel, fitted with the then new variable pitch, bridge controlled propeller, made headlines when it lurched forward onto the streets of Los Angeles because, in the process of backing her out of her berth, the officer on the bridge inadvertently tipped the control levers forward. In 1960, a large ore/oil carrier equipped with self-unloading equipment, including conveyor belts that ran in tunnels under the cargo compartments, sank following an explosion in mid-Atlantic. The unique conveyor tunnels made it impossible to have the watertight compartmentation of the standard tanker or ore carrier and no doubt contributed to the vessel's demise less than nine hours after the explosion. In 1970, a containership sank at her berth in New York because an automatic valve opened while the main condenser covers were off for inspection. During the past few years, we have witnessed initial structural problems in certain of the large size bulk carriers, and the mammoth tanker explosion phenomena is another costly example that lessons are not all to be learned on the drawing boards and in the test tanks. One of our first and largest claims on the new LASH vessels was for the loss of a deck gantry, underdesigned and possibly mishandled, as the entire unit catapulted overboard into the harbor of Piraeus. Machinery and vibrational problems are currently plaguing several new barge carriers and containerships. These are but a few examples of losses related to technological change.

In the face of the unknown, we might consider now how the underwriter goes about rating the new design - what he takes into account in performing what can only be described as a study in qualitative analysis.

First, from periodicals, technical studies and discussions, we must acquire as much knowledge as is available about the new design. What is it, and in what particulars is it similar or dissimilar from established designs? What untried features does it contain and what testing of these features has been undertaken before their adoption? Also, we must consider how these features will stand up against the human element. Will they be understood and are they capable of being properly employed by the men on board who will be responsible for their utilization?

If the ship is being specially constructed for the transport of a new product, it is imperative that we learn as much as possible about that potential cargo. What is it, and how will it travel at sea or react in the face of perils to the possible detriment of the ship?

Second, with this background of basic knowledge, we must endeavor to evaluate the hazards which this new ship and cargo present in an attempt to determine whether they are greater or less than hazards we are accustomed to dealing with in the case of more conventional ships and cargoes. The basic hull design, the machinery and the cargo handling apparatus must be regarded from this aspect. The exposures brought on by the ship's size and speed, her product, the ports she will serve and the routes she will follow are all parts of the assessment.

Third, we must construct a "rating model" at the outset, and we build this off rating levels of vessels already on our books. The containership rates were originally based upon those of similar size dry cargo vessels with adjustments made primarily for the unique cargo handling features and in some cases for the fact that the vessel imperilled at sea, on the strand or in a port of refuge may not have the facility to help herself in any required off-loading process. The barge carriers coming along afterward were initially rated off the containerships, but with special attention to their intricate, expensive and vital barge handling and stowage mechanisms, plus the fact that their in-port operations would be substantially different in nature. The VLCCs were rated off the smaller tankers, with primary concern being given to the difference in their handling characteristics, their tank size and deep drafts, and the lack of tug and drydock facilities available

in the emergency. Most recently, the LNGs are being considered from the basis of the VLCC rate levels, with particular emphasis, however, on their exotic and much more specialized and expensive cargo carrying compartments. Frankly, the nature of the exposure which the LNG product itself presents remains something of a puzzle at this stage. Despite all that has been written and surmised on this score, we have deferred making any judgments, adverse or otherwise, up to the present.

Accepting that the initial rating must be something of an inexact appraisal, you may ask at what point in time "informed judgment" shows itself with recognition given for the safety features which should make one vessel better or worse than another. Within recent months, comments have been made in a technical journal that underwriters have been remiss in this regard and ought to grant more immediate reduction in premium for incorporation of safety features.

To answer this, the role of the underwriter should be examined in perspective.

THE UNDERWRITERS' ROLE IN TIME OF CHANGE

At the outset, it is important to repeat that our service to shiponwers is one of financial support --- the protection of his most valuable asset, the vessel. It would be neither wise nor proper for us to interpose our ideas in other areas prematurely for several reasons.

First, not being shipowners, we should not be using his funds - meaning a portion of the premium he has paid - to perform research functions he is perfectly capable of performing himself. Because we would be primarily concerned with safety measures, these would invariably be given preference over economic factors. The extent to which double bottoms are utilized in tankers to the detriment of cargo carrying capacity, for example, must be left to the owner to determine, notwithstanding how much we might favor the incorporation of this added protection.

Second, we are not designers, nor are we omniscient to the extent of being able to determine at the outset that a given feature or piece of equipment will, in fact, live up to its promise of efficient performance.

We have had to bear this latter fact in mind when faced with inquiries from developers of navigational equipment who seek our support and approval to a new item, usually with the thought in mind that they will then have an added selling point - the carrot of a rate reduction. To the promoter we will bring up the example of radar which was so highly touted at the time of its introduction as the device which would forever eliminate collisions at sea. We said then that if radar worked and accomplished what its developers foresaw, loss records would soon bear out that fact. We know now that as valuable as radar has become, it is no panacea. Collisions still occur and there is the additional dismaying phenomenon of the radar-assisted collision. Probably more than any other cause, overreliance upon and misinterpretation of radar was responsible for the ANDREA DORIA - STOCKHOLM collision off Nantucket lightship in July, 1956.

In the same vein, it would be presumptuous of us at this point to take a firm position in favor of one system for gas-freeing tanks over another, particularly since we cannot yet be sure the basic cause of tanker explosions has been fully uncovered. Similarly, it is not our place to conclude that the spherical tank is superior to the membrane tank for the carriage of liquified natural gas, or vice-versa. It is far too early to make any such differentiation. If anything at this time, we can only express disappointment that the tendency appears to be toward as few and as large tanks as can be fitted. A system of smaller tanks would seem to be preferable purely from the standpoint of safety.

These comments should not be taken to mean, however, that we do not have thoughts on the subject of desirable features or that we are quite unprepared to make distinctions. Perhaps a brief description of a vessel we would favor is in order.

The underwriters' vessel would be able to survive an opening of the shell anywhere in its length, under any conditions of loading, and it would have a double bottom. It would have dual propulsion and provision for independent lateral movement, such as thrusters. There would be direct control from the bridge of propulsion machinery, including such control on the wings. There would be adequate provision for observation from the forecastle, and the wheelhouse would have full circle visibility. A public address system would be installed. The ship would be fitted not only with audible water depth indicators, but also a similar horizontal ranging Sonar-type beam forward to provide for indication of obstructions ahead. Its radar would be augmented with an automatic plotting system, which would include an audible collision avoidance alarm. If the ship were to have salt water ballast spaces, these would be substantially coated to avoid thinning of structure through stress corrosion. Configuration of internals would also be such as to reduce the likelihood of stress fractures. Hog/sag indicators would be employed and loading manuals would also be available to insure proper distribution of weights within the vessel to provide proper stability and minimize longitudinal strains. If frequent dockings were contemplated, wire mooring winches would be installed with deck edge controls.

Further, if it were a tanker, there would be a double hull as well as bottom. It would be inerted, and in addition it would have installed a soon-to-be-announced system for dissipating electrical charge buildup, thus controlling both the atmosphere and the ignition sources within

cargo tanks. The tank sizes would be limited to less than those set forth in the IMCO standards. There would be remote reading gauges in all cargo areas, adequate air compressor capacity to force water from flooded tanks, and fire fighting capabilities on deck as well as in the engine room.

The underwriters' vessel, wet or dry, would be manned by a qualified crew, specially trained for their tasks and certificated by the most responsible authorities. The ships would be built and maintained to the highest standards of the most demanding classification society. Whether these ships would make money is a matter of conjecture, but there would be every expectation that their premiums would be less than those paid for other vessels now operating. It is unfortunate that this statement must be qualified at all, but there is still the assured's overall record to consider, plus the fact that the best ships in the world are exposed to marine perils which sometimes cannot be avoided. Also, and even more regrettably, it remains a fact that the great majority of accidents are caused by human failure. This is why we lay such stress on training and qualification of crews of every nation. Human engineering must be regarded as even more important than design engineering.

Turning now to incentives, it seems to us that there are already many and varied reasons for the owner to strive to build the safest ship he can within the limits of his operational expectancies. Imposition of governmental requirements in the face of disinclination of owners to act voluntarily is always a strong inducement. On the purely economic side, the charter an owner may have at stake, or the long and expensive delay his ship may suffer while undergoing repair would seem adequate reasons for his interest and concern about the kind of ship he operates. We know also that the best owners have adopted a very enlightened view toward the incorporation of safety features and equipment without the explicit urging of underwriters. On the other hand, the individual who insists on being "paid" first before he acts will, unfortunately, not ordinarily do more than he feels he can get by with in any case.

Another problem with incentives, from the underwriting viewpoint, comes in the attempt to quantify them. How much and from what base? If we were underwriting by tariff, i.e., set schedules for the insurance cost of a particular type of vessel, it might theoretically be possible to advertise a five percent discount for this or a ten percent discount for that. But remember, hull insurance rates are not established by tariff, they are determined by judgment--and no shipowner has ever expressed to us the wish that we develop rates for his vessel in the same manner they are assessed for the protection of his home or automobile. While we must be careful of advance recognition of features, and though we

must begin our thinking about a new design from
what is essentially a common base, as described
earlier, please be assured the qualitative distinctions will be taken into account as well.

One of the important tools which we employ
to assemble information and make initial assessments can also assist us in making the qualitative distinctions just mentioned. This is the
evaluation questionnaire we developed for the
mammoth tanker. This questionnaire has been revised from time to time and now includes the
ore/oil vessel as well. In addition, we take
this occasion to announce that a new form has
been developed for dry general and bulk cargo
vessels as well. Copies of these questionnaires
are available to all, and our assureds are encouraged to utilize them to inform us, in greater
detail than we would ordinarily obtain, about
their vessels and their unique characteristics,
their trades, operation and personnel, both crew
and shoreside. Through this means, the fullest
consideration of every risk can be promised.

There is one particular area where underwriters
can be of assistance to the maritime community
in these times of change, and it also relates
to an exchange of information. Feedback of operational experience to design agents and engineers has too often been sadly overlooked and,
because of this, problems which could be avoided
are built back into new ships. Our records contain extensive data on maritime casualties, and
we have authorized our technical and surveying
organization, United States Salvage Association,
Inc., to undertake a program of damage survey
analysis based on casualty data they develop
through surveys made on our behalf. This program of coding casualty information by vessel
type, cause, nature and extent of damage provides a source of valuable reference material
which the Association is prepared to make available to the worldwide shipping industry upon application. We hope you will agree that this is
a worthwhile undertaking, and that you will make
use of the opportunities it offers.

Hopefully, also, these comments today will have
provided you with some food for thought. Please
keep in mind particularly the direct, insepara-
ble relationship between maritime losses and the
cost of hull insurance. Safety, efficiency and
economy--these three elements do relate and in-
teract upon one another. Even in the changing
times, this truth, at least, remains unchanged.

# # # # #

ERGONOMIC STUDIES AFFECTING SHIP CONTROL

AND BRIDGE DESIGN

Ronald E.F. Lewis
D.A. Attwood

A.V. Churchill
D. Beevis

Defence and Civil Institute of Environmental Medicine
Downsview, Ontario

ABSTRACT

This paper summarizes several ship control and
related studies conducted by human engineers
(ergonomists) of the Defence and Civil Institute
of Environmental Medicine (DCIEM) in recent
years. These include (a) the design of a
unique bridge for what may be one of the largest
and most powerful ice-breakers in the world for
the Canadian Coast Guard; (b) sea trials aboard
a Canadian destroyer in which direct bridge control was compared in terms of manoeuvring performance with the conventional fighting ship
voice-ordered system; (c) the use of CCTV in
several marine situations to complement voice
communication and to improve external vision in
areas normally blind to bridge personnel; (d)
a human engineering review of a small submersible; and (e) the importance of sea trials as a
means of obtaining data is discussed.

INTRODUCTION

This paper will describe a series of ship control studies that have been conducted in recent
years by the Defence and Civil Institute of
Environmental Medicine, in Canada. The authors,
who have each carried out one or more of these
studies, are members of the human factors
engineering group at the Institute.

"Old habits die hard." That is a very old
saying unquestionably true of seagoing people
everywhere. Unfortunately it is also true of
ship designers because, with few exceptions,
ship control designs change very slowly,
relatively speaking, as the years roll by.
This situation occurs, we would suggest, for
one main reason. Ships are controlled by
captains who, for the most part, are conservative in attitude. Often they dictate in large
measure how a new ship shall be manned and
controlled, at least in terms of the bridge
complement.

It is in the face of this attitude that the
human factors engineer brings suggestions to
better achieve more effective man-machine
systems designs in the marine environment. We
are, however, slowly achieving success and
several of the studies to be described have

resulted in systems installation in recent ship
designs. The examples to be presented have in
common a simple fact. They all deal with fundamental principles of human engineering that,
generally speaking, have been overlooked in
ship control designs.

DESIGNING THE SHIP CONTROL POSITION
FOR A LARGE POLAR ICEBREAKER

The first example undertaken for the Canadian
Coast Guard has concentrated on identifying
those areas of the icebreaker control task where
human factors expertise can most usefully contribute, in developing a valid design philosophy,
and building a representative mock-up of the
proposed bridge design[1].

The bridge design has been developed around the
outline specification originally provided by the
Coast Guard, namely:- 600 ft. overall length,
up to 100 ft. beam, 100,000 plus. S.H.P.

Observations at sea on current icebreaker
bridges during icebreaker handling caused the
authors to conclude that visibility from the
bridge, particularly when running astern during
escort work was less than desirable. It was
concluded that the current style of full width
bridge is not ideally suited to icebreaking:
the major disadvantages of such a layout, namely
inadequate visibility, particularly astern, and
the constant movement about the bridge necessary
to compensate for this, became progressively
more serious with increasing size. A design was
therefore developed based on the principle that
the officer in charge should be able to see the
majority of the ship's perimeter from one point,
either seated or standing, rather than building
up a mental image of the situation round the
ship by a series of "looks" through individual
windows.

This one point would be a station on a small
conning bridge, at the top of a stepped, or
pyramidal superstructure, allowing vision all
around the ship's perimeter. The basic geometry
of such a layout, and the way in which it dic-
tates the overall design of the ship's superstructure are illustrated.

It was originally hoped that a small conning bridge could be designed which would accommodate all necessary navigating equipment [2], and fulfill all necessary wheelhouse/bridge functions. However, it became clear that the space requirements for normal bridge equipment were much greater than those of a small conning bridge designed for icebreaking work and ship berthing only. It was therefore decided to separate the two bridge types, the conning bridge being mounted above the main navigating bridge, access being via a stairway.

With the need to accommodate at least two persons on the conning bridge, the minimum deck size must be approximately 8 ft. square. With such a layout it was found impossible to provide a view of both sides of the ship from one position. Therefore a compromise layout was adopted to allow three closely spaced conning positions around one set of helm and power controls. The ship may then be conned from either side, allowing a clear view along the whole side of the ship, or from the centre line, from which position either side of the ship may easily be seen by moving only two feet to port or starboard.

Following a mock-up review meeting with Canadian Coast Guard personnel in December 1972 the Coast Guard concluded that while in agreement, in principle, with the pyramidal super-structure/small bridge concept, the conning position should be designed to accommodate at least four persons. A deck area provided by the initial design is therefore insufficient, and the conning bridge should be enlarged.

DCIEM Human Engineering personnel have serious reservations regarding the number of bridge personnel required for icebreaking/escort duties, but were asked to investigate the ramifications of such an enlargement. Enlarging the design has three major associated penalties;
- reduction in the extent of the ship's perimeter immediately visible from any one position,
- two or three sets of power and helm controls are required to allow conning from either side or the centre line,
- the increase in size and window area increases the difficulty of keeping all windows clean and frost-free at all times.

Taking these problems in reverse order, little can be done about window frosting, apart from a very rigorous approach during the engineering design stage using heated window glass, forced air warming, etc. The farther away that windows are from the observer, the less he is able to compensate for any dirt, rain or frosting by small movements of the head and eyes. While this may be stated as a generalization, we cannot estimate the effect on visibility to be expected by increasing the viewing distance to the far side windows from 6 ft. to, say, 10 ft.

The second problem, the need for more than one set of power controls, again must be accepted. Just as it is believed to be wrong for the officer in charge to have to move about the bridge in order to see out, so it is thought wrong for him to have to move from vantage point to controls and back again. The controls should fall readily to hand whether the ship is being conned from the centre line or either side of the bridge. An initial analysis indicates that two sets of controls should be sufficient, if they are placed convenient to both centre line and side conning positions. With one set of controls in the lower, navigating bridge, this is still no more, in total, than is fitted in current full width bridges.

Reduction of visibility is the most serious drawback related to an increase in size. It is not, however, as serious as at first suspected. Due to the length of the proposed ship, the majority of the ship's perimeter is viewed through the front and rear windows, rather than those at the side.

Thus, if only the width of the wheelhouse is increased, no more of the ship's perimeter is obscured than at present; the distance to the nearest visible point on the sea-surface to the far side of the ship is increased, however, which is in itself undesirable. With a 12 foot wide bridge the nearest visible point on the far side would be some 270 ft. away, i.e., 220 ft. from the ship's rail. Crossing the 12 ft. width of the bridge reduces this distance to 20 ft. but this is obviously a less desirable solution than the existing design. The amount by which the width of the initial conning bridge can be increased is therefore limited.

Similarly, remembering that the majority of the ship is seen through the front and rear windows, comparatively little increase in the length of the conning bridge can be tolerated. Study of the lines of sight shows that the present design could be increased to about 11 ft. 6 in. long overall without seriously affecting vision ahead or astern.

The overall dimensions can therefore probably be increased to 12 ft. 3 in. interior width, and 11 ft. 6 in. interior length without compromising the conning position concept too much. This should provide sufficient room for up to four persons, plus equipment.

SEA TRIALS TESTING THE EFFECTIVENESS OF DIRECT CONTROLS ON THE BRIDGE OF A DESTROYER

Until recently the navies of the world have relied on voice orders from the bridge to the engine room to change engine revolution. The same voice-ordered procedure was used to pass below changes to the helmsman (quartermaster) sometimes situated with the wheel, below decks.

In the course of early familiarization at sea aboard a destroyer it was quickly judged that the delays and, more important, the error that would inevitably occur with this system would, sooner or later, be the cause of accident. (Icebreaker design personnel had put direct control of engines on the bridge wings of ice-breakers years before, but their reasons, we think, were different.)

The question at the core of this study was: could DCIEM, by means of sea trials, demonstrate through human performance measurement, the manoeuvring advantages of the direct bridge control system as opposed to the conventional voice-ordered system?

When the Canadian Navy made available a des-troyer and frigate exclusively, for a six week sea trials period, DCIEM entered upon a fascinating period of research activity.

Six experienced captains controlled HMCS SASKATCHEWAN for a week each and performed various manoeuvres about the frigate HMCS NEW GLASGOW. They controlled the destroyer from a seated position on the centre-line in a small gazebo bridge and from that position used both the "direct" or "voice-ordered" system. Per-formance was measured by taking aerial plan pictures of both ships and reconstructing the captain's station-keeping ability.

Results were, we think, impressive [3,4]:
(a) Manoeuvring performed was significantly better using the "direct" system except for one condition in which no advantage or disadvantage was shown.
(b) After just three hours of practice with the "direct" system, each captain de-clared himself ready to be tested using it.
(c) Using the "direct" system totally inex-perienced people manoeuvred the destroyer in simulated dockings at sea (alongside drifting logs) with comparative ease.
(d) It was estimated by one officer that the "direct" system could reduce the total crew complement by eighteen.

This sea trial is not recent. It is described here because it clearly demonstrated two points:
(a) that human performance data obtained at sea are a convincing means of persuading design authorities of the need for change, and
(b) that field trials data regarding human performance can indeed be obtained in quite difficult operational situations.

We are pleased that the new Canadian destroyer escorts designated DDH 280 do have direct con-trols on the bridge.

THE USE OF FULL-SCALE MOCK-UPS IN HUMAN FACTORS DESIGN FOR SHIPS' BRIDGES

Through our studies we have made considerable use of the full-scale mock-up. We have found the mock-up invaluable as a research tool for "instant" changes can be made. It is useful

as a vehicle for professional discussions with potential users, e.g., ships' captains, and is of course a very good demonstration and lecture exhibit. We would not hesitate to use the full-scale mock-up whenever man-machine interaction studies are performed. Mock-ups need not be expensive and extremely handsome effects can be achieved using materials such as Foam-core.

THE STANDARD NAVIGATING BRIDGE FOR COAST GUARD VESSELS

This study has been the basis of a "standard" bridge design for several classes of vessels within the Canadian Coast Guard [5]. With it, the Coast Guard entered a new era of bridge and bridge interior design, and seriously embarked on a programme that would inaugurate the several basics to good design mentioned previously. Captains could now see more efficiently from the bridge. Displays were legible. Communications were systemized, etc. Compromises had to be reached when a ship class became very small, e.g., a rescue cutter. Nevertheless, the principles of good design were not affected.

THE USE OF CLOSED CIRCUIT TELEVISION IN A SHIP CONTROL ENVIRONMENT

There are many uses for CCTV but in a marine environment it can be especially useful.

Where the vision aft from the bridge is re-stricted by the funnel and superstructure (especially in older vessels) it is highly desirable for bridge personnel to be able to "SEE" using CCTV. If the ship carries a heli-copter, the departures and arrivals of the helicopter can be seen [6]. Communication does not always deal effectively with the problem. Similarly CCTV can be used to better show the perimeter of the ship, especially astern, and so permit better manoeuvring. Indeed one Canadian captain, using such a display docked his vessel from 1000 yards out completely blind but for the CCTV monitoring picture [7].

CCTV can be used in its traditional role to monitor remote activity on the ship, and also to monitor activity such as hull and propellor examinations. DCIEM proposes to use TV to show ice conditions in an otherwise unseen area at the side of the polar icebreaker.

One cautionary word. In our recent opinion CCTV can give confusing information if distance judg-ments are made between closing vessels unless the user is practiced and vigilant.

DESIGN PROBLEMS IN THE SUBMERSIBLE SDL-1

Though not directly related to ship control, our most recent study is perhaps interesting because the entire submersible has been reviewed by one of our human factors engineers [8].

This little submarine is controlled from a forward sphere joined by a tunnel to a smaller rear lock-out sphere (which accommodates divers) and from which the divers exit. All controls and displays concerning manoeuvring are in the forward sphere.

This study again was carried out using a full-scale mock-up of the submersible as a research tool.

VISION

When submerged, external vision from the control sphere is poor due to the poor placement of viewports. Operators assume contorted positions to obtain adequate vision forward and their comfort has been largely ignored as it has in most other submersibles.

New generation submersibles are fitted with large plexiglass domes which provide a panoramic view to a seated operator. Some older submersibles, containing viewports similar to those in the SDL-1, have been fitted with passive optical systems which permit the operator to sit comfortably back from the ports and still receive an adequate view.

Neither of the above solutions is feasible in the SDL-1. Moreover, active sensors (i.e., CCTV) have not proven satisfactory for remote guidance due to the lack of depth and colour perception and resolution and are not viable solutions.

Operator seating was redesigned in the DCIEM mock-up around the existing viewports. The pilot seat comfortably supports the pilot in a semi-prone position by distributing his weight over his chest, seat and knees. The co-pilot and observers are provided with prone couches which utilize a hammock support principle to minimize fatigue.

External vision on the surface is non-existent at present. The pilot relies solely on surface controllers for guidance when manoeuvring. DCIEM has recommended the use of CCTV as an aid for surface vision. The external camera would be mounted on a platform which would rotate in both the horizontal and vertical planes. The camera would provide all around vision on the surface and would be used as a search and navigation aid underwater.

CONTROLS/DISPLAYS

As a general comment, DCIEM proposes that the majority of controls and displays within the submersible be redesigned.

The majority of the controls now in the submersible are multiturn valves which operate the independent air systems in the vehicle. The controls which serve an on-off function were replaced by quarter turn valves in the mock-up. The controls and displays were also grouped according to individual air systems to improve identification. Control labelling in the submersible is misguiding in many cases and the shape and colour coding of the controls is poor. Displays also suffer from poor labelling, only a few are lit, and none are colour coded. Each of these problems is addressed in the mock-up.

Beta lighting, for example, has been recommended for the few displays that should be monitored in the event of a power failure during a lock-out mission. A few of the important displays would be edge-lit while most would be designed with high letter to background contrast and large alphanumerics to be legible under low level ambient illumination.

The controls and displays required by the pilot to manoeuvre the vessel are presently scattered throughout the control sphere. The controls for trim and ballast, for example, are so widely separated that they cannot be easily operated by the same man at the same time. The DCIEM redesign groups the pilot's controls within his work envelope and locates the critical displays as close to the viewports as possible.

The lock-out personnel are presently provided with information and controls to perform functions that are either unnecessary or redundant and that can be controlled more precisely and conveniently from the command sphere. Since space is a premium in the lock-out, it was important to delete unnecessary equipment. The number of controls and displays recommended for the lock-out has been reduced to a minimum. The resultant space savings had created enough seating area to comfortably house three divers; the original design complement.

EXTERNAL COMMUNICATIONS

The individual handsets of the underwater and surface vessel-to-vessel communication systems are routinely tangled and often confused. The location of the handsets of all communications systems are widely separated and awkward to reach from the pilot and observer positions. A redesign of the peripheral communication equipment has been recommended. Each occupant will be provided with headphones, a boom microphone, and an integrated switching facility that will permit him to use each communication system from his working position.

It is important to have emergency power for communications in the event of a major power failure. At the present time, a power failure in the SDL-1 severs communication between it and the diver. The DCIEM design recommends that diver-vessel communication remain unaffected by a major power failure.

In addition to the main topics discussed above, DCIEM has suggested many minor improvements to the design. Stowage areas, for example, have been designed to increase the usable volume of the lock-out sphere. Fold-down tables and stowable seats have been provided to enhance operator comfort without interfering with the operation of the vessel. Handholds have been recommended for operator safety during entry and exit.

Where possible, we have strived to design around the present systems using the simplest and least expensive techniques. When it became impossible to use the original systems, the new systems that were recommended were either off the shelf items or were within the state of the art and could be developed quickly and inexpensively.

Most of the recommendations and solutions listed above will be put into effect as the SDL-1 undergoes conversion. Since none of the shortcomings create dangerous conditions, these can be put into effect as and when convenient.

Recent submersibles will, we hope, have fewer human factors engineering problems remaining after construction.

In conclusion, wherever possible we utilize the many design criteria that have been determined by researchers in the past. Where new man-machine systems are proposed that can significantly change performance we advocate the use of carefully prepared sea trials.

REFERENCES

(1) Beevis, D. and R.E.F. Lewis, "The Design of a Bridge for a Large Polar Icebreaker," Third Ship Control Symposium, 26-28 September, University of Bath, U.K., 1972.

(2) Scott, R.L., "Modern Destroyer Bridge Design," U.S. Naval Institute Proceedings, March, 1968.

(3) Lewis, R.E.F. and D.M. Sweeney, "Direct Bridge Control of Engines and Helm on a Destroyer: Sea Trials Results," DRET Report No. 718, 1969.

(4) Lewis, R.E.F., W.D. de la Riviere and O. Logan, "Sea Trials of Direct Bridge Control of Engines and Helm: A Summary of Test Captains' Opinions," DRML Report No. 630, 1966.

(5) Churchill, A.V., "Ship Control: Navigating Bridge Design," DRET Report No. 682, 1967.

(6) Lazet, A., "Some Applications of Closed-Circuit Television in Ships," DRET Report No. 690, 1968.

(7) Dean, P.J., R.E.F. Lewis and R.O. Morphet, "Closed-Circuit Television as an Aid in Ship Control," *Journal of the Institute of Navigation* (U.K.), 1967, 20, 121-130.

(8) Attwood, D.A. and Carol McCann, "Human Engineering Evaluation of the SDL-1 Submersible," DCIEM Technical Report (In preparation.)

ABOUT A PLAN OF "NAVIGATION RECORDER"

Torao Mozai
Prof. Dr.
Department of Navigation
Tokyo University of Mercantile Marine
Tokyo, Japan

INTRODUCTION

The surrounding sea of Japan islands is so worse of rapid variation in the weather and the sea condition. Especially in the winter it happen so many sea casualties in this area, in every year.

In January 1969, we lost an ore carrier, the Bolivar-Maru, of 54,271 DWT, and in February 1970, sank another big ore carrier, the California-Maru, 62,147 DWT, one after another. These sea casualties have stimulated the opinions of people so strongly, who desire to trace the causes of these accidents, and make the results

of it to raise up the safety of ship in future. But it was so difficult a problem, because all evidences were completely lost into the very deep sea of 6,000 metres.

Usually, the sea casualties will happen by the reasons of meteorological and oceanological conditions, manoeuvering conditions of the ship, the capacities and the abilities of the hull and engine, the abilities or knowledge of the crew. And, all of these causes used to have relations each other in complicating figure. But, only if we can get the evidences, it may be possible to analyse the true reasons of the accident.

The Ministry of Transportation of Japan has suggested to investigate about a method of remaining the evidences of the accident, for avoiding the future sea casualties of same reasons.

The Japan Ship's Machine Development Association has set up a committee, by this suggestion.

Officers, professors, ship-builders, shipping companies, instrument makers and investigators were collected for the members of the committee, which discussed this problem.

It is well known that there is a "Flight Recorder" which is being used in areoplanes already. The committee decided that, as this idea must be applied to the ship too, it must be investigated about the possibility of the "Navigation Recorder" and also, what data must be recorded in it too.

BASIC PLAN

By a study of the statistical report of 1970, which concerns the causes of the sea casualties in Japan, we learned as follows:

(1)	Mistakes of Manoeuvering	1,376	ships:	52%
(2)	Mistakes of engine handling	434	"	16%
(3)	Bad constructions	244	"	9%
(4)	Irresistibles	170	"	7%
(5)	Careless for cumbustibles	136	"	5%
(6)	Bad stowages	86	"	3%
(7)	Unknown origines	67	"	3%
(8)	Others	133	"	5%

In total   2,646 ships:100%

In this table, we noticed that the sea casualties which were occurred by human works, including (1), (2), (3), (5), (6), occupy about three thirds of all.

Considering these conditions, we consolidated our basic ideas about the "Navigation Recorder".

First it must not only be useful for surveying the causes after the accidents, but also be useful for avoiding the accidents themselves which should have occurred, by getting the information in advance, necessary for the normal maintenance and the safety adjustments.

Secondly, it must be floated on the sea, separate from the ship, even if at the worst, with the useful recorded information, accompanied by the automatical SOS transmitter. Thirdly, the recorder itself must have the alarm systems for the purpose of normal ship manoeuvering, not withstanding to the over limitations of circumstances.

SELECTION OF RECORDING ITEMS

We discussed the items, which must be recorded on the "Navigation Recorder". At first, so many items were considered, but we focused the works of discussion to the 22 items as follows:

(a) Weather condition   6 items

   (Atmospheric pressure, air temperature, sea temperature, wind direction, wind velocity and sea condition).

b) Navigational condition   4 items.

   (Latitude, longitude, ship's course and speed).

c) Hull condition   5 items.

   (Drafts of fore and aft, pitching and rolling angles, dynamical forces).

d) Engine condition   3 items

   (Propeller revolution, temperature of exhaust air, pressure of lubricating oil).

e) Actual state   1 item.

f) Spares   3 items.

After many discussions we got a conclusion, showed on table 1. But the true meaning of showing these items is:

a) At least, these items which are shown on the table 1, are the recognized ones about the possibilities of realization.

b) These items are simply the recommendable ones for the aim mentioned above, and not means the unchangeable factors.

c) The selection of items may be changed in case by case for every ship by its own way.

CONSTRUCTION

The "Navigation Recorder" will be divided into two main parts. One is a container for recorders, including automatical SOS transmitter, which will be floated on the sea, separate from the sinking ship. And the other is a display unit, which will indicate information necessary to prevent accidents in advance, by watching the conditions of the hull and the engine. As shown in Fig. -1, the former will be set on the flying bridge, just upward of the wheel house. And the latter will be set in the chart room of the bridge, with CPU & I/O. And of course every sensor will be set in every part for the aim. All the signals from sensors for emergency and for maintenance will be collected into I/O, which is directly connected to CPU. From I/O via a cassette tape controller, the digital data will be recorded on the cassette magnetic tapes in the container. Only the voice and the sound signals from the microphone will be recorded and stored in the container via sound recording controller, instead of via I/O.

On the other hand, from I/O via a plotter controller, some data will be plotted on a X - Y plotter. Some other data of navigation and engine condition will be indicated on some indicating panels connected with I/O. Those data will be able to help the officers and engineers to keep the conditions concerned normal.

SENSORS AND THE MINI-COMPUTER

The author does not consider that it is necessary to make mention of the methods of fitting the sensors one by one here, and also about the problem of what type of mini-computer will be selected for this purpose. These problems could be variable in each case, even though we investigated them precisely in our own way. And consider that only to see the table-1 is enough to understand this work.

CONCLUSION

In the case of realization of the "Navigation Recorder", it must be necessary to make an international agreement of cooperation, at least for collection of the floating container. But we investigated only about the fundamental technical feasibility, except that such kind of human problems. One must investigate about the economical problems, methods of its usage or the selection of items, more and more, before realization.

As we aimed two objects at the same time, we selected so many items for recording and indicating, that it caused the apparatus itself to be rather expensive. But it can easily be changed by selection or reduction of numbers of items in case by case.

In conclusion, it can be said that the idea of the "Navigation Recorder" will be finished in an academic argument only, but we really believe that this idea must be realised in the near future, for the better safety on the sea.

ACKNOWLEDGEMENT

This work was done by the Research Committee
of the "Navigation Recorder", which was set
up in Japan Ship's Machine Development
Association, under the leadership of the Ship
Bureau, Ministry of Transport of Japan.

The author is greatly indebted to every member
of the Committee, who worked separately in
every professional section.

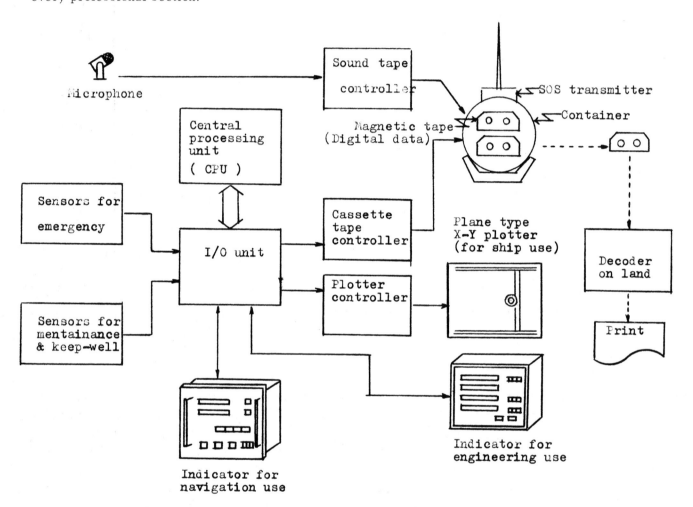

Fig. - 1 (Block diagram of NAVIGATION RECORDER)

TABLE - 1 (RECORDING ITEMS)

	ITEMS	RANGE	ACCURACY	SENSOR	SIG. RANGE	OBS. PERIOD	DATA PROCESS
W E A T H E R * S E A	ATOMOS. PRESSURE	940-1040 mb	± 2.0 mb	Aneloid	0-10 mV	1 hour	Inst. value
	AIR TEMPERATURE	(-20)-(+60)	± 1.0 C	Thermo couple	"	"	"
	SEA TEMPERATURE	(-4)-(+40)	± 1.0 C	"	"	"	"
	WIND DIRECTION	All direct.	± 5%	Vane	"	10 & 1 min.	1 min. mean by hard
	WIND VELOCITY	0-62 m/sec	"	Anemo	"	"	"
	WAVE			Manu. imp.		4 hours	
	SWELL			"		"	
N A V I G A T I O N	LAT. & LONG.			"		"	
	CARGO LOAD.			"		Depart. time	Case by case.
	SPEED	(-5)-(+50)kt	±1%	Mag. log	(-4)-(+4) mA	10 & 1 min.	Mean of 10 in eve.1 min
	COURSE	0-359°.8	±0°.2	Gyro.	0-5 V	"	"
	RUDDER ANGLE	(-35)-(+35)	± 0°.5	Rud. indi.	(-5)-(+5) V	10 min.	Inst. value
H U L L	PITCHING	(7) - (+7)	"	Pitch. indicator	"	"	√E of data of 3 min. in eve.2 sec.
	ROLLING	(-35)-(+35)	"	Roll. indi.	"		
	DRAFT (2)	0 - 30 m	±0.5%	Draft gauge	2-10 mA	Dep. time	Fore & aft.
E N G I N E	DINAMIC FORCE	0-1.5 g	0.001g	Accelero meter	(-1)-(+1) V	10 min.	Max. of 10 min.eve.2 s.
	PROPELLER REVO.	± 150 RPM	±0.5RPM	Revo. mtr	±5 V	"	
	TEMP. EXHAUST GAS	0°-500° C	±1°.0 C	Thermo couple	0-10 mV	"	Data of 10 cylinders
	PRESS. LUB. OIL	0-3kg/cm²	±0.02kg/cm²	Press gauge	2-10 mA	"	
	TIME	0-23.59.30		Contact		30 Sec.	
	VOICE & SOUND						
T E M P E R A T U R E	AIR COOLER INLET	0-150° C	±1°.0 C	Thermo couple	0-10 mV	1 hour	Inst. value
	" OUTLET	0-100° C	"	"	"	"	"
	CYLINDER LINER	0-200° C	"	"	"	"	"
	THRUST BEARING	0-100° C	"	"	"	"	"
	STERN TUBE B'G	"	"	"	"	"	"
	ROOM	(-20)-(40)	±0°.5 C	"	"	"	"
	REV. SUPER CHARGER	0-12,000 RPM	±1.0 %	Tacho meter	0-25 mV	"	"
	SCAVENGING PRESSURE	0.4-1.3 kg/cm²	±0.1 kg/cm²	Pressure gauge	2-10 mA	"	"
	FUEL CONSUMPTION	0-5,000 L/Hr	±10 L	Flow mtr.	Contact pulse	30 min.	Count outside
	BRAKE HORSEPOWER	0-50,000 BHP	±100BHP	Tortion meter	0-25 mV	1 hour	Mean of 30 min in eve. 10m.

Note:--- The 22 items of upper side (from WEATHER to VOICE & SOUND) are for emergency use,
and the other 10 items of lower side are for mentainance and keep-well.

CHARACTERIZATION AND IDENTIFICATION
OF THE MOTIONS OF SHIPS IN CONFUSED SEAS

Claude A. Bozzo
Laboratoire d'Automatique
GESSY
Centre Universitaire de Toulon - France

ABSTRACT

The motions of a ship in an irregular sea are very nearly linear and gaussian. This permits the direct application of the theory of Kalman filtering to prediction in real time of the response of the ship and to estimation of parameters of ship motions.

INTRODUCTION

The motions of a ship travelling obliquely to the direction of waves are complicated series of translational and rotational oscillations. These motions are considered as the summation of six components, three translational and three rotational. The translational motions are surging ξ along the x-axis, side-swaying η along the lateral or y-axis and heaving ζ along the vertical or z-axis. The rotations about these axes are rolling θ, pitching φ and yawing ψ.
In the mathematical analysis of such a motion, six simultaneous differential equations are written. The motion of a ship, as a rigid body, is completely described by these six components which are six degrees of freedom of the body. However, a practical ship is not an uncontrolled and unpropelled body but has an additional degree of freedom in movements of the rudder.

In this paper we assume that the rudder is fixed in neutral position : The motions of a ship travelling obliquely to the direction of wave crests can therefore be described by six coupled differential equations.

A ship travelling in a direction normal to the wave crests will experience only motions in the plane of symmetry ; i.e surging, heaving and pitching. The oscillatory surging motion along the x-axis has no effect important in practice on the heaving and pitching motions and does not appear to be of direct interest in defining the seagoing qualities of ships.

A ship at zero speed in beam seas will experience only rolling, side-swaying, and heaving. In side waves in these conditions, many coupling effects are inactive, heaving motions can be neglected and coupled rolling and side-sway equations can be written. The coupling effects come into play with increase of ship's speed and with obliqueness of ship's heading to wave crests.

By extension, ship motions in irregular seas can be characterized by a Gauss-Markov process
$$(1) \quad dx_t = F(t) \, x_t \, dt + f(t) + G(t) \, d\beta_t \quad t \geqslant t_o$$

where x_t is the 9 vector state
$$(2) \quad x_t^T = [\, \theta, \dot{\theta}, \ddot{\theta}, \varphi, \dot{\varphi}, \ddot{\varphi}, \zeta, \dot{\zeta}, \ddot{\zeta} \,]$$

F and G are non random continuous matrix time-fonctions and $\{\beta_t, t \geqslant t_o\}$ is a vector Brownian motion process with $E[d\beta_t \, d\beta_t^T] = Q(t) \, dt$.

Discrete linear observations are taken at time instants t_k
$$(3) \quad z_k = H(t_k) \, x_{t_k} + v_k \quad \text{with } v_k \sim N[o, R_k]$$
with (4) $H = [1,o,o,1,o,o,o,o1]$ $\quad x_{t_o} \sim N[\hat{x}_{t_o}; P_{t_o}]$

$\{\beta_t\}$ and $\{v_k\}$ are assumed independant.

$f(t)$ is a fixed bias included in the dynamics to account for errors due to :
- coupling effects (obliqueness of ship's heading to wave crests and effect of the speed)
- non linearities in rolling and in yawing (and yawinduced rolling) , difficulties caused by transient and multiple responses,
- hypothesis that the waves are a stationary random process which excit a linear system (ship) and produces a stationary and random process (ship motions)
- reduction in the system dimension in the characterization of each decoupled motion
- difficulties caused by the directional properties of the waves and by the fact that the spectrum that must be considered is the encountered wave spectrum.

The true value of the bias $f(t)$ is unknown. The purpose of estimation will be to find a bound for $f(t)$[1], to study the effect of $f(t)$ on the Kalman filter and to introduce a general measure of actual performance of a suboptimal, but low sensitive, filter by a sensitivity analysis. A promising approach based on the innovation property of an optimal filter is also available to determine the covariance Q of these artificial noise sources added to account for model uncertainties and non linear effects. The purpose of adaptive estimation will be to update the estimates Q and R in such a way that they converge to Q and R in the mean square sense or with probability one.

SPECTRAL ANALYSIS OF SHIP MOTIONS

A large amount of statistical data on ship motions has been collected and observations have been made on many ships with a permanently installed instrumentation. The instrumentation used is shown, for instance, in Fig.1. A gyroscopic instrument was used for recording, rolling and pitching angles and general types of accelerometers for measuring accelerations of surging, of side-swaying and chiefly of heaving.

These measured data (14 parameters) were recorded on a magnetic analog tape in FM. It was also possible to use on board a digital computer to compute in real time the correlations, spectra and cross spectra of the motions, the continuous signal being sampled with a judicious choice of sampling interval. ($\Delta t = 0,160$ ms for instance)

Ships response have been measured in a series of wave lenght and wave directions at a series of forward speeds. Observations were made for sea conditions (wind, average wave height and lenght encountered, wave direction and so on ..) Wave lengths also were estimated from the periods of encounter using relationships valid for trochoidal waves.

The ship was travelling on an octagon, each side of this octagon being travelled in a time τ (τ varying form 3 to 45 minutes). The observations made with a large τ have shown that it was possible to reduce this time to a τ_{min} value that was sufficent to have good estimates of the correlations of the observed processes.

The autocorrelation function of the rolling and of the pitching motions of a ship of 500 tons displacement and 45 m long BP (fig.1) appears in fig.2. The spectra for various relative ship and wave positions appears in fig.3 with the frequencies of the maxima of each spectrum. Fig.4 shows real spectra and computed spectra when a Gauss-Markov process model is used.

SENSITIVITY ANALYSIS OF DISCRETE AND CONTINUOUS KALMAN FILTERS

The estimation of system data as developed by Kalman presupposes knowledge of the underlying system structure which generates the data and knowledge of all statistical and dynamical parameters which characterize the data generation model.

If we consider, for instance, the case of a discrete process, the real or actual system is described by :

$$(5) \quad \begin{vmatrix} x_{k+1} = \Phi(k+1,k)x_k + \varphi(k) + \Gamma(k)w_{k+1} \\ z_k = H(k)\ x_k + v_k \end{vmatrix} \begin{vmatrix} w_k \sim N[o, Q(k)] \\ v_k \sim N[o, R(k)] \\ x_o \sim N[\hat{x}(o), P(o)] \end{vmatrix}$$

The process is assumed to be represented by the linear vector difference equation (5) where $x(k)$ is a state vector of dimension n, $\Phi(k,k-1)$ is the $n \times n$ state transition matrix, $\Gamma(k)$ is an $n \times r$ matrix and w_{k+1} is a stochastic input vector of dimension r; $z(k)$ is a m-vector observation, $H(k)$ is an $m \times n$ matrix and $v(k)$ is a stochastic observation error vector of dimension m. $\varphi(k)$ is a fixed bias included in the dynamics to account for errors due to nonlinearities, reduction in system dimension and so on.. In what follows $\{\varphi(k)\}$ could be treated as a random sequence. The stochastic processes are uncorrelated with one another and assumed to be gaussian sequences with zero mean and covariance matrices.

The model used in the filter design is assumed to be known and to be characterized by the two difference equations

$$(6) \quad \begin{vmatrix} x_{k+1} = \Phi_c(k+1,k)x_k + \varphi_c(k) + \Gamma_c(k)\ w_{k+1} \\ z_k = H_c(k)\ x_k + v_k \end{vmatrix}$$

Using equation (6) and standard results in linear estimation theory, then :

$$(7) \quad \begin{vmatrix} \hat{x}_{k+1}^k = \Phi_c(k+1,k)\ \hat{x}_k^k + \varphi_c(k) \\ \hat{x}_k^k = [I-K_c(k)H_c(k)]\ \hat{x}_k^{k-1} + K_c(k)\ z_k \end{vmatrix}$$

with
$$(8) \quad \begin{vmatrix} K_c(k) = P_c(k/k-1)H_c^T(k)[H_c(k)P_c(k/k-1)H_c^T(k)+R_c(k)]^{-1} \\ P_c(k+1/k) = \Phi_c(k+1,k)P_c(k/k)\Phi_c^T(k+1,k) \\ \qquad\qquad + \Gamma_c(k)\ Q_c(k+1)\ \Gamma_c^T(k) \\ P_c(k/k) = [I-K_c(k)\ H_c(k)]P_c(k/k-1) \end{vmatrix}$$

The computed matrix $P_c(k/k)$ is not the estimation error covariance matrix, since the filter model differs from the real.

This filter is not the minimum variance filter for the actual system characterized by the error covariance $P(k/k)$, but a suboptimal filter.

A mesure of the filter performance is provided by the actual estimation error covariance matrix.

$$(9) \quad P_a(k/k) \triangleq E[(x_k - \hat{x}_k^k)(x_k - \hat{x}_k^k)^T] \quad \text{with}$$

$$P(k/k) \triangleq E[(x_k - \hat{x}_k^k)(x_k - \hat{x}_k^k)^T] \quad \text{and}$$

$$(10) \quad P_c(k/k) \triangleq E[(x_k - \hat{x}_k^k)(x_k - \hat{x}_k^k)^T]$$

Difference equations for the actual errors in the estimate can be found in [1] and [4].

Under appropriate conditions, the actual error variance is less than or equal to the computed variance. For instance, we have :

Theorem : if $P_a(o) \leqslant P_c(o)$ and $Q(k) \leqslant Q_c(k)$ $R(k) \leqslant R_c(k)$ all k, then $P_a(k/k) \leqslant P_c(k/k)$ and $P_a(k+1/k) \leqslant P_c(k+1/k)$ for all k

$P_c(k/k)$ may be precomputed to determine whether the conservative estimates of $P_a(o), Q(k)$ and $R(k)$ give satisfactory filter performance, or whether somewhat less conservative estimates are desirable.

Various special cases of the actual estimation error covariance matrix equations have been developed and numerical simulations have shown that qualitative results can be developed to account for errors in coupling effects non linearities and so on (the bias $\varphi(k)$ can be included in w_k by changing $Q(k)$).

An example is given for a second order model (rolling motion); the results are indeed much more easy to show. Thus, the study was achieved with 4 or 5 order models for the different motions (rolling and so on..) and with 2 or 3 order models for coupled parameters. The steady state is only considered. In this occurence, it is easy to show that the continuous case is equivalent to the discrete case. The sensitivity analysis leads to identify in real time some of the parameters and introduces a general measure of the accuracy of this identification stage on the actual performance of the suboptimal filter.

If the difference between the model used in the computation of the state estimate and the model of the actual process are small, then a small scale

or differential matrix sensitivity function may be defined as :
$$\left[\frac{\partial P_a(k/k)}{\partial \zeta_i}\right]_\zeta$$
where ζ_i is a vector of parameters in the actual system and ζ its value in the filter model.

In the steady state case, sensitivity equations can be developed trivially by differentiating the continuous or discrete Wiener filter equation (11) and (12).

Theorem : The algorithm for solving the discrete and continuous Wiener filter equation are equivalent. The sensitivity analysis made for the continuous steady state filter is valid for the discrete filter.

Proof : At steady state the error covariance matrix P satisfies :

- The continuous Wiener filter equation for (1)

$$(11) \quad \dot{P} = o = FP + PF^T - PH^T R^{-1} HP + GQG^T$$

- The discrete Wiener filter equation for (5)

$$(12) \quad P = \Phi P \Phi^T - \Phi P \Phi^T [HPH^T + R]^{-1} HP\Phi^T + \Gamma Q \Gamma^T$$

The algorithm for solving the continuous filter equation is a quasi-linearization algorithm which proceeds as follows :

$$(13) \quad \left| \begin{array}{l} \theta_i = F - K_i H \\ \theta_i P_i + P_i \theta_i^T = - K_i R K_i^T - GQG^T \\ K_{i+1} = P_i H^T R^{-1} \end{array} \right.$$

and for the discrete case

$$(14) \quad \left| \begin{array}{l} \theta_i = \Phi - L_i H = \Phi(I - K_i H) \\ P_i - \theta_i P_i \theta_i^T = L_i R L_i^T + \Gamma Q \Gamma^T \\ L_i = \Phi P_i H^T [H P_i H^T + R]^{-1} \end{array} \right.$$

The existence of a unique, positive definite solution of the steady state Wiener filter equation[1] and [2] and the convergence of the above algorithms are not established here.

The equation (13) can be rewritten as :

$$(15) \quad \alpha X + X \alpha^T = \beta \quad \text{with} \quad \alpha = \theta$$

By using the linear fractional transformation $\frac{1-\zeta^{-1}}{1+\zeta^{-1}}$ (Laguerre transform[5]) which maps the left half complex plane into the unit disc, equation (15) becomes:

$$(I-\alpha) X (I-\alpha^T) - (I+\alpha) X (I+\alpha^T) = - 2\beta$$

$$(16) \quad X - (I-\alpha)^{-1}(I+\alpha) X (I+\alpha^T)(1-\alpha^T)^{-1} = -2(I-\alpha)^{-1}\beta(I-\alpha^T)^{-1}$$

The following expression is equivalent to (14)

EXAMPLE. ANALYSIS OF ROLLING - CONTINUOUS FILTER

The selected model is a second order model : we add artificial noise to account for model uncertainties.

The data generation mechanism is described by

$$(17) \quad \dot{x} = \begin{bmatrix} o & 1 \\ -\omega_o^2 & -2 z \omega_o \end{bmatrix} x + \begin{bmatrix} o \\ \sigma_Q \omega_o^2 \end{bmatrix} w_t = F x + G w_t$$

$$z = \begin{bmatrix} 1, o \end{bmatrix} x + v_t \quad \text{with} \quad w_t \sim N[o,1] ; v_t \sim N[o, \sigma_R^2]$$

The filter consists of the following equations :

$$(18) \quad \dot{\hat{x}} = F \hat{x} + K(z - H \hat{x}) \quad \text{with} \quad K^T = \begin{bmatrix} \dfrac{P_{11}}{\sigma_R^2}, & \dfrac{P_{12}}{\sigma_R^2} \end{bmatrix}$$

$$(19) \quad \left| \begin{array}{l} \dot{\overline{P}}_{11} = 2 \overline{P}_{12} - \overline{P}_{11}^2 \\ \dot{\overline{P}}_{12} = \overline{P}_{22} - \omega_o^2 \overline{P}_{11} - 2 z \omega_o \overline{P}_{12} - \overline{P}_{11} \overline{P}_{12} \\ \dot{\overline{P}}_{22} = -2\omega_o^2 \overline{P}_{12} - 4 z \omega_o \overline{P}_{22} - \overline{P}_{12}^2 + \omega_o^4 \dfrac{\sigma_Q^2}{\sigma_R^2} \end{array} \right. \text{with } \overline{P} = P \times \frac{1}{\sigma_R^2}$$

$$\text{and} \quad \frac{\sigma_Q^2}{\sigma_R^2} = E$$

The steady state solution is given by[2].

$$(20) \quad \overline{P}_{11}(\infty) = \omega_o \sqrt{2} \left[(1+E)^{\frac{1}{2}} - (1-2 z^2)\right]^{\frac{1}{2}} - 2 z \omega_o$$

With similar equations for $\overline{P}_{12}(\infty)$ and $P_{22}(\infty)$.

Sensitivity equations can be developed trivially by differentiating (20). For instance :

$$(21) \quad S_\omega^{12} = \frac{\partial \overline{P}_{12}(\infty)}{\partial \omega_o} = 2\omega_o \left\{ 4z^2 - 1 + (1+E)^{\frac{1}{2}} - 2z\sqrt{2}\left[(1+E)^{\frac{1}{2}} - (1-2 z^2)\right]^{\frac{1}{2}} \right\}$$

Theorem - The actual estimation error variance are bounded by the computed variances which are generated as a part of the filter solution.

- if $P_a(o) \leqslant P_c(o)$ $\quad K_a^2 \sigma_a^2 \leqslant K_c^2 \sigma_c^2$ and $\sigma_{R_a}^2 \leqslant \sigma_{R_c}^2$

for all k
- or if $\dfrac{1}{z_a} \leqslant \dfrac{1}{z_c}$

The proof is trivial and is not developed here.

Sensitivity functions

If the continuous linear system described by (17) is sampled at discrete time instants t_k, then the sampled data x_k satisfy :

$$\left| \begin{array}{l} x_{k+1} = \Phi(k+1,k) x_k + w_{k+1} \\ z_{k+1} = H x_{k+1} + v_{k+1} \end{array} \right.$$

with $\Phi(k+1,k) = e^{FT} = \dfrac{e^{-\beta T}}{\omega}\left[F \sin \omega T + I(\omega \cos \omega T + \beta \sin \omega T)\right]$

and $EM\left[w_k w_k^T\right] = Q_k = \displaystyle\int_o^T e^{F\theta} GG^T e^{F^T\theta} d\theta = \sigma_Q^2 \left| \begin{array}{cc} q_{11} & q_{12} \\ q_{12} & q_{22} \end{array} \right|$

$\lambda^2 + 2\beta\lambda + \omega_o^2 = o \Longrightarrow \left| \begin{array}{l} \lambda_1 \\ \lambda_2 \end{array} = - \beta \pm j\omega \right.$

Fig.5 shows the form of the sensitivity functions for the steady state discrete filter. Numeric values are those corresponding to the ship considered in fig.1 and in fig.4.

It is easy to show that the filter performances are very sensitive to variations of parameters ω_o and σ_Q and not very sensitive to variations of the parameter z.

ω_o is a well known parameter : the natural frequency in rolling motion at small amplitudes is nearly constant. The damping parameter is a function of sea conditions (wave height and lenght) and of the relative ship and waves position. Therefore, the variance σ_Q^2 of the bias included in the dynamics must be identified.

Adaptative parameter identification

It has been shown by Mehra that a necessary and sufficent condition for the optimality of the Kalman filter is that the innovation sequence be white. The assumption made in arriving at this result was that the Φ matrix of the system was known and the variances of the state and observation noise sequences were to be identified.

In the problem considered, we can assum that R is known (off line analysis of the noises on the measure by gyroscopic instrument and accelerometers). The values of z and ω_o can be determined by a sensitivity study.

We now consider the innovation sequence r_i

$$r_k = z_k - H_k \hat{x}_k^{k-1}$$

which has a theorical covariance $(H_k P_{k/k-1} H_k^T + R_k)$

If we notice that the actual covariance of r_k is much larger than $(H_k P_{k/k-1} H_k^T + R_k)$ obtained from the Kalman filter, then the process noise covariance Q should be increase.

An equation for Q can be written

$$H P_{k/k-1} H^T + R = H[\Phi P_{k-1/k-1} \Phi^T + Q] H^T + R = E[r_k r_k^T]$$

$$HQH^T = E[r_k r_k^T] - H\Phi P_{k-1/k-1} \Phi^T H^T - R$$

$$\sigma_Q^2 = \frac{1}{q_{11}} \left[F(r_k r_k^T) - (\varphi_1^2 P_{11} + 2\varphi_1 \varphi_2 P_{12} + \varphi_2^2 P_{22}) - \sigma_R^2 \right]$$

with $\Phi(k+1,k) = \begin{vmatrix} \varphi_1 & \varphi_2 \\ \varphi_3 & \varphi_4 \end{vmatrix}$ and $P_{k-1/k-1} = \begin{vmatrix} P_{11} & P_{12} \\ P_{12} & P_{22} \end{vmatrix}$

q_{11} is a function of β and ω_o .

Notice that $P_{k-1/k-1}$ do not represent the actual error covariance. Correlation methods can also be used. They are not developed here.

CONCLUSION

Different approaches to the characterization and identification in real time of the motions of ships in confused seas have been described. The essential idea is that the motions are very nearly linear and gaussian and that, therefore, the direct application of the theory of Kalman filtering is possible. Applications to prediction in real time of the response of the ship and to estimation of parameters of ship motions have been presented. Applications of the method are possible for the correlation of stresses in structural members or for problems of stabilization.

REFERENCES

(1) JAZWINSKI A.H."Stochastic process and Filtering Theory" Academic Press - NEW YORK - 1970

(2) BUCY R.S.and JOSEPH P.D "Filtering for Stochastic Processes with Applications to Guidance" Interscience publishers. NEW YORK - 1968

(3) KORVIN-KROUKOVSKY S.V. "Theory of Seakeeping" - The Society of Naval Architects and Marine Engineers - NEW YORK - 1961

(4) BOZZO C. LEGRAND W. "Différents aspects des problèmes de Modélisation et de sensibilité en filtrage linéaire" Journées sur le filtrage numérique et ses applications - Proceedings - TOULON - 1972

(5) BOZZO C. "Notion de transformée de Laguerre d'un signal continu"
RAIRO J1 page 35 Dunod - PARIS - 1972

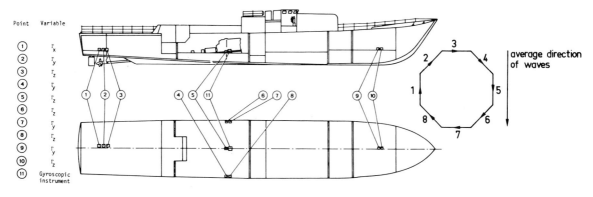

Locations of Instruments

Figure 1

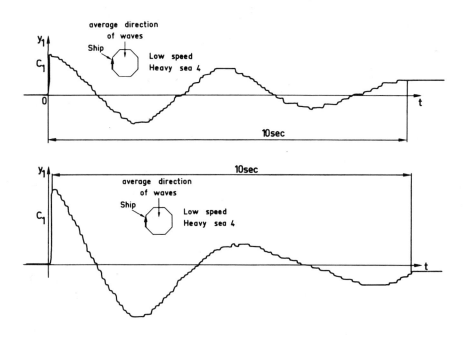

average direction of waves

Ship

Low speed
Heavy sea 4

C_1

y_1

0

t

10sec

---

average direction of waves

10sec

Ship

Low speed
Heavy sea 4

C_1

y_1

t

Figure 2

1 Maximum			2 Maxima			3 Maxima			1 Maximum			2 Maxima			3 Maxima		
Obser-vation	Characte-ristics	Frequencies of the maxima	Obser-vation	Characte-ristics	Frequencies of the maxima	Obser-vation	Characte-ristics	Frequencies of the maxima	Obser-vation	Characte-ristics	Frequencies of the maxima	Obser-vation	Characte-ristics	Frequencies of the maxima	Obser-vation	Characte-ristics	Frequencies of the maxima
1		0,2	3		0,1 0,2	12		0,01 0,06	4		0,07	6		0,18 0,25	1		0,12 0,25 0,21
2		0,2	4		0,075 0,2	11		0,05	8		0,07	7		0,18 0,27	2		0,16 0,25 0,23
6		0,2	8		0,07 0,2	10		0,1 0,1 0,07	5		0,1	19		0,26 0,08	3		0,1 0,3 0,25
7		0,2	5		0,1 0,2	9		0,15 0,1	12		0,05	22		0,24 0,31	9		0,08 0,35 0,28
13		0,2	26		0,08 0,22	19		0,03 0,22	11		0,05	31		0,26 0,36	25		0,17 0,36 0,16
23		0,22	32		0,22 0,29	18		0,12 0,07 0,22	10		0,07	30		0,33 0,2	13		0,29 0,13 0,22
24		0,22	35		0,03 0,22	17		0,03 0,8 0,21	18		0,05	41		0,25 0,34	15		0,12 0,19 0,33
25		0,22	28		0,03 0,22	16		0,03 0,15 0,22	17		0,02				21		0,17 0,06 0,32
27		0,2	43		0,01 0,22	20		0,15 0,22	16		0,05				33		0,32 0,19 0,24
21		0,22	15		0,12 0,22	29		0,03 0,18 0,24	23		0,25				35		0,03
22		0,22	36		0,03 0,22	42		0,22 0,1	24		0,25				44		0,03
31		0,21							26		0,08				29		0,19 0,24 0,13 0,32
33		0,2							27		0,07				37		0,12 0,26 0,2
34		0,2							20		0,08						
30		0,22							32		0,3						
41		0,25							34		0,07						
37		0,22							28		0,05						
38		0,21							45		0,27						
39		0,24							43		0,03						
40		0,22							38		0,25						
									40		0,3						

Low speed
Average speed
High speed

Heavy sea (3 to 4)
Light sea (1 to 2)

Figure 3

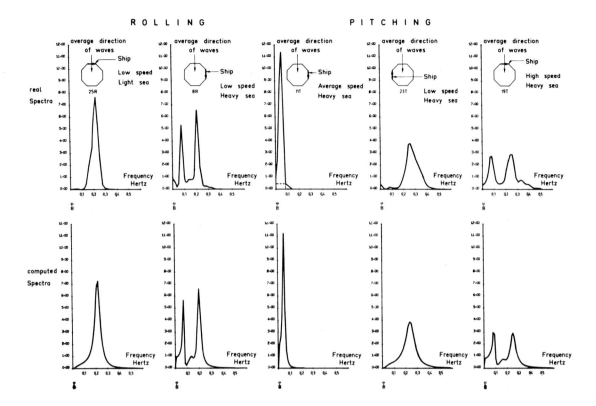

Figure 4

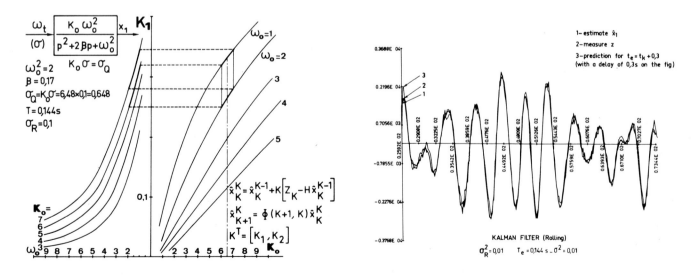

Figure 5

Figure 6

ON THE CONTROL OF A SUBMERGED VESSEL USING THE SIDESLIP ANGLE

ESTIMATED BY AN OBSERVER

Yoichi Ogawara

Control Research Laboratory
Kobe Technical Institute,
Mitsubishi Heavy Industries, Ltd.
Kobe, Japan

ABSTRACT

A ship motion in a horizontal plne is affected
largely with its sideslip angle, but as the sideslip angle is difficult to measure, it has been
not used for the cotrol of a ship motion. In this
paper it is investigated with the simulation to
estimate the sideslip angle from obtainable variables by an observer, and to use the estimated
sideslip angle for the autopilot system. The subject vessel is a submarine ore carrier, and its
automatic course control and the method to correct
the effect to the depth and the pitch angle in the
turning motion are inquired. There is a fair prospect of practical use.

INTRODUCTION

The automatic course control apparatus of a ship
has been constructed with the feedback of the yaw
angle and the yaw rate. On the other hand, when a
submerged vessel turns, its longitudinal motion is
affected by the sidewash effect. Then the depth
and the pitch angle of the vessel change. This effect is corrected by adjusting the angle of the
fairwater plane and that of the stern plane relatively to the rudder angle and the yaw rate.

These methods are not sufficient. As hydrodynamic
forces acting on the vessel in the lateral motion
are caused largely by the sideslip angle and the
yaw rate of the vessel, it is the suitable method
to use these variables as feedback signals or as
the inputs to the sidewash compensator. But the
sideslip angle has not been used on account of
difficulty to observe. As a result of this, in the
automatic course control system the feedback gain
of the yaw rate should be very large in order to
eliminate the overshoot at the course change, and
to restrain the steady-state error in the long
periodic disturbance by tidal current. This is not
desirable for the noise reduction in the apparatus.
Though the turning effect is corrected by the simple method as has been stated, the compensation is
not enough in the transient state.

Here it is tried with simulation to estimate the
sideslip angle by an observer and to use it to the
control of the vessel as the first step to the
practical use. The subject vessel is a submarine
ore carrier. The simulation study was conducted

with an analog and a digital computers.

SUBJECT VESSEL

Until now various kinds of submerged vessels such
as a submerged tanker, a submerged cargo boat and
a submarine ore carrier have been designed or
proposed. Here the subject vessel is supposed as a
submarine ore carrier. The principal particulars
are decided refering to the submarine ore carrier
designed in England which is considered to be one
of the vessels making the best use of the characteristics of a submerged vessel.[1]

The rough arrangement of the model is shown in Fig.
1 and the principal particulars are shown in Table
1. A parallel middle body forms 29.4 % of the
length overall, and it has a cylindrical section.
On the upper part of the parallel middle body
there is a superstructure with a cargo hatchway.
In front of the superstructure there is a conning
tower. The depth and the pitch angle of a vessel
is controlled with both a fairwater plane installed on the side of the conning tower and a stern
plane, and the course control is conducted with a
rudder. Derivatives of equations of motion were
obtained with the wind tunnel test of the model
and with the reference to the results of similar
actual ship tests carried out up to this time. The
details are omitted here. Coefficients of equations
of motion described in the following section are
shown in Table 2.

OBSERVER

Formulae of Observer

The method of the estimation of the state variables of a linear system with the obtainable inputs
and outputs is divided into two main classes, that
is, the one is a stochastical dealing and the
other is a deterministic dealing. The former is
well known as "Kalman-Bucy filter" considering the
existence of noise. The latter has been proposed
by D.G.Luenberger and it has been formulated as
"Observer". The both are the way to estimate system parameters with a filter from observable variables instead of using a differentiation or a
model.

An observer has the following characteristics.

1. An observer is by itself a linear system. (But recently a nonlinear observer is investigated.)
2. To the n dimensional control system, an observer can be constructed as less than n dimensional system.
3. An observer can be utilized in several problems concerning with the deterministic linear system.
4. It is considered that the observer is less affected by an initial value in the parameter estimation than the method using a model of a system.

Considering these characteristics it is decided to use an observer for the sideslip angle estimation.

An observer is given as follows.[2] The system to be observed is supposed to be linear and to be expressed by the following equation.

$$\dot{x} = Ax + Bu \tag{1}$$

where x is an n state vector, u is a r control vector, A is an n×n matrix and B is an n×r matrix. Suppose an observable state vector y, and y is obtained from x by the equation (2).

$$y = Cx \tag{2}$$

where y is a p output vector and C is a p×n matrix. Assume that n ≥ p and rank C = p. In this time the estimated state vector $\tilde{x}$ is obtained from the equation (3).

$$\left.\begin{array}{l} \dot{z} = Dz + Ey + Gu \\ TA - DT = EC \\ G = TB \\ \tilde{x} = \begin{pmatrix} C \\ T \end{pmatrix}^{-1} \begin{pmatrix} y \\ z \end{pmatrix} \end{array}\right\} \tag{3}$$

where z is an n-p vector, D is an n-p × n-p matrix, E is an n-p × p matrix, G is an n-p × r matrix and T is an n-p × n matrix.

Suppose that initial values of z and x to be $z(0)$ and $x(0)$ respectively, then the following equation is obtained.

$$z(t) = Tx(t) + e^{DT}\left[z(0) - Tx(0)\right] \tag{4}$$

That is, if the relation

$$z(0) = Tx(0) \tag{5}$$

is satisfied, from (4) and (5) the constant linear transformation

$$z(t) = Tx(t) \tag{6}$$

is obtained. The equation (5) is a desirable initial condition for an observer. When the condition (5) is not satisfied, an error in a transient state occurs according to the equation (4).

Estimation of The Sideslip Angle

Suppose axes of coordinates shown in Fig. 2 for the description of a motion of a submerged vessel in a horizontal plane. In Fig. 2 a frame of reference o'x'y' is fixed to the earth, and that of

oxy is fixed to a submerged vessel and moves with it. A center of gravity of a vessel is assumed to coincide with the origin o. Assuming the small perturbation from the reference steady state, the equations of a submerged vessel lateral motion can be linearized as follows.

$$\left.\begin{array}{l} D_1 V\dot{\beta} + D_2 V^2\beta + D_3\ddot{\psi} + D_4 V\dot{\psi} = D_{13} V^2\beta_r \\ E_1 V\dot{\beta} + E_2 V^2\beta + E_3\ddot{\psi} + E_4 V\dot{\psi} = E_{13} V^2\beta_r \end{array}\right\} \tag{7}$$

where $D_1, \ldots, D_{13}, E_1, \ldots, E_{13}$ are coefficients of equations of motion, V is the advance speed of a vessel, β is the sideslip angle, ψ is the yaw angle and β_r is the rudder angle. The rolling of a vessel is neglected considering that it has little effect on the turning motion.

Suppose that

$$\left.\begin{array}{l} x = \text{col.}(\beta, \psi, \dot{\psi}) \\ u = \beta_r \end{array}\right\} \tag{8}$$

then the equation (7) is expressed in the form of the equation (1) using the following matrices A and B.

$$\left.\begin{array}{l} A = \begin{pmatrix} a_{11} & 0 & a_{13} \\ 0 & 0 & 1 \\ a_{31} & 0 & a_{33} \end{pmatrix} \\ B = \text{col.}(b_1, 0, b_3) \end{array}\right\} \tag{9}$$

where

$$\begin{array}{ll} a_{11} = -V(D_2 E_3 - D_3 E_2)/\Delta & \Delta = D_1 E_3 - D_3 E_1 \\ a_{13} = -(D_4 E_3 - D_3 E_4)/\Delta & \\ a_{31} = -V^2(D_1 E_2 - D_2 E_1)/\Delta & \\ a_{33} = -V(D_1 E_4 - D_4 E_1)/\Delta & \\ b_1 = V(D_{13} E_3 - D_3 E_{13})/\Delta & \\ b_3 = V^2(D_1 E_{13} - D_{13} E_1)/\Delta & \end{array}$$

As the yaw angle ψ and the yaw rate $\dot{\psi}$ can be measured, the output equation (2) takes the form

$$\left.\begin{array}{l} y = \text{col.}(\psi, \dot{\psi}) \\ C = \begin{pmatrix} 0 & 1 & 0 \\ 0 & 0 & 1 \end{pmatrix} \end{array}\right\} \tag{10}$$

so that in the equation (3), n = 3, r = 1, p = 2 and the dimension of the observer is 1.
Let

$$\left.\begin{array}{l} D = D \\ E = (\tilde{E}_1, \tilde{E}_2) \\ T = (T_1, T_2, T_3) \end{array}\right\} \tag{11}$$

then the estimated sideslip angle $\tilde{\beta}$ is given by the following observer system.

$$\dot{Z} = DZ + \widetilde{E}_1 \psi + \widetilde{E}_2 \dot{\psi} + G \beta_r$$

$$\widetilde{\beta} = l_1 \psi + l_2 \dot{\psi} + l_3 Z \qquad \Bigg\} \quad (12)$$

where

$$G = b_1 T_1 + b_3 T_3$$
$$l_1 = -T_2/T_1, \quad l_2 = -T_3/T_1, \quad l_3 = 1/T_1$$
$$T_1 = -a_{31}(\widetilde{E}_1/D + \widetilde{E}_2)/\gamma$$
$$T_2 = -\widetilde{E}_1/D$$
$$T_3 = (a_{11} - D)(\widetilde{E}_1/D + \widetilde{E}_2)/\gamma$$
$$\gamma = (a_{11} - D)(a_{33} - D) - a_{13}a_{31}$$

Decision of Coefficients of The Observer System

As seen in the equation (3), there are several parameters which cannot be decided uniquely. In this case these parameters are D, $\widetilde{E}_1$ and $\widetilde{E}_2$. A method to decide them suitably has not been found. Here it is tried to decide them considering the following.
1. D governs the decay of an arror owing to an initial value as seen in the equation (4), so that it should be decided without obstruction in relation to the response speed of the controlled system.
2. These parameters must be arranged so that the coefficients of the equation (12) may be neither very large nor very small beyond the restriction of the hardware which constructs the observer.

On the other hand though the equations of motion of a vessel are linear as shown in the equation (7), those coefficients vary according to the vessel advance speed, so that the coefficients of the observer should be altered simultaneously with the advance speed. The response characteristics of a submerged vessel to the rudder angle input approximates to the first order lag. The time constant T varies as shown in Fig. 3 according to the vessel advance speed V. From Fig. 3 it is found that the relation between T and V is

$$1/T \propto V \qquad (13)$$

As has been stated $1/D$ corresponds to the time constant of the observer system, so that it seems to be reasonable for D to be in proportion to $1/T$, that is

$$D \propto V \qquad (14)$$

Moreover in order that the change of the coefficients of the observer to the vessel advance speed can be done as briefly as possible, $\widetilde{E}_1$ and $\widetilde{E}_2$ are selected in the following way.

$$\widetilde{E}_1 \propto V$$

$$\widetilde{E}_2 = \text{const. to } V \qquad \Bigg\} \quad (15)$$

From the equation (14) and (15), the equation (12) can be expressed in the following form.

$$\dot{Z} = V(k_D Z + k_{E1} \psi + k_G \beta_r) + k_{E2} \dot{\psi}$$

$$\widetilde{\beta} = k_{11} \psi + \dot{\psi}/(k_{12}V) + k_{13} Z \qquad \Bigg\} \quad (16)$$

where k_D, k_{E1},..., k_{13} are constant coefficients to V.

AUTOMATIC COURSE CONTROL

Here the estimation of the sideslip angle with the observer is investigated on the automatic course control system. First the coefficients of the observer system were calculated according to the given values of D, $\widetilde{E}_1$ and $\widetilde{E}_2$. D, $\widetilde{E}_1$ and $\widetilde{E}_2$ were changed in the following range respectively.
$$D = -1/(0.1 \text{ T}) \sim -1/(5T) \quad \text{sec}^{-1}$$
$$\widetilde{E}_1 = 0.1 \sim 20.0 \quad \text{sec}^{-1}$$
$$\widetilde{E}_2 = 0.1 \sim 20.0$$
The effect of V was also inquired in the range of $5 \sim 25$ knots. From the results of these calculations the parameters of the observer are decided as follows.
$$D = -1/(0.5 \text{ T}) \quad \text{sec}^{-1}$$
$$\widetilde{E}_1 = 0.3 \quad \text{sec}^{-1} \text{ when } V = 15 \text{ knots.}$$
$$\widetilde{E}_2 = 1.0$$
The block diagram of the automatic course control system which uses an estimated sideslip angle together with the yaw angle and the yaw rate is shown in Fig. 4. The steering servomechanism approximates to the first order lag system with a time constant of 1 sec. The rudder angle is restricted within $\pm$ 20 deg. to prevent a vessel from an excess turning. The result of the simulation is shown in Fig. 5. This is one example when $V = 15$ knots. Coefficients of the observer in this case are shown in Table 3. The feedback gains are adjusted so that the yaw angle can reach the desired value in a minimum time without an overshoot. In this case $K_\psi = 4$, $K_{\dot{\psi}} = 5$ sec and $K_\beta = 5$. It is found that the sideslip angle is estimated by the observer very well. The result of the conventional system without the sideslip angle feedback is also shown in Fig. 5 compared with the proposed system here. In this case $K_\psi = 3$ and $K_{\dot{\psi}} = 50$ sec. The proposed system is superior to the conventional one as shown in Table 4. It is summarized as follows.
1. The response speed of the new system is faster than that of the conventional system.
2. The feedback gain of the yaw rate can be reduced without an overshoot of the yaw angle.
3. The satisfactory controllability can be obtained without changing the feedback gains according to the vessel advance speed. This is made sure in the range of $5 \sim 25$ knots for the subject vessel.

In the case shown in Fig. 5 the condition (5) is satisfied so that the sideslip angle can be estimated without an error in a transient state. But in general there is no assurance for the condition (5) to be realized. Now we investigate about the cases that the condition (5) is not satisfied. As one example it is assumed that the initial value of the yaw rate is 0.5 deg/sec with some disturbance when the initial value of Z is equal to 0. The result of the simulation is shown in Fig. 6. Here $\widetilde{E}_1$ and $\widetilde{E}_2$ are constant and equal to the values in the case of Fig. 5, and D is altered. The coefficients of the observer are shown in Table 3. It is found that when the absolute value of D becomes large, the estimated value converges to the exact value rapidly but the initial error becomes large owing to the values of coefficients, and that when the absolute value of D becomes small, the initial error becomes small but the convergence to the exact value is getting slow. In the setting of an initial value and the selection of coefficients as described here it seems to be desirable that D is selected to $- 1/T \sim - 1/(0.5T)$.

Besides, the effect of the disturbance affected by an ocean wave has been also investigated. The controllability of the new system is almost equivalent to that of the conventional system, and it has been found that there is no problem for the use of the estimated sideslip angle. The details are omitted here owing to limited space.

TURNING EFFECT COMPENSATION

There is interaction between the lateral and longitudinal modes of the submerged vessel.(3) This is the effect of bridge fairwater sidewash which causes lateral sideslip or yaw to produce downward forces that affect the depth and trim of the submerged vessel. The purpose of the turning effect compensation is to counteract this effect. The heaving force Z_{sw} and the pitching moment M_{sw} produced by the sidewash effect are given in the following forms.

$$\left.\begin{array}{l} Z_{sw} = - B_{21}V^2\beta^2 - B_{22}V\beta\dot\psi - B_{23}\dot\psi^2 \\ M_{sw} = - C_{21}V^2\beta^2 - C_{22}V\beta\dot\psi - C_{23}\dot\psi^2 \end{array}\right\} \quad (17)$$

where $B_{21},\ldots,B_{23},C_{21},\ldots,C_{23}$ are coefficients. On the other hand the longitudinal motion of a submerged vessel is expressed as follows.

$$\left.\begin{array}{l} B_3V\dot\alpha + B_4V^2\alpha + B_5\ddot\theta + B_6V\dot\theta \\ \quad = B_{11}V^2\beta_{ef} + B_{12}V^2\beta_{ea} + Z_{sw} \\ C_3V\dot\alpha + C_4V^2\alpha + C_5\ddot\theta + C_6V\dot\theta + C_7\theta \\ \quad = C_{11}V^2\beta_{ef} + C_{12}V^2\beta_{ea} + M_{sw} \\ \dot H = - V(\theta - \alpha) \end{array}\right\} \quad (18)$$

where axes of coordinates shown in Fig. 7 are taken, and assuming the small perturbation from the reference steady state, the equations of motion are linearized. $B_3,\ldots,B_{12},C_3,\ldots,C_{12}$ are coefficients of equations of motion, α is the attack angle, θ is the pitch angle, H is the depth, and β_{ef}, β_{ea} are the deflection of the fairwater plane and that of the stern plane respectively. Though strictly speaking there are the effect of the change of the vessel advance speed and that of the nonlinearity owing to the turning motion in this case, it is considered for them to have a minor effect and they are neglected.

The turning effect is compensated by making the force and moment equal to $-Z_{sw}$ and $-M_{sw}$ with the deflection of the fairwater plane and the stern plane by β_{efc} and β_{eac} respectively.

$$\left.\begin{array}{l} B_{11}V^2\beta_{efc} + B_{12}V^2\beta_{eac} = - Z_{sw} \\ C_{11}V^2\beta_{efc} + C_{12}V^2\beta_{eac} = - M_{sw} \end{array}\right\} \quad (19)$$

Until now as the sideslip angle cannot be obtained, it has been impossible to solve the equation (17) and (19) and to decide β_{efc} and β_{eac}. By this reason the following simpler computation process has been adopted. First, the relation between the constant rudder angle β_r and the final values of β and $\dot\psi$ to that β_r, and the required β_{efc} and β_{eac} to compensate Z_{sw} and M_{sw} yielded with the prescribed final value of β and $\dot\psi$ are computed. Then, the control signals corresponding to these computed β_{efc} and β_{eac} are given to the servomechanisms of the fairwater and stern plane through the first order lag elements which have a time constant equal to that of a vessel lateral motion. By this method the compensation is completly carried out at the final steady state, but at the transient state the desirable result cannot be obtained.

Here, it is tried to estimate the sideslip angle by the observer and to obtain the required β_{efc} and β_{eac} by solving the equation (17) and (19) directly. The block diagram of this process is shown in Fig. 8. The control system of a longitudinal motion of a vessel was investigated separately and was decided as shown in Fig.8. One example of the result is shown in Fig. 9 together with the usual method. The conditions adopted in Fig. 9 are as follows.
  V = 15 knots
  the input of the steering servomechanism
    = 8 deg (step input)
  parameters of the observer
    $D = -0.1$ sec^{-1}
    $\tilde E_1 = 0.3$ sec^{-1}
    $\tilde E_2 = 1.0$
The result of the controllability is shown in Table 5. The proposed method adopted herein has the desirable faculty to the compensation.

SUMMARY AND CONCLUSION

It is found that the method to estimate the sideslip angle by the observer and to use it to the automatic course control or to the turning effect compensation is effectual compared with the conventional way. Because the observer is a first order lag system, it seems to be comparatively easy for us to construct it as a hardware. Here, only the simulation study is carried out, but it is intended to apply this system to an actual vessel in future.

As problems remained for the practical use the followings should be inquired carefully.
1. A criterion to the decision of the observer parameters.
2. The effect of the estimation error in the coefficients of the equations of motion.
3. The nonlinear effect in the turning motion.

REFERENCES

(1) P.R. Crew, etc., "The Submarine Ore Carrier,"
    R.I.N.A., Vol.104, No. 4, 1962

(2) M.M. Newmann, "Optimal and sub-optimal control
    using an observer when some of the state varia-
    bles are not measurable," Int. J. Control,
    Vol. 9, No. 3, 1969

(3) R.J. Kochenburger, etc., "Alternative Autopilot
    Configurations for Automatic Submarine Control,"
    General Dynamics / Electric Boat, Research &
    Development Department, 1961

Table 3 Coefficients of observer   V = 15 kt.

D s^{-1}	$\widetilde{E}_1$ s^{-1}	$\widetilde{E}_2$	G s^{-1}	l_1	l_2 s	l_3
-1.0	0.3	1	0.003871	-29.88	-80.76	99.58
-0.5	0.3	1	0.005188	-19.92	-37.36	33.19
-0.2	0.3	1	-0.08778	0.7565	-11.32	-0.5044
-0.1	0.3	1	0.005268	-0.9262	-2.637	0.3087
-0.03333	0.3	1	-0.9219	-0.2617	3.150	0.02908
-0.02	0.3	1	-7.205	-0.06765	4.307	0.004510

Table 1 Principal particulars of subject vessel

Length overall (m)	170.0		
Breadth maximum (m)	22.0		
Displaced volume (m³)	47,497.0		
Center of buoyancy Ahead of midship (m)	7.720		
Over vessel's bottom (m)	11.113		
	F.P. *	S.P. **	R. ***
Total area (m²)	75.9	196.7	231.0
Movable part area (m²)	75.9	90.9	92.1
Designed speed (kt)	25.0		

* Fairwater plane
** Stern plane
*** Rudder

Table 2 Coefficients of equations of motion

B_3	143.7	C_3	2.936	D_1	143.8	E_1	-4.67
B_4	0.879	C_4	-0.411	D_2	1.265	E_2	1.0856
B_5	105.8	C_5	5705.0	D_3	-168.4	E_3	5830.0
B_6	-56.30	C_6	150.5	D_4	74.5	E_4	95.9
		C_7	12.74	D_{13}	-0.225	E_{13}	0.488
B_{11}	-0.171	C_{11}	0.167				
B_{12}	0.228	C_{12}	0.546				
B_{21}	-0.1339	C_{21}	-0.6008				
B_{22}	29.668	C_{22}	219.7				
B_{23}	-2822.3	C_{23}	-7917.3				

These coefficients are derived in the following
units.

β : rad α : rad
ψ : rad θ : rad
β_γ : rad H : m
V : m/s β_{ef} : rad
time : s β_{ea} : rad

Table 4 Comparison of characteristics of
automatic course control system

		Conventional method		Proposed method		
		K_ψ	$K_{\dot\psi}$ (s)	K_ψ	$K_{\dot\psi}$ (s)	K_β
Feedback gain	5 kt	1	65	4	5	5
V =	15 kt	3	50	4	5	5
	25 kt	5	35	4	5	5
Time constant (s) (Response speed)						
	5 kt	96		32		
V =	15 kt	20		10		
	25 kt	6		6		

Table 5 Comparison of result of turning effect
compensation   V = 15 kt , δ_γ = 8 deg

	without compensation	with compensation	
		Usual method	Proposed method
Max. depth change (m)	6.64	2.05	0.05
Max. pitch angle chnge (deg)	3.1	1.1	0.03

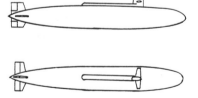

Fig. 1 Rough arrangement of subject
vessel

205

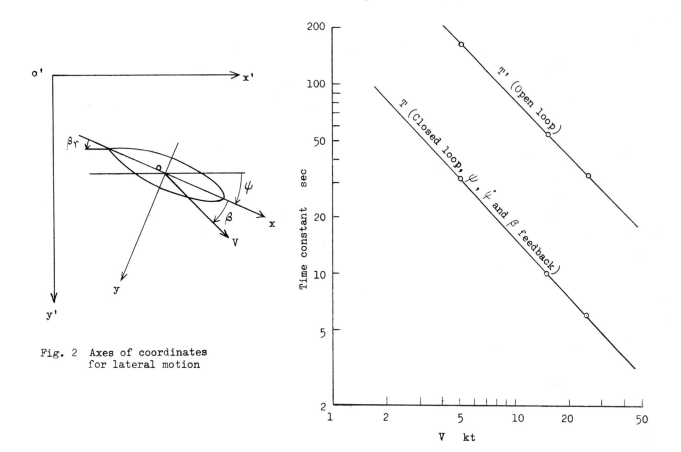

Fig. 2 Axes of coordinates
for lateral motion

Fig. 3 Time constant of response speed of subject
vessel

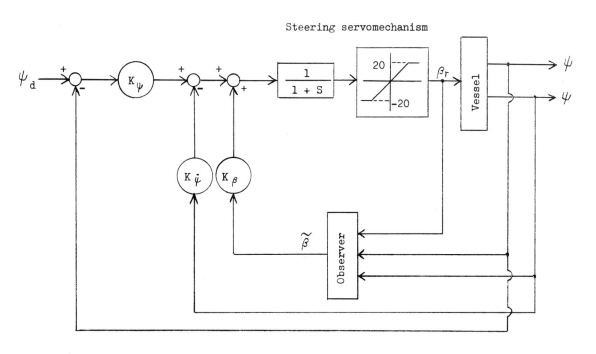

Fig. 4 Block diagram of automatic course control system

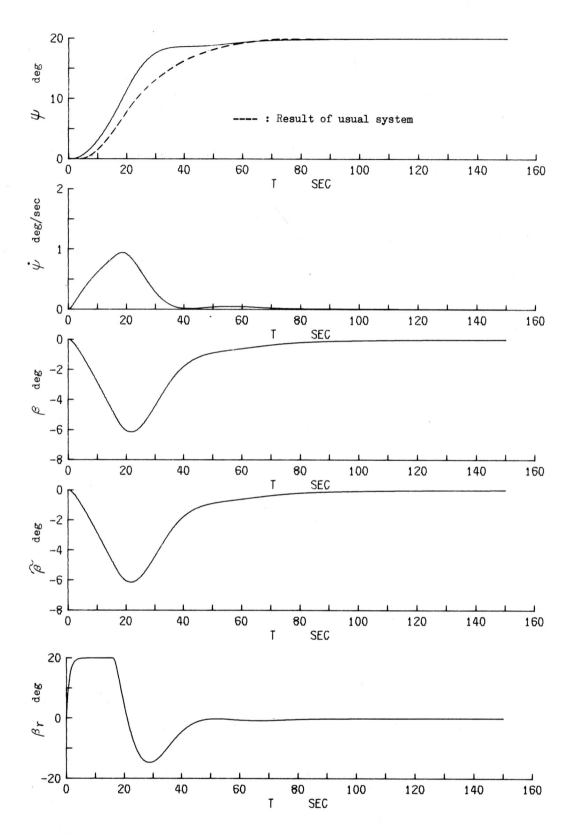

Fig. 5 Result of simulation of automatic course control system

V = 15 kt, ψ_d = 20 deg

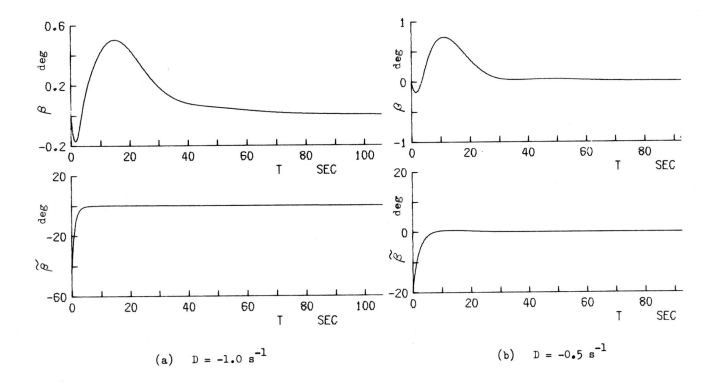

(a) $D = -1.0$ s^{-1}

(b) $D = -0.5$ s^{-1}

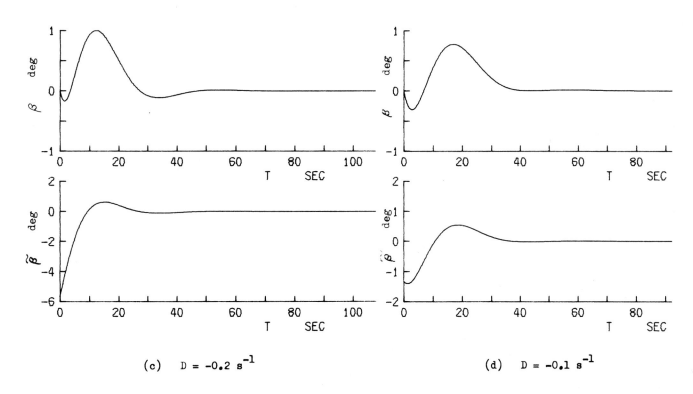

(c) $D = -0.2$ s^{-1}

(d) $D = -0.1$ s^{-1}

Fig. 6 Effect of observer coeffecients in estimation for course control
$V = 15$ kt , $\dot{\psi}(0) = 0.5$ deg/s , $\widetilde{E}_1 = 0.3$ s^{-1} , $\widetilde{E}_2 = 1.0$

208

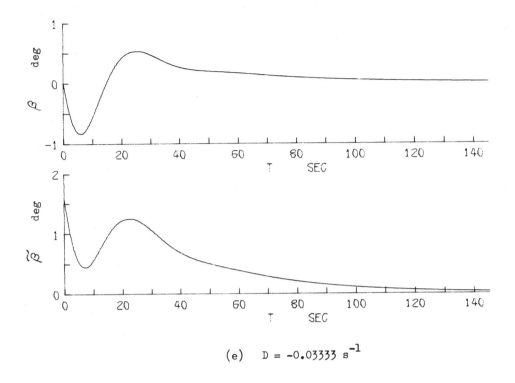

(e) $D = -0.03333 \text{ s}^{-1}$

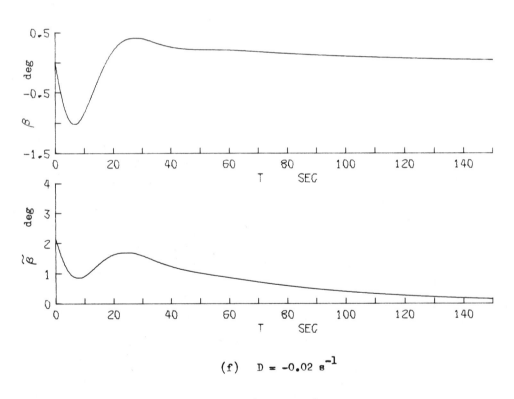

(f) $D = -0.02 \text{ s}^{-1}$

Fig. 6   (continued)

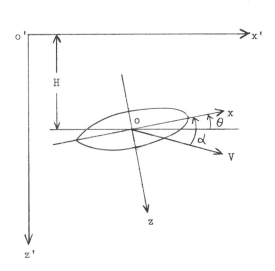

Fig. 7 Axes of coordinates
for longitudinal motion

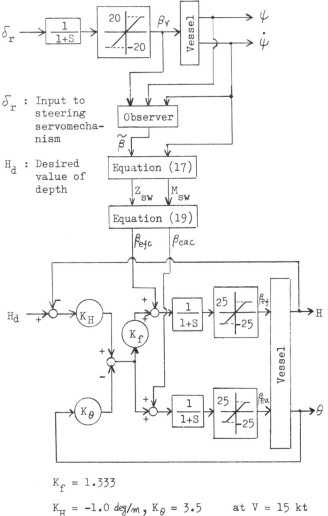

δ_r : Input to steering servomechanism

H_d : Desired value of depth

$K_f = 1.333$

$K_H = -1.0 \ deg/m$, $K_\theta = 3.5$ at $V = 15$ kt

Fig. 8 Block diagram of turning effect
compensation system

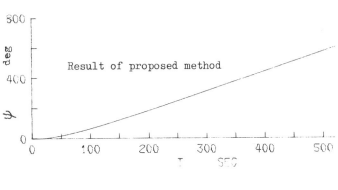

Result of proposed method

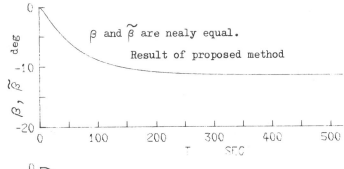

β and $\tilde{\beta}$ are nealy equal.
Result of proposed method

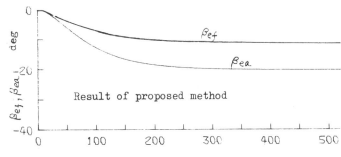

β_{ef}

β_{ea}

Result of proposed method

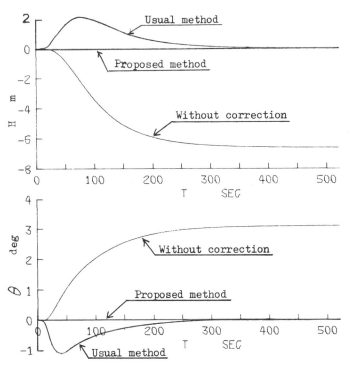

Usual method

Proposed method

Without correction

Without correction

Proposed method

Usual method

Fig. 9 Result of simulation of turning effect
compensation $V = 15$ kt , $\delta_r = 8$ deg

OPTIMAL MANAGEMENT POLICIES FOR SHIP'S ENGINE SYSTEMS
"An automated Decision- maker under optimal maintenance policy"

P. Dagnino, G. Soncin, A. Tiano
Laboratorio per l'Automazione Navale
National Council of Researches
Genoa, Italy

ABSTRACT

A criterion for performing the controlled maintenance is proposed in this paper.
The approach refers to a diesel main engine system, for which a failure functional model is presented.
The method employs a simulation model for starting
the maintenance procedure and for forecasting, during the real operation of plant, the failures or
the effects of maintenance actions.
The mathematical hypothesis about the system's deterioration process are discussed.
A few hints on automated failure diagnostic and
naintenance decision are also given hereafter.

INTRODUCTION

A new criterion for the implementation of an automated maintenance decision-maker is presented hereafter. No attempt to show even intermediate solutions
is made in this paper, since our research project
is still in its initial stages. Nevertheless, earlier
applications of such a criterion are eagerly expected
in the near future and some contacts with other technical and shipping staffs are about to be taken in
order to realize a concrete joint plan.

AN APPROACH TO THE GENERAL PROBLEM OF DATA ACQUISITION

Any statistical analysis on the behaviour of a ship,
regarded as a system, and in particular about the
ship's propulsion engine, as her sub-system, requires a great deal of data, opportunely chosen, accurately acquired and continually updated.
But those data, for motives we need not to discuss
here, are not usually available but a few and often
show their unreliability, because "retouched" for
misunderstood reasons of convenience. Thus, the
task of the statistician and researcher, ever star-
ving for data, becomes almost frantic in the general
techno-economic context of Ship's Management.
Nevertheless that job has to be done anyway: it
then appears to be reasonable and realistical some

criterion for the Simulation of the system behaviour, with respect to its faults and failures, in
order to supply the predictable initial deficien-
cy of collected data.
Even the technical and scientific literature about
the most recent theory and techniques of reliability and maintenability applied to ship's propulsion engine is lacking or hardly accessible, particularly when concerned with unmanned engine rooms
during the whole 24-hours.
In this paper, the objective is to develop a comprehensive survey of a new heuristic approach to
the solution of the problem which arise from the
scarce availability and trustworthiness of collected data, previously taken into account, in order
to start a statistical analysis of general failures and maintenance interferences on ship's engine
operation.
Such an approach makes use of a Simulation of the
real controlled system operation, of its perturbations and of all decisional actions that can be
performed on the engine to preserve its reliability and operational efficiency.
A new possible implementation of the continual
observation of the state of any component or significant unit belonging to such sub-system, during
its real or its simulated operation, is introduced
and described hereon, in order to determine a system state index at any instant.
A sequence of such state indexes, suitably ordered,
together with a proper sequence of decision indexes,
are consequently meant for the prediction of components Reliability and System Availability obtainable through the prognosis of failing states.
The same index sequences are also used for the
next phase of seeking an Optimal Surveillance-
Maintenance Policy, according to Derman's basis
and under a Markovian Deterioration hypothesis, in
order to point out the whole some advantages of a
Controlled Maintenance Criterion over the conventional routine-programmed maintenace procedure.
This work refers to an automated ship's propulsion
plant (powered by a large-bore, slow, two-stroke,

single acting, supercharged Diesel Engine) equipped with a central process computer which, of course, has fully available knowledge of all, or almost all, the parameters requested for the state identification of the component blocks considered and, thus, of the whole system.

The same criterion can be obviously applied to a steam or gas turbine marine plant as well.

Further data we might need for the computerization, when specifically meant for fault-monitoring, are to be taken by suitable sensors and transducers already existing on the market or some-how easily to design by a specialist.

Immediate purpose of such elaboration of the data so available is to acquire all informations about the deterioration process of a component block,to make the progressive forecasts of its failures and, eventually, to provide the programmed directions for its preventive maintenance or repair. Such instructions must take into account all constraints imposed by ship's service and safety rules, by any maintenance priority, by a certain shifting hierarchy of failures, by the actual availability of spare parts in the ship's stores of shipboard facilities and handy technical staff. Moreover, this procedure is supposed to suggest the requisitions of spares, to be forwarded to the Company's Office, and is to provide the prompt recording of all significant data and events to be next used in a statistical analysis of ship's engine behaviour, with respect to failures, and of the costs of ship's engine maintenance and operation.

The simulation criterion, hereafter presented, pursues a double goal: it begins to supply a former set of sufficiently reliable data, as first reference, it then proceeds to corroborate, sharpen or deny them by means of the adaptive system feedback. It also provides, on board of ship, an implement for a statistical prediction of the ship's engine behaviour, as a controlled system, in its evolution from one state to another of its operating cycle.

Extremely interesting, besides that, is the capability of the system to attain, by means of a relatively simple stretch-out of its earlier programme, a fast function of diagnostic of the simulated system operation and/or of the real system actual operation.

Yet, the most important feature to be noticed remains the final opportunity to implement a decisional function, through an automated decision programmed-device following the diagnostic device,organized and planned so that the most advisable action can be suggested and/or simulated, at any time, according to the optimal maintenance policy.

REAL ENGINE SYSTEM MODELLING

In fig. 1 is shown a diagrammatic arrangement of

the ship's propulsion plant, composed of a 12.000 HP, at 133 RPM, 8 cylinder, 2-stroke Diesel Engine and its auxiliaries.

The particular distribution of blocks reflects the engine behaviour, with respect to its failure, and justify the fact that a failing block inserted in a certain modular unity doesn't directly interfer with other units, while prevents the operation of the following blocks of its own unit: that is a shunt-series connection is justified.

It's expedient to point out that said blocks are empty of any controllistic significance, which we are not concerned with right now, while they have a mere logical relevance.

SYSTEM SIMULATION MODELLING

Some attempts to build up an effectual mathematical model, based on classic Reliability Theory,showed up their draw-backs, as soon as we moved away from simpler systems with a number of components.

While the complexity of such systems as ship's main engine plants causes the formulization to become cumbersome and produces such a massive computational overwork that not even a large and powerful electronic computer can be able to carry out, though on long terms.

However, fault and failure prediction obtainable from reliability considerations, can't be but little accurate and below the aims of this work, though it remains remarkably important in the study of ship's general management.

The other classic approach, through Stochastic Control, since it requires full knowledge of the transfer function of any component block, appears to be clearly unfeasible: indeed, while for some of said blocks we might find a certain transfer function, for most of them we aren't even able to formulize the physical aspect of their process involving chemical, mechanical, electrical and thermodynamic phenomena.

Thus, to represent our large-scale system we have been compelled to adopt a stochastical model for the simulation of ship's engine operation, its failure diagnostic and decision making.

Referring to Fig. 2 we shall outline the whole logical scheme of the decision procedure we proposed.

We can see, in detail, that within the so called "simulated system" there are two separate blocks: the first one stands for ship's engine supposed to be free of failures, while the other represents a "failure source" or "fault generator".

The "failure-free system" block has two vectorized inputs: the reference vector $[X]$, i.e. the set of all setpoints or references controlled by the central processor, and the "off-limits" probability $P_X(x)$, viz the integral probability that the value of unfailing output of component block is kept within a $X_i \pm \delta x_i$ interval, properly fixed. Such probability P_X makes it possible to reckon the variance σ_X of a certain gaussian distribution, having $\bar{X}$ for mean and mode, which characterizes the steady state control error ε, or, in another scale, the undisturbed block output X.

The "failure source" block, analogously, has two vectorized inputs: the mean value $\bar{Y}$ of the fault-noise magnitude, which being a function of time so takes into account the "aging" of the component block, and the probability P_Y (y), where the quantity $(1-P_Y)$ is the probability that the fault-noise reaches a certain threshold so to exhibit the presence of failure.

In fact we define failure, according to its ethymology, as the event after whose occurence an unaccettable shifting of the output characteristics of components out of the prescribed ranges of tolerance arises and becomes detectable. This way we may consider failures at any level: from the light malfunctioning or anomaly, through various degrees of stated failures, to final or catastrophic failure or breakdown.

The two blocks previously mentioned then have as vectorized outputs, respectively, the unperturbated outputs and fault additive noise distribution. We then proceed to an algebraic sum of homonymous vector components, under hypothesis of linearity, for the two stochastic independent variables X and Y, so to obtain a new random variable Z=X+Y stochastically distributed according a new gaussian pattern and having P_Z (z) as density function. Where:

$$P_Z(z) = P_X(x) * P_Y(y) = \int p(x) \cdot p(z-x)\, dx$$

is the convolution of the two original density functions.

The resulting distribution of r.v. Z, has then the following parameters:

$$\bar{Z} = E(z) = \int z \cdot p(z)\, dz$$

$$\sigma_Z = \left[\sigma_X^2 + \sigma_y^2 \right]^{1/2}$$

Such gaussian distribution, resulting sum of the two indipendent former distributions, is then used as imput to next logical block, which provides at the output, through standard guided Monte Carlo Simulation Method of Congruence, a sequence of random distributed values of the magnitude for any simulated quantity, as time goes by.

It's to note that, within every component block, one or more physical quantities are considered and so measured to characterize the block behaviour or performance. All these measures are carried out by a system of sensors and transducers interfaced with the central processor input. This can be done as partial simulation on board of ship or as full simulation on a shore computer.

At this stage is clearly feasible to calculate or estimate the Performance Index for any component Block (B.P.I.).

Besides, the State index Y_t of the whole system, consisting of a number of orderly sets of such component blocks according structural groups and modules, can be now obtained by means of an apt superposition of the single normalized performance indexes.

The value of said system state index Y_t, so obtained, is then fed into the logic block for the "diagnostic" whenever it appears to be abnormal i.e. $\neq 0$: in such a case, that implies that one or more block performance indexes have gone out of the range of permissible variability. Then, on account of the particular built-in connection, every time that $Y_t \neq 0$, all the necessary informations are automatically demanded and received by the diagnostic block, in order to realize the failure and find out its cause through its effects.

SIMULATED OBSERVATIONS PROGRAM

The simulation criterion used can be accepted as a first approximation, since only by means of the data obtained during the plant operation it will be possible to decide whether or not the gaussian distribution is fit.

Afterwards, by system's story, reconstructed according to stored data, we can analyse different distributions which reflect as faithfully as possible the best failure model with respect of the actual phenomena.

According to fig. 3, we have a tabulation representing an intermediate result from which it is possible to calculate all the Availability parameters.

Besides, we can draw, although under the hypothesis of instantaneous repair and maintenance actions, the following quantities referred to every component block:

a) rate of failures (at different levels, from light faults up to the final one) and their distribution

b) mean time between failures and their distribution

c) corresponding failures flow; where the term flow stands for a certain sequence of failures.

Moreover, such distributions would verify the validity of the Markovian Deterioration hypothesis hereafter presented and, at the same time, justify the Poissonian model of failure.

Then, although as first approximation, this procedure allows us the permanence time in every marginal state, from which particular costs and penalties can be derived.

Besides, we can draw how many times, in every operating cycle, the system moves into a certain state and how long it would take to reach the condition identifying such a state. That is meaningful

expecially when it concerns the final absorbing
state, which actually is a pseudo-absorbing one,
because only repairable systems are considered
hereby.
Disposing now of a good deal of results, in connection with the particular quantization's step and
sampling frequence chosen, the transition probabilities from a state to another and the mean stay
time in every state can be drawn.
Along with this simulation an operative period of
about one year, spread over some hundreds of various width temporal units, has been considered.
As a final result, an identification of the
system's observed state is accomplished
$(Y_t /t=0,1,...)$ and a classification among the
possible decisions $(D_i, {}_{jk})$ is performed.
Once the above parameters are known, it becomes
feasible, indeed, to formulate and solve the befo-
re-mentioned dynamic programming problem, seeking
an optimal maintenance policy. Such an optimum
being considered in the minimization of both system
unavailability and expected repair costs.

OBSERVED STATES CLASSIFICATION

The observation's block performs firstly a quasi-
qualitative appraisal of system state, based on
the analysis of a set of measured and discretized
quantities, and then proceeds to quantify its
observation according to a prearranged code.
For istance, it might be convenient to assign for
the system conditions:
'state 0' to Main Engine Plant at the beginning of
         a new operating cycle
'state 1' to the conditions in which the systems
         is found after general maintenance or
         repair requiring substitutions
'state 2' in presence of a light and/or temporary
         failure, without secondary effects, that
         neither requires urgent repairs nor bia-
         ses engine efficiency
'state 3' to system suffering one or more light
         failures or faults, with possible secon-
         dary effects, but not yet requiring
         immediate works (tipically, cleaning)
'state 4' after maintenance work and general
         checkout of unities
'state 5' after standard works on failed unities
         only
'state 6' after major maintenance, repairs, repla-
         cements, before check up or testing
'state 7' in presence of a failure requiring
         supporting maintenance and next but not
         immediate repair
'state 8' in presence of a light failure requiring
         urgent but not immediate maintenance
'state 9' in presence of a serious, or multiple
         failure.
However, it's not easy to tell, a priori, which

one is the best among all possible criteria of
assignation of level indexes to observed states.
It is noticeable that the "decision" block optimi-
zes its "suggested actions" taking into account
the general operative and environmental conditions,
the real ship's service constraints and the actually available resources.
Much easier it can be the definition of possible
decision indexes, such as:
with no break in on the engine
'decision 0' keep on standard alert
'decision 1' intensify alert on disturbed block
'decision 2' start extended and intensified alert
            on engine section
'decision 3' as before, but on the whole engine
            and with visit planning (all constra-
            ints satisfied)
'decision 4' as before, but with none but emergency or manoeuvring constraints
emergency situation
'decision 5' break in on the engine right away
            (no constraint but safety)

DIAGNOSTIC AND MAINTENANCE

Appropriate standard tables supply us with the
characteristics of maintenance: mean repair time
for any unit, number of unit components, kind
of required maintenance team. Further informations
on men-perhours cost for every single maintenance
work and its corresponding annual cost must be
given.
We have now rather detail the criterion, which
provides the decision to maintain the engine, organize its components repair or replacemente and
plan a visit.
As shown in fig. 2, the system state information
enters the diagnostic block, preceeding the decision block. This information about system state
is obtainable through the operations already indicated, by the earlier information on state or performance indexes of components belonging to the
systems.
Anytime it's required, the complete information
is demanded by the diagnostic block and answered
by the sensors installed on the component which
has conditioned the switching of the system, that
within or beyond a non-contemporaneity hypothesis.
In such a way the cause of failure shall be strictly
identified through the observation of its effects
on engine operation. Thus, the diagnostic block
represents a phase of critical analysis of the
failure, summarized as a rule in a proper subroutine.
This routine contains all instructions to read
those and only information bits concerning that
failing block and its parts interested by a fault.
Implicitly, a certain function of memorization of
the system story, which was purposely ignored

while considering the Markovian theory of deterioration, is now considered and implemented.

In order to confront the proposed controlled maintenance performance with that of the conventional routine maintenance, a few hints on both procedures are certainly to be given.

While the proposed criterion supplies the directions and programs for maintenance visits, according to an efficiency policy, the routine program requires scheduled visits, performed at regular intervals, viz according to the progressive amount of operation time. This is clearly either precarious or wasteful. It is indispensable to integrate such program with a continual smart direct surveillance of the various engine parts, in order to be able to promptly cut in, when it is necessary, to prevent an unimportant fault, easy removable, to turn into a serious failure. With the former criterion, the whole system and all its parts are always under control for a total survey and no visit is wasted, if unnecessary.

Marine engineering experience suggests the advantage to proceed, before performing a maintenance visit, to some easy and quick checks on the engine stopped and opened. Such checks and inspection may well give a realistic picture of certain engine parts situation and so let the engineer decide to maintain some component even before the scheduled time or delay it beyond that deadline.

The controlled maintenance, through the sensor-transducer system, is aware of the actual conditions or state of the engine during its running,too,therefore the decision block needs no scheduling but the one which concerns Classification Institutes inspections, now ordinarily convertable into an agreed continual visit.

It is a rule, however, never to postpone a maintenance visit, when the engine or its component conditions make it advisable, since, besides lowering the engine efficiency and silly risking an heavier failure, the unattending such rule certainly helps to increase the maintenance cost.

The new controlled maintenance criterion proves itself favorable when confronted with the conventional maintenance routine scheduling, right from the above mentioned intuitive benefits,namely:

1) system state is known all the time, with operating engine, too
2) failure is promptly detected, quickly diagnosticated and all directions are given to amend it in the best possible way
3) repair stage is reduced to the minimum actual repair time
4) diagnostic and decision blocks serve the ship's staff with an handy device based on the experience of best marine engineers, on the accounted suggestions of engine and plant builder.

All these benefits are then considered essential to fulfill any economical and technical requisite implicit into the optimal maintenance policy

selected.

THE DECISIONAL PROCESS

The decision block or process has to be fed, as to its inputs, not only by the failure-information flow, already mentioned, but must be aware of the actual ship's operation constraints also.

In fact, these further data to be known for a correct decision making can be so classified:

a) environmental constraints, like sea-state winds, currents, etc.
b) logistical constraints, like the actual availability of spares maintenance crew,lifting gears, etc.

Of course, for those data acquisition an adequate information flow must be organized.

As illustrated in Fig. 3, it is possible to formalize, by means of a number of blocks, the progressive evolution of the decisional process while taking into account either a failure hierarchy, related to the environmental constraints, or a maintenance priority, depending on logistic and operational constraints.

However, some difficulties may arise owing to the presence in the problem of qualitative variables, such difficulty mainly based on the conversion to the equivalent quantitative expression.

The decision eventually consists on settling whether to maintain the engine and, in the positive case, when and how. The modalities of the maintenance action are suggested, complying with the constraints imposed while a given cost function is optimized.

CONCLUSIONS

A new procedure for coping with the controlled maintenance criterion has been proposed widely employing simulation models.

The state of the art being in its early stage,this work, just from previously given hints, already shows the intuitive convenience of the controlled maintenance which can be realized when disposing of a shipboard central process computer.

The basic grounds on which such procedure is based, and this paper deals with, are not only those peculiar simulations that provide us with a realistic approach to the controlled maintenance implementation but also appears to be the concrete feedback system information meant for the maintenance optimal policy.

A slow diesel main engine has been preliminarily examined, but, of course, a possible extension to a steam or gas turbine marine plant is soon expected to be carried out.

Therefore, we can actually think of extending on solid grounds the automation to optimal policies determinations concerning several ship's operation processes.

Noticeably, the availability of first quality
sensor and transducers, the presence of one or two
process computers onboard, the progressive improvement of the failure know-how, the development of
adavanced programmation techniques can feasibly
be introduced. By means of such features it is
possibly not only to find the engine system optimal behaviour, the optimal route choice or the best
procedure of cargo handling, but also to search
for a maintenance policy which can give the maximum
service continuity, the highest ship safety and minimum management costs.

REFERENCES

E.COTTI, Recent Fiat Experience in the large marine
        Diesel Engine Maintenance - ASME,London
C.DERMAN,Optimal replacement and maintenance under
        Markovian Deterioration
Proceedings of a Conference on Reliability and
Maintenance 1971, Ist.of Marine Engin.,London
SHINNERS, Techniques of system Engineering
        McGraw Hill, N.Y.
Shipping World,April 1972: The computer system for
engine monitoring and control aboard "Höeg Multina"
SITZIA G.-G.SARTIRANA, Computerized automation of
        the containership Lloydiana IFAC/IFIP,
        Oslo 1973
E.VOLTA,M.PIATTELLI, The Progetto Esquilino of C.N.R.
        ISME,Tokyo, Novembre 1973
VINOGRADOV, Analysis of Maintenance of Marine Diesel
        Engine USSR Merch.Marine Research Inst.

fig.1

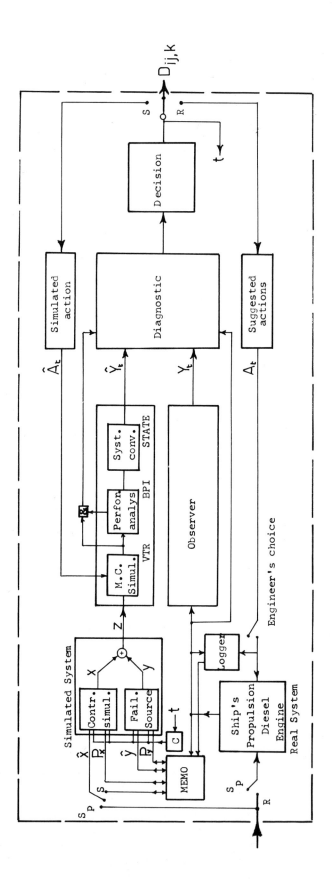

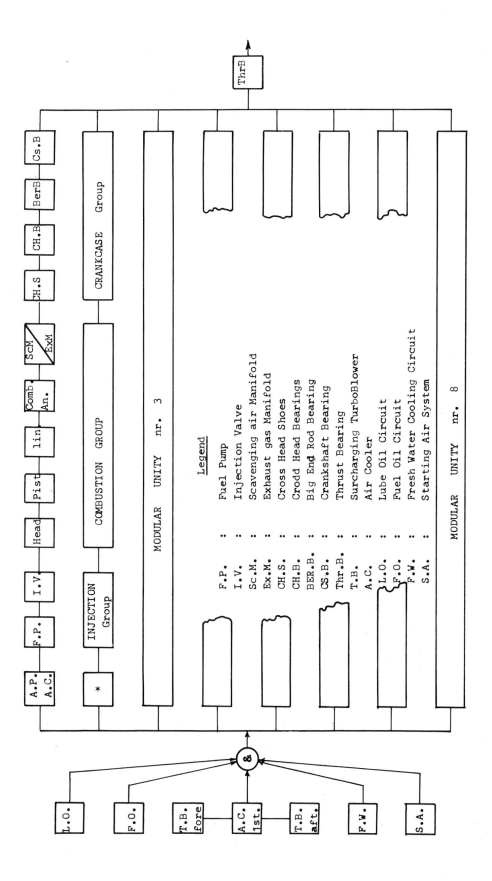

fig. 2

218

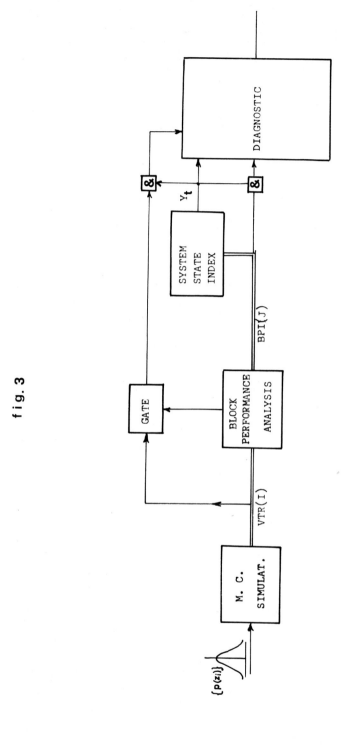

fig. 3

fig.4

ISTAB	TESTATE	CAMICIE	PISTONI	CARTER	CS	CL	T1	T2	R1	R2	REFR.PA.	POMPE IN.	POLVERIZZ.	LO	FW	SA	RPM	FO
BLOCCO	1 3 5 7 2 4 6 8	9 12 15 10 13 16 11 14	17 20 23 18 21 24 19 22	25 28 31 26 29 32 27 30	33	34	35	36	37	38	39 42 45 40 43 46 41 44	47 50 53 48 51 54 49 52	55 58 61 56 59 62 57 60	63	64	65	66	67
TEMPS	********	********	********	********	*	*	*	*	*	*	********	********	********	*	*	*	*	*
T= 65*	00000000	00000000	22001002	10000101	2	1	1	1	0	1	01201010	00000000	20110012	0	0	1	1	1
T= 129*	11111111	00000000	01011000	01101000	1	0	0	1	1	1	01000001	00000000	01201010	0	0	0	1	0
T= 257*	00000110	00100001	02001200	00011100	0	0	2	0	0	0	01000102	00000000	02200100	0	0	0	1	1
T= 321*	00000001	01000100	00101000	10000000	0	0	0	1	0	0	11100010	00100000	01000001	0	0	0	1	0
T= 385*	11121111	01000200	02021000	10000100	1	0	2	1	0	0	10000000	10000000	11012100	0	0	0	0	1
T= 449*	00000000	00000000	00001101	00010100	0	1	2	0	1	0	00001110	00000010	00011101	0	0	0	1	1
T= 577*	00000000	10010011	20010111	00011000	2	0	1	0	0	0	10202001	00010010	11110101	0	1	0	1	1
T= 705*	00100000	01000000	00000010	10100100	2	0	1	1	0	0	10113000	10010000	10000000	0	0	0	1	0
T= 897*	00011000	00000000	02000001	00002010	0	0	1	1	0	0	10010000	00000010	10111200	0	0	0	1	0
T= 961*	00000000	00020101	20000011	10030002	2	0	2	2	0	0	00000210	00010000	02001101	0	0	0	1	1
T= 1025*	11111111	00110100	00011100	00220000	0	1	2	1	0	0	00001001	00000000	00000012	0	0	0	1	0
T= 1153*	00100000	11100001	00000020	11000101	1	0	0	1	0	0	10100100	01000000	01100012	0	0	0	1	0
T= 1345*	00000000	00020001	01100110	10101100	0	0	0	0	0	1	12100100	00010100	03120112	0	0	0	1	1
T= 1409*	00000001	00000000	02300100	00100100	1	0	0	3	0	0	10010101	00100000	02112101	0	0	0	1	0
T= 1473*	11211111	11111111	01001011	12010011	2	0	0	1	0	0	02100000	00100000	10001001	0	0	0	1	0
T= 1537*	00000001	00010000	00000101	01001120	2	0	2	0	1	0	11000000	00000101	11111100	0	0	1	1	0
T= 1729*	11111111	10010000	00000001	00021000	1	0	1	1	0	1	10002000	00000100	20002121	0	1	0	1	0
T= 1793*	00011000	00000000	00010110	10100000	1	1	0	1	0	0	10001001	00000100	10001100	0	0	0	1	0
T= 1857*	00000100	21311122	00002000	01001001	1	0	1	1	0	0	00000010	10000100	11110100	1	0	0	1	0
T= 1921*	00000000	01110100	01011010	10101000	2	1	0	0	0	1	10000101	00100000	01200010	0	0	0	2	0
T= 1985*	01000000	00011000	00001110	01100000	0	0	3	0	0	0	10002111	00000000	22000002	0	0	0	2	0
T= 2241*	00100000	00110000	00000011	00000000	2	0	0	0	1	1	11101002	01010001	10100011	1	0	0	0	1
T= 2433*	00000000	00100000	10111100	11000000	1	0	0	2	0	0	02311120	00000000	00100001	0	0	0	2	0
T= 2497*	12111111	10001000	01101110	00010002	0	0	1	0	1	0	00110010	00001000	01000201	0	0	0	2	0
T= 2689*	00000000	01000101	10000010	11001010	0	0	1	0	0	0	11110001	00000000	10023110	0	0	0	1	1
T= 2817*	00000000	00100110	00012000	10010111	0	0	1	0	0	0	01110100	00000001	01121122	0	0	0	2	0
T= 2945*	01100000	01010000	00000010	10101011	0	1	1	1	0	1	00012000	00000000	11211210	0	0	0	1	0
T= 3009*	10000000	00010001	10003100	00110000	1	0	1	2	0	1	00000000	00000000	11011200	0	0	0	1	0
T= 3073*	01000000	00101000	00110000	01010110	0	0	0	0	0	0	00001011	10010000	01112111	0	0	0	2	0
T= 3137*	10000000	00010110	01000001	00020011	0	0	2	2	0	0	01011000	10000000	11001010	0	1	0	1	0
T= 3265*	01000000	00000000	00110010	10010110	0	0	0	0	0	0	01001011	00100000	11001110	0	0	0	1	0
T= 3329*	10100000	00000000	10000111	00000003	0	0	2	2	2	0	10000100	00000001	00110200	0	0	0	1	0
T= 3393*	00000000	11212211	12100000	00101000	0	1	1	2	0	1	00000100	00000000	11110011	0	0	0	1	0
T= 3457*	11111111	11000001	01101100	00110011	2	0	0	1	1	0	00001101	00000010	12001211	1	0	0	2	0
T= 3521*	00100000	00000101	00000100	12000021	1	0	1	0	1	0	10000200	00010000	00101010	0	0	0	0	1
T= 3585*	10000000	01100000	00300000	00011000	0	0	0	1	0	0	01102001	00000000	10000010	0	0	0	1	0
T= 3713*	00100000	01000000	11201100	00100111	0	0	2	0	0	0	11120000	00010000	00001011	0	0	0	0	1
T= 3969*	00000000	11111211	00010001	10010011	1	0	0	1	1	1	00010100	00000000	20000111	0	1	0	1	0
T= 4097*	00000000	00020000	00010002	00100010	0	0	0	2	1	0	00010010	00000000	11102030	1	1	1	2	0
T= 4417*	00000000	11212111	11001010	00000000	0	0	0	0	0	0	00100010	00000000	10000200	0	0	0	1	0
T= 4481*	00000100	00000000	01002100	01110000	0	0	2	0	2	0	00011000	00100000	00100111	0	0	0	1	0
T= 4609*	01001000	10100000	01010000	12101012	0	0	0	2	0	0	00011000	00000001	00100011	0	1	0	1	0
T= 4673*	00100000	10010000	01011100	00100000	2	0	1	1	0	0	00001001	00010000	00001021	0	0	1	1	0
T= 4737*	00000000	00001000	01010001	00000000	1	1	2	1	0	1	10100001	00011010	12100000	0	0	0	1	0
T= 4801*	10000000	00101011	00011110	00100010	1	0	2	0	1	1	00001000	01000000	20110111	0	1	0	2	0
T= 4865*	01000000	01001000	10000001	00001000	1	0	1	0	0	1	12000000	00000100	00000000	0	0	1	1	0
T= 4929*	00010000	01000011	00011001	00110001	2	0	1	0	0	0	00101000	00000000	11100101	0	1	0	1	1
T= 4993*	00000000	00000001	20011000	20000101	1	0	2	0	0	0	01000010	00000000	11011100	0	0	0	1	0
T= [illegible]	[illegible]	[illegible]	[illegible]	[illegible]	1	0	2	1	1	0	[illegible]	[illegible]	[illegible]	0	0	0	0	1

"NEW DEVELOPMENTS IN ENGINE ROOM AUTOMATION"

PER B. FISCHER
Head of the Marine Dept.
SØREN T. LYNGSØ LTD.
Copenhagen, Denmark

Contents

1. What started automation in ships?

Ten years ago an acute need for seagoing personnel among Scandinavian shipowners arose, owing to a substantial enlargement of the merchant fleet taking place and numerous seagoing engineers leaving the fleet simultaneously to obtain attractive shore jobs offered by power stations, refineries and industrial plants.

Consequently shipowners had to replace these men, since legislation and safety did not provide for staff reductions.

One immediate way of compensating this loss was to improve the control and supervisory equipment in the engine room, since the unproductive night watch could then be abolished without impairing safety, where the practice so far had been that 2 members of the engine staff were on the night watch where they carried out normal routin work as for example filling of fuel oil tanks, check of the machinery and entering the loogbook.

This expansion of control- and supervisory equipment was tried out in varying degrees in a number of ships. Experience gained soon showed that whilst the idea was a sound one i.e. it was possible to obtain reliable centralized super- vision, it also gave an indication of what equipment was necessary, and what could be descarded.

Operating with unmanned engine rooms at night (and weekends) soon resulted in legislation changes in many countries, so that a reduction of the engine room staff was legal. Classification Societies became simultaneously engaged in tests and trials of this form of operation.

A number of recommendations on this mode of operation were drafted by the Classification Societies, and these recommendations soon became rules after necessary experience had been gained.

Even though there are differences in the degree and function of control- and supervisory equipment recommended by the various Classification Societies, the equipment which today is regarded as both necessary and sufficient for unmanned operation, can be condensed to the following points:

a. A fire detecting and extinguishing system.

b. A bridge manoeuvring system for the main engine

c. An alarm system by which the alarms can be transferred to the bridge and/or the duty engineers' cabins.

d. Electric power generation security.

e. Automatic control of important temperatures.

f. Means of manual control.

In retrospect an enormous development has taken place since automation on board was introduced. This has led to the majority of today's new- buildings being equipped for unmanned engine room operation.

2. Experience to date.

What experience has been gained to date with the installation of electronic automation equipment for unmanned operation on board ship?

Many analysis have been made and much has been written since automation began, partly concerning the   engineer's attitude to automation, and partly about the durability and environmental suitability of the equipment.

Generally it can be stated   that the attitude on the part of the engineers has become more and more positive. Today automation is accepted as an invaluable aid and a mean of obtaining better working conditions. Automation is no longer regarded as an attempt by shipowners to rationalize in order to create redundancy amongst seagoing engineers.

Experience shows that when a Scandinavian marine engineer takes hire nowadays, he prefers to be onboard a vessel equipped with automation providing conditions for an unmanned engine room. This attitude should naturally be seen in relation to the experience engineers have hitherto gained with respect to equipment reliability and durability. This experience would indicate that when electronic equipment is designed specifically for the marine environment, especially the engine room, there normally is a great reliability.

A statistical analysis of, for example, a number of bridge manoeuvring systems for the control of the main propulsion machinery from the bridge (one of the more complex systems manufactured for the marine environment), over a service period of 500.000 hours, showed that a MTBF(mean time between failures) of approximately 13.500 running hours had been obtained.

A number of faults had been rectified on board by engineers without having to call for assistance, and the average running time between the requested service calls (MTBF), amounted to around 19.000 hours with increasing tendency.

Since a Bridge Manoeuvring System comprises electronic/electrical/mechanical/pneumatic components, it is possible to split the figures up between electronic/electrical faults and mechanical/pneumatic faults. For both groups the figures show around 38.000 running hours between each service call.

3. Running problems.

Automation for unmanned engine room operation provide, as mentioned, for an engine room crew reduction, besides an environmental improvement for the crew and a more qualified machinery maintenance. Today this degree of automation is regarded as a fully acceptable and normal part of the ship's installation.

Unfortunately, this has not proven to be the panacea for all the problems connected with the running of the machinery. If one takes a look at the conditions and the trends which are most predominant in the merchant fleet today, the following will be concluded:

a. The average time a chief engineer remains at sea is still decreasing. It would not be far wrong to state that most chief engineers "go ashore" before they are 35 years of age. This means that the experience gained with the machinery on the part of the chief engineer, from the time of his examination until he leaves the fleet, is relatively limited.

b. The thermic and mechanical load on the machinery, especially the main propulsion machinery, increases concurrently with new engine designs and the increased mean pressure (in diesel engines), and steam conditions (in steam turbines).

Furthermore, machinery is becoming more and more complicated concurrently with demands placed to higher speeds of the ships.

c. Demands on the part of owners to a reduction of the off-hire time are intensified owing to competition and the costs of the vessels.

Due to the aforementioned unmanned means of operation, the engine room crew is reduced in size in comparison with earlier years and the ship's stay in the port is down to a minimum thanks to the use of modern loading- and unloading facilities.

Viewed singularly these points are well known and are in fact generally accepted as a result of the trends nowadays. Yet on the other hand when considered as a whole, a more complex problem arises which must be made subject to an exact examination in an attempt to rectify and improve these conditions.

"Why are we to make piston overhauls at fixed intervals if supervision equipment can be installed to inform us when it is really necessary", was the recent remark from a chief engineer. "What often happens is that we renew piston 4, which could still have run for quite some time, and a couple of days later piston 6 burns out", he added.

This remark seen in relation to the aforementioned points shows that there is a need for an aid which can be of use when maintenance work is to be planned. This could replace the periodical maintenance work partly of fully with a system which can indicate, when maintenance on the machinery is necessary. In brief, when the button for cylinder 6 is pressed, the system indicates on a viewing screen or the like, how many running hours cylinder 6 has left before the piston need to be renewed.

4. Computers in ships.

If we for a moment turn away from the described running- and maintenance problems and take a look at the application of computers on board ships, it is so that in later years where "conventional" automation for unmanned engine room operation has become more and more advanced concurrently with developments of the engine and electronics, the computer has found a natural position in a number of ships.

The first of these installations were not at all successful. The fault probably lies in the fact that owners failed to define the purpose of the installation. Furthermore, early computers were designed to meet static mercantile purposes, and as such proved incompatible with the special demands made to durability and environmental correct design necessary when installing in ships. Initially, most installations were carried out according to the motto, "now we have a computer on board, how can we best make use of it?"

A better approach would of course be to evaluate computer tasks in connection with the propulsion machinery, and thence a sober consideration of whether or not there are at all reasons for the installation.

There are hardly any conditions which can be
changed with respect to the optimal running of
diesel machinery, and increase of the efficiency
since most running conditions are determined by
the engine's design and mode of operation.

However, if we consider the running- and maintenance problems outlined above which occur on
board ships, then it would not be unnatural to
imagine a computer being used advantageously, since
a system which informs when engines components are
to be repaired or exchanged must demand the sampling
and processing of a great amount of data, all of
which is not available from conventional propulsion
machinery and its instrumentation.

As an example of the application of a micro
computer, which is a "small" cheap computer, in
conjunction with conventional automation equipment,
it can be mentioned that a micro computer can be
relatively easily connected to an alarm system
containing a number of binary and analog alarm
channels.

The analog alarm channels are automatically
scanned by the computer at intervals of 30 seconds,
and the collected values are stored in the
computer's memory for a period of, for example,
10 minutes. Every 15 minutes the measure values
for each channel are fed on the magnetic tape.

In the event of a binary channel being activated,
the measurings from the last 10 minutes are fed
on to the tape, and measurings taken every 30
seconds are also fed on to the tape as long as the
alarm remains.

The tapes with this "historical" run of the alarm
condition can be despatched to the owners, where
an analysis of the collected data can be carried
out on a larger computer so that "trend calculations and report printing" can be read out.

5.   Condition control.

From the above the conclusion can be drawn that it
would be advantageous for the supervision of the
propulsion machinery and the planning of its maintenance, if a system based on the collection and
processing of numerous data were installed to
inform the engineers on the state of the machinery.

In the design and construction of such as system
of condition control, the following points must
be borne in mind:

a.   based on accessible knowledge it must be
     decided which data is to be collected from the
     machinery in order to obtain a relevant picture
     of the condition, or put in another way, where
     should we measure on the machinery?

     The determination of measuring points must
     naturally take place through a close co-
     operation between the owners, engine builders,
     the classification society and automation
     equipment suppliers. Not only are the desired
     measuring points to be specified, they are to

be chosen so that the necessary types of sensors
can be constructed in a simple yet robust manner,
and there mounting in the machinery as a permanent
installation can be carried out without great
difficulty for the engine builder and for the
normal maintenance in the ship.

b.   The collected data found necessary to describe
     the state of the machinery must be processed
     in a computer or the like in such a way, that
     the results are presented in a form
     understandable by the chief engineer. In other
     words, it must be possible for the user to
     operate and use the system without having
     expert knowledge, and without having to draw
     too many conclusions.

     It is here where the greatest difficulties
     mainly lie in the use of a condition control
     system.

     There are not greater technical problems
     connected to the construction and installation
     of the sensors thought to be necessary. It is
     also not at all difficult to install a great
     or a number of smaller computers for the
     processing of the collected measurings. The
     problems arise when the processing base for
     the measuring data is to be decided so that
     results can be presented in a comprehendable
     manner. Here it is of paramount importance
     that owners and engine builders make available
     the material which has been collected during
     the daily running of the ships over the years.
     It is this material which provides the in-
     formation on condition changes which lead to
     machinery break-downs, and which have formed
     the basis on which today's maintenance routines
     have been compiled.

     Only after one has understood how to formulate
     measuring data in their correct mutual
     dependance and in such a way, that fully
     unambiguous information is presented to the
     chief engineer, it can be said that demands
     placed on a condition control system are
     fulfilled.

c.   After a condition control system for propulsion
     machinery has been carried out as a case study,
     or better as an installation on board a ship,
     economy calculations for the hardware and
     software contained in such a system must be
     made. The investments must be weighed in
     relation to the economy by applying the system.

     The result of such calculations will probably
     show that it can pay to install condition
     control for a limited part of the propulsion
     machinery only, for example, on the main
     engine or perhaps only a part of it, for
     example, on the cylinder liners with pistons.

6.   Other examples of automation equipment.

Whilst the development of a condition control
system for propulsion machinery has proven to be
of interest among the shipowners,development and
improvement of the "conventional" automation

equipment continues to take place.

The prime reason for this activity are changes and improvements in the types of ships and thus also in machinery. An example of this is automation in connection with ships having 2 or more main propulsion engines, where synchronizing equipment ensures that crank shafts have a constant phase angle,thereby minimizing vibrations.

Furthermore, such ships demand greater integration of the machinery's various control systems in a centralised control system than is the case today. Centralisation would also comprise the bridge manoeuvring system, control of the turbo- and diesel generators, start- and stop of pumps and other auxiliary machinery.

A further increase in the application of electronic automation in connection with the electrical control of exhaust valves and fuel pumps, besides electrical control of the start air distributor, can be foreseen in conjunction with the constant improvement of diesel engines.

7. Conclusion.

Owners' interest in a condition control system for diesel engines has resulted in
a co-operation between Burmeister & Wain Engineering Company Limited, Copenhagen, the Technical University of Denmark and Søren T.Lyngsø Ltd. with the aim of developing and constructing an automatic diagnostic system for marine diesel engine plants, primarily with respect to the main engine and its systems.

This diagnostic system must be able to carry out the following functions:

a. detection of any development toward critical engine conditions, to enable advance intervention to be made.

b. continual supervision of components' working state in order to provide in a practical manner for the planning of overhauls (maintenance), thereby extending the permissable working hours of the individual components.

Computers in future engine rooms are to be regarded as a reality in connection with systems where storing of data is necessary, as for example in condition control systems and the trend shows that a decentralization of the computers in smaller units probably will be more appropriate than the use of big process computers.

Copenhagen

12th February, 1973

GENERAL HARDWARE AND SOFTWARE FOR ENGINE ROOM MONITORING

AND CONTROL SYSTEMS

Steinar Espestøyl - Ove M. Sivertsen
N O R C O N T R O L
division of NORATOM-NORCONTROL A/S

INTRODUCTION

The system hardware philosophy is a totally integrated system where the computer, the input/output electronics, the power supplies and the process termination racks are contained within the engine room control console.

Further aims in the design has been:

a. High reliability
b. Good serviceability
c. Modular construction
d. High noise rejection
e. Special consideration to the shipboard environment

The system software philosophy has been to create a set of software modules allowing easy generation of different system configurations.

Further aims in the design has been:

a. Powerful on-line testing facilities
b. System configuration by data tables
c. High efficiency software (time and space)

SYSTEM DESCRIPTION

1.   Computer

The computer in the system is the NORD-4E, which is a shipboard version of the NORD-1, with an integrated power supply by NORCONTROL.
   The NORD-1 is a 16 bit computer with a powerful instruction repertoire. This includes hardware floating point arithmetic and bit manipulating instructions.
   Standard software includes a powerful symbolic editor, an assembler with several debugging features (on-line and off-line), a FORTRAN IV compiler and the SINTRAN real time executive. A small time-sharing system specially suited for system development, off-line testing and system generation is being used in the software production.

2.   Hardware

Computer with I/O-equipment
General description

The DataChief Hardware Configuration is shown in fig. 2.1.

The main components are:

- Central Processing Unit with two input/output channels.
- Ferrite Core Memory with 8K to 64K word capacity.
- Paper Tape Reader or Magnetic Tape Reader for program loading.
- Channel 1 I/O-system interfacing all the equipment necessary for operation of the DataChief and its sub-systems.

The main parts in Channel 1 I/O-system are:

- Operators Panel including:

  CRT-displays
  Logging typewriters
  Pen-Trend recorder (optional)

- Interface electronics for panel servicing
- Interface electronics for analog and digital process inputs and outputs.
- System Monitor allowing several operational tests and simulations to be performed on-line.

Power for all the hardware units, except for the Teletype, the Paper Tape Reader or Magnetic Tape Reader, is supplied from a centralized source made up of a Charging Unit, Buffer Batteries and DC/DC-converters. In case of battery breakdown or servicing, a Back-up Supply for vital circuity is also provided.
   All units used are built with the most modern solid state components, and the system is designed to meet the highest standards specified for marine environment.

The following environmental specifications apply:

Relative humidity: 0-96% without condensation

Temperature: 0-55°C

Vibrations: Frequency range: 5-50Hz.
Vibration velocity amplitude: 20 mm/sec.

2.1 Modular digital and analog input/output system

Digital Input Module

The digital input module has 16 or 32 channels with parallel input. Each input channel is filtered to improve noise margin and to eliminate contact bounce. Standard timeconstant is about 40 ms.

The module will normally interface to process contacts. But as the input circuitry responds to the contact current, it may be used with any kind of current source. The contacts are supplied with 10mA max. current, and the trigger point will be at approximately 5 mA.

A optic/electronic coupling (GaAs-diode and phototransistor) is provided on each channel input. This results in complete isolation between different channels.

Digital Output Module

There are two kinds of output modules all having latching registers:

16 channel lamp and relay drivers.

Driving capability 1 A/50 Volts.
Operation: "Sinking" to ground.

2 channel pulse-width circuit, programable pulse-width output variable in 128 steps.

Output 20 mA, sourcing from +24volts.
Used for driving solid state AC-relays.

The 2 channel pulse-width circuit contains also limit-timer function for fail to safe operation after certain hardware or software failures.
(Deenergizing system switch-over contactors).

Analog Input Module

The analog input system consists of a 12 bit A/D converter of the successive approximation type. Conversion time is about 40 µs with a through-put rate of approx. 6000 channels/sec.

The measured values are converted to binary numbers with negative numbers on 2's complements form.

The A/D converter takes signals from a multiplexer. The multiplexer has random access addressing and is of modular design,

16 channel modules are normally used. For differential inputs, there are 8 channels per module.

Input filtering elements and calibration channel for gain and offset drift is provided.

Input signals from the process sensor to the multiplexer are fed through special modules containing bridges and normalizing elements. Separate isolated power supplies are used for most of the sensor types.

Analog Output Module

The analog output module contain two 10 bit channels with latching registers and reference supplies. The current output is available in several ranges such 0-10 ma, 4-20 ma and 10-50 ma. Optionally, there will be "a watch dog" for each channel.

System Monitor Module

The System Monitor will allow several test functions to be performed on-line. The hardware loop control allows the CPU to test the operation of the input/output bus and the control functions.

A stable voltage reference supply is provided allowing on-line testing of the analog input system.

"Watch dogs" will check the repeatability of critical software clock routines and false operation will cause a system switch over to back-up operation.

Power System

The power supply is centralized for the whole system and is made up of a charging unit connected to NiCd floating buffer batteries, which again supplies DC/DC converters. The batteries and the DC/DC converters are providing all the necessary voltages to the system. Because of the batteries, the system will operate during black-out periodes of more than half an hour and operation will be highly insensitive to the types of noise and transients always existing on a ship's mains supply.

In case of battery breakdown or servicing, a back-up supply is provided. Normally the battery voltage will override that of the back-up supply. See fig. 2.1.2.

2.2 Man/Machine Hardware

The man/machine communication section, see fig. 2.2.1., consists of an alarm panel (upper) and a communication panel (lower).

The alarm panel is made up of group alarm lamps/push-buttons and an alpha-numeric display. The communication panel is made up of a graphical/alpha-numeric display, an alpha-numeric keyboard and "communication push-buttons".

All devices are using the ASCII character code. The most interesting device is the graphical /alpha-numeric display system shown in fig. 2.2.2.

SOFTWARE

The general software consists of the following parts.

3.1 Executive and I/O Driver Routines

The executive used is the Norwegian developed SINTRAN II which is a modular real time multiprogramming operating system, see fig. 3.1.

The operating system can be divided into three parts:

    a. Interrupt handling including alphanumeric I/O-driver routines providing buffered input and output.
    b. A monitor providing "job" scheduling. To obtain re-entrancy and dynamic data allocation, a data stack common to all programs is used.
    c. Interactive programmer's communication for on-line system testing and debugging.

3.2 Digital and Analog Input/Output Routines

Under the direction of the analog input routine, MEAS, the modules scan the various plant variables on a prescheduled periodic basis.

The analog input routine will for every measured variable carry out the following standard operations where applicable.:

    a. Measurement linearization
    b. Instrument limit check
    c. Rate of change limit check
    d. Digital filtering of measurement
    e. Process variable limit check

The digital input/output routine is specially developed to easily handle the great variety of digital signals from system to system by "reorganizing" the inputs to fit the standard programs, see fig. 3.2. Interfacing routines allow the process programs to extract or set data in the digital I/O-tables.

The process control output driver routine is designed to handle outputs from multi-variable control schemes, PID algorithms and specially written algorithms.

3.3 Man/Machine Software

This software is developed to handle in the most flexible way the different requirements of a complex communication.

The communication is push-button initiated and is carried out by using the alphanumeric keyboard and display. Each communication task is specified by table elements containing points to text, variables, limits and special program sequences.

3.4 Alarm Handling Software

This software is made to handle a larger number of alarms than usual onboard ships in the past. In addition, emphasis is placed on having a flexible and accurate alarm presentation.

The basic idea in the design of the system is the logical arrangement of the alarms in groups according to the process sub-systems. It is felt that this improves the alarm presentation in a large system and allows the operator to get better over-all view of the actual situation.

In order to give detailed description of the alarm point and alarm cause, a 32 character message is given for each point. On request, the system will display the value of the process variable together with the alarm limit. Typical examples of the alarm presentation for a diesel ship are shown in fig. 3.4.

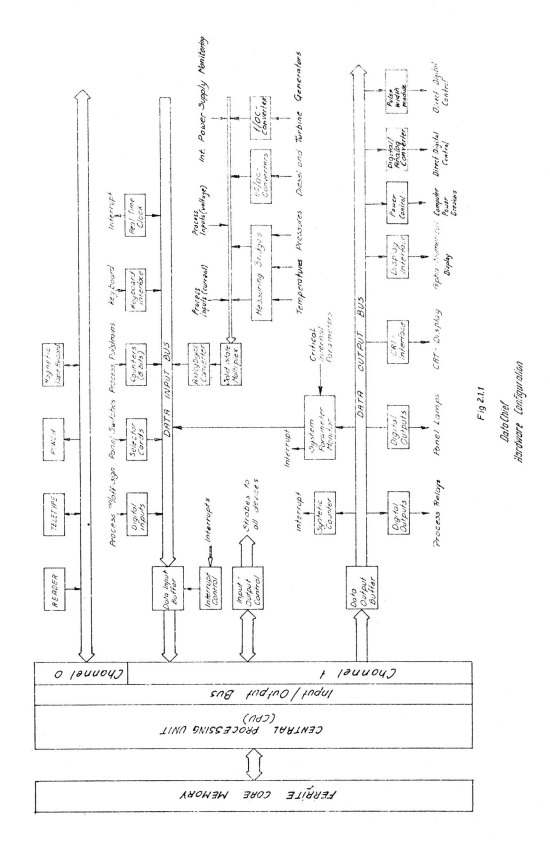

Fig 2.1.1

DataChief
Hardware Configuration

228

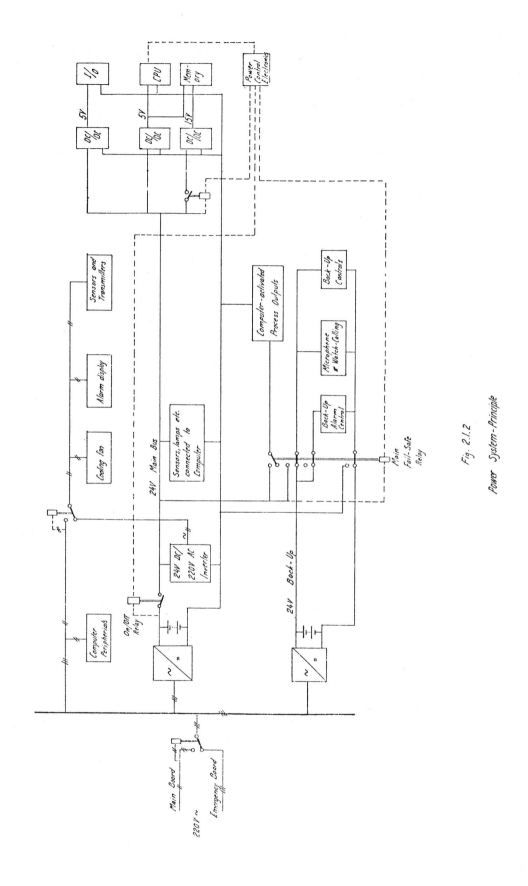

Fig. 2.1.2

Power System-Principle

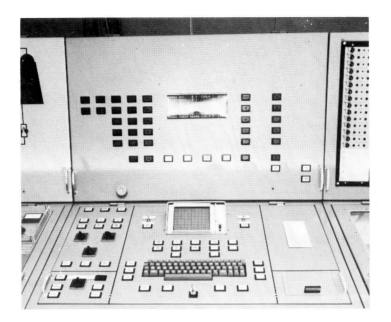

Fig. 2.2.1 Man/Machine Communication Section

230

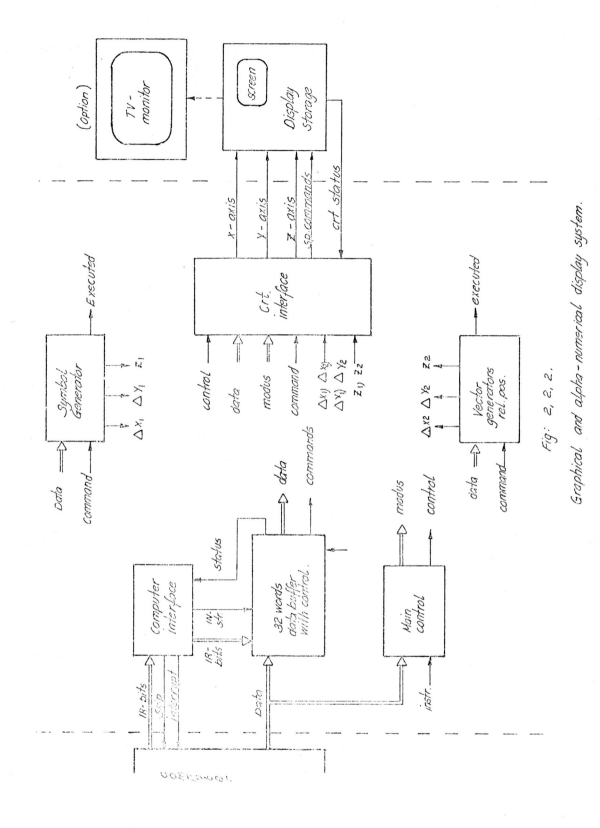

Fig: 2, 2, 2.

Graphical and alpha-numerical display system.

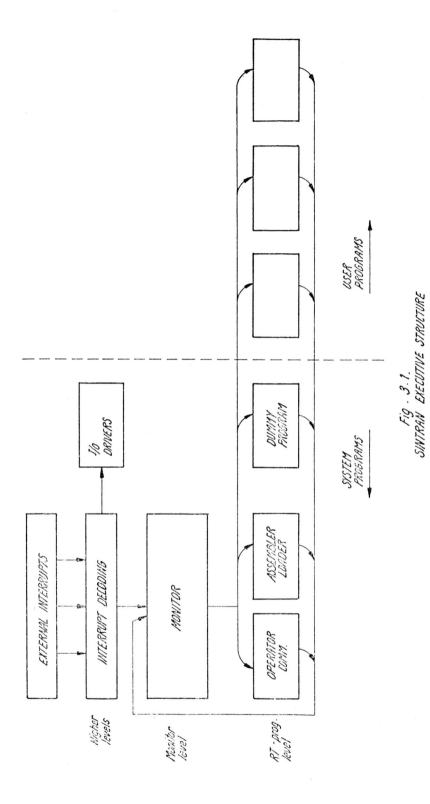

Fig . 3.1.
SINTRAN EXECUTIVE STRUCTURE

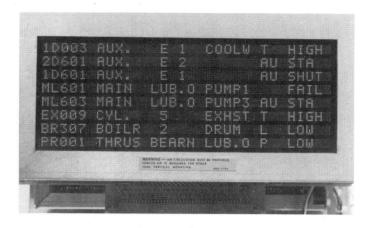

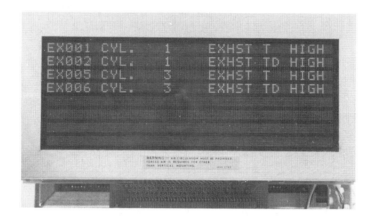

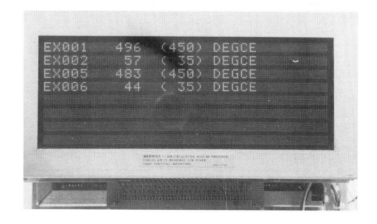

Fig. 3.4
ALARM PRESENTATION

COMPUTERIZED SYSTEMS IN DIESEL ENGINE ROOMS

INSTALLATION, TESTING AND OPERATION

Arild Andreassen - Svein K. Johnsen
Project Engineers
N O R C O N T R O L
Division of NORATOM-NORCONTROL A/S

INTRODUCTION

The latest development in a growing line of computer systems developed in Norway for use onboard merchant ships is the NORCON-TROL system named DATACHIEF. The process knowledge built into the system has been a joint effort by THE SHIP RESEARCH INSTITUTE OF NORWAY and NORCONTROL.

The DataChief system consists of a family of sub-systems for engine room automation and maintenance prediction as follows:

- A condition monitoring system designed to monitor the condition of certain engine room components, like turbochargers, coolers, cylinders etc., as well as to predict the future date of the components' maintenance by the DataTrend sub-system.

- Monitoring, alarm handling, auto start/ stop of pumps and compressors, and logging by the DataSafe sub-system.

- Complete electric power generating plant automation by the DataPower sub-system.

- Main engine remote control system, AUTOCHIEF II, may be integrated with the DataChief. The AUTOCHIEF II is a "self-contained" system with tie-in to DataSafe and in the future to DataTrend.

TECHNICAL ASPECTS

All inputs from the process are conducted through the interface into the computer. Here the various programs take over; and after a large number of comparisons and calculations, the result are presented as output to the process or to communication devices, or they may be stored in the computer's memory.

As all logics are executed in a programmed computer, necessary changes and adjustments are made in the programs, not in the hardware.

The computer is placed in a Control Desk located in the Engine Control Room, thereby being close to the process.

The various remote controls and communication and alarm devices, along with the process interfacing equipment, are all located in the Control Desk.

The computer used in DataChief is specially designed to withstand rough conditions, as are all the modern electronic circuitries used throughout the system.

In DataChief, analogue sensors are used exclusively in the process. Besides that information for multiple functions may be obtained by the same sensor, several possible sensor failures may be detected by the computer. In addition, the input signals are easily filtered to reduce for instance false alarms.

DataChief has some very important built-in safety features. Besides checking that the inputs are correct, it also checks its own outputs by a special technique. Furthermore, the system's power supplies, fuses etc. are continously monitored. Even more important is the checking of correctly executed program sequences. If any serious failures are found, the output channels will be closed and the control left over to the back-up systems, always failing to safety. Such system failures are not very likely to occur, but when they do, the operator will be informed on the cause so that the malfunctioning unit may be replaced.

BRIEF SYSTEM DESCRIPTION

DataSafe

DataSafe is based upon the UMS/E0/AUT-class requirements, but on several items goes far beyond these rules. Major features:

- Total process monitoring with a number of automatic safety actions, and alarm presentation with logically correct alarm blocking and dynamic limits.

- Delayed start of major power consumers until sufficient power available (eventually start of stand-by-generator).

- Automatic restart of pumps after black-out.

- Purifier automation

- Compressor automation

- Exhaust boiler automation

- Automatic filling-up of tanks

- Complete engine room logging

For typical installation, the number of alarm points totals about 300. To deal with all the information received, a sophisticated alarm system is designed, where the alarms and messages are instantly presented on a display unit and an automatic logger.

All alarms and action limits are stored in the computer's programs, making it very convenient for the operator to make adjustments.

DataPower

The DataPower sub-system monitors and automates the ship's electric power generating plant. Major features:

- Minimizing the risks for black-out, by always keeping a certain minimum extra power available. However, it is continously checked whether this surplus is too high, so that a generator eventually may be stopped.

- Automatic start of stand-by auxilliary engines, automatic synchronizing, connection and load sharing.

- Automatic disconnection and stop

- Logging of all actions

- Alarms if failures detected.

The stand-by generator is started up and connected automatically under the following conditions:

a. Overload on one of the duty generators
b. Shut-down on one of the duty generators
c. Power supply insufficient to allow connection of heavy consumer
d. When turbo generator is running, steam pressure inlet gets low.

DataPower makes a vital contribution to additional reliability of operations and also better economy. One generator can be kept in operation and the others will start and stop automatically when needed.

DATATREND - PERFORMANCE MONITORING AND MAINTENANCE PREDICTION

The development of the DataTrend system is based partly on experiences from the "Large Bore Diesel Engine Project" and partly on practical experience achieved through measurements and tests carried out after completion of this project as well as a pilot project onboard M/S "VIANNA".

Principle of Performance Monitoring

DataTrend is a plant condition monitoring system designed both to monitor the actual state of certain engine components such as the thermal loading on the cylinders and to predict when maintenance should be carried out and on which components.

Based upon the continous on-line recording of relevant process parameters, the computer calculates a set of present condition parameters, PCP. These are derived by comparing actual performance data with ideal performance data. Actual data are either directly measured or deduced from a measured relationship. Ideal data is obtained from on-line mathematical model simulations where the models are excited by measured input parameters. The input parameters are process loads, temperatures, pressures and ambient conditions.

Condition parameters are turbo-charger efficiency, a cooler's heat transfer coefficient, cylinder liner temperatures etc.

Maintenance prediction is carried out by performing a linear least square regression on successive PCP's. When demanded by the operator, this mean line is extrapolated until it intersects with a preset limit. This point of intersection gives the data for overhaul.

A very useful feature is that if changes in the operation conditions are expected, for instance when sailing from Nothern Europe to the Persian Gulf, the influence on various parameters may be checked very conveniently by a question-and-answer procedure. Furthermore, when some maintenance has to be done, but the time available does not allow for all components in the system to be overhauled, DataTrend will simulate the effect of overhauling on specific components pointed out by the operator. By this means, irrelevant components may be skipped, and the few hours available may be used where they best pay off.

A more detailed explanation will be given in a seperate lecture.

AUTOCHIEF II

The main engine remote control system is integrated with the DataChief computer system. Major features:

- May be installed in already commissioned ships.

- Stepless RPM regulation

- Fully programmed, does not demand any training of navigator.

- Built in electronic RPM controller

- Automatic program for running of cold engine

- Protects the engine by automatic reduction of RPM for 4 variable conditions

- Protects the engine by automatic stop for 4 variable conditions

- Automatic stop after 3 starting attempts

- Over-load protection.

- Adjustable barred RPM range

- "Fails to safety"

- Built in "Crash Manoeuvre"

- Built in fault finding procedure, does not demand any knowledge of electronics.

- Simulation of the system possible without running the engine.

- Built up with Integrated Circuits

- Pre-programmed logic for several main engine makes and types.

- Start air pressure indication in Bridge panel

- Revolution counter included.

DESCRIPTION OF THE PROTOTYPE INSTALLATION

As the first system delivered by a commercial company and for commercial use, the DataChief system have been installed onboard in a 280 000 tons tanker M/S "THORS-HOLM" owned by A/S Thor Dahl, Sandefjord and built by Mitsui Shipbuilding & Engineering Co. Ltd., Chiba Works, Japan.

This installation includes DataSafe, DataPower, DataTrend and AUTOCHIEF II and on bridge DataBridge system and was put into service 15th. of February 1973.

All equipment such as computer, I/O-system, panels and sensors have been delivered by NORCONTROL as owners supply, and the yard has been responsible for the installation. The project started medio 1971 and during the project planning it has been 3 technical discussions with the yard in order to discuss installation and to give yard system knowledge. During the same period system solutions have been discussed with owner and yard, so we may say that how the system operates today is based upon cooperation between NORCONTROL-Mitsui and owner.

The system comprises 286 analog inputs 236 binary inputs and 127 binary outputs. The analog inputs are mostly pressure, temperature and levels and the binary input mostly levels and information concerning pump status, such as pump running, stop push button or start push button pressed. The binary outputs are used for start and stop of pumps, connect or disconnect main circuit breakers, governor motor up or down and start or stop of aux. diesel engines, etc.

Sensors used are standard pressure transducers, diff. pressure transducers, temperature sensors, (platina - termistor - thermo - elements) and inductive sensors for piston ring control.

As mentioned it has been 3 technical discussions during the project planning period. In the first technical discussion mainly systemsolution, sensor specification, installation, (location of sensors, cable arrangement, cable specification) and time-schedule were discussed. In the second, further discussion concerning installation and details around drawings were discussed, and in the third, details around system and final discussion concerning installation were the main items.

As a result of these technical discussions no people from NORCONTROL attended during the installation period. It shall also be mentioned that NORCONTROL have a similar delivery to the same yard, and for this project there will be no technical ¨ discussions.

As mentioned the yard have been responsible for the installation, i.e. installation of all sensors, cable arrangement and connection to sensors and alarmpanels and assistance during testing period. In order to have same type of sensors and equipment in system delivered by Mitsui, the yard have ordered sensors from same manufacturers.

For computersystem, ordinary ships cable with twisted pair can be used. Analog and binary signals should be transferred in seperate cables. For cable installation the following recommendations should be followed:

- The cable shall not run parallel with a 100KVA, 440V cable, more than 10 meter and with a min. distance of 0.1 meter. If the min. distance is more than 0.1 meter, the parallel run may be decreased proportionally.

- If the cable must cross a high voltage cable (as mentioned above) the min. distance should be 0.1 meter.

- If the cable passes near a high voltage transformer, the cable should be, as far as practical, led straight by and the distance should be more than two times the transformer's main dimensions.

- Cable screen shall be earthed to the system's common earth system.

Otherwise the ordinary recommendation for installation of signal cable to be followed.

For future installation it should only be necessary with one technical discussion, as during this project all necessary documents and drawings have been completed.

TESTING

The testing of the complete DataChief system may be regarded as being carried out in two phases:

Phase 1:

Official testing of the automation and safety systems, i.e. AUTOCHIEF II, DataSafe and DataPower.

This testing does not differ very much from the testing of conventional systems in any particular way, except perhaps in one respect: As the system gives no false alarms during making the engine room stand-by or during maneouvering, most of the criteria for cancelling non-appropriate alarms must be simulated since the testing is carried out at various stages of completion of the plant. The system software is designed with this in mind, and all simulation is done by our system engineers as the testing proceeds and later verified during mooring trial and sea trial.

Phase 2:

Testing of the DataTrend system. All sensor connections are checked by the yard before delivery of the ship. The various functions of the system requires the main engine to be running for some time, and can at the earliest be started on the sea trial. But as the sea trial often can be rather stressed and with a tight schedule, most of this testing is carried out during the ship's maiden voyage. This also allows for sufficient time and opportunity to train the ship's crew in how to get the best advantages of the system.

With the necessary assistance from the yard in checking of cabling and sensor calibration, 2 systems engineers from NORCONTROL will be required for the testing of a complete DataChief system.

OPERATION

Even though the system may be considered complicated with all the functions included, this does not appear in the operation of the system.

To start with maintenance, this is limited to replacing malfunctioning sensors and electronic cards, and routine service on the logger.

Continous self-checking and off-line check programs help locating possible system failures.

The alarm system is designed so as to supply detailed information with a minimum of manual operation. Only a few lamps are used, instead most information is presented on a easy-to-read display.

All setpoints for alarms and automatic actions, and all time delays, are conveniently adjusted by the common communication devices (display, keyboard, pushbuttons), with automatic logging of all adjustments made.

The man/machine communication is made with emphasis on getting a fool-proof operation. The engineers will need very little training before having full confidence in using the system, as it is quite impossible in any way to disturb the proper execution of any programs by for instance pressing wrong push-buttons or giving wrong input. But, as in any system, limits may be erroneously adjusted.

All data collection for DataTrend is automatic, except for the cylinder indication. The transducers for cylinder pressure and f.o. pressure are not continously connected, so this must be done periodically by the engineers. The pressures are then read in by the ocmputer and analysed.

The outputs from DataTrend contain well-known engine parameters, and can be used by the engineers without further information. However, to achieve the best usage, detailed documentation is included in the delivery, as well as training of the crew by one of our systems engineers during the maiden voyage. Training of future crews can also be arranged.

Our experience regarding operation of the first installation is interesting. Probably because a computer is involved, the system is assumed rather complicated to operate. However, after only a short introduction and a few demonstrations, the crew seemed to be gaining confidence very quickly.

DIRECT DIGITAL CONTROL OF A DIESEL ENGINE

Pier Paolo Puliafito
Department of Electrical Engineering
University of Genoa

Fulvio Tosi
At the time of experiment with the Laboratory of
Naval Automation (Genoa) and now by the CE.TE.NA.
(Genoa)

INTRODUCTION

Aim of this paper is to describe a controllistic experiment on a ship propulsion diesel engine performed by the shipboard computer.
Such experiment has been carried out within "Pro getto Esquilino" Programme, which was meant for studying the opportunity of a ship global control. As well known, the problem of main engine automatic control has already produced interesting solutions which, from an industrial point of view, may guarantee, by means of up-to-date control devices, a conspicuously efficient and safe service.
Some important realizations of european and overseas builders have recently been treated in the techno-economical literature, to which the reader addressed: see the included bibliography at (1) and (2) . Unfortunately much rarer are the realizations of on-line computer control.
The experiment, which is dealt with in this paper, has been carried on a 12000HP, 8 cylinder, simple acting, supercharged FIAT B758 Diesel Engine. Ms/Esquilino, built in 1963, belongs to Lloyd Triestino Shipping Company and has been put on freight service on Italy-Far East routes. The ship was already originally equipped with relatively modern telemetering and telecontrol devices. Photographs no. 1 and 2 show two details of our realization: they present, respectively, the fuel handwheel setting and the manoeuvring lever pneumatic servo-positioning.
During the experiment a 1800 IBM (16-bit word lenght, 24 kwords core memory and 4 microsecond cycle time) computer has been employed. Since its installation had to be performed a few years after ship's fitting, the computer room couldn't be arranged but relatively far from the bridge and from the control room.
From the bridge messages can be sent to the computer through the engine telegraph; while a teletype can receive messages on the bridge no such typewriter is equipped in the control room where all communications are carried out through an alarm display provided with illuminated windows.

AIMS OF THE EXPERIMENT

Ship propulsion diesel engine automation chiefly consists of such phases:
a) warming-up and debugging
b) control during manoeuvring
c) control during navigation
d) logging

Only phase a), or engines warming up, has been neglected in the experiment while all others have been considered.
Screw speed is the controlled variable during manoeuvring while during free navigation, as output variable, mean of cylinders exhaust gas temperature was chosen, being a quantity related with the shaft power. It has been done so because, along the free navigation phase, it is expedient to proceed to a constant power control, i.e. in open loop, since shaft speed is subject to random variations, as much relevant as heavier is the ship's pitching.
The functions, assigned to the control programs during the manoeuvring phase, can be summarized like this:
- execution of ahead and astern starting, including one or more, up to three, attempts in case of failed starting.
- execution of bridge order, as to telegraph pointings, and keeping up the requested speed according to this code:

Ahead or Astern Telegraph Pointer Position	Required Speed R.P.M.
DEAD SLOW	42.5
SLOW	50
HALF	60
FULL	80

- execution of reverse and stop orders.
Then, the programs are partly sequential and partly closed loop in order to control the screw propeller shaft speed, here called Ω .
Also in this phase of operations, a certain number of physical quantities, peculiarly important for the engine operation, must be kept under control. Adequate thresholds, beyond which red alarm indications up to engine stoppage orders are provided, have been purposely set on such quantities values.
During the navigation the programs functions are the following:
- reaching out of steady-state conditions, skipping any critical speed range: such forbidden speed ranges are set, on this engine, one about the 90 RPM and the other from 106 to 109 RPM.
- keeping up said steady state conditions and scanning checks of engine operative conditions (logging).
Crash arrest are expected to be feasible right

from the available programs, though no trial has been made as yet.

Fig. 1 schematically shows control and output process variables, which are:

p = manoeuvring handle pointings (five possible positions)

ϑ = fuel pump cam angle

T = average of mean cylinders exhaust gas temperatures

Ω = shaft speed

Evidence is also given to the blocks which put on the orders: the engine room telegraph during manoeuvring or the bridge teletype during free-navigation.

The request of the dynamic characteristics of control actions are simple enough: during the manoeuvring steady-state conditions must be reached without overshoot, i.e. an underdamped responce is compulsory. Indeed, it is mostly undesiderable that the system happens to be overperturbated, as it would be owing to the overshoots.

Cut frequency is ordinarly found of some cycle/sec, during the manoeuvring phase, whereas during open-sea navigation, because of the upper limit on Ω, shaft speed increments or decrements must be very gradually performed. Such constraints on Ω is complied with by small spaced variations of Ω, in order not to produce dangerous thermal overstresses. Taking into account that the slow speed range ($\Omega \leq 80$ RPM) usually attends to manoeuvring, whereas the upper speed range refers to free navigation, said constraints requires that the upward transition from $\Omega = 80$ RPM to $\Omega = 116$ °/. 122 RPM steady state is performed in about 2 hours.

CONTROL DIAGRAM

In Fig.2 a simplified block-diagram of the shaft Ω speed control is illustrated. Manoeuvring lever control block and signal have been purposely omitted: which implies that none of the sequential phase is there represented.

It appears not to be necessary to give here more details on the sequential aspect of the problem, indeed quite tipical and simple: it shall suffice to remember that the five pointings or pointer positions of the manoeuvring handle are the following:
- STOP (fuel is cut-out)
- AHEAD and ASTERN STARTING (starting air is cyclically admitted to cylinders)
- AHEAD and ASTERN RUNNING

As shown in Fig. 2, the computer is also employed within the handwheel positioning loop: block R represents the controller which elaborates the signal to be fed in the servomotor G_m, that actually performes the positioning.

Block D.E. represents the Diesel Engine which outputs the driving torque C_m. After naming J the inertial momentum said diagram evidences the feedback due to the screw propeller characteristic.

Such characteristic is, of course, non-linear since the propeller resistant torque varies according Ω^3 i.e. a cubic law.

The possibility that some external factor may perturbate Ω has been identified with the noise: for instance, N could be the rudder angle.

Naturally, the system, as a whole, is non-linear. Actually, such non-linearity is due to the fact that $\Delta\Omega$, related to $\Delta\vartheta$, heavily depends on working engine conditions.

Also the response readiness depends on those conditions: therefore the non-linearity has been located in the outpart of Fig. 2.

Keeping N = cost., ϑ and Ω may be regarded, respectively, as input and output of a single block, which then represents the whole diesel engine, shafting and propeller.

Block F then means to take into account such non-linearity and has to compensate it.

SYSTEM IDENTIFICATION

As shown in Fig. 2, system comprehends two blocks only: one for the actuator and its feeding. This block is indicated with G_m and its structure can be approximated by the following transfer function:

$$G_m = K_m \frac{e^{-\tau s}}{s} \qquad \text{where} \qquad \tau = 1 \text{ sec.}$$

The other block, indicated with G_e, being intented for the propulsion diesel engine itself, has ϑ as input and Ω as output.

Its structure depends on many a factors, which make it difficult to formulize. Most of said factors are entirely uncontrollable and hardly measurable: that's why it is pratically impossible take them into account when numerical values are to be given to the system parameters.

Among such factors, all those physical quantities acting on the screw propeller characteristic (like sea water temperature and density, depth contour, ship's draught) or certain particular "states" (like ship's bottom foulness or engine cylinder compression) are to be included.

Obviously, the weight of these factors is by no means easy to evaluate quantitatively: anyhow, roughly speaking, when ship's operation is set far from boundary conditions (as, for instance, shoals or inefficient engine cylinders) those factors can be properly negletted, i.e. their effects are not relevant and can be disregarded.

On the contrary, ship's rudder angle heavily weighs on Ω and is therefore considered a noise-input in Fig. 2.

By the logged data of engine trials and the technical literature, where the terms "rise-time" and "gain"[3] are widely used, a very simple small-signal linearized model can be introduced:

$$G_e(s) = \frac{\Delta\Omega(s)}{\Delta\vartheta(s)} = \frac{K_e}{1 + s \cdot \tau_e} \qquad (1)$$

On such grounds, the limits of the model, in which K_e is mainly influenced by the propeller steady state characteristic while all the above mentioned factors act prevailingly and unknownly on τ_e, are clearly defined.

Notwithstanding its uncertainty, the model remained sufficient for its duty and the parameters identification obtained results mostly interesting. It is also noticeable that such model, already valid for increasing running speeds, can be fairly assumed to be valid also for decreasing speeds though with much a greater value for τ_e, owing to the propeller inertia.

The indicated values for τ_e are meant for increasing Ω running upward variations.

When the model (1) is accepted, the global transfer function of the system to be identified and of zero-order hold can be expressed in terms of z-transform, by:

$$G_e(z) = K_e \frac{1-\exp\ (-Tc/\tau_e\ )}{z-\exp\ (-Tc/\tau_e\ )}$$

from which this recurrent relation can be drawn:

$$\Delta\Omega(n+1) = A \cdot \Delta\Omega(n) + B \cdot \Delta\vartheta(n) \qquad (3)$$

where

$$A = \exp\ (-T_c/\ \tau_e)$$
$$B = K_e(1-\exp(-T_c/\ \tau_e)\ ) \qquad (4)$$
$$T_c = \text{sampling period}$$

In this case T_c = 200 ms
Actually, besides K_e and τ_e, it is also unknown the operating point in whose neighbourhood the linearization has been performed, i.e. that $\bar\Omega$ value which corresponds to the steady-state intermediate position $\bar\vartheta$ of fuel handwheel.
As a matter of fact, $\bar\vartheta$ might be unknown, too, but its determination is quite easy to reckon, whereas the measure of $\bar\Omega$ is affected by more relevant errors due to the non-uniform propeller rotation.
A parametric identification has been accomplished, according to the minimum-square criterion in two subsequent steps. The regression method has been used, by means of (3), in order to find a minimum with respect to $\bar\Omega$, having fixed $\bar\vartheta$.
Indeed, assumed that measure errors have zero mean value and unity covariance matrix, from:

$$\begin{bmatrix}\Delta\Omega(n+1)\end{bmatrix} = \begin{bmatrix}\Delta\Omega(n), & \Delta\vartheta(n)\end{bmatrix}\begin{bmatrix}A\\B\end{bmatrix}$$

where $\begin{bmatrix}\Delta\Omega(n+1)\end{bmatrix}$ is a 199-element vector (array)
$[\Delta\Omega(n), \Delta\vartheta(n)]$ is a 199 x 2 matrix
A, B are given by (4)
A and B can be obtained (4):

$$\begin{bmatrix}A\\B\end{bmatrix} = \begin{bmatrix}\begin{bmatrix}\Delta\Omega(n)\\\Delta\vartheta(n)\end{bmatrix}\begin{bmatrix}\Delta\Omega(n), & \Delta\vartheta(n)\end{bmatrix}\end{bmatrix}^{-1} \begin{bmatrix}\Delta\Omega(n)\\\Delta\vartheta(n)\end{bmatrix}\begin{bmatrix}\Delta\Omega(n+1)\end{bmatrix} \qquad (5)$$

Equation (5) gives A and B. Thus K_e and τ_e are obtained, for a certain value of $\bar\Omega$: it is then possible to determine the square error.
A further search for the value of $\bar\Omega^*$, which minimize, such error, has been carried out by means of a 8-step Fibonacci search procedure, i.e. with a certain approximation.
Identification next step, now for a fixed $\bar\Omega^*$, provides a sharper search for the minimum, according to an "hill climbing" procedure consisting in computing such error at points set on a certain network. Said network is centered on the point corrispondent to the minimum error previously computed, where every point represents a couple of K_e and τ_e values. This way permits a quick convergence since the procedure moves from a point close enough to the minimum.
Fig. 3 and 4 show the identification results: they are clearly referred to recordings in which the rudder angle remains almost unchanged.
The values of gain K_e, which is the ratio of corresponding transducers, appear to individuate quite well a third-order curve (a cubic): from its contour it can be seen how the gain decreases with an increasing shift speed, accordingly to the physic reality.

Instead, the values of time constant τ_e are a little bit spread, because this parameter is certainly more subject to the particular conditions in which data were logged.
Fig. 5 compares, for same inputs, the actual system and the model outputs.

CONTROL PROGRAMS AND THEIR ORGANIZATION

The organization and function of the main programs implemented on the ship's computer, in order to achieve the diesel engine control, are discussed hereafter.
It is noticeable that the programs linkage is actived only on account of the functions to be performed or in relation with certain external causes, because the research project included the contemporary operation of other programs, on a time-sharing basis.

Switching to Automatic Control

This program is called up by merely pressing a push-button in the control room and performs a sequence of checks on the positioning of the telegraph handle, of the manoeuvring lever and its pneumatic lines, on the running engine operation and ship's running, etc.
Switching to AUTOMATIC is permitted only if certain congruity conditions are complied with and if circuits can guarantee the engine control. Such switching then happens automatically in the control room: it consists of the pressurization of pneumatic circuits on the manoeuvring lever and servomotor clutch on the fuel pump regulation spindle.
A mere cut-out of said compressed air, through the MANUAL switch, produces the process computer cut-out.
This program also prepares the execution of other programs, according to the actual phase of manoeuvring on free-navigation.

Orders decoding

A displacement of telegraph handle initializes, through a process interrupt, this program which is effective during manoeuvring operation or in case of "crash arrest".
A comparison between the former and the actual telegraph handle position is performed by the program, which, taking into account such indication, classify the orders in one of these five type:
- engine starting
- charge of running speed
- inversion (reversal)
- stop the engine
- finished with engine.

Manoeuvring Control

This supervision program is cut-out and in by the orders decoding program: i.e. it is a sequential control and closed loop control mixed-program.
During the manoeuvring phase, any position of the telegraph handle implies the settling of a certain set-point for shaft speed, according to the code mentioned before.
Linkage among the various phases (as to starting and speed control, etc.), as soon as the previous phase has been completed, is performed by the program itself.

Said program also provides a scanning control of all most important quantities interesting the engine operation and safety.

Bridge orders

By means of a simple conversational program from the bridge teletype, the following options can be made on the type of control during open sea-going:
1. average speed control and logging;
2. mean of average cylinder exhaust temperatures and logging;
3. logging without any control.

Navigation Control

This program provides the engine control during free-navigation, bringing up the engine to its steady-state after the manoeuvring of departure or slowing down the shaft speed upon arrival at port.

A logging, which takes into account the trend of any measured quantity and then helps the prediction of its possible further abnormal values, is also effectual, within this program.

SOME COMMENTS ABOUT SEA TRIALS AND CONCLUSIONS

On-line tests and trial have been performed on the voyage Piraeus – Venice and Venice – Trieste, during the regular commercial service of the ship. Unfortunately, an imperfect functioning of the recorder prevented us from presenting some data registration taken on the first part of the trials (that Piraeus – Venice voyage) the registered data shown in Figg. 6 are all referred to the Venice – Trieste voyage.

All registrations have been performed during the manoeuvring phases, while very few trials have been made during free-navigation since, in such cases, the registration would lack of evidence: in fact, being the shaft speed constant or almost so, the average cylinder exhaust temperature are also nearly constant and, anyhow the phase is an exceedlingly long one.

Some consideration about such trials can be interesting:

- All engine starting have been performed on a fixed time period (800 msec) air admission into engine cylinder, regardless of the environmental conditions (headway or sternway ship, etc.). Results have proved to be very good, although more trials could have supplied an optimum (or more than one) of such starting time period.
- Reversal manoeuvrings are not "hard", i.e. no counterstroke air admission was allowed: that's why some reversals are quite long.
- The structure of the simply proportional (with variable gain) type regulator is not entirely satisfactory, as it cannot expected to be but so. Such fault becomes so much more evident as lesser the ship draughts: in fact, during the Venice – Trieste passage, because of the light draft, emerging screw blades "slapped" the sea-surface and cavitational phenomena occurred, particularly during astern running and on speed changes. Instead, a deeper draught have made these phenomena less relevant, although satisfactory results could not yet have been recorded. The scantiness of disposable time prevented possible improvements and variegated trials.

Considering all mentioned topics, some although not definitive conclusions about the so gathered experience can be eventually drawn.

First of all, it is mostly advisable, in this kind of applications, to dispose of a minicomputer entirely destined for the engine control: it thus shall be feasible to use a more efficient programmation technique, for instance, through cyclical programmed tests of congruity conditions. This being the case, no more problems of promptiness are to be faced and the ship's plant safety is increased.

Besides that, with reference to Fig. 2, it may be expedient to dignify the ship's computer by not letting it to perform any function within the inner loop.

The fuel handwheel position control can be obtained, via hardware, by using circuits and devices already exixting on the market and so leaving to the computer those peculiar duties of identification, elaboration, prediction and, eventually, optimization.

As observed before, many parameters depend on environmental or contingent conditions: to realize those controls which deeper take into account all such various conditions appears to be the scope of better exploiting computers capabilities, in order to improve the safety and reliability of the ship's engine plant.

REFERENCES

(1) Ragazzini, W., "Sguardo generale sull'automazione degli apparati motori diesel per navi mercantili", Boll. Tecn. FIAT G.M.N., n° 1-2, vol. XX, 1967.

(2) Gavazzi, R., Fedrigo, G., "Pylotron new approach to ship automation", C. Gavazzi Tecn. Report.

(3) Ogawara, Y., Iwata, S., Tsujita, T., Sasaki, K., "Governing operation of diesel engine for high-speed ship in rough sea", Japan Shipbuilding and Marine Eng., vol. 6, n° 4, 1972.

(4) Jenkins, G.M., Watts, D.G., "Spectral analysis and its applications", Holden-Day, 1969.

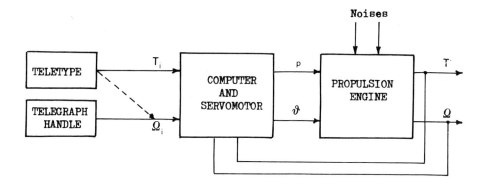

FIG. 1

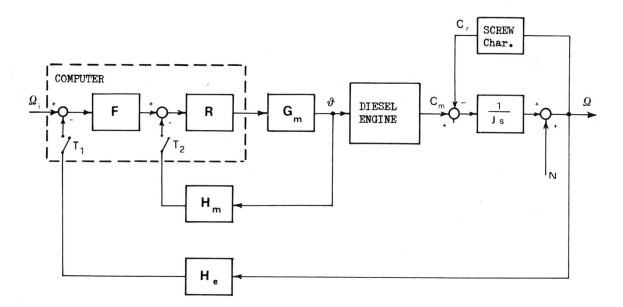

FIG. 2

242

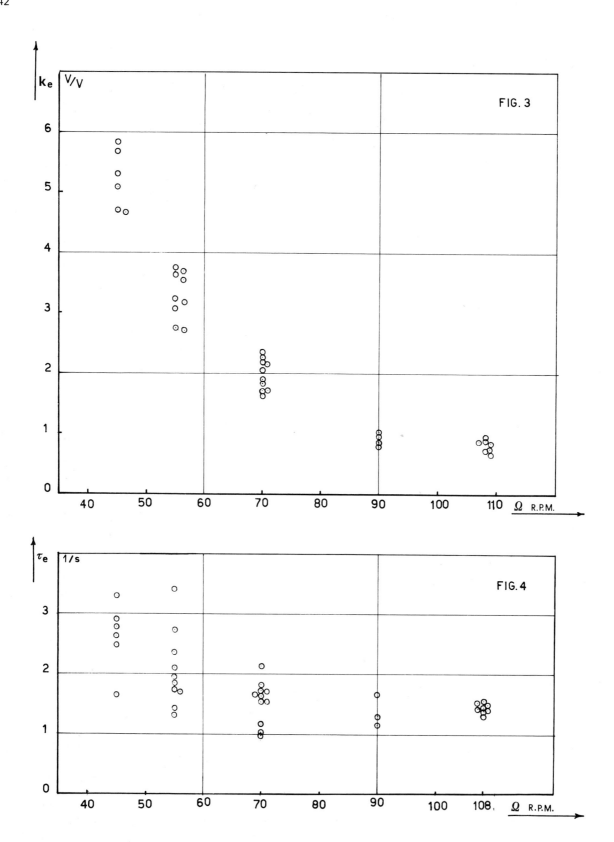

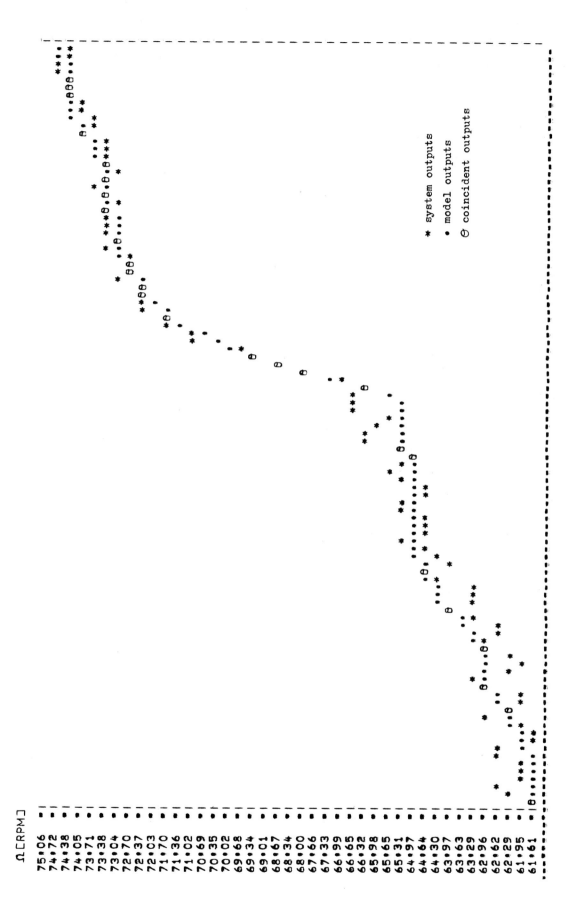

FIG. 5

* system outputs
• model outputs
Θ coincident outputs

FIG.6a

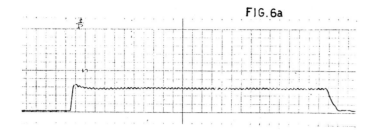

Avviamento Avanti Molto
Adagio - Fermo

**Ahead start - dead slow
ahead - Stop**

Fermo - Avviamento Avanti
Tutta

**Stop - Ahead start -
Full Ahead**

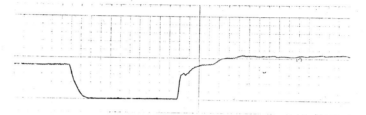

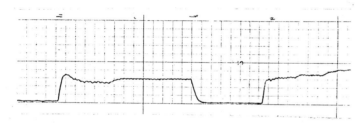

Avviamento Addietro Molto
Adagio - Fermo - Avviamento
Avanti Mezza

**Astern start - Dead slow
astern - Stop - Ahead start -
Half Ahead**

Avviamento Addietro Molto
Adagio

**Astern start - Dead slow
astern**

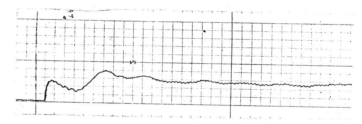

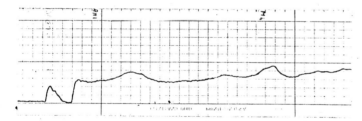

Avviamento Addietro Molto
Adagio (riuscito al secondo
tentativo) - Addietro Mezza

**Astern start - Dead slo
astern (first attempt failed) -
Half astern**

Avviamento Addietro Molto
Adagio - Avviamento Avanti
Molto Adagio (inversione)
**Astern start - Dead slow
astern - Ahead start - dead
slow ahead (reversal)**

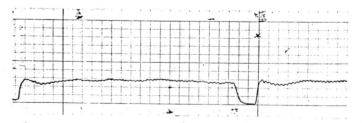

FIG. 6b

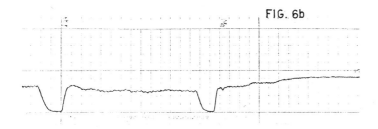

Avviamento Addietro Molto
Adagio – Avviamento Avan-
ti Mezza (2 inversioni)

**Astern start – Dead slow
astern – Ahead start –
Half Ahead (2 reversal)**

Avanti Molto Adagio –
Avanti Mezza

**Dead slow Ahead – Half
Ahead**

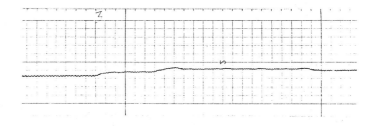

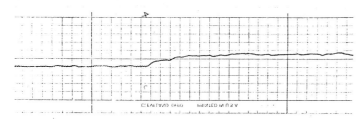

Avanti Mezza – Avanti
Tutta

Half Ahead – Full Ahead

Addietro Molto Adagio –
Addietro Adagio – Addie_
tro Mezza

**Dead slow astern – Slow
astern – half astern**

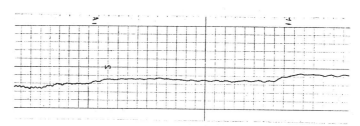

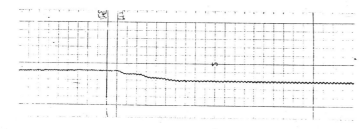

Avanti Mezza – Avanti
Molto Adagio

**Half Ahead – Dead slow
Ahead**

Avanti Tutta – Avanti
Molto Adagio – Fermo
**Full Ahead – Dead slow
ahead – Stop**

**scale: time 5sec/div
         speed 15RPM/div**

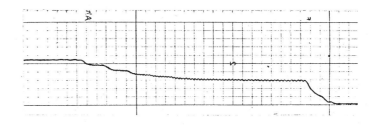

DIRECT DIGITAL CONTROL OF DIESEL ENGINE FUEL INJECTION

Arnold Hansen
senior research engineer
The Ship Research Institute of Norway

Introduction.

Vital functions in a diesel engine such as fuel injection and valve operation are controlled by cams driven from the engine crankshaft. Control functions are optimized at the design stage and cannot be altered during running of the engine.

Absolute and relative load for a ship propulsion engine will vary with time. Ambient condition, fuel quality and engine condition (component and overall condition) are also time dependent. The ideal control concept should therefore incorporate a continuous process optimization. This could possibly be achieved using digital computers to perform the necessary measurements, process analysis and controls.

A research project aiming at evaluating the potential process improvements using direct digital control (DDC) of

- exhaust valve operation
- cylinder lubrication
- cylinder cooling
- v. p. propeller pitch
- fuel injection,

is carried through by The Ship Research Institute of Norway (NSFI) in collaboration with The Institute of Internal Combustion Engines, NTH.

As indicated by the title, the present paper will concentrate on DDC of fuel injection, however, a few remarks regarding the benefits of DDC on some of the other functions mentioned, will be given.

Cylinder lubrication.

Piston ring malfunction resulting in gas leakage past the rings is a serious problem on large slow-running diesel engines. This gas leakage causes a temperature increase in the lubricated surface of the liner, reducing the loading ability of the lube oil film. Frequently the gas leakage, therefore, is the transition to piston ring scuffing (1).

Extensive investigations made by NSFI have shown that it is possible to normalize the piston ring function by a temporary increase in lube oil feed rate (2). Gas leakage is sensibly detected by temperature sensors in the liner and could therefore be the controlling parameter in an automatic feed rate control, preferable in today's unmanned engine rooms. This feed rate control could be further improved by utilizing the information about piston ring behaviour given be proximity transducers located in the liner (2).

The transducer signal, however, requires rather intelligent treatment. Thus this control task can best be realized using a micro-computer.

Cylinder cooling.

Cylinder cooling control strategy today is to keep cooling water inlet temperature, alternatively outlet temperature, constant. Metal temperature measurements in liner and cylinder cover has been made by us during sudden load increase and decrease, (also full power to stop and stop to full power) testing both alternatives. The temperature histories in liner and cover are practically the same for both alternatives, figure 1.

During low load, however, we found the metal temperatures in the lower part of the liner so low that a potential risk of sulphur condensation existed. To prevent this happening, the cooling water temperature should therefore be adjusted upwards as the load decreases. This could be achieved using a load dependent cooling water temperature set point or better in a multi-variable control system using metal temperatures in liner lower part and cylinder cover as controlling parameters.

Fuel injection.

Background.

Experience gathered during two years running of a slow-speed 2-stroke engine with a comprehensive instrumentation and a computer (later on referred to as the Vianna-project) revealed that excessive thermal loading of the components surrounding the combustion space is created by abnormal combustion (2). The same kind of observations were made during the extensive investigations performed during The Large Bore Research Project, Ref. (1) and (3).

(3) describes in particular the temperature distribution in piston during stable and unstable combustion. Transition to unstable combustion causes a temperature redistribution, giving higher temperatures at the peripheral parts of the piston top and slightly lower temperatures in the centre.

Considerable temperature increases caused by bad injectors have been measured in cylinder covers, pistons and upper part of liners during the "Vianna-project".

Periods with excessive thermal loading have also been experienced at the same time in more or less all cylinders. Rate of heat release analysis based on very accurate cylinder pressure measurements showed slightly lower burning rates in the initial phase and especially longer total burning times. These observations, together with other facts, lead to the conclusion that the fuel was the primary reason for the excessive thermal loading.

Burning of residual fuel

Experimental and theoretical studies of burning drops reported by Chen and El-Wakil in (4) have contributed to better understanding of residual fuel burning. The drop histories can be divided into four phases: 1 pre-ignition, 2 self-ignition and combustion, 3 thermal decomposition and 4 carbon residue burning.

Their findings showed that the asphaltene constituent of the residual fuel contributed greatly to burning irregularities. The burning rates of the fuel minus asphaltenes were also slightly faster than those of the regular fuel. Drop lifetime is substantially dependent on initial drop size.

Phase 4 referred to as the carbon residue phase is probably the most interesting one with regard to burning of residual fuel in diesel engines. Burning occurs at the surface of the solid residue, and the rate is low, the length of combustion being comparable to that of the liquid phase. The initial drop size, however, greatly affects the burning times of the solids.

The excessive thermal loading referred to above, attributable to the fuel quality, is possibly caused by a drastic increase in radiant heat during the carbon residue phase. This in turn probably being caused by a high content of asphaltenes in the residual fuel used.

The burning rate during the liquid phase when running a diesel engine on residual fuel having a high content of ashpaltenes and resins can be increased to normal by decreasing the spray mean drop size.

The greatest benefit, however, would then obviously be the reduction in thermal loading as a result of higher burning rate during the carbon residue phase.

Controlling drop size and spray penetration

Experiments referred by Komaroff and Melcher (5) verifies the well-known dependence the injector nozzle diameter has on the drop size. Their results also showed that the nozzle length and injection pressure affect the drop size. Doubling the pressure nearly halves the mean drop size.

Knight's formula for calculating mean surface diameter (6) gives a less pressure dependence on drop size than (5). His formula also shows that the fuel viscosity slightly affects the mean drop size and that the nozzle coefficient has a great influence.

This latter fact is probably the reason for the injector-created excessive thermal loading reported above. The nozzle wear causes an increase in nozzle coefficient and consequently reduced injection pressure, both factors contributing to increase in mean drop size.

Despite the discrepancy between (5) and (6), in to what power the mean drop size is affected by the injection pressure, the latter parameter is the obvious one in controlling drop size distribution and thereby burning rate.

Fuel control system and strategy

A fuel injection system according to figure 2 basically consisting of a high pressure pump, accumulator including maximum pressure control valve, an electronic timing and pressure control valve (later referred to as "injection control valve" and a normal injector makes it possible to control timing and pressure time function during the fuel injection.

The fuel injection cyclic control and the process optimization can be performed according to the principles shown in figure 3. Reference signal input R 1 is required mean indicated pressure or in other words, fuel injected per cycle. Based on this input a set of reference signals: injection timing, accumulator pressure and pressures during injection are calculated. These reference signals are fed to the cyclic control which works according to the feed-back principle.

Superior to this cyclic control acts a process optimization based on measured thermal loading and rate of heat release during the combustion. This information is used to adjust a model predicting the optimum combustion process for the actual fuel and engine condition and accordingly adjusting the algoritmes calculating the reference signals necessary to achieve this process.

Work in progress

A fuel injection system according to the lines drawn in fig. 2 has been developed and tested to see that the pressure variations required could be obtained. The result was positive. The system is later on implemented on one cylinder of a two-stroke cross scavenged engine, 280 mm bore and 420 mm stroke, to perform extensive tests. This computer controlled system is also used in fuel spray investigations utilizing laser holographie.

The objectives with the engine experiments are to study heat release during combustion and thermal loading for a systematic series of injection timing and pressure time functions. The results will firstly be used for evaluating the process improvements this computer controlled fuel injections system makes possible. Secondly they will be utilized in verifying a mathematical combustion process model primarily intended for control software development.

Preliminary engine test runs have been made. The main purpose being, firstly to test hardware and software, secondly to gather data for planning the actual extensive test runs. However, interesting results were obtained already at this initial stage and they will be discussed in the next chapter.

The hardware configuration used during these initial tests are given in figure 4. The fuel injection control hardware functioned as expected (or more correctly, as hoped) and showed to be reliable. So did the new developed system for recording of the crank angle which has an accuracy of $\pm$ 0.025°.

However, during the extensive test runs nearly all the measurements will be performed directly by computer as this has proved labour-saving. The high sampling rate and continuous data reduction required for making very accurate rate of heat release analysis and the fuel injection control task, keeps one computer busy and does not allow any extension in the measurements. We have therefore decided to use two computers, one taking care of the fuel injection control and engine protection, the other performing data acquisition and test analysis.

The control software used at present, controls directly the fuel injection based on a manual input to the computer of required fuel amount per cycle. Fuel injection timing and pressure function are predetermined, but can also be altered manually during running. Both timing and pressure function are automatically adjusted according to engine speed.

Results of preliminary engine tests

As indicated in figure 4, cylinder pressure measurements were performed already on the initial test runs. The transducer's analog signals were digitized by the computer controlled analog to digital converter every one degree crank angle and mean values based on 15 successive sycles calculated. Heat release was calculated on a step-by-step basis, from the measured mean values of cylinder pressure at the beginning and end of the step. Step size of 1 degree crank angle has been used.

The method generally used by us for heat release analysis treats the cylinder as a single zone, values of temperature and gas composition being taken as cylinder average values. Gases are treated as perfect, but variable specific heats are used. Heat transfer to cylinder walls are included using the approach described in (7). The values of the coefficients being chosen to give the proportion of heat to heat transfer obtained by heat balance.

Rate of heat release (ROHR), cylinder pressure (Pcyl) and fuel injection pressure (Pinj) are presented for three of the tests performed, fig. 5, 6 and 7. The curves are mainly presented to demonstrate the ability of this fuel injection system to give a variety of injection time pressure functions and thereby also the ability to adjust the rate of heat release or in other words burning rate.

Test 6 shows an injection time pressure function almost like the one produced by the standard Bosch type system for this engine.

In test 7 the injection control valve signal input was slightly modified to eliminate the pressure drop shortly after injection opening experienced in test 6. Figure 6 clearly demonstrates that this was achieved.

Test 8, fig. 7, has a high injection rate at the beginning, giving a great part of the heat release during premixed combustion (fuel evaporated and prepared to burn before ignition). Injection pressures are low (large drop size) in the last half, resulting in a slowly decreasing rate of heat release compared to test 6 and 7. This is clearly demonstrated in figure 8 which compares relatively cumulative heat release for the same tests.

The last part of the ROHR-curve from test 8 is very much like that found on large slow-running engines burning residual fuel, figure 9. The reason for the slowly decreasing rate in that case being thermal decomposition and carbon residue burning.

The inplementation of this fuel injection control system presented very few problems. Optimum performance could be achieved after only a few test runs. Compared to the time consuming process during engine development which a fuel injection system optimization normally is, this computer based system also offers great advantages in this respect.

The initial tests, some of them referred above, have already verified the ability of this test fuel injection system to control burning rates. It therefore seems probable at this stage that the system will contribute to significant combustion control improvements for engines burning residual fuel.

Summary and Conclusions.

The paper has presented some of the vital control problems of importance for efficient operation of large slow-running marine diesel engines.

Methods of controlling the cooling of thermally loaded parts and cylinder lubrication are outlined.

Problems experienced with burning of residual fuel have been referred and it has been concluded that improved combustion control will benefit. A computer based fuel injection system is presented. An experimental system has been built and preliminary engine tests have been performed. The results clearly demonstrate the system's ability to control burning rates. Significant improvements in combustion control for engines burning residual fuel therefore seem possible.

References:

(1)   Sarsten, A. et.al.: "Thermal Loading and Operation Conditions for Large Marine Diesel Engines", IMAS, London 1969.

(2)   Hansen, Arnold: "Condition monitoring using minicomputer". Experience from M/V "Vianna". (Norwegian) NSFI-seminar June 1972.

(3)   Langballe, M.: "Some observations on combustion problems in large, slow-running diesel engines". DnV-report No. 68-30-M.

(4)   Chen, C.S. and El-Wakil, M.M.: "Experimental and theoretical studies of burning drops of hydrocarbon mixtures." Paper 10, Diesel Engine Comb. Symposium, London 1970, TIME.

(5)   Komaroff, I.and Melcher, K.: "Messung des Strahlkraft und bewegungsgrösse zum Beurteiling der Zerstäubungsgüte von Einspritzstrahlen". Bosch Techn. Berichte 3 - Heft 6 - Dec. 1972.

(6)   Knight, B.E.: "Communication on the Performance of a Type of Swirl Aromizer." Proc. Inst. of Mechn. Engr., 1955, p. 104 - 105.

(7)   Hansen, Arnold, et.al.: "Thermal Loading of Diesel Engine Components and its Prediction, Paper 30 CIMAC 1971.

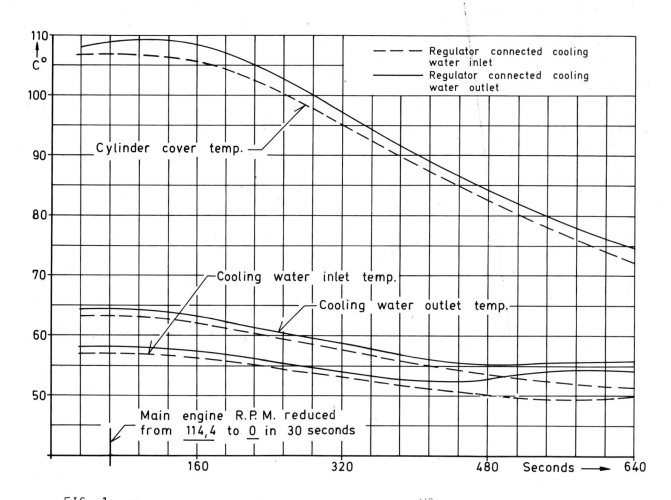

FIG. 1: CYL COVER AND COOLING WATER TEMPERATURE VS. TIME DURING SUDDEN
LOAD DECREASE, REGULATOR CONNECTED TO INLET ALT. OUTLET.

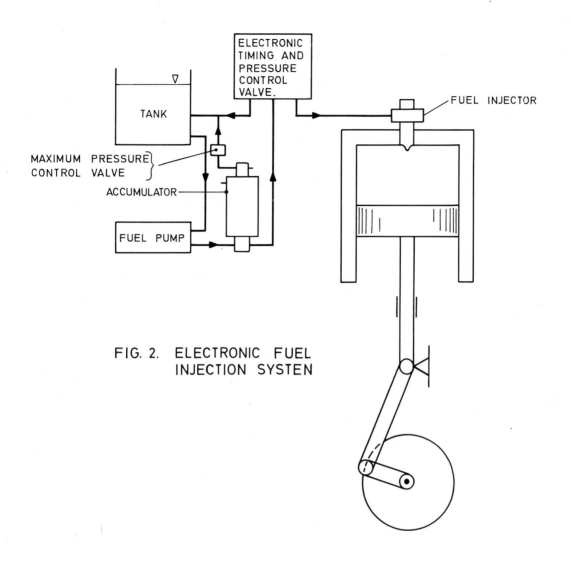

FIG. 2. ELECTRONIC FUEL
INJECTION SYSTEM

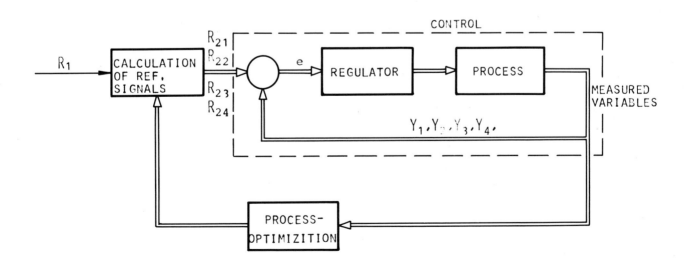

FIG.3: FUEL INJECTION CONTROL AND PROCESS OPTIMIZITION
PRINCIPLES.

254

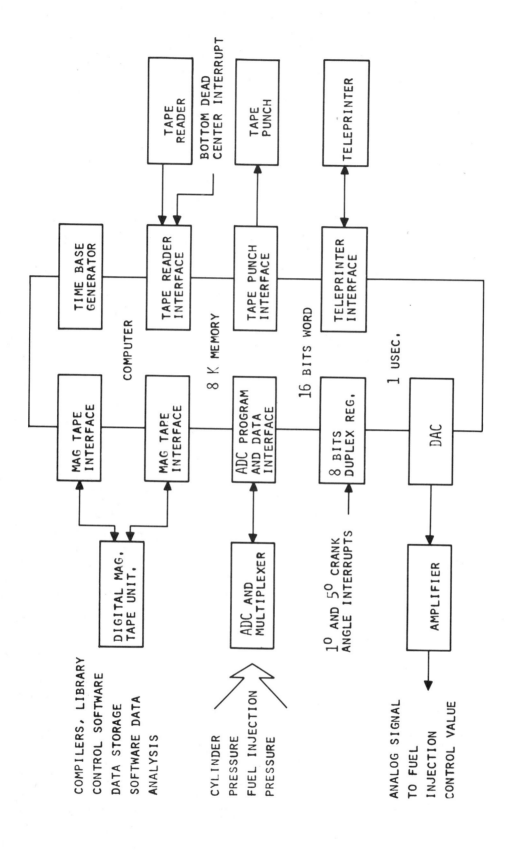

FIG. 4: HARDWARE CONFIGURATION FOR PRELIMINARY TESTS OF COMPUTER
CONTROLLED FUEL INJECTION.

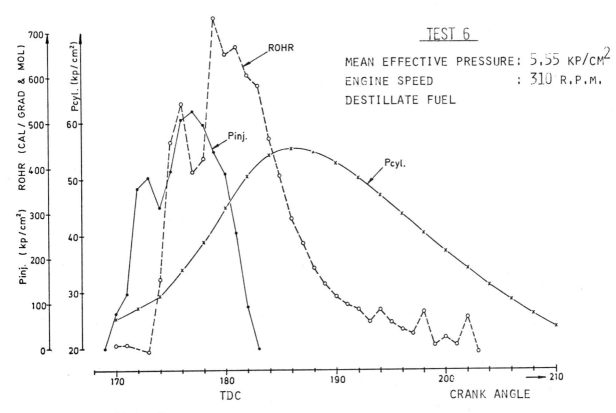

FIGURE 5: RESULTS FROM ENGINE TESTS WITH DIRECT COMPUTER
CONTROLLED FUEL INJECTION.

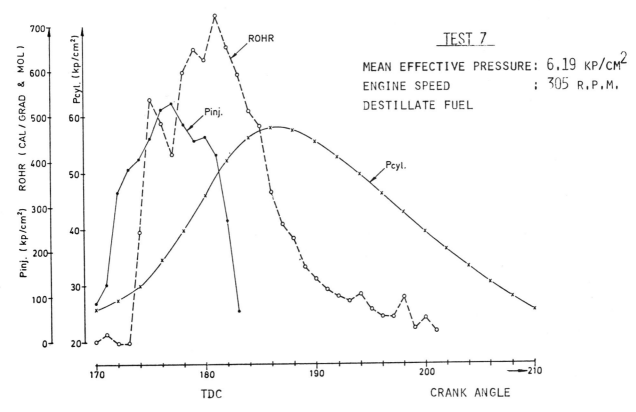

FIGURE 6: RESULTS FROM ENGINE TESTS WITH DIRECT COMPUTER
CONTROLLED FUEL INJECTION.

256

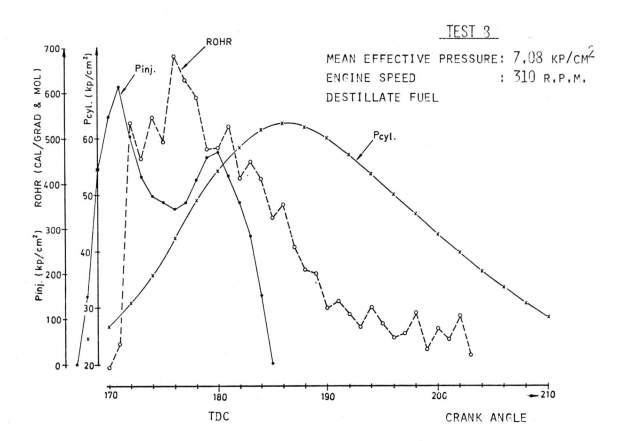

FIGURE 7: RESULTS FROM ENGINE TESTS WITH DIRECT COMPUTER
CONTROLLED FUEL INJECTION.

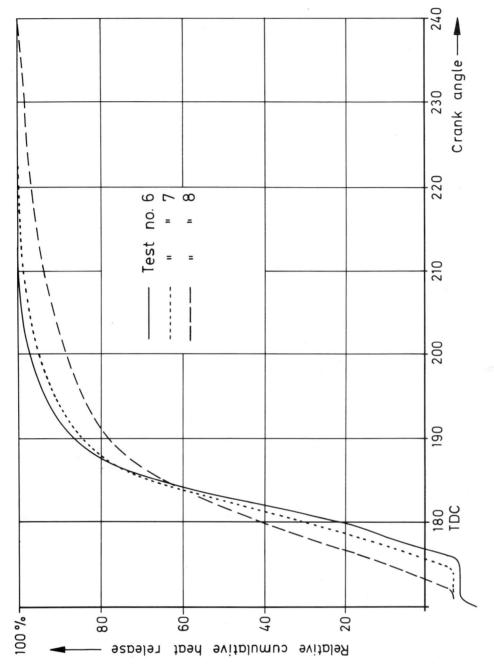

FIG. 8 Results from engine tests with direct computer
controlled fuel injection.

258

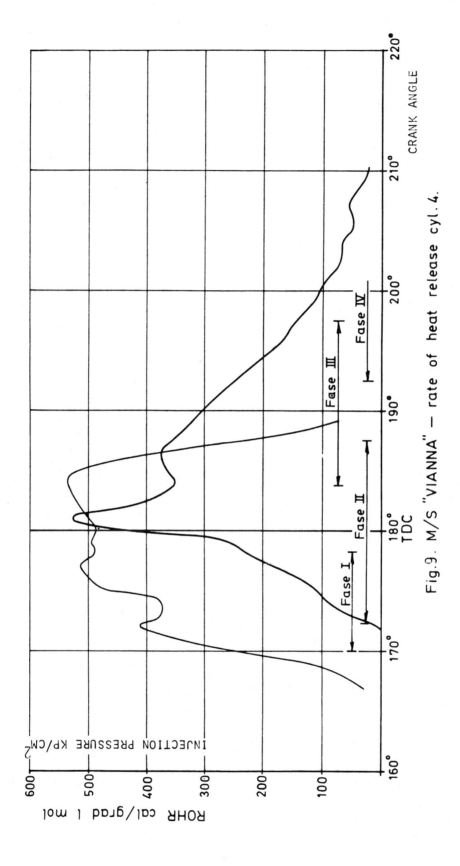

Fig.9. M/S "VIANNA" — rate of heat release cyl. 4.

DATATREND, A COMPUTERIZED SYSTEM FOR ENGINE CONDITION MONITORING AND PREDICTIVE MAINTENANCE OF LARGE BORE DIESEL ENGINES.

H. Sandtorv
The Ship Research Institute
of Norway

G. Fiskaa
The Ship Research Institute
of Norway

M. Rasmussen
The Div. of Marine Eng.
The Technical University
of Norway

ABSTRACT.

There is given a description of a Computer System designed to monitor the condition of the Main Engine and certain auxiliaries, as well as predict the future date of recommended maintenance.
This includes a survey of the methodology used, the measuring equipment and the various major software elements.
The development of this system is based on several years of research work into the field of advanced automation, which includes a two-year test-run with a shipboard computer installation. The paper includes some of the results achieved from this installation.

1. INTRODUCTION.

This paper describes a computerized system for Condition Monitoring and Predictive Maintenance of Large Bore Diesel Engines. Other auxiliary engine room systems may also be included.

This system is called DATATREND. It may be part of a computerized engine automation system or be used as a stand alone computer system.

The system is based on a Condition Monitoring System which was developed during the periode 1969 to 1972, as a result of cooperation between The Ship Research Institute of Norway (NSFI) and The Division of Marine Engineering at The Technical University of Norway, Trondheim. The further development of this condition monitoring system into DATATREND was done in cooperation with Norcontrol, Norway.

The instrumentation used is mainly conventional but some of the sensors are especially developed for condition monitoring purposes.

2. BACKGROUND.

During the three years 1966 through 1968 a Norwegian large bore research project was carried out as a cooperative undertaking with research personnel from a variety of research institutes in Norway. The work was centered around problems encountered in thermally loaded components and included 19 series of shipboard measurements on nine engines. (1), (2).

This work has continued in several areas, making use of the vast amount of data and know-how from the previous project. (3). The mathematical background and measuring equipment used in this system is to a large extent a result of know-how achieved during the above mentioned project.

The first comprehensive condition monitoring system based on the know-how in the milieu at the University in Trondheim was realized with the Computer installation onboard M/V "VIANNA" in November 1970.

This installation included the major elements now incorporated in DATATREND, but it was mainly intended to be an experimental installation with the following aims:

- Further development and testing of electronic measuring equipment and measuring methods to be used on shipboard installations.

- Further development of mathematical models and software for condition monitoring.

- Collection of data to establish the connection between measured values, changes in component condition, failures and break downs and executed maintenance.

Some of the results from this installation are discussed in section 6.

3. CONDITION MONITORING METHODOLOGY AND EXTENT.

General.

Today the normal practice in maintenance of the two-stroke diesel engine is to decide the time of maintenance actions from fixed maintenance periods. Previous experience supplemented with data from the engine manufacturer is used as a basis for stipulation of the length of the maintenance periods. The length of the periods may be somewhat adjusted according to information provided through simple measurements and inspections.

The result of the increase in cylinderdimensions and specific loading, is that the deviations from normal working conditions that can be allowed before damage occurs, have been drastically reduced. Parts with high thermal loading, like pistons, exhaust valves, liners and cylinder covers are specially conserned. This makes it difficult to decide upon justifiable and economical maintenance periods from previous experience. With a fixed number of running hours between maintenance, varying working conditions (variation in pressure, temperature or thermal loading) in each period may in one case result in damage, in another case a too frequent maintenance.

The ideal time for a maintenance action on a certain component is determined from it's operating condition and from information about the influence of a reduced component condition on the efficiency and reliability of the total system. With the traditional aids that have been available up to now, a good judgement of a component's technical condition has required dismantling of the component. This is not always acceptable from an economical point of view.

With the system described in this paper it is possible through a systematic manipulation of data from the various measured equipment to determine the condition of a component without dismantling it. Trend analysis performed on calculated condition deviations is then a good basis for establishing the right time for the maintenance action.

By using a system of maintenance scheduled by condition monitoring we expect to achieve the following:

I   detect and correct faults and irregularities before secondary damage occurs.

II predict maintenance by assessing the future change in condition. This will result in better planning for maintenance and eleminate unnecessary maintenance work.

III replace time-consuming inspections by a system of measurement and analysis to determine the cause(s) of the faults correctly.

Together this will result in the reduction of "off-hire" and in reduced expenses for repair and maintenance.

Assessing the Condition.

The principle of assessment of the technical condition of a component is illustrated in figure 1.

Based on measurements of physical state of a component a number of characteristic parameters are calculated. Examples of such quantities are efficiency of the turbocharger compressor, over-all heat transfer coefficient (K-value) of a heat-exchanger. The value of these parameters gives an expression of the condition of the components at that moment. These values are called the "service values". The characteristic service value of each parameter will at a given instant depend on the prevailing operating conditions, some of which are considered external to the component being checked. Their effect on the characteristic parameter will therefore have to be compensated for. This is necessary to get a unique relation between the characteristic parameter and the physical condition of the component itself, without any influence of the conditions under which the component is running (e.g. engine room temperature, sea water temperature etc.). Compensation for external effects is achieved by calculating the same characteristic value for a best possible (usually new) component under running conditions. Data for such a calculation is normally obtained on the trial trip. This means that we ask ourselves the question: "What would be the value of the characteristic parameter (overall heat transfer coefficient, efficiency etc.) if the component was in new condition, but working under the same external conditions?" This value is called the "reference value". Comparing the service value and the reference value of the characteristic quantity gives a unique measure of the condition of the component at the moment of performing the check. For a heat exchanger this could be represented by a certain percentage reduction in over-all heat transfer coefficient relative to new condition value. The difference between the reference and the service value is referred to as a "condition parameter".

Trend Analysis.

The calculated condition parameter describes the present condition of the actual component. To plan a maintenance action it is desireable to decide the expected future development of the condition. What is aimed at is to predict the correct time for a maintenance action based on predicted future component condition.

This can be achieved by storing the calculated changes of condition (deviations) from consecutive condition analyses. By performing a trend analysis on these data and extrapolating the calculated trend the future condition is estimated.

The actual time for maintenance is then fixed according to prefixed trendlimit not to be exceeded. Exceeding this limit may in some cases involve a certain risk of break-down, whereas in other cases there is no risk of break-down for the component concerned. For example if the limit is exceeded for the over-all heat transfer coefficient of an air-cooler or for pressure loss through an air-filter due to dirt, this will not involve an essential risk of damage to these components, but it will lead to increased thermal load on associated components on the main engine. The limit for this kind of components is then fixed on the basis of their influence on the thermal load of associated components.

Components and Parameters included in the condition monitoring.

As previously mentioned the main purpose of this condition monitoring system is to control the thermal load of the main engine. This is done directly by measuring the actual metaltemperature in the thermally loaded components and indirectly by monitoring the condition of components which have an influence on the thermal load.

In addition some auxilliary engine-room systems are included in the condition monitoring.

In table 1 is given a survey of the various components and parameters included.

On a 9-cylinder engine with 3 turbochargers a total of 184 parameters is included in the calculations, while 58 of these are used in further trend analyses to schedule maintenance.

Figure 2 shows the structure of this system, i.e. components and systems giving input to the computer, major software elements and a survey of various types of output.

4. HARDWARE EQUIPMENT.

General.

All communication with the computer connected to the condition monitoring system is carried out through a separate panel on the engine-control desk.
This panel contains a keyboard, two displays, and a variety of pressbuttons to be used when initiating the various program elements in the system.

Instrumentation.

As mentioned previously all instrumentation used is conventional. The thermocouples especially developed for usage in this condition monitoring system will be described in some detail.

The following gives an impression of the variety of sensors used.

- Dynamic pressure recordings of cylinder - and injection pressure by piezo-electrical sensors.
- Three thermocouples in each cylinder unit to measure metal-temperatures.

- Two proximitysensors in each cylinder unit to detect the piston ring behaviour.
- Approximately 90 analog sensors for measuring pressures and temperatures.
- Binary counters for measuring fuelflow and RPM on main engine and turboblowers.
- Measurment of cranckshaft-position.

In addition the system makes use of some manually given information.

Measurment of metaltemperatures.

To establish the thermal load, measurements of the metaltemperature in thermally loaded components is carried out.

A total of three sensors are used in each cylinder unit. Two of these are situated in the liner opposed to each other on the maneuvre and exhaust side and at the top ring top dead centre. The actual measuring point is situated 7 mm below the inner surface of the liner. These sensors detect an increase in the liner temperature due to blow by and/or scuffing. An increase in this temperature is experienced when the liner wear increase and may be used in assessing the liner and piston ring condition.

The third thermocouple is situated in an area above the piston, either in the top of the liner or in the cylinder-cover and thus measures the temperature in areas exposed to the combustion. The thermal load expressed by this temperature is mainly dependent on the weight of air available for the combustion and the condition of the injection equipment. High measured temperatures indicates reduced efficiency in one or more of the components in air, exhaust or injection system. These defects may then be detected by the condition monitoring carried out in these components.

The design of the thermocouples being used is shown in figure 3, and figure 4 shows actual locations of these elements in thermally loaded components.

5. SOFTWARE.

General.

The complete software connected to the condition monitoring make up a totale of 10K core memory. This includes both program and data. All programs are written in Assembly language for a maximum utilization of available core.

Extensive work has been laid down in making the software as modulare as possible. The result is that the major program elements easily may be used as stand alone elements, furthermore debugging, replacing and extending the various program elements are easily achieved.

All data are stored in tables located in a central data area. This includes as well all constants and limits to be used in the various mathematical models and calculations.

The location of the wide variety of data thus stored is defined in a central adress tabel. This lay-out gives easy access to all kinds of data for changing or updating while the central software remains unaffected. Access to dataarea is possible at any time through panel on the control desk.

Monitoring and Measuring Program.

DATATREND makes use of the SINTRAN II Monitor System. This is a real-time, multi-programming operating system for the NORD-Computer. (4).

The analog inputs are handled by a Analog Input Program System called MEAS. This is a general program system for process control. The MEAS Program System is to be run under control of the SINTRAN Monitor. (5).

Data Aqusition System.

This part is a program-system that acts as a software-link between the measured values (analog or digital signals) and the process analyzing programs. The main functions of this system are as follows:

1. Continuous monitoring of all temperatures, pressures and flows.

The measured values are checked against instrument limits, high variation and process limits. If any of these limits are exceeded the operator is informed via a fault-message on one of the display, a flashing lamp and in some cases also an audio-alarm signal.

The metal temperatures, especially in the liner, may for a short period increase considerably above the steady-state value. These short-time increases are generally considered harmless to the sylinder condition. Therefore no alarm is given unless the temperature has continously been above some preset level for a certain period of time. In some cases the process limits are set dynamically as surrounding condition may affect the allowable deviations and therefore have to be compensated for. All signals are filtered in software to supress arbitrary noise and to generate a representative mean value for a certain period of time. (2-4 hrs.). The momentary value of the signal (in physical unit) can be presented at any time on one of the displays. A log print-out of some selected data may be obtained by pressing a push-button.

2. Warning-messages.

A warning-message is given to the operator for some process variables when the deviation from normal do not require immediate action but still seems high enough to be checked out when convenient.

3. Cylinder- and fuel injection pressure.

These pressures can be recorded on demand. The piezo-electric pressure transducers are mounted on the cylinder which is to be checked, and the communication with the computer for executing the measurements properly is done via a local panel located on the upper platform of the main engine. Any instrument- or operator-fault will flash an error-lamp on this panel.

The cylinder pressure is recorded every 4th degree of cranck-angle in the low pressure range and every degree in the high pressure range. The latter also applies to the injection pressure.

Both pressure diagrams may be presented on the graphical display. In addition some caracteristic parameters as mean indicated pressure, max. pressure, fuel needle opening pressure etc. will be printed out.

4. Piston ring measurements.

The piston ring functioning is continously monitored by measuring the ring's distance from the inner liner surface. Each liner is equipped with two proximity sensors sensing this distance. These are mounted flush with the inner surface of the liner just above the scawenging air ports. Each of them are located vertically below one of the termocouples in the liner. The value of the signal level gives a measure of the sealing efficiency (see fig. 5). A signal level below normal means that the ring is not sealing properly and a signal below zero means that the ring may be partly broken. The rings generally tends to oscillate in their grooves. Hence, a ring-gap may occasionally pass the transducer giving low signal level for a shorter time. Hence, the number of registrations below an upper limit and below zero level is counted for some period of time. The judgement of the ring function is thus not based on momentary values but on an abnormal condition lasting for a certain period of time. However, on demand the momentary values for one cylinder may also be continously visualized on the graphical display. If a piston ring has continously been in an abnormal state for a given time period, the operator is given a warning message. A temporary increase in the cyl.-oil feed rate will then usually return the ring functioning to normal.

5. Miscellanous.

In addition to the instrument check on each sensor there is performed a correlation-check between some of the most important measurements used in the main engine condition calculations. This is done to prevent any systematic error-development in the measurements to give misleading result from the condition calculations.

There is also kept a continous record of the engine operating conditions for the last 3-4 hours to prevent any condition analysis to be performed based on measurements from a period with unstable engine load.

Engine condition Analysis.

The main principle for evaluating the current engine condition is described in section 3. The analysis is based on a time period of 3-4 hrs. with stable engine load. The analysis is separated in 4 main groups:

- Cylinders
- Main Engine generally
- Turbocharger-system
- Auxilleries

Within each group there is a number of components or process-parameters which are analyzed. One component may also have more than one parameter to describe it's conditions. For each parameter the following values are presented in the print-out:

- Service value
- Reference value
- Deviation from reference value (condition in present analysis)
- Deviation from reference in the previous analysis
- Deviation limit.

Fig. 6 shows an example of the print-out for one turbocharger group. The deviation value is presented in percentage of the reference value.

The condition of the cylinders and the combustion process efficiency are considered to be the major factors expressing the total efficiency of the main engine. Each cylinder therefore undergoes a thorough analysis divided in 5 groups:

- Analysis of the combustion process (cylinder pressure diagram)
- Analysis of fuel-oil injection (injection pressure diagram)
- Thermal load
- Piston ring functioning
- Resultant judgement of the cylinder condition in 3 levels (normal, less satisfactory, bad)
- Diagnosis (possible faults).

The main engine condition software also incorporates a program system for calculating the ships speed loss (referenced to condition of loading) due to hull fouling. These programs have been tested ashore for some years based on data reported from the ships.

Before the main engine analysis is started the computer warns the operator if such an analysis is not recommended (the period with stable engine load too short, cyl.-press analysis not performed or data too old etc.). Before the actual computation starts the operator has to input a few data via the communication keyboard (ships speed, draught and the weather condition). When the computation is completed the deviation values for some selected parameters are stored to be used by the programs that perform the trend-analysis.

Programsystem to Update Calculated Deviation Data.

The calculated deviations connected to the various parameters are to be used in establishing the future trend. This requires that data calculated over a certain periode being available. In the central data area it is possible to store up to 20 deviation data for each of a totale of 58 parameters used in the trendanalysis. This cor-

responds to a periode of 3 to 5 months.

The main purpose of this program is to transfer calculated data from the last engine condition analysis into the data-area, and updating the former stored data with these new values. In addition informations concerning last executed maintenance on all components are stored. It is possible to get a printed survey of these informations on the teletype.

The program system is initiated by a press-button. Checking of data during storage is not performed. This is the responsibility to the operator before initiating storage, and he ought to reject an updating when for some reason a majority of calculated data are obviously wrong.

Calculation of Date for Future Maintenance.

Based on a linear regression of the stored deviation data a trend in the future condition is established for each parameter. As mentioned above, deviation data are avaiable for a period of the past of up to 3 to 5 months. Intersection between the established trend and the trend limit determines the date of maintenance.

This trend is normally calculated based on all valide deviation data for the actual parameter. Data being obviously wrong are rejected before this calculation. In addition a calculation based on the last five stored deviation data is executed. Based on the result of this analysis it is possible to detect any accelerated trend of the condition in any component and thus in due time give informations thereof so that necessary actions may be taken.

This system is initiated by a press-button and a man/machine communication takes place before the actual calculations starts.

In figure 6 is shown a part of a printout from this program. The accuracy of the analysis is indicated by asterics (x) and is based on the calculated correlation-coefficient combined with the actual number of data available. Bad accuracy (x) results in no calculated date of trend limit.

In addition to calculated date it is possible to get an estimate of deviation from normal condition at a future date (second column from right).

Calculation of Future Thermal Load.

This program performs a calculation of future thermal loading, given as temperature in thermally loaded parts. It takes into account the predicted degradation in condition of all components which have influence on the thermal load, as well as changes in the ambient condition. The programme also takes into account the running condition of the main engine and the influence of any maintenance carried out. The programme is conversational and thus the operator can propose maintenance of the components one by one and see the influence of the proposed maintenance on the thermal loading. This feature gives the engineer the possibility to predict and possibly prevent unwanted load reductions in the future due to degraded components and also to optimize the maintenance work.

Program execution is initiated by a press-button.

In figure 6 is shown an example of printout from this program system.

6. PRACTICAL RESULTS OF A COMPUTER-IZED CONDITION MONITORING SYSTEM.

Over a period of 2 years an experimental PREDIKT installation has been in use on a 100.000 ton OBO-carrier.

The monitoring covered the components already mentioned. In addition a detailed set of instruments were installed in order to register the temperature on different areas of the thermally laded components. The instrumentation system included transducers on some of the cylinders to register the functioning of the piston rings as well.

Some of the results are described below. Further informations given in (6).

Piston overhaul.

Due to necessary software development the system was taken into operation approx. 2 months after leaving the shipyard. At this time high levels of temperature were registered on two of the cylinders. Inspection revealed scuffing marks on the piston rings and a later times measurement showed great wear.

Figure 7 shows the development of the condition parameter (increase in temperature at Top Piston Ring Top dead center) during a period of fourteen months on one of these cylinders.

On 1/6-71 a trend analysis (prediction) was carried out on the basis of the collected data. The trend which was found indicated that the limit for the condition parameter (70° C) would be exceeded in the first half of August (dotted line in top of graph). The results in the period up to this date confirmed the estimated change, as seen in the diagram. When the piston was overhauled (1/8-71), it was found that the three top piston rings were broken (this cylinder was not equipped with piston ring sensors) and that the wear of the cylinder liner was considerable. The bottom graph in figure 8, shows the results at the same level on the liner but on the opposite side (manoeuvring side as opposed to exhaust side).

After the piston had been overhauled, the temperature on the exhaust side stabilised, while after a short periode a marked increase in temperature level was registered on the manoeuvring side. This was due to increasing blow-by on parts of the piston circumference due to poor functioning of the new piston rings. This in turn was caused by the extensive and uneven wear on

the liner. To avoid secondary damage the amount of lubrication oil in the cylinder was increased to its maximum for fortyeight hours. This resulted in the stabilisation of the liner-temperature at a level which made it relatively safe to go on until docking in the first part of December month.

The liner was replaced and after a running in periode we find temperatures on the liner close to normal value.

Thus the measurements can be used as a basis, not only for registering changes in condtion, but also for assessing the effect of direct action as shown in the above example.

It may be added that the additional liners show completely satisfying wear rates. This is mainly to the use of trend analysis on registered data when deciding when an action is to be taken to stop and reduce an increase in thermal load. The kind of action taken may be a temporary reduction of the service load of the cylinder or/ and an increase in the amount of lubrication oil to the cylinder liner.

Development of the condition of charge air coolers and air filters.

Figure 8 shows the development of the condition parameter for scavenge-air cooler and air filter. (Reduction in K-value and increased pressure-drop across the air filter and cooler.)

On the basis of the great reduction in K-value it was decided during July to clean the cooler on the seawater side about the end of July or beginning of August. The pressure drop was reasonably low so it was found unnecessary to wash the air side. During this cleaning it became apparent that the lowest element was very barnacled on the seawater side and could not be cleaned properly in position. This element was therefore replaced at the end of September, and a considerable improvement of the coolers K-value was observed. On the other hand the pressure drop across the cooler was now high, so the cooler had to be washed on the air side around 20th October. After this the pressure drop on the cooler was reduced to near its normal level.

These examples should demonstrate clearly the advantages of these analyses. Maintenance work can be planned in good time, the type of work to be done is indicated by the analysis and so is the quality of the maintenance work which has been done.

References.

(1) Sarsten, A., Hansen, A., Langballe, M. and Martens, O. 1968. "Varmebelastning og driftsforhold for store skipsdieselmotorer". NSTM-68, Trondheim, Norway.

(2) Sarsten, A., Hansen, A., Langballe, M. and Martens, O. 1969. "Thermal Loading and Operating Conditions for Large Marine Diesel Engines", IMAS-69, Institute of

Marine Engineers, Proc. 4c, p. 64-80.

(3) Hansen, A., Rasmussen, M. and Sarsten, A. 1971. "Thermal Loading of Diesel Engine Components and its Prediction", CIMAC-71, paper A-30.

(4) SINTRAN II, Users Guide 1971. A/S Norsk Dataelektronikk.

(5) MEAS - An Analog Input Program System for Process Control. Application Manual. The Engineering Research Foundation of the Technical University of Norway. 1971.

(6) Hansen, A. 1972. "Tilstandskontroll basert på Minidatamaskin, Erfaringer fra M/S "VIANNA". SFI-Seminar. "EDB, Prosess-kontroll og Elektronikk".

SYSTEM	COMPONENTS	PARAMETERS
Auxilliaries	Fresh-water cooler.	Over-all heat transf. coeff.
	Oil cooler	Over-all heat transf. coeff.
	Evaporator	Over-all heat transf. coeff.
	Boilers	Over-all heat transf. coeff. Pressure drop.
Hull	Wetted surface.	Fouling.

TABLE 1.

SYSTEM	COMPONENTS	PARAMETERS
Main Engine	General	Thermal Efficiency. Relative Load. Nominal Thermal Load. Total Amount of Air. Total press-drop across Engine.
Cylinders	Cylinder Pressure	Various characteristic pressure data.
Thermally loaded components	Cylinder Cover Cylinder Liner Piston Ring	Metal-Temperature. Metal-Temperature. Piston Ring Functioning.
	Piston Exhaustvalve	Metal-Temperatures as measured above give general information of thermal load of the other thermally loaded components as well.
Injection Equipment	Injection Pumps. Injection valves.	Efficiency Various characteristic pressure data.
Scaw.air system	Air Filter Compressor	Pressure drop. Efficiency
Scaw.air system (cont.)	Air Cooler	Pressure drop. over-all heat transfer coefficient.
Exhaust system	Turbine Exhaust-Boiler	Efficiency Over-all heat transf. coefficient

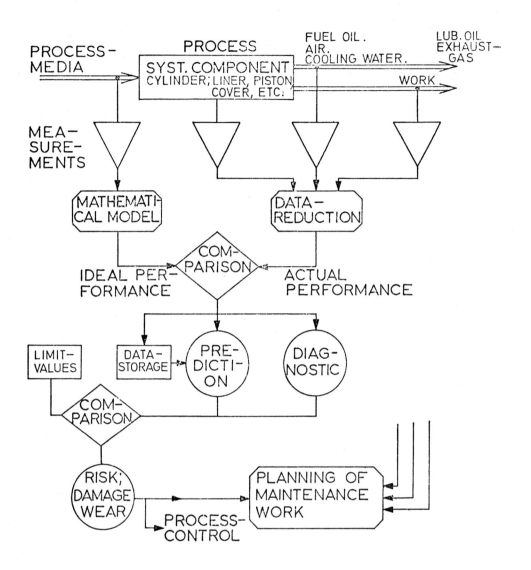

FIGURE 1.

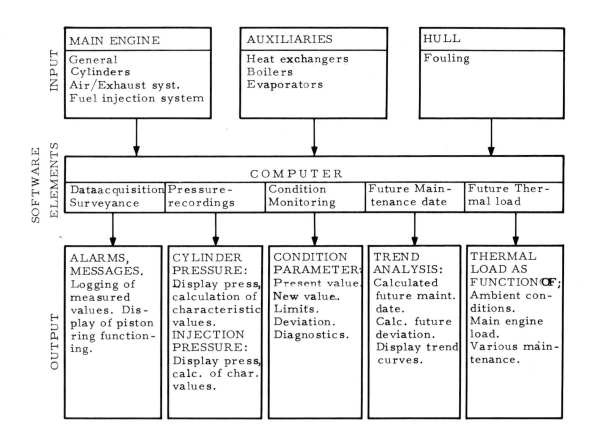

FIGURE 2.

268

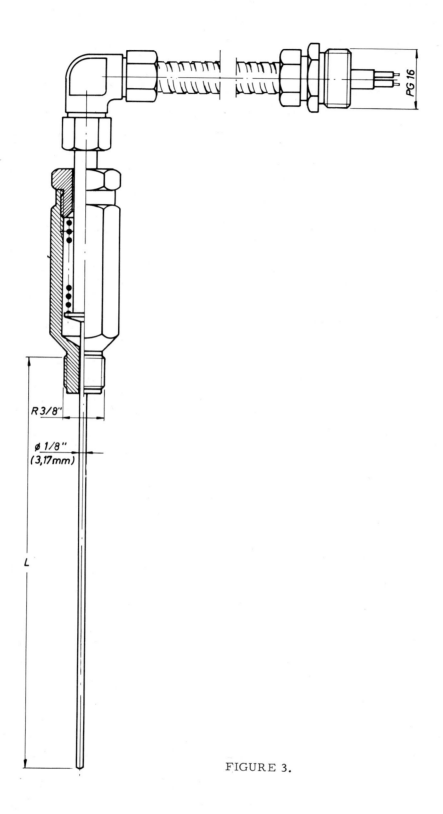

FIGURE 3.

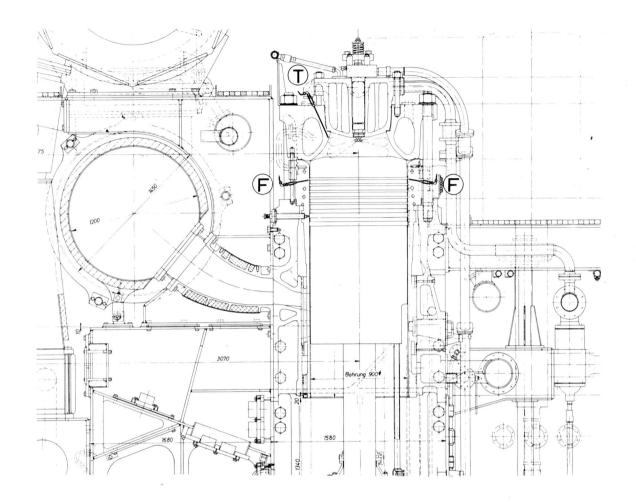

FIGURE 4.

MONITORING OF PISTON RING FUNCTIONS

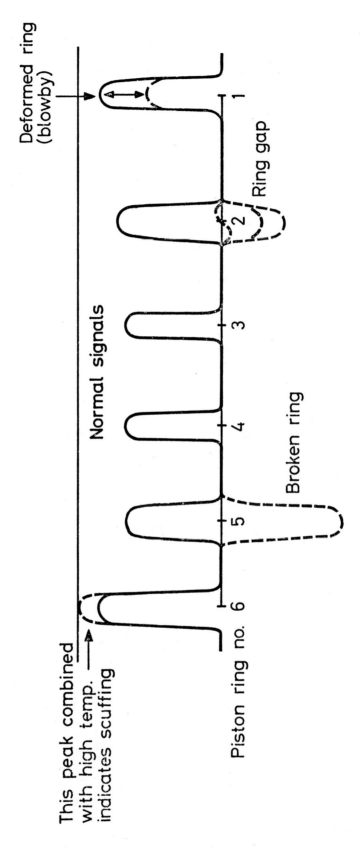

FIGURE 5.

EXAMPLE PRINTOUT: ENGINE CONDITION

-- TB.CH SYSTM COND. --

- TB.CH NO. 1 -

```
              ETURB  COMPR  AFILT  ACOOL  ACOOL
       RPM    EFFIC  EFFIC  PDROP  K-VAL  PDROP
MEAS:  6845   76.2   79.4   58     235    89
NORM:         81.2   83.2   50     350    40
DEV%:         -7     -5     16     -30    105
LAST
DEV%:         -5     -2     12     -21    85
LIM%:         -10    -10    60     -50    85
```

-- TB.CH NO. 2 -

(ETC.)...............

EXAMPLE PRINTOUT: CALCULATED FUTURE MAINTENANCE DATE

----PRED. MAINT. M/T 'HAPPY' 73.01.15 19.07.12 ----

-- INJEC. --

```
                    ----ALL DATA---- ---FIVE DATA---- DEVI DATE
                    DATE      ACCUR   DATE      ACCUR 73  5 25 LIMIT

TR 801  EFFIC                 *                 *     000.0    -10
TR 802  COMBC   73  6 20  ***  73  4  5  ***    37.5    30
TR 803  EFFIC   73  4 27  **                ***  -12.1   -10
TR 804  COMBC   $$ $$ $$  ***  73  4 25  ***    32.1    30
TR 805  EFFIC   73  5 14  ***  73  3 16  ***    -14.7   -10
TR 806  COMBC   $$ $$ $$  **                ***   21.1    30
TR 807  (ETC.) ...............
```

EXAMPLE PRINTOUT: FUTURE THERMAL LOAD

-- MAIN ENG. DATA --
```
                 REL.
 IHP   RPM   MIP  LOAD
25300 116.2 10.16 106
```

-- ESTIM THERM LOAD DATE 73.04.20 --

```
CYL.NO.      -1- -2- -3- -4- -5- -6- -7- -8- -9-
TEMP COMBC:  352 363 345 372 390 360 358 354 369
TEMP LIMIT:  380 380 380 380 380 380 380 380 380
TEMP DIFF.:  -28 -17 -35  -8  10 -20 -22 -26 -11
```

REDUC MIP 0.1 KP/CM2 = REDUC TEMP 11 DEGCE

FIGURE 6.

272

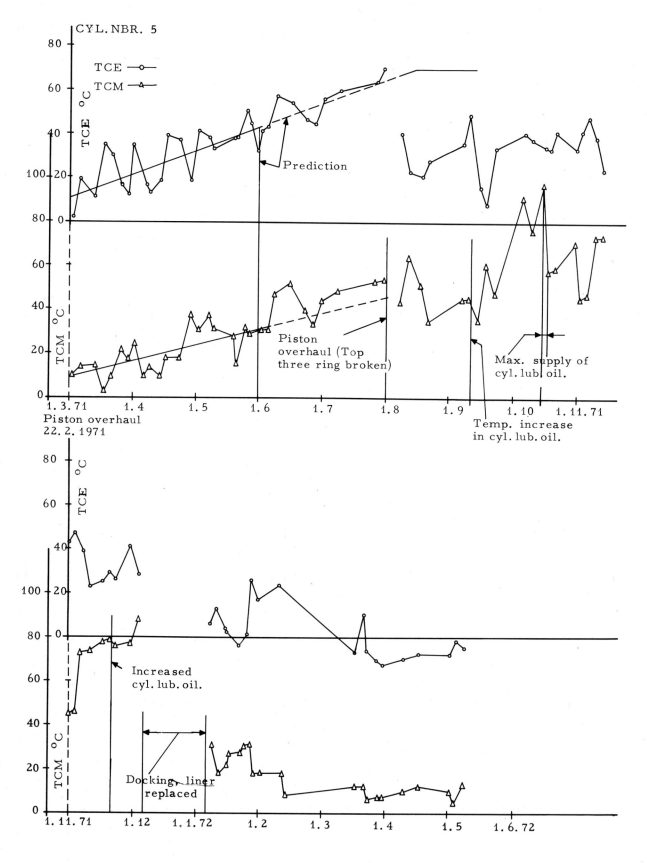

FIGURE 7.

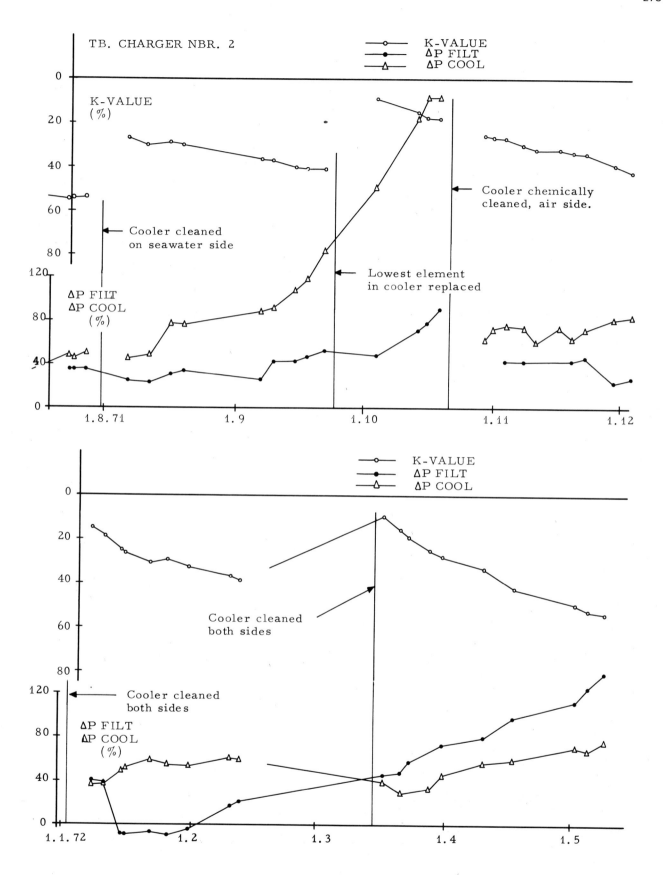

FIGURE 8.

CYLDET, ASEA'S SYSTEM FOR MONITORING
THE COMBUSTION PRESSURE IN DIESEL ENGINES

Åke Madesäter and Nils Hammarstrand
Marine Automation Department
Transport Division
ASEA
Västerås, Sweden

INTRODUCTION

The increasing interest being shown in recent years in the monitoring of different systems on board ship underlines the need for a system capable of continuously monitoring the combustion pressure in the cylinders of diesel engines. Many attempts have been made on the basis of modern measuring techniques to design a transducer which can be continuously connected to the combustion chamber. However, the severe environment with hot, corrosive gases and the greatly pulsating pressure have limited the application of different transducers. In addition, the special environment on board a ship is a limiting factor for certain types of transducer, since a powerful signal unaffected by the noise generated by other electrical machines is desired.

ASEA has developed a transducer that is insensitive to the surroundings, yields an adequate electric signal and is resistant to the pressure and temperature occurring in the combustion chamber. This transducer does not contain any moving parts, has a linear output signal subject to only insignificant hysteresis and is easy to adapt to different makes of diesel engine. No extra cooling circuits are required and it is not necessary to drill any holes in the combustion chamber. The experience hitherto obtained from several installations with ASEA's transducers over a period of more than one year has been very good.

TECHNICAL DESCRIPTION

The transducer is built up around a PRESSDUCTOR® sensor, which has been used for many years within industry to measure forces, as well as a heat insulating shield and a diaphragm. All these parts are enclosed in a steel housing and those parts exposed to high temperatures and corrosive gases are made of stainless steel. The transducer housing fits most types of indicator cock and valve available on the market and is attached to the cock or valve with a Maihak connector having a diameter of 27 mm.

The small movement of 10-15 μm of the diaphragm resulting from the pressure is transferred direct to a steel piston and from this via a heat-insulated piston to the PRESSDUCTOR transducer. This is an ASEA invention, whose operating principle is based on the fact that the permeability of a magnetic material is altered when pressure is applied. A number of thin transformer sheet laminations are bonded together to form a package. Four holes are arranged symmetrically in this package and two windings, the primary and the secondary, pass through these holes at 90° to one another, see Fig. 1. The primary winding is fed with alternating voltage, while the secondary winding is connected to the measuring equipment. As long as there is no load on the transducer, the measuring equipment will not receive any signal. When a load is applied, the measuring equipment receives a signal that is directly proportional to the mechanical load acting on the PRESSDUCTOR transducer, see Fig. 2.

This transducer forms the heart of a measuring system - CYLDET 1800 - which has now been introduced on the market. CYLDET 1800 is an abbreviation of "CYLinder pressure monitoring and condition DETection system", where 1800 stands for 18 cylinders, which is hitherto the largest number of cylinders on a marine diesel engine.

The transducer as described above can be connected to the indicator cock or valve of all makes of diesel engine. It has been possible to satisfy the demands made on a transducer of this kind such as no extra cooling, no extra drilling, etc. However, to meet the need of the engine builder and engine room crew to be able to "blow" the engine prior to starting, it is preferable to install double indicator cocks or valves. The simplest solution is therefore to fit a Tee or the like, which means that it will not be necessary to dismount the CYLDET transducer. The electrical connection of the transducer is made with a flexible steel armoured cable insulated with silicone rubber fitted with a watertight plug-in connector (see Fig. 3) by the transducer and a junction box at the other end. This junction box is mounted in a well-protected position, preferably beneath the platform on the diesel engine. The cable between the engine and the power supply and electronic equipment consists of a conventional marine cable, 4x1.5 mm^2, where the conductors are connected crosswise to eliminate induction between the primary and the secondary conductors. The length of the cable between the junction boxes on the diesel engine and the terminal blocks in the electronic equipment must not exceed 50 metres. Noise tests have been performed in laboratories with 2 kV surges on parallel conductors 100 m long without any disturbing effects.

The transducers are fed from a power supply set up in a central position. This power supply includes a mains transformer, rectifier and convertor. The normal ship supply voltage, single-phase 110/220 V, 50/60 Hz, is stepped down, prior to rectifying, to ±15 V. This direct voltage is then used for feeding both the convertor and the signal processing and indicating modules. The convertor, which is of solid-state design, converts the direct voltage into 12 V, a.c., 1000 Hz, for feeding all the transducers in parallel. The power supply should preferably be mounted on a vertical plane inside the engine room control console. The terminal blocks supplied with the equipment are preferably set up in the vicinity. These terminal blocks and the power supply are interconnected with 2x2.5 mm² cables for feeding the transducers. The secondary signal circuits are also connected to the terminal blocks. The connections to the electronic equipment are made as standard with 3-m-long cables fitted with multi-pin connectors at both ends fitting the corresponding connectors in the electronic equipment and terminal blocks.

The electronic equipment is of modular design for panel mounting. Each section of the electronic equipment consists of one indicating module and at least one signal processing module. In turn, each signal processing module contains printed-circuit boards for six transducers, where the signals of each transducer are processed individually on each board. To allow the signal variations from the transducers to be used, the signal is rectified and filtered before being displayed either as a time-pressure diagram on a CRT, oscilloscope screen, or in the module on a pointer instrument. In addition, the signal processing boards incorporate automatic zero-point correction. The zero point has been set equal to the scavenging air pressure to avoid irregular differences between the cylinders. The signal processing boards also contain alarm logic with alarm lamps and a resetting pushbutton. The latter functions in addition as a selector pushbutton for presenting the pressure of the desired cylinder. When the signal is connected up to the indicating module, a lamp for the cylinder involved shines.

The signal processing and indicating modules (see Fig. 4) are interconnected by a cable fitted with multi-pin connectors. The indicating module can be connected to three signal processing modules, which means that in all 18 channels can be connected to one indicating module - CYLDET 1800. In addition to the instrument and CRT output already mentioned on the indicating module, this contains an instrument selector for selecting the peak pressure, the mean value of the peak pressure of all the cylinders, the integrated time average value from the time-pressure curve and alarm limits. There are also pushbuttons for alarm reset, alarm test and lamp test. The printed-circuit board included in the indicating module contains circuits for setting the upper and lower alarm limits, and automatic blocking of the alarm at low speed and low pressure. To allow a relatively simple oscilloscope to be used, the indicating module incorporates a triggering circuit, which starts the oscilloscope sweep

within a very short space of time. The equipment complies with the standards of the leading Classification Societies for automation equipment and has a group alarm contact function, which is intended for connection to the alarm system of the diesel engine.

In addition, the CYLDET 1800 system is prepared for the connection of a digital display instead of a pointer instrument as well as for connection to the analog inputs of a computer to allow the checking of the state of each individual cylinder.

The CYLDET 1800 system does not require any special calibration or the services of a specialist during commissioning. Each transducer is calibrated on delivery and anybody who has participated in the commissioning of the alarm system can adjust with a screwdriver the alarm limits according to the instructions given in the manual provided with the equipment. All connections except those between the junction boxes on the diesel engine and the terminal blocks in the engine room console as well as two conductors between the power supply and the terminal blocks are fitted with multi-pin connectors.

EXPERIENCE

The first complete transducer equipment was installed on board the M.S. Höegh Multina in October, 1971, as part of a research project involving condition monitoring. The first standard CYLDET equipment was installed in September, 1972, on board the M.S. Finnhansa, a passenger/car ferry belonging to Finnline, and has been operating satisfactorily ever since. It has been established that the equipment is very insensitive to electromagnetic noise.

The equipment on the Finnhansa was installed on all eight cylinders of the port engine, a Sulzer RD 56, 180 r.p.m. diesel engine, see Fig. 5. To permit blowing of the engine prior to starting, branches were fitted direct on the cylinder covers with the original indicator valves mounted in the same way as before. In addition, Klinger indicator cocks were fitted for blowing of the engine with the transducers mounted on the original cocks. The transducers were arranged vertically to check the heat distribution in the most unfavourable position.

The junction boxes for the connecting of the external cable to the transducers are mounted on an angle iron close to the engine on the upper platform on the manoeuvering side.

The electronic equipment was installed in the control room with only a visual alarm, since there was not any alarm channel available in the ordinary alarm system. A very simple oscilloscope, type Tektronix 310, set up above the electronics cubicle has been provided for displaying the time-pressure diagram. Typical examples of the time-pressure diagram are shown in Fig. 6. The screen could have been larger, but even so it gives a very clear picture of the combustion process. To begin with, the engine room personnel questioned the accuracy of the CYLDET system, but they have now become aware of its possibilities and regularly check the com-

bustion process in all the cylinders of the port
engine. When the pressure was checked with a mechanical indicator, it was found that the CYLDET
system indicated a pressure that was about 4 bars
higher. The reason for this is the larger moving
mass of the mechanical indicator and consequently
its poorer response.

Before the CYLDET system reached its present form,
it underwent a number of development stages. Different variants were tried out on various makes
of diesel engine, both low-speed and medium-speed
ones. There are, however, certain limitations when
higher speeds are involved. Nevertheless, tests
performed on auxiliary 600 r.p.m. diesel engines
have given such good results that a good reproduction of the time-pressure characteristic of 720
r.p.m. engines is anticipated. Applying the CYLDET
transducer to diesel engines running at still higher speeds will require a different and considerably
more expensive supply system for the transducers
and their mounting would probably have to be modified. Nevertheless, continued development work is
taking place and undoubtedly further applications
of the CYLDET system will be found in the future.

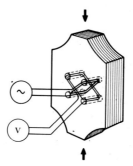

Fig. 1. Schematic diagram of PRESSDUCTOR force transducer with windings.

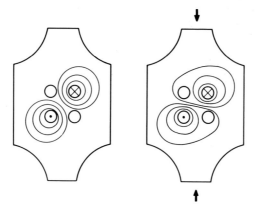

Fig. 2. Schematic diagram of PRESSDUCTOR transducer.

     a) unloaded

     b) loaded

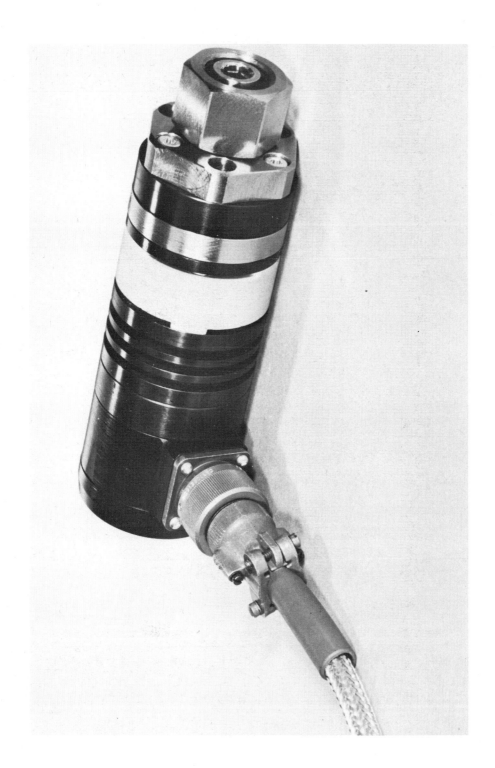

Fig. 3. CYLDET transducer shown with water-tight plug-in contact and steel armoured cable. (85244)

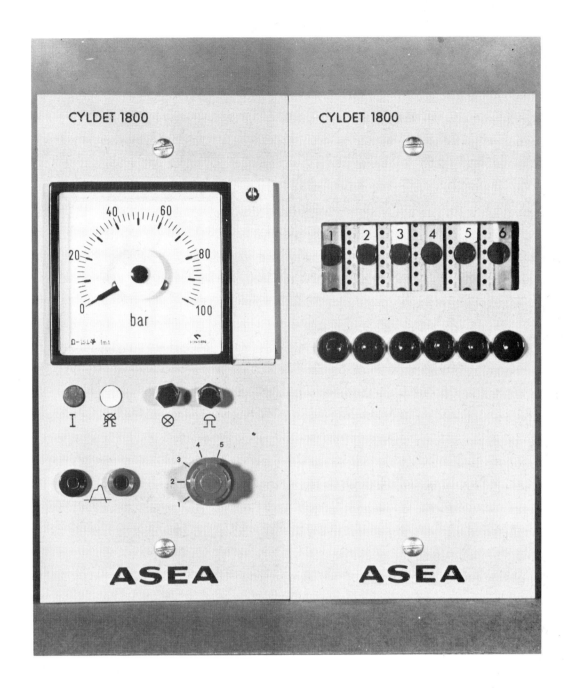

Fig. 4. Processing and indicating modules forming a complete display
unit. (85831)

Fig. 5. Transducer fitted on board the M.S. Finnhansa. (86256B)

Fig. 6   Different time-pressure diagrams for typical faults

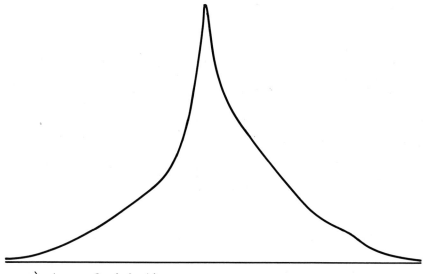

a) too early injection

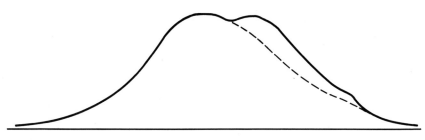

b) too late injection

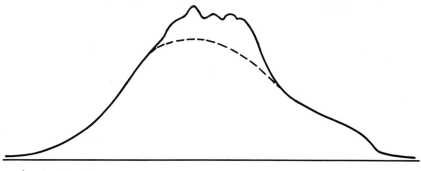

c) faulty injector

A DIGITAL COMPUTER BASED ENGINE ROOM AUTO-
MATION SYSTEM FOR TURBINE DRIVEN SHIPS

Kjell Lind
Project Manager
The Ship Research Institute of Norway
Trondheim
Norway

ABSTRACT

This paper treats one aspect of the shipboard
automation, namely an automated engine room
for turbine driven ships. The automation system
presented compromise the result of a Norwegian
research and development project which started
in 1970.

The system is based on one standard type process
control computer. The general goals of such an
automated engine room system are stated. A
description of the automation system is given,
and the advantages of digital computer applications
are pointed out.

Special attention is made to on-line condition
monitoring and trend analysis of steam turbine
plants, and to the optimal Direct Digital Control
(DDC) of the main boiler.

The computer system has conventional back-up.
A brief discussion on the back-up philosophy
and the method of swtiching from computer mode
to conventional mode is carried through.

Complete computer system simulation testing of
the automation system before entering the ship
is very important and some space is devoted to
this matter.

The qualifications of the operating personnel is
explained.

The necessary training in addition to the basic
education and experience of the engineers will
be given.

The paper concludes with a summary of the
importance of the new developments which are
implemented in this automation system.

INTRODUCTION

This computer based engine room automation
system is the result of a research and development project which started at The Ship Research
Institute of Norway in 1970, as a natural following
of the computerized cargo ship M/S TAIMYR
completed in 1969. Today several interests are
working together to produce a prototype installation to be completed in September 1974. The
system company Noratom-Norcontrol will be
responsible for the installation of this system.
The ship, a 285.000 tdw tanker, is being built
by the Aker Group to the Hagb. Waage shipowners.
The Ship Research Institute of Norway has the
project responsibility, and the following institutes
at The Technical University of Norway, Trondheim, are participating in the project:

> SINTEF, Division of Automatic Control
> Division of Industrial Heat Engineering
> Institute for Industrial Social Research
> Division of Marine Engineering.

Working in the group are also Svenska Maskin-
verken, delivering the CE-V2M9-13 boiler
to this ship, and Staal-Laval delivering the turbine, gear and condenser system.

The resulting prototype installation is not an
experiment installation, it is only the first one
of several systems planned to be built by Norwegian system companies. The engine room
computer automation system is carefully planned
in detail and is meant to represent the state of
the art in ship steam power plant automation.
Additions will be made to the system as one
gains experience with operation of this and
other similar systems, but these additions
are mainly expected in software, and not in
the design of the automation system.

The system is based on one Norwegian made
NORD-4E process control type computer with
32 K of core memory. The computer has been
thoroughly tested for shipboard use, and is presently working in at least 30 installations on
ships. The computer has proven a good MTBF
(MeanTime Between Failure) and is easily ser-
vicable by the people on board. The reason for
basing this automation system on one digital
computer with conventional back-up, is that it is
felt that one has very little experience with dual
digital computer systems (digital back-up), and
that the problems in making reliable switching
from one computer to another are not solved. It
is also felt that the dual software and hardware
necessary for this system will at the present
time make them too expensive for commerical use.

The importance of extensive testing of the computer system before entering the ship should be stressed. Both static and dynamic tests by simulation will be carried through in a special test laboratory. This is important because most of the hardware and software problems occur during the first hours of operation. The system does not require a computer specialist to be present on board, but will be operated by the same people as is now operating conventionally automated turbine ships.

PROJECT GOALS

Due to larger ships and increasing capital investments, one will have to expect a higher degree of instrumentation and automation in order to ensure safe operation of the ship. The purpose of this project was to develop and install a computer based engine room automation system for steam driven ships and improvements are to be made in the following areas:

1. Safer ship operation
2. Reduction in maintenance costs and down time
3. Increase knowledge with respect to social and organizational problems in highly automated ships
4. Reduce the work load of the operating personnel and investigate the possibilities for manning reduction
5. Gain experience in utilizing digital computers in advanced shipboard automation.

The system was to be commerically attractive with respect to installation costs seen from an economical point of view.

SPECIAL ADVANTAGES OF THE COMPUTERIZED AUTOMATION SYSTEM

Many advantages are apparent when using computers for monitoring and control functions [2, 3]. The main advantages are the following:

- Possibility of more advanced supervision of process equipment. On-line calculation of performance and efficiency of the main propulsion system. On-line calculations of performance and efficiency of important parts in the auxiliary system. This will lead to better planned maintenance and more economical operation.

- Direct Digital Control (DDC) of the boiler and the throttle control system, utilizing more advanced control techniques. This will result in safer plant operation and reduced wear of important components.

- Improved man-machine communication system presenting more information about the process in an easily understandable form. This may be specially helpful during emergency operation.

- Self-checking of the computer system control circuits and measuring equipment result in more reliable operation.

- Highly standardized electronics integrated on few cards make the system service and repair easy.

- On-line and off-line diagnostic routines simplify the system maintenance.

- The system may easily be expanded or changed due to the nature of the digital computer.

- Collection and logging of data that are demanded or desired by the operator, the shipowner or authorities.

The system discussed in this paper has been designed to compete with conventional automation equipment, and results show that it really is compatible seen from an economical point of view. The initial system cost is somewhat higher than existing conventional systems. But, because of the additional features included in this computerized system, it will be more attractive as one learns to appreciate the new features. The new condition monitoring and trend analysis package should be mentioned in this respect. Several manually operated condition monitoring systems have been installed and are giving promising results.

The earlier computer system disadvantages of high initial costs and unproven MTBF (Mean Time Between Failures) are no longer true for the type and size of system considered here.

SYSTEM DESCRIPTION

This digital computer based engine room automation system is based on one computer to perform monitoring, control and plant performance calculations. The following main features are included in the automation system:

1. Condition Monitoring and Trend Analysis of main propulsion system and auxiliary system.

2. Multivariable Direct Digital Control (DDC) of the boiler, and computerized logic for burner management.

3. DDC of Main turbine throttle control including control modes for warming-up and securing the main turbine.

4. Computerized monitoring, alarm and logging.

5. Man-machine communication system including alpha-numerical display and graphical display.

These main features, which represent the important new developments, will be discussed in the following sections. Figure 1 shows the computer process control configuration.

Condition monitoring and trend analysis

This condition monitoring and trend analysis sub-system [5] is a further development of a manually operated system for steam-turbine ships developed jointly by the Division of Marine Engineering at The Technical University of Norway and The Ship Research Institute of Norway (NSFI). The results from the installations of the manually operated system are promising and important for the development of this automated system. It is also based on a computerized condition monitoring and trend analysis system for diesel engines developed in a cooperation between the same two groups above during a period from 1969 to 1972.

Experience shows that computerized condition monitoring and trend analysis systems are advantageous. This is because the data collection routines are fast and accurate, and that the complexity of calculations and signal filtering have almost no limits. It should also be mentioned that it is considered as a big advantage to avoid the individual judgements by human operators, as in the manually operated systems.

The purpose of this condition monitoring and trend analysis system is to:

- Detect faults and irregularities before serious damage occurs.

- Based on trend analysis, estimate the future change in condition. This will make it possible to predict and plan necessary maintenance.

- Avoid inspections or extend the intervals of inspections which require opening of components.

This will increase the life of the machinery, decrase the maintenance costs and reduce the "off-hire" for the ship.

The principle of this condition monitoring and trend analysis system is that several service parameters are calculated based on continuous measurements made on the respective components These parameters are an expression of the component condition at the moment. Each parameter is then compared with a reference parameter having the value of a new component operating under the same condition. The reference parameter may either be calculated before the ship leaves the yard, or may be calculated based on various tests during the ship's sea trial. A simplified flow diagram is shown in Figure 3.

The difference between the reference parameter and the currently calculated parameter is a measure of the condition of the component considered. The changes in condition may be presented as percentage reduction or a change in

an absolute value (heat transfer coefficient).

A lot of work has been done in finding ways to present these values such that they will appear meaning full to the process operator. The system has two displays, one alpha-numerical and one with graphical capability. Current component conditions are preferably displayed on the alpha-numerical display whilst trend curves are presented on the graphical display.

The measuring elements used in this system are mostly of standard quality, the same usually found in shipboard installations. Most of the measurements required are already existant in conventionally intrumented turbine plants, and the additional measuring equipment is in large standard "of the shelf" type. An extensive theoretical analysis was carried through to find the required accuracy of the various measurements. The automatic checking of the measuring elements and transmitters by the computer is very important for the reliability of the component condition data presented.

Based on the calculated condition parameters stored over a period of time it is possible to develop a trend in the deviation of a certain selected component. From this trend it is possible to estimate the time of overhaul for the component. In this way it is possible to plan the future maintenance of vital components on the engine room system.

The most important components considered in this condition monitoring and trend analysis subsystem are:

- Main boiler including superheater, economizer and air preheater
- Main turbines
- Feedwater preheaters
- Main condenser
- Condensate pumps
- Feedwater pumps
- Feedwater turbines.

The system is mainly programmed in assembly language and requires approximately 8 K of the computer core memory.

The boiler control system

At the present time, most shipboard propulsion systems are controlled entirely by pneumatic or electric analog controllers. Either of these could be converted to a corresponding digital computer control system by merely duplicating the control functions implemented on the pneumatic and electric controllers to digital computer algorithms. A much more important method, however, would be to apply the techniques of modern control theory in order to develop a discrete multivariable optimal control system for the propulsion plant as the basis for digital implementation.

The main boiler in this system is controlled by such a multivariable Direct Digital Control (DDC) method, [4]. DDC means that the control action is performed by the digital computer and that the computer establishes the signal to the final controlling element. The computer is on-line in the control loop and replaces the conventional analog electric or pneumatic controllers. Figures 4 and 5 explain in a simple way the difference between multivariable control and conventional control.

The features of this multivariable computer control system are the following:

- The boiler is treated as an integrated process and the interactions between the various control loops are accounted for.

- By utilizing a Kalman filter one can assure optimal signal filtering and estimation of process state variables which are difficult to measure but important for the control system (e. g. flow, enthalpy).

A great number of real time simulations of the control system on the non-linear process has been performed and the following advantages are seen:

1. A quicker, safer and more consistent response to bridge orders.

2. Reduced wear of equipment and simplifications in instrumentation.

3. Extension of operating range.

4. Great flexibility in changing control parameters.

5. Compensation of non-linear effects in process and process actuators.

6. Estimation of state variables gives the possibility for the control system to control the process for a period of time with some of the important measurements (transmitters) out of order.

7. Adaptive control (compensation of control parameters as physical parameters and conditions of the "Plant" changes with time).

The difficulty in handling the "shrink and swell" effect in conventional control systems are well known. In this system where the control system is based on a mathematical description of the process, the information contained in the control system makes it easier to handle this problem within the limits of the boiler design criteria. This is of special importance when in manoeuvering mode, and especially under low load condition.

The computer control system has conventional back-up, that is, conventional electric analog controllers are ready to take over if something should happen to the computer. The process is interfaced to the computer through Computer-Automatic-Manual CAM-stations (Figure 2). These stations will automatically switch from computer control to conventional PI (Proportional Integral) automatic or manual control in case

of computer failure. The back-up is automatic, but the system allows the operator to transfer one or more control loops from the computer mode to manual or automatic conventional mode and vice versa. That is, one may have control loops both on the computer and on conventional controllers at the same time.

Some of the functions in the boiler control system are not included in the multivariable control system, but implemented on the computer by specially designed algotihmes. The reason for this is that some loops require logic operation, some require ratio control of some require special attention because of non-linearities.

These algotihmes operate on signal from the multivariable system. The separate loops are:

- Combustion control algorithmes ensuring accurate control of air fuel ratio. Included here are control of air flow, control of fuel flow and control of differential pressure across fuel oil valves. Also the drum pressure is controlled by a separate algorithm based on signal from the multivariable system.

- Feedwater control including separate loops for controlling feedwater valve and feedwater pumps.

- Burner management system including logic operations for ignition and extinguishing of burners.

These individually controlled loops also work through the CAM-stations and in this way have the same possibility for conventional back-up.

The remote throttle control system

The throttle control system is also implemented on the computer as DDC-functions. The different modes of operation are the following:

- preparation for getting underway
- turbine warm-up
- manoeuver
- full power
- finish with engines.

All these functions are implemented according to specifications made by the turbine manufacturer. The system will in general perform all the functions of the conventional system only in a more elegant way.

It is very natural to implement on a computer ramp function generators as required to limit the rate of change of valve position and time dependant load ceilings during warm-up. Important features as automatic gradual throttle reduction when critical parameters reach alarm level and automatic breaking by means of astern steam based on RPM request or other criteria have also been included.

The turbine plant may either be controlled by valve positioning (open loop) or by revolution/min. feedback control (closed loop). The closed loop method is normally used, but the system provides automatic switch over to open loop if the speed feedback loop should fail.

Monitoring, alarm and logging functions

This computer based automation system is designed to meet the requirements of periodically unmanned operation (EO) by The norske Veritas classification society. Extended requirements (rules) are now being worked out specially for digital computer installations, and this ship will be the first turbine ship classed by these rules. The system also includes important features in addition to the EO requirements.

A computerized monitoring system as developed by Noratom-Norcontrol [1] is superior to conventional systems for several reasons. For instance, the man-machine communication part consists of two displays, one alpha-numerical and one graphical, both serviced by the computer. The alpha-numerical display is used for current process information obtained through analog sensors. Calculated values, process limits and instrument limits may also be displayed. The graphical display is specially useful in presenting trend curves from the condition monitoring and trend analysis sub-system.

In addition to the alpha-numerical display the alarm system consists of group alarm lamps. Important system parameters and limits may be changed by using various push-buttons and/or teletype.

Mainly due to economical considerations, the design of the man-machine communication part is a compromise between what the operator wants and wnat the designer finds possible within his constraints. It should be mentioned that the success of a process control system is to a large extent dependent on how the man-machine communication part has been solved.

Most of the signal inputs are preferred as analog signals because of the filtering and check procedures performed by the computer. Still there are the following digital inputs:

- Start and stop button positions
- Manual/auto switches
- Motor contactors
- State of relays
- Valve limit positions
- Pulse inputs as RPM and frequency.

These signals also go into the computer and may initiate various actions.

One other reason why a computer system is superior to conventional systems is the various tests that may be performed on the analog input signals. Examples of such tests are the following:

- Instrument range
- Digital filtering
- Alarm limits (high, low)
- Integration limits
- Rate limits
- Deviation from mean value
- Variable limits depending on operating conditions
- Process variable limit check.

The computer may also perform linearization of special non-linear signals. The reason for all these tests and operations on the incoming analog signals are:

1. Increases the information about the process and the instrumentation system to be presented for the operator.

2. Improves the various control functions.

The alarm system is designed to give the operator the possibility of obtaining all required information to quickly find the cause of the alarm. Four things happen when an alarm goes off. An audible alarm sounds, the group alarm flashes, the alpha-numerical display shows where it occurred and a permanent record is printed out on the teletype.

The operator may now request additional information about the alarm if necessary.

The system alarm logging includes the following:

- process variables in alarm condition.
- equipment which has failed
- instrument failure
- controlled variables not responding correctly
- start and stop of equipment
- changes in control set points, instrument limits and process limits.

Additional information may be printed out if desired by the operator or the shipowner. One should recall that this automation systeam will operate under EO condition and very little information is printed out during normal operation.

Back-up philosophy

Because of the state of the art of dual digital computer system (i. e. one computer as back-up for the other) a conventional back-up was chosen. This means that the development of dual digital computer systems has not reached the point where it is justifiable to be utilized in shipboard automation systems neither from a reliability nor from an economical point of view. This is of course an interesting development, but further research has to be done before commercialization. The special weak points with dual digital systems are the difficulties with switching operation from one computer to the other, and the expence of the double-up of software necessary.

The analog controller back-up through the Computer Automatic Manual (CAM) stations (Figure 2) brings you back to well known conventional techniques, and the price is just a fraction of another computer system.

The system also has conventional alarm back-up in case of computer failure. The alarms are based on the same sensors as the computer system.

Software - hardware considerations

The computer uses a SINTRAN II operating system specially designed for on-line real time operation in process environment. Most of the 32 K of core memory is programmed in assembly language. This means a relatively high initial investment in programming effort as compared to systems programmed in FORTRAN or other similar languages. But since the system will be made commercially available, several similar systems will be produced. Then the intial extra cost in programming is paid by the extra core space space required for a high level language. Because of reliability problems, rotating mass memories do not seem to be an alternative yet for shipboard applications.

The reason for choosing this Norwegian NORD-4E computer is that it has been thoroughly tested in rough environments and that the computer today is in operation in at least 30 shipboard installations. The computer and the input-output (I/O) hardware have been designed based on the latest developments in electronic components. The computer and the I/O consist of only a few cards and are easy to service.

SYSTEM TESTING AND SIMULATION

The system is being extensively tested over a long period of time at the Noratom-Norcontrol test laboratory before being shipped to the yard. Experience has shown that most of the hardware problems occur during the first hours of operation. Therefore these initial hours of operation have to be spent in the test laboratory and not on board the ship.

During the project, extensive tests of the control system have been performed at the real time simulation laboratory[6]. The system consists of two process control type digital computers interfaced together. One is used to simulate the process, whilst the other performs the multivariable control functions. Very useful results and experience have been gained from the simulation work at this laboratory. A complete software test, both dynamically and statically, will be performed by the system company responsible for the installation. That is, the computer is temporarily interfaced to another computer which simulates all relevant shipboard functions both statically and dynamically. Really this is a computerized testing of the engine room computer based automation system.

OPERATING PERSONNEL AND QUALIFICATIONS

This computerized system is designed to be operated by the engineers operating similar conventional steam turbine automation systems today. A short course of one week's duration is considered sufficient to learn the new system. During the project period, developing the prototype system, engineers with long experience in conventional turbine plant operation are actively working with design and testing procedures.

The on board service and repair are based on a "cook book" procedure. Simple operations on the computer as loading and punching of paper tape are considered necessary to be performed by the operator. The computer is hidden behind the control panel, and the engineer has no special feeling of operating a computerized system, except in the fact that the system may appear extremely intelligent to him.

CONCLUSION

A digital computer based automation system has been designed for a marine steam power plant. The system represents the state of the art of shipboard automation, both with respect to hardware and software developments. Modern control techniques have been applied and real time simulation tests show promising results. The importance of real time simulation should be noted both in the control system's design and in the final testing of the complete automation system. As mentioned before the purpose of this project was not to experiment on new techniques, but to develop a realistic computer based automation system which will be commercially attractive. Potential manning reduction on this EO ship is being considered, but it is too early to draw any conclusion from this work. The real gain is expected to come from the condition monitoring and trend analysis part, which will make safer ship operation and better planned maintenance possible.

REFERENCES

(1) Aas, T. and Sivertsen, O. M., "Data Chief/ Turbine - System Manual", NC publication No. 6-72-11E, Norcontrol, Horten, Norway (1972).

(2) Lind, K. and Williams, T. J., "A Survey of the Present Status and Future Needs of the Ship Automation (Computer Control) Field", PLAIC Report No. 38, The Purdue Laboratory for Applied Industrial Control, Purdue University, Lafayette, Indiana (January 1971).

(3) Walters, R. C., Lind, K. and Williams, T. J., "Engine Room Automation for Turbine Driven Ships", IFAC Paper No. 15.4, 5th World Congress of the International Federation of Automatic Control, Paris, France (June 1972).

(4) Tyssø, A., "Design of a Multivariable Con-
     troller for a ship boiler system", internal
     report, The Ship Research Institute of Norway,
     Trondheim, Norway, 1973.

(5) Øyvang, K., Løken, J. and Rasmussen, M.,
     "Thermodynamic Condition Monitoring",
     internal report, The Ship Research Institute
     of Norway, Trondheim, Norway (1973).

(6) Brembo, J.C., "Steam Boiler Control and
     Simulation", internal report, The Ship
     Research Institute of Norway, Trondheim,
     Norway (1973).

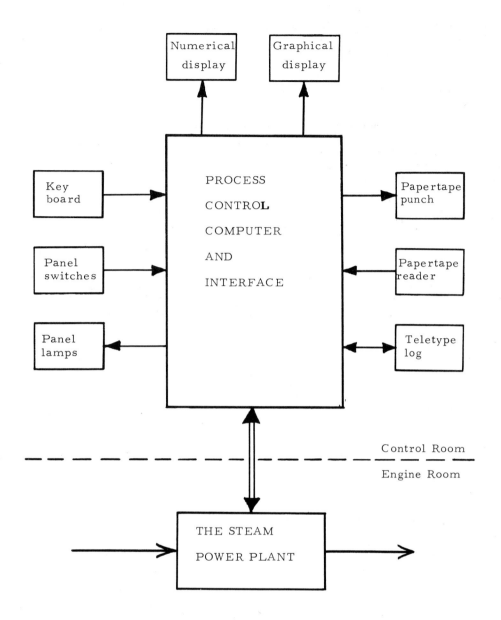

Figure 1.

THE COMPUTER PROCESS CONTROL CONFIGURATION

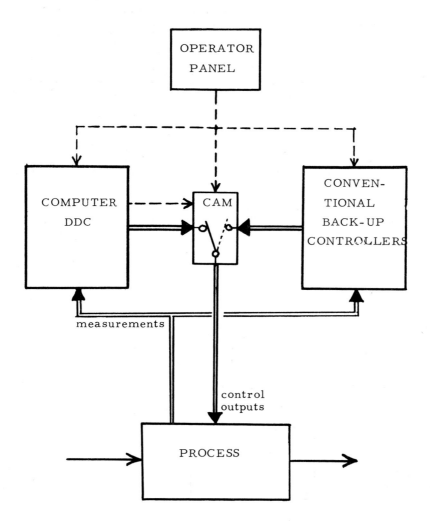

Figure 2.

CONTROL SYSTEM ARRANGEMENT THROUGH COMPUTER -
AUTOMATIC - MANUAL (CAM)
STATIONS

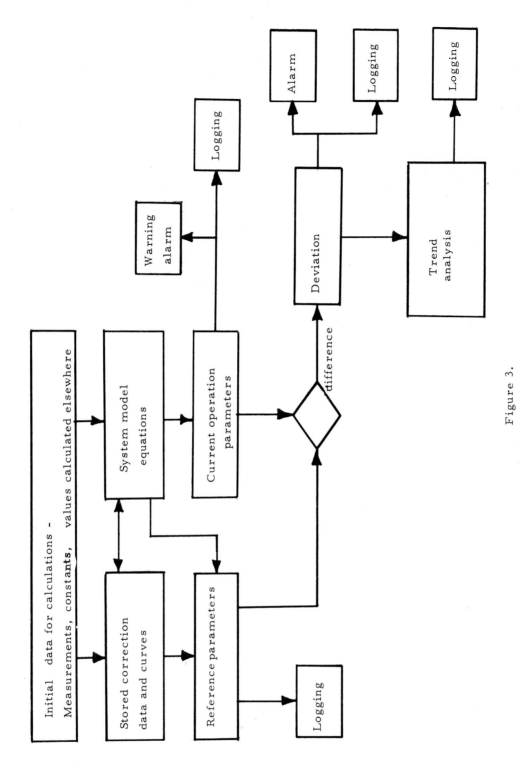

Figure 3.

CONDITION MONITORING AND TREND ANALYSIS SYSTEM.   SIMPLIFIED FLOW DIAGRAM.

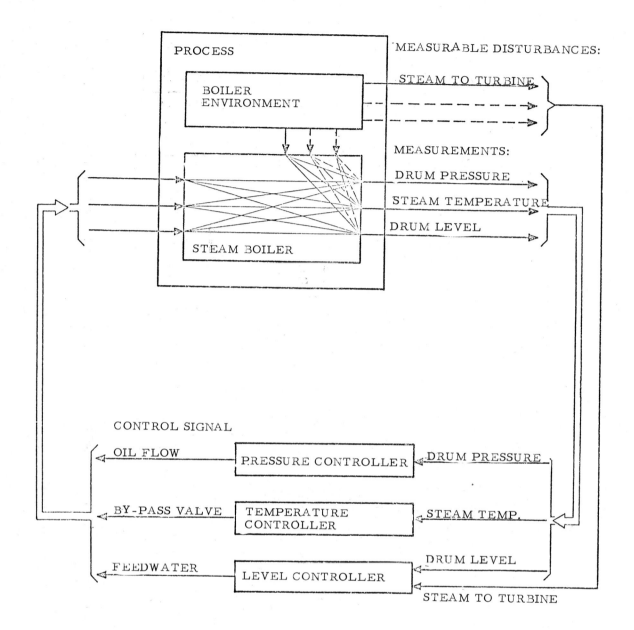

Figure 4.

CONVENTIONAL CONTROL SYSTEM

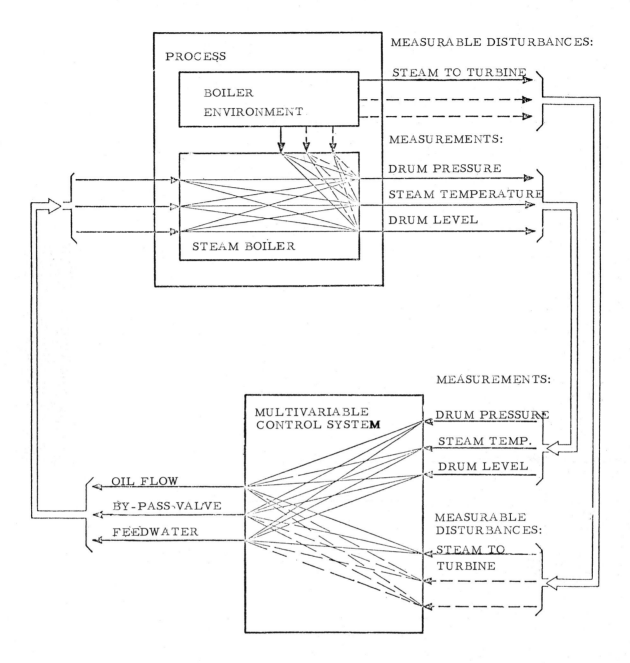

Figure 5.

MULTIVARIABLE CONTROL SYSTEM

THE LIQUID NATURAL GAS CARRIER
AUTOMATION SYSTEMS

Albert A.Ardley M.Inst.M.C.

Marine Specialist

Foxboro-Yoxall Limited

Redhill, Surrey, England

INTRODUCTION

With the discovery of large concentrations of natural gas in many parts of the world, coupled with the rapidly declining resources of conventional fuels in the world, particularly for those countries with high industrial commitment, comes the requirement, and increasing demand, for special ships to transport L.N.G. to those areas, urgently and in large quantities.

The development of the "L.N.G. Carrier" over the last twenty years, has introduced to the shipbuilding world problems of construction especially related to materials and manufacturing techniques, for a variety of cargo tank designs.

Before taking a look at the history of L.N.G. development and transportation of L.N.G. by sea, across the world, what is it that creates such interest in this particular fuel?

The advantages of L.N.G. in both domestic and industrial sectors are that methane is a remarkable fuel. Its calorific value is about twice as high as that of conventional town gas. It contains no carbon monoxide, it is clean and the products of combustion do not pollute the atmosphere, which are qualities certainly appreciated in all western countries where the fight against pollution is being strongly waged.

As an industrial fuel, natural gas can be used for instance, for firing electric power plants. Because of its purity, it is also the ideal fuel for use in the steel and glass industries and in many applications in the field of chemistry.

In the U.S.A. there is an increasing philosophy that natural gas could be used as an automobile fuel which for them and the world at large would eliminate a major source of atmosphere pollution.

In this general picture, the advantages of L.N.G lie in the reduction of volume brought about by liquefaction ($1m^3$ of liquid representing $600m^3$ of gas) which provides a solution of two problems which might have slowed down the growth of the natural gas market.

The first problem is that of storage of the gas. Its solution resides in peak-shaving installations. Near major builtup areas the swings in demand make conventional gasometers inconceivable. For 200-300 days a year the peak-shaving plant liquefies quantities of gas which are stored before being regasified just for a few days to meet peak demands. Storage space under these circumstances is minimised.

The second problem is one with which we are concerned, that of making available to our consumers overseas resources through maritime transportation. Methane tankers enable large amounts of energy to be carried in compact form.

THE HISTORY OF L.N.G. DEVELOPMENT.

It will be of interest to look at the history of L.N.G. development especially in relation to the carriage of L.N.G. by sea, the number and type of ships in service and the rate of growth of this fleet.

'Fig. 1': shows the growth of the worlds L.N.G. tanker fleet. It will be seen that in 1965 there existed only five ships, whose total carrying capacity was something of the order of a quarter of a million barrels (oil equivalent). By 1970, that is in five years, the number of ships was eleven with a carrying capacity of just over half a million barrels. Jumping to mid 1973, it is expected that some twenty-one ships will be in service with a carrying capacity of over three and a half million barrels. The graph illustrates that the increase in number of ships is of the order 5-6 per year and that the carrying capacity dramatically increases from 1972 on.

It is also interesting to consider the types of cargo tank that have been fitted and will be fitted in new construction. Figure 2. lists design company, tank type, tank shape, ships in service in 1973 and ships on order for future delivery.

Whilst it is not the purpose of this paper to discuss the merits of the various designs it is interesting to note that up to 1973 most ships in service will have either the free standing 'Prismatic' type of tank or the 'Membrane' type but that ships on order for delivery after that date would seem to be more or less equally divided between the spherical tank design (free standing) and the 'Membrane' type.

The U.S.A. is currently building an increasing number of L.N.G. carriers which will, it is reported, use the spherical design. Japan likewise is moving into the building of L.N.G. carriers, but which design will be used?

The purpose of this paper is to consider and present some of the interesting and important measurement and control systems utilised in the machinery and cargo areas of the L.N.G. carrier. The large numbers in which these special ships will be required augers well both for the shipbuilder and the automation equipment manufacturer. Fig. 3 gives information which shows the development of L.N.G. ocean transport.

As long ago as the year 1920 Godfrey Cabot issued a patent covering insulated containers for transport by barge, but it was not until 1952 that a serious study was conducted by "Union Stockyard" of Chicago for transport of L.N.G. by barge.

In 1957 Constock & North Thames Gas Board made a joint study on use of large L.N.G. carriers.

1958 records the conversion of the 'Methane Pioneer' from a dry cargo ship to an L.N.G. prototype.

'Methane Pioneer' made successful delivery of L.N.G. to Canvey Island (U.K.) in 1961.

1962 sees the order by Conch & U.K. Gas Council of two 24,400m3 ships to carry L.N.G. from Algeria to U.K.

1964, 1965 sees the completion of 'Methane Princess', 'Methane Progress' and 'Jules Verne'.

These ships and all subsequent new buildings are making increasing use of automation systems. Sea transport of L.N.G. is poised exactly between 'The Stage of Development' and 'Large Scale Commercialisation' and it is important from the operator point of view that these expensive, specialised ships, be run economically, efficiently and above all safely.

When comparing the extent of instrumentation required with that in use on the average V.L.C.C., the L.N.G. carrier requires as much instrumentation for the cargo side as for the propulsion plant and in consequence should be given highest attention in the design stage.

When an owner orders these ships they are usually planned to operate regularly between definately assigned pick-up and delivery terminals. Consideration should therefore be given by the shipbuilder to the use of equipment that can be serviced without difficulty. This must mean choosing manufacturers who can provide service in the ship operation areas.

It is good policy to give maximum consideration to the following general and important points:-

1. The use as far as is possible of standard equipment sea-service proved and to Classification Society approval.

2. Minimising the type and variety of equipment in order to simplify the 'Spares' inventory.

3. Keeping control loops as simple as possible, within the requirements of the control function needed.

4. Providing overall guarantee for satisfactory operation of the plant within the limits defined by the control system specification.

5. Providing customer training in the understanding of the particular system installed.

There is a tendancy by certain instrument and control equipment manufacturers and others, to produce packaged systems for such specific duties as 'Boiler Combustion Controls'. These packages do not necessarily provide the ideal in a comprehensive automation system such as that required for an L.N.G. carrier.

Boiler Combustion Control like many of the other systems required, can be provided by using the same type of equipment throughout, whether using electronics or pneumatics. The use of the same type of equipment throughout would appear to be more acceptable to both the shipbuilder and the shipowner.

CONSIDERATION OF TYPICAL INSTRUMENT LOOPS

Fig. 4 shows details of boiler instrumentation.

The most important feature of the boiler combustion system on an L.N.G. carrier, having steam turbine propulsion, is the burning of 'Boil-Off' gas from the cargo tanks in the boiler(s).

In considering the control loops shown in Fig's 4 and 5, bear in mind a number of important matters, among them for example:-

(a) Rate of "Boil-Off".

(b) Change of calorific value of "Boil-Off" gas during voyage.

(c) Gas availability.

(d) Safety features.

(e) Ecology - current requirements.

"L.N.G. as a cargo is usually carried at near atmospheric pressure and at its corresponding boiling point of about -160°C. As a liquid it is extremely light, with a specific gravity of about 0.45; it is also crystal clear and colourless. In composition, L.N.G. contains a mixture of methane, ethane, propane and butane, with methane predominating. The percentage of the constituents varies according to the geographical source." *

USE OF BOIL-OFF AS FUEL

Several of the classification societies have formulated rules, 'Guidance Regulations' or 'Provisional Requirements' applicable to the use of L.N.G. boil-off as a fuel for the main propulsion machinery. These require that a dual fuel system be installed and that when operating under gas firing a minimum of 10% fuel oil is burned simultaneously. The USCG will allow 'Boil-Off' burning in port and whilst manoeuvring, provided that means of disposing of excess energy is available, such as steam dump, oversize condenser or controllable pitch propeller.

Apart from classification society rulings, some port authorities will not permit burning of boil-off whilst in port.

Obviously the control system design must allow operation of boiler plant to suit permissible conditions. Rate of boil-off from cargo tanks is about 0.25% per day.

I Cargo Tank Maximum Pressure Control

Cargo tank pressure is measured with an absolute pressure transmitter PX-1 calibrated 950-1300 mbars absolute to an accuracy of $\pm 0.5\%$ of span. The proportional signal is transmitted to controller PC-1 which in emergency would operate the vent to atmosphere valve V1, however, the set point of the controller PC-1 is manually set by SP-1 at a higher value than SP-3 on the gas availability loop to controller PC-3.

Low selector relay LS-3 passes to Gas Availability controller PC-3 the low value signal set by SP-3.

EXAMPLE:-

SP-1 = 1100 mbar abs and cargo tank pressure = 1060 mbar.

PC-1 = 20% proportional band.

V1 = 0.2 bar (valve closed).

If:- Cargo tank pressure rises to 1065 mbar, valve V1 would receive 0.2 bar and remain closed, if cargo tank pressure rises to 1070 mbar V1 would receive 0.26 bar and thus vent to atmosphere.

For safety reasons pressure transmitter PX-1 is duplicated. The high selector relay HS-1 monitors both transmitters, passing the highest value forward.

II Compressor Discharge Pressure Control

Discharge pressure of the compressor is measured by transmitter PX-2 (also duplicated for safety reasons) and the signal passed via high selector relay HS-2 to controller PC-2.

PX-2 is calibrated:- 950-1700 mbar abs, and in order to maintain good gas flow control the discharge pressure will be kept constant through modulation of valve V2 by controller PC-2. This controller will have P+I action and be fitted with an anti-integral saturation device to avoid overshoot when the valve closes.

III Gas Availability

Gas available for combustion is a 'status' which is created by adjustment of setpoint to controller PC-3 by SP-3 for control of pressure in tanks.

The status condition provides a level of control via PC-3 which is proportional to the deviation between the pressure in the tanks and the setpoint SP-3. The set point adjustment is 950 to 1300 mbar abs.

The low selector relay LS-3 will ensure that the lowest setting is passed to controller PC-3.

IV Steam Demand

The typical system shown in Fig. 4 is based upon a linear function of steam flow QS corrected in 'closed loop' by superheated steam pressure PS. Computing relay CR-1 accepts steam flow and steam pressure signals and provides an output representative of total calorific value demand.

The output of CR-1 acts as a master signal for fuel and air flow to the boiler. The controller PC-4 has P+I control action. The relative values of steam and pressure signals may be adjusted in computing relay CR-1.

V Combustion Controls

Combustion controls are designed to adjust the fuels to the steam demand in order to maintain steam pressure. However, in this instance preference is given to the 'Gas Available' signal, in order that all gas available is burned in the boilers. Set point SP-3 adjusts the level of availability, for example when the cargo tank pressure equals 1060 mbar abs and set point is 1060 mbar abs availability signal equals 0.6 bar. If it is desired to adjust set point to say 1060 mbars, the availability signal would then be 0.72 bar (with PB of 20% on PC-3).

(a) Where demand is greater than availability.
The demand signal is used to set the fuel gas controller FC-5 and control valve V7 will open to supply the required gas flow under pressure drop shown by the process. Since there is insufficient fuel gas, the difference between the demand and the calorific input is sensed by computing relay CR-2. The output of this relay will now provide the set point to the fuel oil controller FC-6.

If the set point is lower than the allowable minimum for fuel oil (as set by precision regulator on HS-3) the high selector relay will pass the precise set pressure to the fuel oil flow controller FC-6. In this case too much gas is sensed and the gas valve V7 will move to a more closed position, so that the incoming fuels are equal to the demand.

(b) Where demand is below gas availability

In order that all available gas is sent to
the burners, the set point to the controller
FC-5 is equal to availability. The fuel oil
set point will then be negated and the controller restricted to the minimum (as set by
precision regulator on HS-3). Gas set point
being greater than demand, increases steam
pressure.

If steam dumping is not immediately author-
ised, gas pressure in the cargo tanks will
increase.

VI Steam Dump Control - See Fig. 5

Controller PC-11a receives superheated steam,
pressure, and its set point must be higher than
that of PC-4. Controller PC-11a output represents the steam pressure above normal setting and
will modulate valve V-10 to pass more or less
steam to the main condenser.

It will be seen that the correct relationship is
required between the cargo tank excess pressure
controller and the excess steam pressure controller, to the point that steam dumping to the
main condenser must take place before excess cargo
tank pressure is vented to atmosphere. Indeed it
may well be necessary in order to avoid pollution,
to run the engines in port at zero propeller pitch.
All is dependant on the pressure of gas available
and the time taken to build-up pressure in the
cargo tanks after continuous 'Full Away' condition
reverting to 'Manoeuvring' condition and Finished
with engines.

Pressure controller PC-11b is included as a limiting controller to prevent excess steam pressure at
the condenser inlet. Pressure downstream of the
dump valve V-10 is limited to 2ATA.

VII Steam Dump Temperature Control

Steam dump flow QSD acts as a set point for spray
water to the desuperheater via controller FC-12.
In addition the temperature control loop TC-12
sends a signal to the computing relay CR-6.
Therefore set point of FC-12 is a linear relationship of steam flow, plus controller TC-12 variations to maintain temperature setting.

The temperature is sensed at the desuperheater
outlet, before the dump valve, to ensure that the
steam to dump valve is slightly superheated. If
saturation of steam is required before entrance to
condenser or in order to be sure of attaining
170°C, an additional temperature loop can be
installed downstream of the dump valve.

VIII Combustion Air Control

Fig. 4 indicates that the combustion air flow is
measured by differential pressure measurement
across a fan inlet venturi rather than pressure
drop across the air register and combustion chamber. The venturi solution provides an accurate,
reliable measurement of total air to the boiler

and gives good control of fuel/air ratio independant of the number of burners in use.

Fuel/air ratio can be either manually adjusted via
manual signal to ratio relay 'RR' or automatically
by use of O_2 analyser and controller.

The set point of the air flow controller FC-7 is
provided from computing relay CR-5 which adds the
two fuel flows to obtain the correct setting.

The increasing steam demand inhibits the signal to
the fuel flow controllers to ensure increased air
flow before increased fuel flow.

Falling steam demand reduces the fuel flow before
a reduction in air flow to avoid smoke.

IX Fuel Oil Pressure Control

The fuel oil pressure control system is designed
to allow wide rangeability in fuel oil flow control and to avoid excessive pressure drop across
the control valve. The controller outputs are
connected to a high selector relay. The output
selected is used as the measured value for a proportional controller SC-1 which operates valve V9
to spill from heater discharge to pump suction.

CALORIFIC VALUE ADJUSTMENT

When using L.N.G. boil-off gas for steam raising,
it is necessary to take account of changes in the
Calorific Value of the 'Boil-Off' which occurs
during the voyage.

Experience in operating marine boiler plant fired
with L.N.G. Boil-Off, shows that manual changes in
fuel/air ratio to compensate for changes in calorific value are required once per watch.

Obviously it is increasingly desirable to make
such adjustments automatically, to meet the
'Unattended Operation' philosophy, which is now
becoming very much the norm.

There are two important reasons why the C.V. of
'Boil-Off' gas will vary during a voyage, they are
gradual enrichment of the gas and effect on boil-
off rate due to ambient variations.

There are two possibilities for the automatic
correction of combustion control related to changes of C.V. in L.N.G. 'Boil-Off'.

The first and obvious method is the use of a Calorimeter directly connected into the cargo gas
line to the boilers, which provides a control signal proportional to the C.V. deviation. This
signal is sent to the gas controller FC-5 via auto
manual station and computing relay CR-4.

Choice of an environmently suitable Calorimeter
for marine application is most important, most
available instruments of this type are more suitable for laboratory usage. However there are
several manufacturers who can provide suitable
equipment.

Accuracies claimed for such instruments are of the order ±1% of value.

The second method makes use of in line single stream chromatographs. The process connected chromatographs, would give a signal proportional to the deviation of C.V. but the signal would be an inferred C.V. based on the assumption that the percentages of nitrogen and carbon dioxide present in the gas sample directly affect its calorific value. A correction factor related to total hydrocarbons present is required.

A typical analysis of L.N.G. is:-

Methane	(CH_4)	=	88%	)
Ethane	(C_2H_6)	=	5.1%	)
Propane	(C_3H_8)	=	4.8%	) By volume
Butane	(C_4H_{10})	=	1.8%	)
Pentane	(C_5H_{12})	=	0.2%	)
Nitrogen		=	0.1%	)

The accuracy required would determine the type of equipment to be used and it is necessary to calibrate a chromatograph to suit the gas sample analysis. This second method of providing automatic adjustment to the combustion system is more costly than the calorimeter but better accuracies are obtainable.

Time does not permit presentation of greater detail, but this brief description serves to indicate the potential possibilities in such an application.

Not mentioned are some of the conventional systems related to propulsion plant, such as condensate systems, evaporator controls and steam range make-up and bleed systems. These systems would be included in the complete automation package, and would be built from standard components in line with the policy previously stated.

CARGO INSTRUMENTATION

Instrumentation related to cargo handling and processing now described, is in reference to the type of L.N.G. carrier using membrane tank design. In general it is applicable to any type of carrier.

The following list summarises the parts of the cargo plant fitted with instrumentation:-

    Gas line to shore heater.
    Gas line to boilers heater.
    Nitrogen storage and distribution.
    Vaporisers.
    Liquid crossovers.
    Main gas line and crossover.
    Cargo tank - pump discharge.
    Nitrogen inlet to interbarrier and
        isolation spaces.
    High duty compressors.
    Low duty compressor.
    Cargo tank temperature measurements.
    Cargo tank level.

Since the instrumentation required for most of these particular parts of the plant is mainly pressure and temperature control, two of the important aspects related to cargo tank measurement are selected.

CARGO TANK LEVELS

Measurement of cargo tank level is important in relation to cargo loading and discharging especially if required for 'Custody Transfer'.

Several methods of level measurement are in use, and have been relatively successful. They include:-

    Mechanical float and tape gauges.
    Nitrogen bubble system.
    Capacitance.
    Ultrasonic.
    Discrete point sensors.

Measurement of liquid cargoes in general is a straight forward operation, in most cases involving simple volumetric tank gauging before and after loading and discharging, with measurements of specific gravity and temperature. In the case of L.N.G. cargo, measurement becomes a somewhat more formidable task.

In relation to 'Custody Transfer' L.N.G. is normally traded on the basis of heat value of the cargo, requiring that the volume and composition of the cargo be known. Having the percentage and heat value of each of the constituents it becomes a relatively simple undertaking to compute the heat value of the total cargo.

Volumetric measurement can be carried out by use of equipment and procedures used for conventional liquid cargoes, modified for the cryogenic aspects of the cargo.

The bubbler gauge system has a reliability that is a function only of the tightness of piping system joints, and the rate at which the operating gas (nitrogen) is passed through the system. Nitrogen is soluable in L.N.G. and if flow rates associated with air-actuated bubbler systems are used, quite erratic results will ensue. It is important therefore to have the higher bubbling rate with nitrogen.

In addition to determining the cargo volume by using level indicators and tank calibration tables it is necessary to find liquid density, and again the bubbler type system may be used.

L.N.G. carriers often use a back-up tank level measuring system of the capacitance type. This system provides total tank level measurement and accurate ullage measurement.

CARGO TANK TEMPERATURES

Other important measurements are temperature within the tank i.e. the cargo temperature and outside the tank for safety reasons to ensure that any leakage of cargo is detected. Leakage of cargo at -160°C could result in structural failures of ships interbarriers and hull brought about by steel fracture. Fig. 6 illustrates a typical system for the monitoring temperatures inside and outside the cargo tanks. Dealing first with the cargo temperatures, these are sensed by resistance probes located at strategic points in the tank to monitor the whole tank area. The number of probes specified by owners varies between ten and twenty per tank.

Platinum resistance probes are screwed into small stainless steel blocks welded to the inside of the tank. The resistance element is housed in a stainless steel sheathed mineral insulated cable of continuous length between the measurement point and the deck mounted junction box, securely clipped to the tank skin.

It is important that the correct grade of stainless steel is used to meet cryogenic conditions obtaining. VIZ: AISI 321 grade.

Each probe and extension cable is a continuous assembly complete with glands to provide seals at deck level and junction box.

Where high accuracy is required, for example when measurement is used in the 'Custody Transfer' calculation, a 4-wire platinum resistance element is used. An accuracy of $0.3^{\circ}C$ is obtainable at the read-out. A multi-core cable is used between the deck mounted junction box and the control room instrumentation (in this case recorders). Zener barriers are included to electrically separate the safe area from the hazardous area to ensure that all circuits are intrinsically safe. The tank outer skin temperatures are monitored by thermocouples placed at carefully selected points. The extension cable and thermocouple are also continuous units from measurement point to deck mounted junction boxes. Stainless steel mineral insulated extension cables are also used for this duty. Fig. 6 indicates that a multipoint temperature indicator is used to scan the ten or so probes fitted to each cargo tank outer skin. A multipoint alarm system continuously monitors each point and in the event of a low temperature would give an audible and visual alarm on the bridge and in the engine room spaces.

PNEUMATICS & ELECTRONICS

The choice between pneumatics and electronics is a matter usually dictated by the owner or shipbuilder, and the majority of ships have so far made use of pneumatics, but the current tendancy is toward electronics and ultimately data acquisition and digital computer systems.

The Immediate Future

Taking a prophetic look into the future the sheer amount and complexity of automation equipment required on L.N.G. carriers, seems to indicate the logical use of a number of computers to give direct digital control in positively assigned areas with an overall management computer.

Perhaps the duties assigned would follow the pattern:-

A. BRIDGE FUNCTIONS

1. Collision prevention.
2. Navigation (NNSS Satellite).
3. Steering (track following autopilot).
4. Administration (custody transfer calculations).

B. MACHINERY & CASUALTY CONTROL

1. Main Turbine (Auto start-up & monitoring).
2. Propulsion (Measured constraints). Turbine/boiler, limiting systems, to maintain boiler pressure, dual fuel firing, power build-up from full ahead to full away, astern/ahead safety.
3. Boilers - (Auto start-up and shutdown, combustion control, feedwater, drum level, steam pressure and temperature).
4. Generators - (Auto start-up, synchronising load sharing and paralleling).
5. Distillation Plant - (Auto start-up and shut-down, auto control of variables).
6. Cargo Handling - Compressors, heaters, pumps, etc.
7. Casualty Control - (Pumps, autoflooding control, bilge levels, fire detection, start pumps and CO_2 control, cargo tank leak alarms).

It is difficult to foresee the size and number of special ships that will be built in the future. What is certain is that shipbuilders and instrument and automation companies will be challenged by the requirements as they develop in the world demand for this most interesting form of marine transportation.

References

*William du Barry Thomas & Alfred H.Schwendtner., L.N.G. Carriers: The Current State of the Art, from LNG/LPG Conference Papers, London 21-22nd March 1972.

Ian Robertson, H.Clarkson & Co., Ltd., L.N.G. Report 1972.

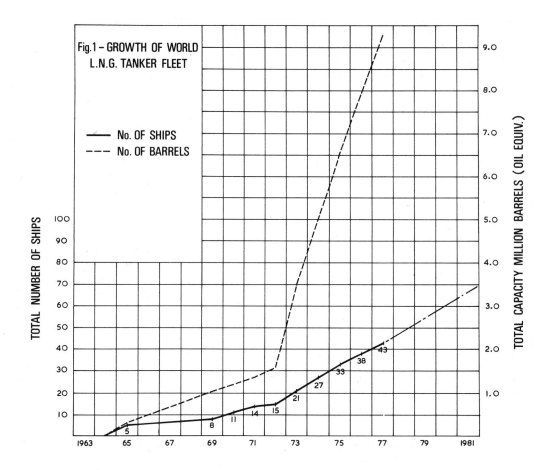

Fig.1 GROWTH OF WORLD L.N.G. TANKER FLEET

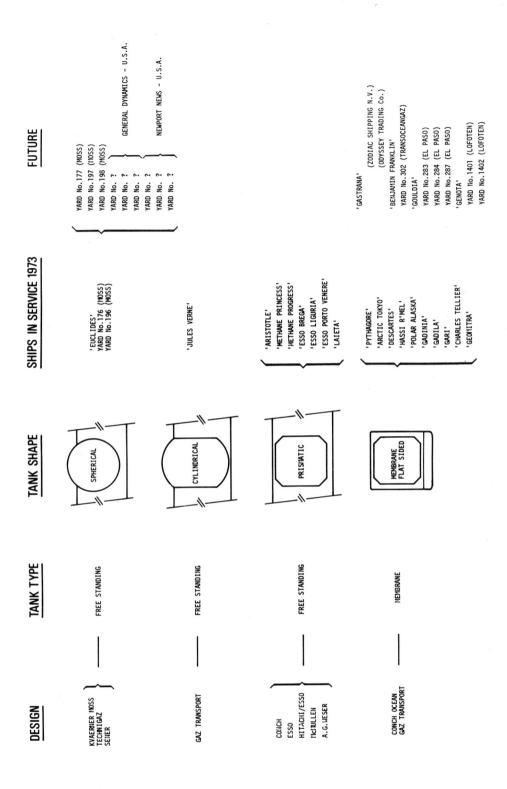

DESIGN

KVAERNER MOSS
TECHNIGAZ
SENER

GAZ TRANSPORT

CONCH
ESSO
HITACHI/ESSO
McMULLEN
A.G.WESER

CONCH OCEAN
GAZ TRANSPORT

TANK TYPE

FREE STANDING

FREE STANDING

FREE STANDING

MEMBRANE

TANK SHAPE

SPHERICAL

CYLINDRICAL

PRISMATIC

MEMBRANE
FLAT SIDED

SHIPS IN SERVICE 1973

'EUCLIDES'
YARD No.176 (MOSS)
YARD No.196 (MOSS)

'JULES VERNE'

'ARISTOTLE'
'METHANE PRINCESS'
'METHANE PROGRESS'
'ESSO BREGA'
'ESSO LIGURIA'
'ESSO PORTO VENERE'
'LAIETA'

'PYTHAGORE'
'ARCTIC TOKYO'
'DESCARTES'
'HASSI R'MEL'
'POLAR ALASKA'
'GADINIA'
'GADILA'
'GARI'
'CHARLES TELLIER'
'GEOMITRA'

FUTURE

YARD No.177 (MOSS)
YARD No.197 (MOSS)
YARD No.198 (MOSS)
YARD No. ?
YARD No. ?   GENERAL DYNAMICS - U.S.A.
YARD No. ?
YARD No. ?
YARD No. ?   NEWPORT NEWS - U.S.A.
YARD No. ?

'GASTRANA'   (ZODIAC SHIPPING N.V.)
               (ODYSSEY TRADING Co.)
'BENJAMIN FRANKLIN'
YARD No.302 (TRANSOCEANGAZ)
'GOULDIA'
YARD No.283 (EL PASO)
YARD No.284 (EL PASO)
YARD No.287 (EL PASO)
'GENOTA'
YARD No.1401 (LOFOTEN)
YARD No.1402 (LOFOTEN)

Fig. 2   CARGO TANKS – DESIGN / TYPE / SHIP

302

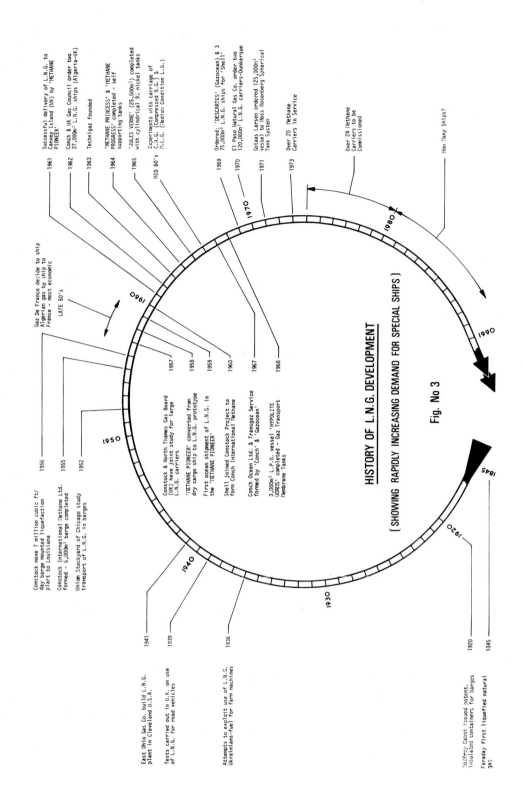

Successful delivery of L.N.G. to
Canvey Island (UK) by 'METHANE
PIONEER'   1961

Conch & UK Gas Council order two
27,000m³ L.N.G. ships (Algeria-UK)   1962

Technigaz founded   1963

'METHANE PRINCESS' & 'METHANE
PROGRESS' completed - self
supporting tanks   1964

'JULES VERNE' (25,500m³) completed
with cylindrical 9% nickel tanks   1965

Experiments with carriage of
C.N.G. (Compressed N.G.) &   MID 60's
M.L.G. (Medium Condition L.G.)

Ordered: 'DESCARTES' (Gazocean) & 3
75,000m³ L.N.G. ships for 'Shell'   1969

El Paso Natural Gas Co. order two
120,000m³ L.N.G. carriers-Dunkerque   1970

Gotaas Larsen ordered 125,000m³
vessel to Moss Rosenberg Spherical
Tank System   1971

Over 20 Methane
Carriers in Service   1973

Over 24 Methane
Carriers to be
Commissioned

How Many Ships?

Constock move 7 million cubic ft/
day barge mounted liquefaction
plant in Louisiana   1956

Constock International Methane Ltd.
formed - 6,000m³ barge completed   1955

Union Stockyard of Chicago study
transport of L.N.G. in barges   1952

Gaz De France decide to ship
Algerian gas by ship to
France - most economic

LATE 50's

1960

Constock & North Thames Gas Board
(UK) have joint study for large
L.N.G. carriers   1957

'METHANE PIONEER' converted from
dry cargo ship to L.N.G. prototype   1958

First ocean shipment of L.N.G. in
the 'METHANE PIONEER'   1959

Shell joined Constock Project to
form Conch International Methane   1960

Conch Ocean Ltd. & Transgaz Service
formed by 'Conch' & 'Gazocean'   1967

3,000m³ L.P.G. vessel 'HYPOLITE
WORIS' completed - Gaz Transport
Membrane Tanks   1968

1950

1940

1930

1920

East Ohio Gas Co. build L.N.G.
plant in Cleveland U.S.A.   1941

Tests carried out in U.K. on use
of L.N.G. for road vehicles   1939

Attempts to exploit use of L.N.G.
Ukrainians-fuel for farm machines   1936

Godfrey Cabot issued patent.
insulated containers for barges   1920

Faraday first liquefied natural
gas   1845

1980

1990

1845

HISTORY OF L.N.G. DEVELOPMENT

(SHOWING RAPIDLY INCREASING DEMAND FOR SPECIAL SHIPS)

Fig. No 3

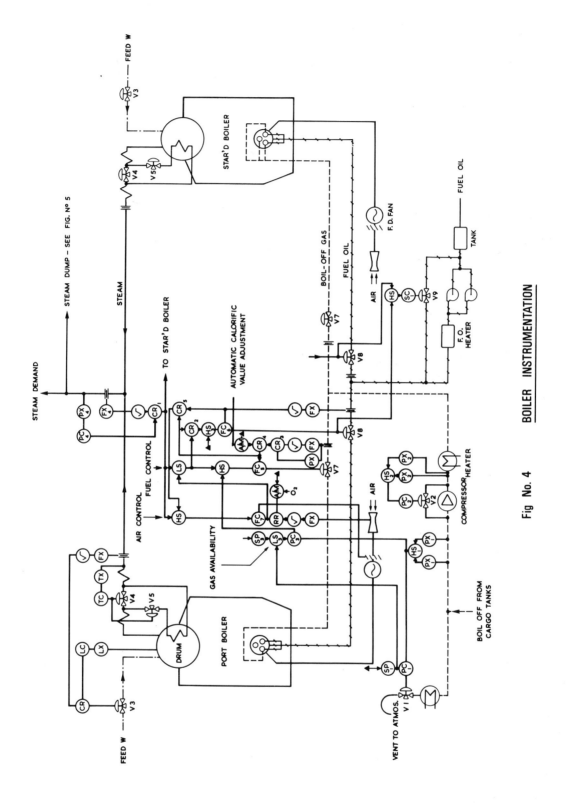

Fig No. 4   BOILER INSTRUMENTATION

304

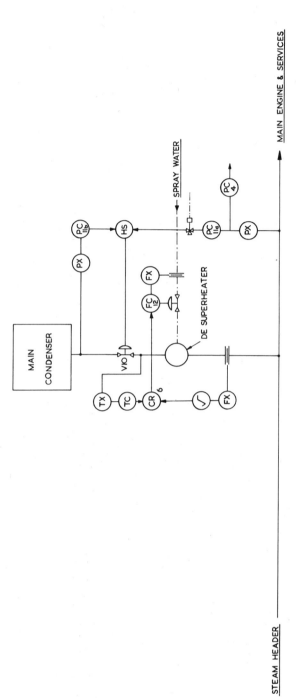

Fig. No. 5.   STEAM DUMP SYSTEM.

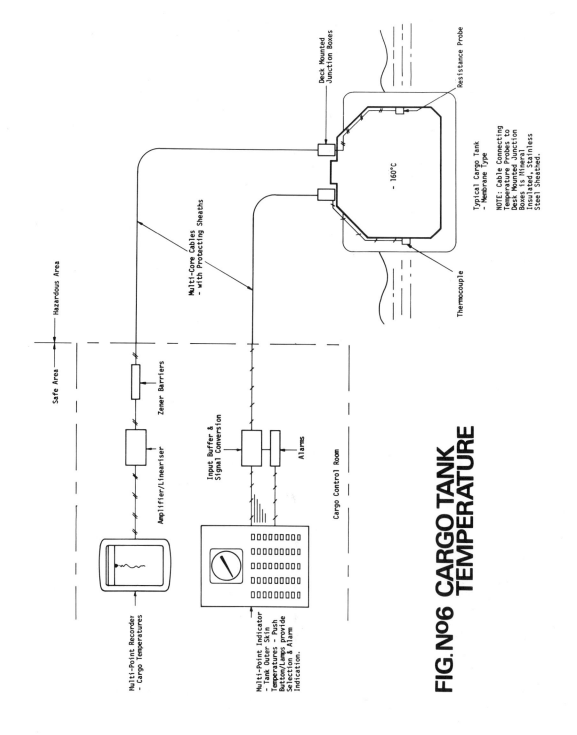

Hazardous Area

Safe Area

Deck Mounted
Junction Boxes

Resistance Probe

− 160°C

Typical Cargo Tank
- Membrane Type

NOTE: Cable Connecting
Temperature Probes to
Desk Mounted Junction
Boxes is Mineral
Insulated, Stainless
Steel Sheathed.

Thermocouple

Multi-Core Cables
- with Protecting Sheaths

Zener Barriers

Amplifier/Lineariser

Input Buffer &
Signal Conversion

Alarms

Cargo Control Room

Multi-Point Recorder
- Cargo Temperatures

Multi-Point Indicator
- Tank Outer Skin
Temperatures - Push
Button/Lamps provide
Selection & Alarm
Indication.

FIG.Nº6 CARGO TANK TEMPERATURE

BOILER FRONT - SHOWING DRUM LEVEL TRANSMITTERS

COMBUSTION AIR FLOW - VENTURI

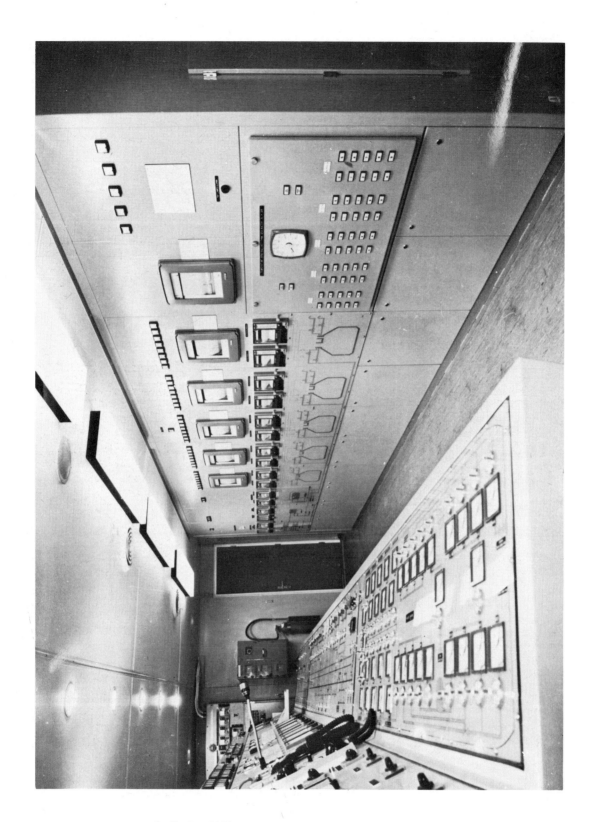

L.N.G. CARRIER – CARGO CONTROL ROOM

L.N.G. CARRIER - ENGINE CONTROL ROOM PANEL

F. Hasselbacher and M. Werner
Siemens Aktiengesellschaft
Erlangen
Germany

INTRODUCTION

The severe competition in world shipping is forcing the owner to have ever larger and faster units built in order to lower freight charges. This leads to the installation of extensive and complex steam generating and machinery plants.

As a plant increases in size, more emphasis is placed on good overall efficiency because the possible savings are no longer negligible. This trend has also resulted in the introduction of higher steam conditions. There were also new technological demands, such as the use of boil-off gas as fuel in liquefied gas carriers or the use of lue gases as an inert gas filling for empty tank compartments, which requires guaranteed 0_2 values even during transient load conditions. What all these innovations have in common is

1. the grater extent of the plants,
2. the greater utilization of the materials, which has lead to closer tolerances for the controlled variables.

As a result, a certain amount of automatic control equipment is indispensible in order to keep such plants under control, even if they are operated by skilled personnel. The rising personnel costs provide a further incentive for progressively extending the degree of marine automation to permit unattended machinery operation which is expected to require a crew of only 12 in the near future.

INTEGRATION OF SUB-SYSTEMS

Extensive automated plants require the application of integrated system technology in order to attain high reliability and thus economy. The term "integrated" has a two-fold significance:

1) Integration of the technologically linked subsystems of the steam generator and turbine with automatic burner, boiler and remote turbine control through exchange of information by associated automatic control systems. (Fig. 1).

2) Modular integration which, however, does not mean the combination of control functions in a single module, but a standardized modular system which permits the solution of similar technological problems with the aid of identical modules.

The information processing structure is shown in Fig. 2. Signal processing takes place along parallel paths and the arrangement of the individual levels is hierarchical in nature. The advantages of such a structure are:

1) Parallel signal processing prevents faults from breaking down the system as a whole. The failure of a component reduces the degree of automation but little.

2) The individual levels are complete in themselves, but arranged hierarchically as regards their function. This means that any desired degree of automation can be attained by the addition of higher levels, without need for modifying a subordinate level in connection with the extension. This provides not only great flexibility in the handling of plants differing in the degree of automation, but is also very beneficial for the commissioning procedure. The individual control loops can be checked and adjusted separately and thus simultaneously.

BURNER CONTROL SYSTEM

The hardware of the burner control system consists of two main parts:

The logic required for starting up and shutting down the boiler and the superordinated components for monitoring and emergency shut-down.

The ignition of the first burner is preceded by purging of the boiler. As soon as the appropriate starting conditions obtain - boiler fan running, normal boiler and deaerator water levels, fuel supply available, etc. - the combustion air control calls for the necessary purging air flow with simultaneous opening of all registers. At the end of the purging period the first burner is ignited: A command is transmitted to the boiler control to provide the necessary oil and air flow for ignition. Upon receipt of the appropriate check-back signals, the register and the oil valve are opened, the ignitor is advanced and the ignition transformers are switched on. An optical/electronic monitor checks for proper combustion. The other burners are ignited by direct control of registers, oil valves and ignitors.

Should abnormal operating conditions arise, such as totale flame failure, low drum water level, fan failure, etc., the safety device interrupts the oil supply to the burners. As a result of today's more stringent demands for safety, the protective devices for quick shut-down are of 2-channel design, from the sensors to the shut-off elements.

Several stages of sophistication are possible for the automatic starting equipment of a boiler, not least because of the differing requirements of the authorities.

BOILER CONTROL SYSTEM

The operating principle of the boiler control system, which consists of main and auxiliary control loops, will be explained by way of the interaction of the load, fuel and combustion air controllers (Fig. 3). The load controller is the superordinated master controller. By changing the command variables of fuel and combustion air it ensures that the desired steam pressure is kept as constant as possible despite load fluctuations. In order to improve the dynamic behaviour, the steam mass flow is fed to all main control loops as disturbance variable. Despite the close relationship between the open and closed-loop control systems or amongst a number of closed-loop control systems, the automatic control system has remained clear in arrangement due to the similar configuration of the individual loops. The functional units of the control loops correspond to the basic modules, such as transducer (1), reference setter (2), differentiating element (3), controller (4), control module (5) and thyristor setter (6). It is also beneficial for planning, commissioning and maintenance of the plant as a whole that a cubicle tier will accommodate a complete control loop.

Electro-pneumatic or electro-mechanical actuators can be used as desired for operating the control valves on the boiler.

The electro-pneumatic actuators are controlled directly from the controller output by 4 - 20 mA signals. The electro-mechanical actuators are fitted with standard three-phase squirrel-cage motors. They are controlled by solid-state thyristor setters which are accommodated in a separate cubicle.

When designing the boiler control system, special attention was paid to overload protection and good manoeuvrability of the boiler.

These considerations lead to the following measures:

1) By applying load and direction-dependent limitations to the derivative-action elements it was possible to obtain better dynamic matching of the individual control loops. For example, the derivative action of the steam mass flow is effective on the fuel controller only when the fuel supply is being reduced, while the air mass flow is given a certain lead over the fuel when the air flow is increasing. This avoids a lack of air which would otherwise cause the protective system of the steam generator to initiate shut-down.

2) The introduction of limiting control loops causes the output signals of the controllers to be compared with the actual values of the controlled variables, thereby providing a certain plausibility check. Thus, the load controller can demand only a fuel flow that is not more than 20% in excess of that related to the associated steam mass flow. This greatly reduces the possibility of over-firing which would also lead to failure of the plant as a whole. Similarly, the active low-air protection derives an additional set value for the fuel and combustion air controllers from the comparison of the actual value of the air mass flow and the output signal of the load controller. Low air causes the set value of the load controller to be reduced, excess fuel that of the combustion air controller to be increased.

TURBINE AUTOMATIC REMOTE
CONTROL SYSTEM

The new development of the automatic remote control system for turbines is based on an automatic control concept that has proved most successful on more than 100 ships.

A speed control loop, which is active over the full speed range, keeps the propeller speed constant at the particular set value. This value is set steplessly on the bridge by means of the engine telegraph and transmitted to the speed controller by an analogue-type rate limiter. The run-up program is adjustable for a maximum duration of up to 1 hour. Either conventional tacho-generators or proximity-type solid state transducers can be used to provide the check-back signals of actual speed.

A pressure limiting control loop for the wheel chamber pressure of the ahead turbine and the admission pressure of the astern turbine limits the output of the speed controller, thereby preventing overloading of the propulsion plant. The pressure limiting control overrides the speed controller only when the actual pressures exceed a limiting curve obtained by plotting the permissible pressure against actual speed.

In addition to this pressure limiting control, there are further protective devices for the main propulsion plant. Upon input of certain criteria, the propeller speed can be automatically reduced or the manoevring valves can be full closed automatically. Another possibility consists of stopping the run-up program with respect to certain external criteria. In order to avoid unnecessary adjustments of the manoeuvring valves when the ship is cruising, it is possible to reduce the sensitivity of response of the speed controller in the upper speed range or to change over to straight valve lift control.

The correcting elements for the turbine manoeuvring valves can be in the form of electro-mechanical, electro-pneumatic or electro-hydraulic actuators. Actuator motors are controlled via solid-state thyristor circuits, electro-pneumatic actuators by 4 - 20 mA signals.

In order to ensure stable speed control in the vicinity of the stop position, say, when setting very low speeds for berthing, the dead ranges of the manoeuvring valves are eliminated electronically. This makes it possible to avoid transient deviations of the controlled variable at speeds as low as 5 rev/min. It is necessary, however, for the operating speed of the manoeuvring valves to be sufficiently high for this purpose.

A zero revolution monitor, which is in action not only during automatic operation, but also during electric manual operation, provides an alarm when an alarm when an adjustable time after standstill of the turbine has elapsed. During automatic operation, the turbine is automatically turned ahead and astern in succession by a turning program.

When there is danger of collision, the bridge personnel can initiate a special emergency manoeuvre program. This automatically increases the reversing speed, i. e. the limiting value for opening the astern manoeuvring valve, reduces the duration of the run-up program and overrides any possible speed reductions.

EXAMPLES FOR THE INTEGRATION OF THE 3 SUB-SYSTEMS

The integration of the 3 sub-systems, "Burner control system", "Boiler control system" and "Turbine automatic remote control system" will now be explained in greater detail by means of a number of examples.

In Fig. 3, the control action on two of the altogether five main control loops is marked in red. For example, the output signal of the load controller is reduced when the failure of a burner is signalled. Furthermore, the burner control system intervenes directly in the fuel control loop to provide a certain amount of fuel for ignition. A separate position control loop is incorporated for the accurate adjustment of this value. To stabilize the combustion process, a momentary additional set value is injected when igniting a burner for compensating the pressure drop occurring when filling the injection pipe.

The burner control system also intervenes in the air flow control. Both the purging air flow and the various ignition air flows during the

starting period are controlled by the inputting of different set values.

A boiler pressure or boiler water level control loop can be superimposed on the turbine automatic remote control system. The actual values of these variables limit the output value of the speed controller by way of limiting controllers, thereby reducing the lift of the manoeuvring valves. This results in a logical interconnection of signals, or exchange of information between the turbine automatic remote control system and the boiler system.

MODULE INTEGRATION

The analogue control loops are built up of components of the TELEPERM C modular system and the digital control loops of components of the SIMATIC C1 modular system. Both modular systems are built up of components with integrated circuits. The mechanical construction is standardized and follows the international IEC recommendations. The electronic components are mounted on plug-in printed-circuit boards (module) of Europa format.

Both systems are electrically compatible; they have the same signal language and the same power supply of 24 V d. c.

The individual modules are self-contained functional groups, all outputs being short-circuit-proof.

The TELEPERM C control system operates externally with 4 - 20 mA standard signals, but internally with voltage signals of $\pm$ 10 V. The use of the internal voltage signals permits the use of parallel signal channels. Fig. 4 shows a proportional plus integral action controller of the TELEPERM C system.

The SIMATIC C1 digital control system - Fig. 5 shows a logic module - is built up of integrated circuits operating within the large voltage range of 14 - 30 V. The outputs are short-circuit-proof against both polarities of the power supply. An extremely high immunity to noise is attained by the high signal level and by dynamic delay. The static signal-to-noise level is 13 V, the maximum limiting frequency to be processed is 100 Hz.

These features, which are possessed by scarcely another integrated-circuit switching system, assure straightforward and reliable operation. The various measures otherwise required for electronic systems to achieve adequate protection against failure and noise, such as the fitting of filters and earth plates, and the use of screened cables, are not necessary.

To complete the standardization of the system as a whole, only transducers are used with 4 - 20 mA live-zero signals and a 24 V power supply.

The combination of the three sub-systems - burner, boiler and turbine control system - ensures uniform documentation. The use of identical, standardized modular systems for all automation equipment of the steam cycle greatly reduces the necessary stock of spares.

The use of the most modern electronic components permitted the automation of the steam cycle in a way which saves both space and costs. The development of the new system incorporated the operating experience with SIEMENS automation equipment on more than 500 ships. The entire signal flow of the open and closed-loop control takes place entirely in solid-state circuits. The necessary switching functions are performed by transistors for the analogue signals. This assures the utmost reliability and service life.

The hitherto customary mechanical devices for the boiler control system have been replaced by electronic components for freedom from wear. This also improves the control stability due to the elimination of mechanical backlash.

In the development of the integrated open and closed-loop control system particular attention was devoted to ease of servicing.

The system was subdivided on a functional basis, the components of any one functional group being installed together in a common 19" chassis or subframe. This provides a clear arrangement, permitting simple commissioning and rapid fault tracing. The use of plug-in modules, the provision of scales or dials for the setting elements and the installation of testing and simulating units which permit the testing of the plant, whether running or stationary, all contribute to ease of maintenance.

The integrated control system for the steam cycle on turbine ships which has just been described, will go into service at the end of this year on a new series of 320, 000 t tankers for Shell.

PROCESS COMPUTER

A still higher degree of automation than so far described can be achieved by the use of a process computer. A characteristic feature of this is the static and dynamic optimization of the process, as well as the necessary adaptive open and closed-loop control. To solve these problems a large number of measuring points must be scanned and a series of protracted calculations performed. A process computer is ideally suited for this by reason of its concept. Such a computer is available in the form of the Siemens 320 process computer. The computer itself and a number of peripheral units, such as an input/output typewriter, a punched-paper tape reader and a paper-tape punch can be seen in Fig. 6. Its performance can be illustrated by a few figures. The use of MSI and LSI techniques permitted a compact design and the short cycle time of 1 μs. The central store can be extended to a maximum capacity of 64 K

for words of 16 bits in steps of 4 K, 2 K or 1 K, according to whether core, semiconductor or read-only stores are used. The 320 computer was tailored specifically for process applications by incorporating special instructions adapted to these functions, such as bit instructions, comparison and jump instructions, input and output instructions.

The following tasks can be performed by the process computer in connection with the steam process:

1) Determination of process efficiency and its optimization by the input of appropriate set values, e. g. by establishing the best condenser vacuum, the optimal fuel/air ratio, the best flue gas temperature, etc.

2) The calculation of guide values from measured values for starting the plant, particularly from cold. The thermal stresses in thick-walled parts exert a limiting influence in this connection (drum, live steam line and turbine admission section). Critical bearing clearances and speed must also be taken into consideration. By appropriate coordination of the steam generator and the turbine, which is obtained by modulating control of temperature and pressure, it is possible to reduce the run-up time and thus effect optimization.

3) Improvement of the control action by feed-forward control. This is done by setting the individual controllers according to computer values, which regard the interaction in the multivariable boiler plant. This improves the transient control action, which results in better manoeuvrability during rapid load changes, e. g. during emergency manoeuvres.

Apart from the way in which control is exercised, a decisive question for the use of process computers is the interface between the computer and the process. The computer produces the greatest savings in the way of equipment if it is coupled directly with the process, which is generally know as DDC. Although the reliability reached by such computers today is already very high (typical MTBF values for computers are in the region of 5000 - 6000 h), it is not high enough to be able to dispense with back-up controllers. The decisive disadvantage lies in the serial structure of the computer which leads to the breakdown of the whole system as the result of a single fault.

It is felt that the computer is best installed at the coordinating level, since calculations are required here and the functional range is extended by the process optimization. In the event of computer failure, the subordinated levels remain fully operational so that the plant can continue to be operated. The use of the process computer is possible both from the automation aspect, as mentioned at the beginning, and from the module aspect. The module systems

314

are compatible with the computer system, so much that small extensions (minicomputers) can be incorporated in single assemblies.

Fig. 1.

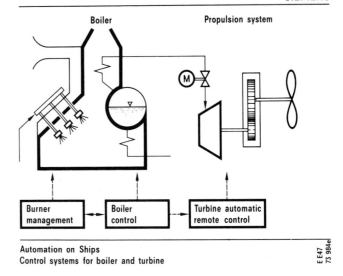

Automation on Ships
Control systems for boiler and turbine

Fig. 2.

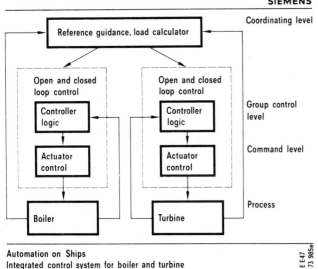

Automation on Ships
Integrated control system for boiler and turbine

Fig. 3.

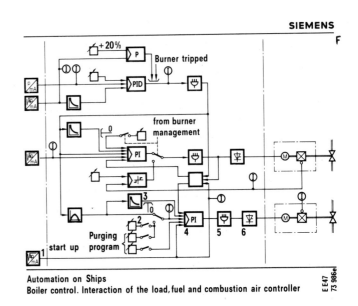

Automation on Ships
Boiler control. Interaction of the load, fuel and combustion air controller

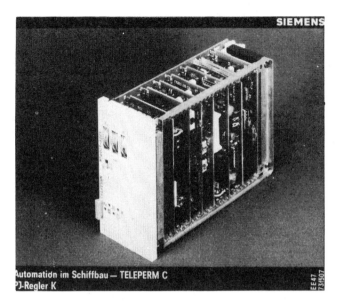

Fig. 4.

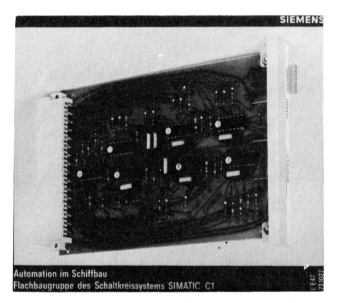

Fig. 5.

Fig. 6.

"ELECTRONICALLY DRIVEN BRIDGE CONTROLS FOR PROPULSION SYSTEMS"

Jay J. Dor
George G. Sharp, Inc.
Marine Systems - Analysis & Design
Hyattsville, Maryland, U.S.A.

ABSTRACT

The paper describes a proposed approach to electronic bridge control, whether for direct control or via engine order telegraph. The configuration presented is drawn from a typical naval ship arrangement, but is adopted to any control system architecture.

A proposed control loop for a marine gas turbine propulsion plant is presented, capitalizing on the advantages of combined speed and power control.

Electronic bridge control are shown to be simple in operation and construction, and are highly reliable. Detail functional flow and hardware configuration are presented and discussed.

Technological advances in electronics applied to marine controls are the means to improve ship operation and reduce manning.

INTRODUCTION

The advent of the gas turbine into naval ships inaugurates an era of engine room automation, made possible by the much simpler control interface of the new prime movers. While traditional naval propulsion control systems are manual, the trend towards automation is caused by a variety of factors, some of which are applicable to those that prompted automation on merchant ships: life cycle cost decrease, through reduced manning and reduced crew skill; equipment safety increase through automated sequencing of start-up, shut-down, and through automatic failure monitoring and switch-over; and increased prime mover performance by optimizing specific thrust. Fast acceleration and maneuvering requirements lead the designers to adopt direct control of the main machinery from the bridge.

With the increased automation aboard ships and the utilization of electronics and digital technology, new concepts should be evaluated for the bridge control systems, whether for direct control or for engine order telegraph.

While the traditional system requires separate instrumentation and control for command and display of standard orders, using heavy, not so accurate and relatively expensive synchros for matching control levers at various stations, capitalizing on the digital technology offers a system which is integrated for command and display and is more accurate, reliable and cost effective.

Traditionally the engine order telegraph is a cumbersome mechanism which requires a dedicated operation. Its operation is dependent on the operator's interpretation of transmitted orders and is therefore a source of possible errors while transmitting, receiving, recording and executing orders.

Thus the old engine order telegraph seems to be somewhat outdated. The designer has to take full advantage of the electronic circuitry at his disposal where commands could be transmitted, received, executed, displayed, and recorded with high accuracy. The paper describes two such systems - one externally similar to the traditional system with control levers, which is normally used for direct control of propulsion from the bridge, tieing to analog circuitry.

The other system discussed is a pure digital system, which uses push buttons for propulsion control, for engine order telegraph, and for display of standard orders. The same push buttons are used for the above three functions, offering: simplicity, high reliability, and low cost, since no heavy mechanical parts are involved.

GAS TURBINE PROPULSION CONFIGURATION

Let us consider a typical naval, one screw, gas installation. The power plant consists of two marine gas turbines driving a controllable reversible pitch (CRP) propeller, through a reduction gear (FIG. 1). The throttle control element controls and/or interfaces with the following systems:

a. Gas Turbine Modules (GTM): Maintains the power level of each by controlling the Power Lever Actuator (PLA) in accordance with the

plant mode. Plant mode is defined as:
Split plant - only one engine on line
Full power - both engines on line

b. Main Reduction Gear: Used for reducing the gas turbine output shaft rpm to the propeller level rpm, and provides clutching and braking capability for each engine.

c. CRP Propeller: Used for reversing ship's thrust. The pitch angle is controlled by a hydraulic servomechanism.

The controls are arranged and interconnected to permit remote single lever control of the propeller's thrust magnitude and direction (shaft speed and propeller pitch), from either the Ship Control Console (SCC) on the bridge, or the Propulsion Control Console (PCC) in a Central Control Station (CCS), which provides the central engineering function in a controlled environment remote from the machinery spaces. Local Operating Station (LOS), in a naval installation, situated near the propulsion turbines have control of all corresponding control elements for testing, maintenance, and emergency back-up features.

Bridge Console Requirements

The propulsion-related function of the bridge is to maintain speed and change it rapidly (for tactical and crash maneuvers) i.e., the bridge capability with regard to propulsion are

1. direct speed control;
2. knowledge of propulsion plant operation configuration for determining available power; and
3. direct communication (voice and non-voice) for commanding desired plant configuration and power levels.

Central Control Station Requirements

The CCS being the central engineering station contains all the monitoring and control required to execute commands, start and stop of plants and auxiliaries, change plant operating configuration, and log all machinery status and alarms. Designed for minimum manning, automatic shut-down of faulty equipment and start of standby machinery are an integral part of the control system. The engineer on watch concentrates on plant monitoring and management only.

Local Control Station Requirement

The local operating stations are provided for maintenance purposes and for emergency backup. As such, they require the capabilities of manipulating the machinery associated with that control station in the manual mode. This means all controls and indicators associated with the power plant.

PROPULSION SYSTEM CONTROL LOOP

The prime consideration in determining the control loop for controlling the propulsion gas turbines, is the ship's intended mission. Thus, one may find gas turbine control loops differ from commercial to naval vessels. The basic control loop for the propulsion plant, whether "speed" control or "power" control, is dictated by the ship operational requirements for maneuvering and steady state, together with ship configuration such as one or more screws and possibly two types of engines per shaft (one for cruise and the other a power boost engine).

Power Control of the gas turbine provides a tight control on the gas generator rpm, by maintaining a constant fuel schedule for a given throttle position. Changes in propeller loading due to sea state, or while maneuvering, will affect only the power turbine section, but will not cause the gas generator to change its constant speed.

Speed Control of the gas turbine provides a tight control on propeller's rpm. For a given pitch this could only be done by appropriate changes in power levels, i.e., changes in gas generator speed via the fuel controller, for varying propeller load.

Power control is advantageous from fuel economy and for longer life of the engine. Speed control is advantageous when a primary requirement is to maintain a constant ship speed. In addition, speed control will provide smoother power transitions when engines are manipulated on and off the line.

It would appear that commercial ships would best use power control for gas turbine installation and naval ships would be advised the same, unless the specific mission requires speed control.

Figure 2 illustrates a throttle control scheme with a combined speed and power control, combining short-term power control with effective long-term speed control. A "sea state adjust" to the rpm compensation network is provided to allow reduction of the speed loop gain, in steps, down to zero. Thus, the operator has the capability to minimize or eliminate the speed portion of the control loop at high sea states in order to minimize gas generator surges.

THE THROTTLE SYSTEM

The throttle system is composed of two elements; one for direct control, and the other for indirect control of the propulsion plant. The two being:

a. Throttle control element
b. Engine order telegraph (EOT)

Throttle control element provides single lever control of the propeller's thrust magnitude and direction in order to affect ship speed; i.e., integrated rpm and pitch control into one command, in the automatic mode. The throttle system manipulates the power lever actuator (PLA) and the CRP propeller's servo, over the full range of ship's operation, from bringing engines on and off the line, and from full ahead to maximum astern ship speeds. Figure 2 illustrates such a system. The throttle movement on the bridge is fed to the power schedule, rpm schedule and the pitch schedule. The pitch schedule is fed directly to the pitch servo in an essential open loop up to that point. The pitch sign is sensed and fed-back to a comparator where it is compared with the pitch command. Unless the two match, the PLA will be kept at idle and the engines will not accelerate. This is particularly important in crash maneuvers when the throttle is moved rapidly from ahead position to full astern and unless we had the pitch mismatch detector, the engines could decelerate and then accelerate again before the propeller has a chance to reverse pitch and thus create a hazardous condition.

The rpm schedule is the closed loop speed control command which is compared with the rpm feedback signal. The resulting error is integrated by the rpm compensation network and then summed with the power schedule to form the automatic PLA command. A "mode change started" signal, then switches the power schedule to the new mode schedule. This, eased by the mode transfer rate limit filter, will cause one engine to accelerate and the other to decelerate until their respective power levels match. A similar rate limiter will protect the engine from fast acceleration when the PLA is brought on line while the throttle is set at high power level commands.

A double overtorque protection system is used. A torsion meter senses shaft torque and interfaces with the engine overtorque computer, (this computer computes engine torque based on engine parameters such as gas generator rpm, inlet temperature and engine pressure ration). Upon receipt of overtorque signal, from either one of the above systems, an alarm will sound and the overtorque signal will cut back on the PLA command, relaxing engine power output. At the same time, the rpm integrator compensation is changed to a first order lag to eliminate the integration of the error in that loop. The two overtorque systems are continuously compared to protect against failure of each.

Engine order telegraph (EOT) is a non-voice communication system provided between the command station (the bridge) and the other throttle control stations, the CCS and the LOS. The system is used to transmit commands from the bridge to the other control stations when the bridge is not in direct control. Commands are normally standard orders and corresponding shaft rpm. For gas turbine installation, the standard orders include pitch angle and plant mode requests. The traditional EOT requires a dedicated operator and all functions are performed manually. Combining the functions of the EOT with those of the throttle element will produce a compact, easy to handle system which will eliminate some of the manual functions required for the traditional EOT. Another advantage of the

combined throttle/EOT is that the control levers at the commanding and the controlling stations (whether CCS or LOS) are always aligned. This system will eliminate the necessity for a relatively expensive and maintenance source hardware which exist using the tracking lever system show in Figure 3, in addition to the manual functions eliminated.

The EOT has to perform the following functions:
1. Alert the control station to command changes from the bridge.
2. Transmit control commands for either plant changes, standard orders, or rpm and pitch changes.
3. Transmit from the control station, back to the bridge, acknowledgment of command received.
4. Transmit command executed message back to the bridge.

Based on the throttle system requirements, the propulsion control capability in the ship control console are:
1. Integrated propeller pitch and shaft speed control into one lever.
2. RPM trim control.
3. Plant operating mode and throttle control mode requesting capability with acknowledgment.
4. Engine order telegraph with acknowledgment.
5. Propeller order (shaft rpm) with acknowledgment.
6. Propeller pitch angle and shaft rpm indication.
7. Plant mode and turbine status indication.
8. Wrong direction and stopped shaft alarms.
9. Alarm indicating override of bridge control by the CCS.

In order to integrate all these functions into one system one can use either an analog or a digital system.

The following paragraphs describe the alternative systems; one analog in nature, using the traditional control levers, and the other digital using illuminated pushbuttons for control and EOT functions (the selection of the above man/machine interfaces is not mandatory to the technique discussed).

ELECTRONIC THROTTLE SYSTEM

With the current state of electronic technology, electronic systems offer better availability, reliability and performance than the mechanical, pneumatic or hydraulic control systems. These, while offering lower weight and space, versatility and self test features, all leading to reduced manning and lower life cycle cost. With the aid of logic circuitry, the throttle system can provide the EOT standard order functions. Both analog and digital electronic systems offer systems superior to the traditional EOT. There is a certain flexibility advantage to digital software controlled system over the analog system, while the analog is less vulnerable. These are summarized in Table 1.

Analog Throttle System

The concept for this system is displayed in Figure 4. Nine illuminated indicators are arranged in line next to the throttle. When the control is directly from the bridge, as the throttle is moved to standard positions, after a small time delay to allow for transitions, the lamp driver will switch on the light of the appropriate indicator standard command, with a steady illumination at all control stations. If the CCS is not in control, the same operation will cause a flashing light to come on at all control station and an audible signal will sound at the station which is in control. When the operator in the controlling station moves his control lever to the position of the flashing indicator, the audible signal will shut itself off and the flashing light will turn steady. With this logic, the control levers are always aligned when the bridge is not in direct control. When the bridge is in direct control, and in one of the standard positions, it is always clear to the other stations where that position is, so that in case of control switch-over from one station to another the control levers could be aligned prior to the switch, and the transfer will be bumpless. If better alignment resolution is desired, a null indicator could be added for dead positioning of control levers.

In addition to the standard orders, the EOT incorporates separate rpm command, separate pitch command, and separate plant command functions. In order to use any of these functions, the bridge operator has separate EOT demand illuminated pushbuttons which he presses. Pressing either one of the rpm or pitch pushbuttons by the bridge operator will trigger an audible signal, and turn on flashing lights on the corresponding EOT pushbutton indicator at the CCS and the LOS. The CCS or LOS operator then presses the flashing pushbutton to acknowledge the receipt of EOT command which will turn off the audible signal and turn the flashing light steady. Using digital display for rpm and pitch, the acknowledgment could be by the execution signal; i.e., setting the commanding order. All EOT functions interface with the bell logger for record keeping.

The analog system described incorporated hard-wired logic circuitry, the system has a substantial interface with the bell logger which is digital in nature, and it may require alignment of control levers before transition. Since the majority of commands are standard orders, if the control system is digital in nature, replacing analog with digital circuitry will reduce the hardware involved, simplify interface and eliminate any problems of misalignment between stations.

Digital Throttle System

Digital computers, with their high density digital integrated circuits, their extreme flexibility through the use of software, their increasing reliability and their expanded operational capability are the next generation logical choice for marine control systems. With the numerous signals to be processed and logged, with the complicated sequences of operations and the growth capability of each system, with the performance monitoring and on-line test and evaluation capability and with the demand to reduce manning and to reduce life cycle cost - computers are the choice. The system described in Fig. 5 could be implemented with or without a digital computer present for ship control. A digital processor though will simplify the interface and eliminate some of the hardware involved. The system utilizes digital logic, clocking and some hardware features that could be provided by a digital processor. The system incorporates illuminated pushbuttons for each of the standard orders (rather than the indicators only of the analog system). The sequence of manual operation is somewhat similar to the analog system, with the exception that the operator presses a pushbutton rather than moves levers in order to execute the standard commands. In addition, the operator has a spring loaded switch to provide continuous incremental signals of rpm and pitch, thus, continuous control over the entire ship speed envelope is maintained. The manual operation of aligning the lever is completely eliminated here. However, pushbuttons are not mandatory and the traditional levers could be used here as well.

The system uses a minimal amount of digital hardware for implementation. The following is part count for the bridge/CCS throttle implementation as shown in Fig. 5 (does not include the LOS).

PART	BRIDGE	CCS
Push buttons (including plant EOT)	16	18
Keyboard encoder (16 positions)	1	2
Pitch display	2	2
RPM display	2	2
Display driver	4	4
Holding register		5 (12 bit ea)
Arithmetic unit		2 (12 bit ea)
A/D converter		2
D/A converter		2

The cost for this system commercially packaged would be around $1,000, for military application the price is assessed to be $3,000. Traditional tracking lever system for military application cost around $7,500 per system in addition to the cost of the independent EOT system.

Fig. 6 is a functional flow chart of the sequence of operations should the throttle system be controlled by a software subroutine. When a pushbutton is pressed an input is received, and the routine will check for the following steps:

1. Is the bridge in control?, determine if the bridge is in direct control ("yes"), or in the EOT mode ("no").

2. If step 1 is positive check the validity of the signal. Is the signal originated from the bridge? If the answer is no, the signal is invalid and is being terminated, if it is a positive, a steady light will turn on in all stations at the appropriate indicator push button, and will send control command to the LOS.

3. If step 1 is negative (EOT mode), and step 2 is positive (valid EOT command) flashing lights will turn on in all stations at the appropriate push-button indicators.

4. Is the CCS in control? If positive, turn on the audible signal in the CCS, if negative, the LOS is the station in control and the audible signal will turn on there.

5. If step 3 is negative, the generated signal is in response to EOT command. Is this signal the same as the one stored in the register? If negative, the signal is an error, alarm will sound until the error is corrected. If positive, go to the next step.

6. Transmit the control signal to the PLA via a D/A converter, turn off the audible signal and the flashing lights on the EOT indicators to steady, in all control stations.

The flexibility in this proccess is that the program could be changed without hardware modification to any desired operational and self test sequence.

Throttle Systems Trade-Off Summary

The pros and cons of the various throttle systems discussed are summarized in Table 1.

SUMMARY

The reliability and low cost of electronics today is such that applying advanced technology and automation to ship controls, will increase availability and reduce manning.

Two electronic throttle configurations have been presented, analog and digital, with different man/machine interfaces. The systems described are simpler, less expensive and more reliable, than the old traditional bridge control systems, while having a direct tie to the bell logger and minimizing the manual operations and the probability of human errors.

Any proposed control architecture for a new ship design, should rely on increased automation. Control stations and console arrangements are a subject to designers trade-off effected by machinery configuration and ship's mission. Basic ship control philosophy should include utilization of electronics for ship control systems.

EVALUATION CRITERIA \ SYSTEM	DIGITAL	ANALOG	TRADITIONAL
Operability	minimum manual functions	moderate manual functions	maximum manual functions
Human Factors	repeatable accurate commands	accuracy depends on operation interpretation of scale	requires tracking levers
Automation	maximum automation	less automation than digital systems	no automation
Weight and Space	minimum weight and space	slightly more panel space than digital	maximum panel space
Mechanization	few moving parts, low tolerance available components	high tolerance for moving parts	highest tolerance for moving parts
Accuracy	1/1000	1/2%	2%
Maintenance	high MTBF with low MTTR	high MTBF with higher MTTR than digital	lower MTBF with higher MTTR
Relative Cost	lowest	higher	highest

TABLE 1   TRADE-OFF SUMMARY

322

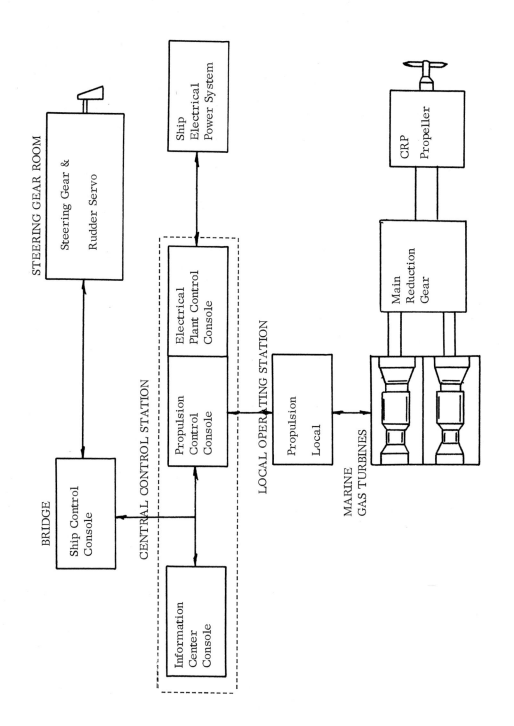

STEERING GEAR ROOM

Steering Gear & Rudder Servo

Ship Electrical Power System

CENTRAL CONTROL STATION

Electrical Plant Control Console

Propulsion Control Console

BRIDGE

Ship Control Console

Information Center Console

LOCAL OPERATING STATION

Propulsion Local

MARINE GAS TURBINES

Main Reduction Gear

CRP Propeller

FIG. 1.   INTEGRATED SHIP CONTROL SYSTEM

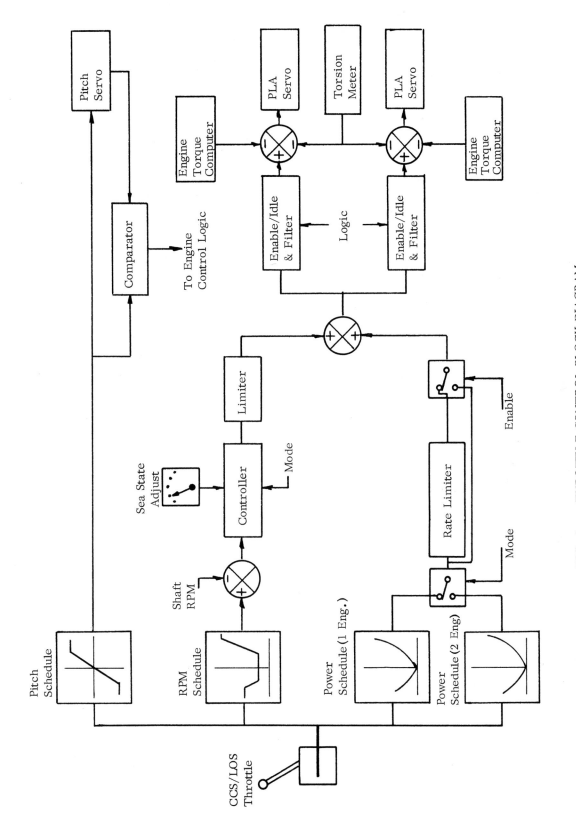

FIG. 2. THROTTLE CONTROL BLOCK DIAGRAM

324

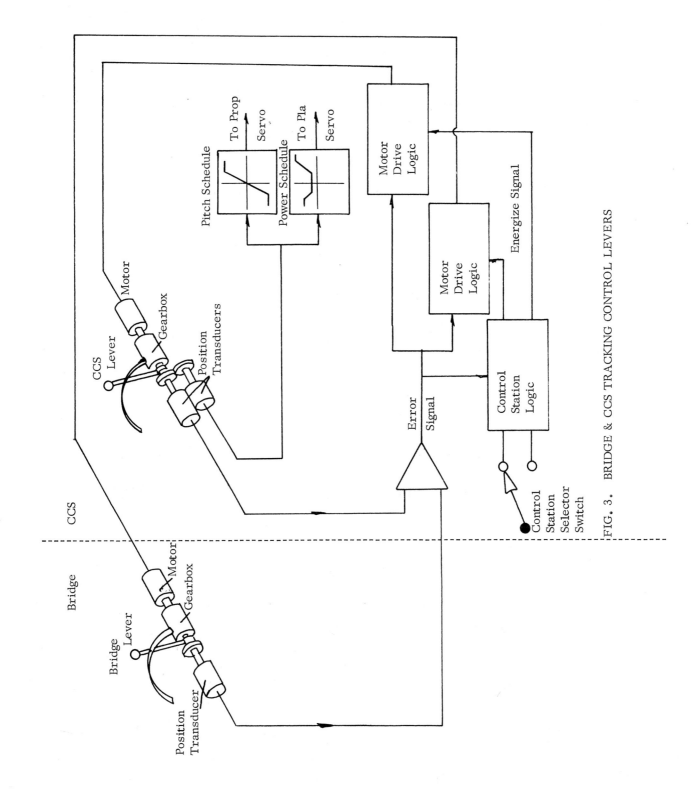

FIG. 3. BRIDGE & CCS TRACKING CONTROL LEVERS

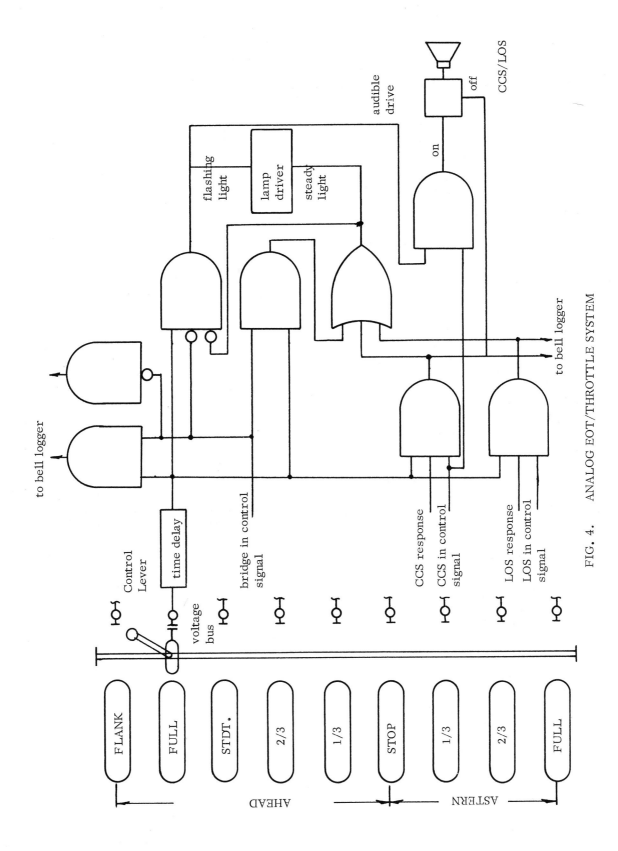

FIG. 4.   ANALOG EOT/THROTTLE SYSTEM

326

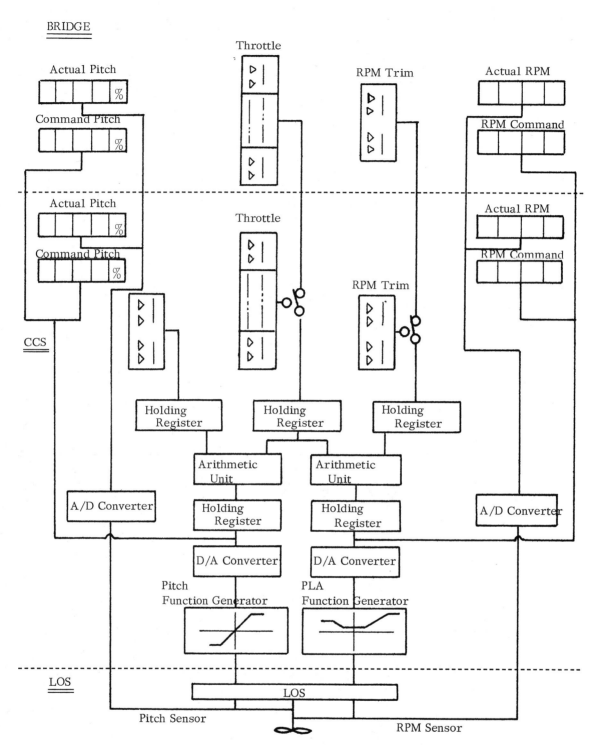

FIG. 5. DIGITAL THROTTLE CONTROL SYSTEM

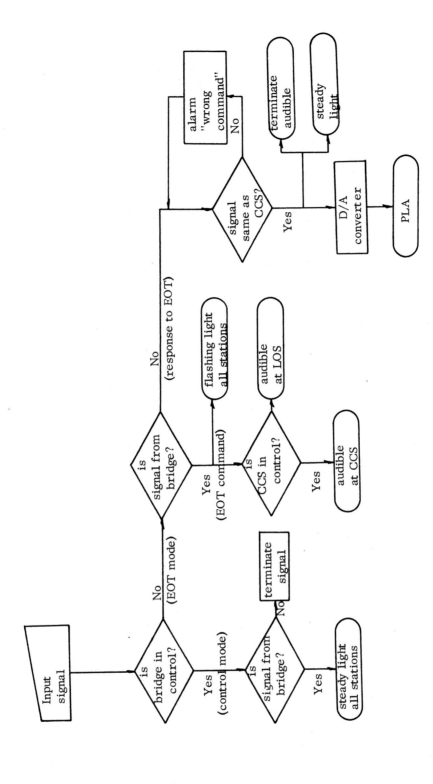

FIG. 6.   EOT & CONTROL FLOW CHART

THE DESIGN OF A DISCRETE MULTIVARIABLE CONTROL SYSTEM FOR

A 35. 000 HP CAPACITY SHIP BOILER

by

Arne Tyssø,
SINTEF, Division of
Automatic Control,
Trondheim, Norway

J. Chr. Brembo
The Ship Research
Inst. of Norway,
Trondheim, Norway

Kjell Lind
The Ship Research
Inst. of Norway,
Trondheim, Norway

A multivariable control system is designed for
a large scale ship boiler. The design is based on
concepts of modern control theory and extensive
use of all digital real time simulation. This
paper describes in particular an application of
linear regulator theory in the design of multivariable control systems for nonlinear processes.

Introduction

The boiler studied in this paper is a Foster
Wheeler ESD III with a normal steam production
of 21. 9 kg/s. The boiler is operated on the
basis of natural circulation. The control system
is designed to maintain the drum level, drum
pressure and the steam temperature at a constant
reference value independent of load and process
disturbances.

There are shown two different ways which provide for integral (reset) control action. Both are
produced by augmenting the state vector. A
Kalman filter for the estimation of the process
state as well as the environmental state vector is
included. The environment is supposed to produce slowly varying disturbances to the process
and coloured noise to the waterlevel measurement (ship-rolling).

By means of simulation facilities it is possible
to examine the behaviour of the control system
for all kinds of manoeuvres and disturbances.
Examples of such tests will be presented.

The integrety of the control system will be discussed, and the digital real time simulation
system which consists of two process control
type computers, will be described in some
detail.

The paper is divided into two parts:

1. The theoretical work necessary for the
    control system's design.

2. The application of the all digital real time
    simulation in evaluating the control system.

1.   THEORETICAL WORK

The boiler model

The original nonlinear dynamic model was of
twentieth order [1]. It was assumed to consist
of lumped energy storage elements comprising
steam drum, downcomers, mud drum, risers,
primary and secondary superheater, desuperheater and economiser. In Figure 1 there is
shown a simplified boiler system. The mathematical model was designed basically for two
following purposes.

a)   To be a basis for a linearized model to be
      used for design of the multivariable control
      system.

b)   To study the multivariable control system
      by means of real time simulation.

For purpose a) it is desirable to reduce the
model to the lowest possible order. This is to
keep the computing time and storage at a minimum, and to reduce the number of state variables
to influence the control system's design. It has
been shown that the optimal controller can be
of rather simple form.

For purpose b) it is desirable to have a nonlinear
model which is accurately describing the actual
boiler system.

The simulated model responses are mostly of
simple form, but the response of the drum level
to a change in steam load is of the expected non-
minimum phase form. We also have an unstable
model. The zero in the right half of the complex
frequency plane qualitatively accounts for the
effects of bubble formation and evaporation in the
riser tubes and steam drum with dynamically
decreasing pressure. This is also known as
"shrink and swell".

The nonlinear model equations were linearized
by considering small perturbations about a steady-
state operating point [2]. The resulting equations
were manipulated by means of a large digital
computer into state space form.

The appropriateness of the model has been verified by comparing model responses with responses on the actual ship boiler in operation.

Reduction of the system order

The aim for the model reduction was to achieve a reduced model, sufficiently accurate for the synthesis of the control system. The reduction was based on a modal method, described in (3) and (4). By neglecting the dynamic effects associated with the small time constants of the system, a reduced model is obtained.

It was found that several variables could be removed, without introducing serious errors in the total system response. Primarily the fast responses and variables of similar character were removed. In this way, it was possible to obtain a satisfactory 8th and 10th order reduced system. The results obtained from the model reduction were utilized in the nonlinear model, and we thus succeeded to reduce the original 20th order nonlinear model to a 12th order nonlinear model. The real time simulation was based on the latter one.

As the response of the 10th order system was very close to the original system response, the multivariable control system was based on this description. In state space form the boiler is described by the vector matrix differential equation:

$$\dot{\underline{x}}_1(t) = A\underline{x}_1(t) + B\underline{u}(t) + C_1\underline{v}_1(t) + C_2\underline{v}_2(t) \tag{1}$$

where

$\underline{x}_1(t)$: the deviation of the process state from steady state (dim = n)

$\underline{u}(t)$: control vector (dim = r)

$\underline{v}_1(t)$: measurable process disturbances (dim=q)

$\underline{v}_2(t)$: unmeasurable process disturbances (dim = p)

The measurement vector (dim = m):

$$\underline{y}_1(t) = D\underline{x}_1(t) + D_B\underline{u}(t) + D_C\underline{v}_1(t) + \underline{v}_3(t) \tag{2}$$

where

$\underline{v}_3(t)$: measurement noise (dim = m)

The noise is of white character but due to the ship rolling and pitching the level measurement will also have coloured noise character.

A, B, C_1, C_2, D, D_B and D_C are matrices of dimension compatible with the dimensions of the associated vectors.

For the original 12th order linearized model the eigenvalues of the matrix A are:

$$\lambda_1 = -1.141 \qquad \lambda_2 = -0.758 \qquad \lambda_3 = -0.590$$

$$\lambda_4 = -0.384 \qquad \lambda_5 = -0.339 \qquad \lambda_6 = -0.146$$

$$\lambda_7 = -0.020 \qquad \lambda_8 = -0.009 \qquad \lambda_9 = -0.007$$

$$\lambda_{10} = -0.006 \qquad \lambda_{11} = 0 \qquad \lambda_{12} = 0.00016$$

We notice the eigenvalue in the origo and the positive one.

The unstable mode depends on how the ratio between mass of steam and water in drum system and how the masses of iron are taken into account. If the steam mass flow is selected no longer to be an input variable, the unstable mode is changed into a stable mode (5). The zero eigenvalue is obviously associated with the drum liquid level.

Environment

The environment which generates the disturbances is described by a Wiener process:

$$\dot{\underline{x}}_2(t) = F\underline{n}(t) \tag{3}$$

$$\underline{v}_2(t) = H\underline{x}_2(t) \tag{4}$$

where

$\underline{x}_2(t)$: environment state vector (dim = 1)

$\underline{n}(t)$: white noise, zero mean vector.

It is reasonable to assume for the steam boiler process that the disturbances vary slowly. This special choice of dynamics of the environment leads to an integral action in the control loop (6).

The state of the "supersystem" encompassing both the process and the environment is described by

$$\dot{\underline{x}}(t) = \begin{bmatrix} \dot{\underline{x}}_1(t) \\ \dot{\underline{x}}_2(t) \end{bmatrix} = \begin{bmatrix} A & C_2H \\ 0 & 0 \end{bmatrix} \underline{x}(t) + \begin{bmatrix} B \\ 0 \end{bmatrix} \underline{u}(t) +$$

$$\begin{bmatrix} C_1 \\ 0 \end{bmatrix} \underline{v}_1(t) + \begin{bmatrix} 0 \\ F \end{bmatrix} \underline{n}(t) \tag{5}$$

and can be written:

$$\dot{\underline{x}}(t) = \tilde{A}\underline{x}(t) + \tilde{B}\underline{u}(t) + \tilde{C}\underline{v}_1(t) + \tilde{F}\underline{n}(t) \tag{6}$$

Time-discrete model

In digital control system the process outputs are measured at discrete intervals of time t = 0, T, 2T ...... where T is the sampling period, and the control inputs are held constant between sampling instants. Equation (6) may conveniently be expressed in the discrete-time form:

$\underline{x}((k + 1)T) =$

$\Phi(T)\underline{x}(kT) + \Delta(T)\underline{u}(kT) + \Omega(T)\underline{v}_1(kT) + \theta(T)\underline{n}(kT)$ (7)

The choice of sampling rate depends on the process and valves dynamics and the noise characteristics. Due to the coloured noise in the level measurement with a period 12 - 16 seconds T is chosen to be 2 seconds.

Control philosophy

The optimal control with state variable feedback is determined from the minimization of the quadratic objective functional (unit sampling interval):

$J = \frac{1}{2}(\underline{x}(N) - \underline{x}_d)^T S(\underline{x}(N) - \underline{x}_d) +$

$\frac{1}{2}(\sum_{k=0}^{N-1} (\underline{x}(k) - \underline{x}_d)^T Q(\underline{x}(k) - \underline{x}_d) + \underline{u}(k)^T P\underline{u}(k))$ (8)

where

$\underline{x}_d$: is the desired state. S and Q are positive, semidefinite symmetric, constant matrices which penalize final state offsets and deviation in the state variables, respectively. P is a symmetric matrix of constants which penalize use of control action and must be positive semidefinite.

The solution of this problem can be separated into two independent problems:

a)   a deterministic control problem
b)   an estimation problem.

The deterministic control strategy is known to be:

$\underline{u}(k) = \begin{bmatrix} G_1 & G_2 \end{bmatrix} \underline{x}(k) = G\underline{x}(k) =$

$= -P^{-1}\Delta^T \Phi^{-T}(R(k) - Q)\underline{x}(k)$ (9)

where R is determined from the discrete matrix Riccati equation:

$R(k) = Q + \Phi^T(R^{-1}(k+1) + \Delta P^{-1}\Delta^T)^{-1}\Phi$ (10)

with boundary condition:

$R(N) = S$ (11)

A necessary condition for an optimal control to exist is that every element in the statevector is available. In our case only 3 components of the state vector are measured, so it is necessary to estimate the others. The estimator is based on a reduced, linear model of the process. The solution will therefore be sub-optimal.

In order to obtain the sub-optimal control, it is necessary to include the dynamical description of the environmental states in the state estimator. To reduce the influence of the coloured measurement noise it is also necessary to include a

model of the ship rolling and pitching in the estimator.

It is known that the least squares estimator is described by:

$\hat{\underline{x}}(k+1) = \Phi\hat{\underline{x}}(k) + \Delta\underline{u}(k) + \Omega\underline{v}_1(k) + \Phi K(\underline{y}(k) - \hat{\underline{y}}(k))$ (12)

where $\hat{}$ denotes estimates. In eq. 12 K is given by:

$K = \begin{bmatrix} K_1 \\ --- \\ K_2 \end{bmatrix} = \Delta X(k)D^T(D\Delta X(k) + W(k))^{-1}$ (13)

where

$\Delta X(k) = E(\Delta\underline{x}(k)\Delta\underline{x}^T(k)) = E((\underline{x}(k) - \hat{\underline{x}}(k))(\underline{x}(k) - \hat{\underline{x}}(k))^T)$

and

$W(k) = E(\underline{\omega}(k)\underline{\omega}^T(k))$

are the covariance matrices of the state estimation error and the measurement noise, respectively. $\Delta X(k)$ can be determined as the solution of the discrete matrix Riccati equation.

The main objective for the multivariable controller is to keep three variables at a constant reference value independently of set point changes and unmeasured process disturbances.

These variables are:

   y_1 = drum pressure
   y_2 = steam outlet temperature
   y_3 = drum level

or expressed in an equation:

$\underline{r}(k) = \underline{r}_{ref}(k) = T\underline{y}(k)$ (14)

where

$\underline{r}(k)$ = reference vector, (dim = 1)

Optimal feedback control

For the boiler application we will use the stationary value of the feedback matrix G(k). The terminal time can be regarded as plus infinity. This also means that S can be set equal to zero.

It is difficult a priori to choose the parameters in the loss functional. As a rule of thumb we use:

$q_{ii} = (\frac{1}{x_{imax}})^2$ $i = 1, 2 \ldots \ldots \ldots n$

$p_{jj} = (\frac{1}{u_{jmax}})^2$ $j = 1, 2 \ldots \ldots \ldots r$

as initial guess of Q and P. Through a simulation it is possible to see if the feedback controller is satisfactory. The constrains and dynamic limitation in the control variables are not taken into account explicitly. Therefore we have to balance a fast response against the realistic magnitude of the control variables. The final answer to this question will be given by the real time simulation in the datalaboratory. It is important that the feedforward terms (see below) are included in the simulation.

Elimination of steady state errors

Depending on the disturbance character we will have the following solutions:

a)   The disturbance vector can be measured directly:

   A feedforward from the disturbance vector.

b)   The disturbance vector is not measured:

   A "feedforward" from the estimated value.

The control law including the feed forward then is:

$$\underline{u}(k) = G\underline{\hat{x}}(k) + G_3\underline{r}_{ref}(k)+G_4\underline{v}_1(k) \qquad (15)$$

The feedforward matrices can be determined from equation 14.

To avoid the problem of selecting weighting elements for the environment state vector, $\underline{x}_2(k)$, also G_2 can be determined from this equation.

In the stationary state we have:

$$\underline{\hat{x}}_1(k+1) = \underline{\hat{x}}_1(k)$$
$$\underline{\hat{x}}_2(k+1) = \underline{\hat{x}}_2(k) \qquad (16)$$

This leads to the following equation:

$$\underline{r}(k) = T(D+D_BG_1)\underline{\hat{x}}_1(k) + TD_BG_2\underline{\hat{x}}_2(k) +$$
$$TD_BG_3\underline{r}_{ref}(k) + T(D_BG_4 +D_C)\underline{v}_1(k) \qquad (17)$$

G_1 is found from eq. 9   and from the condition

$$\underline{r}(k) = \underline{r}_{ref}(k) \text{ we have:}$$
$$G_2 = (TD_B - T(D+D_BG_1)(\Phi_1-I+\Delta G_1)\overline{\theta}^1 = E\theta \,(18)$$
$$G_3 = (E\Delta)^{-1} \qquad (19)$$
$$G_4 = G_3(T(D+D_BG_1)(\Phi-I+\Delta G_1)\Omega -TD_C) \qquad (20)$$

A condition for G_3 to exist is that T has the dimension, $r \times m$. The structure of the complete system consisting of process, state estimator and the feedback - feedforward controls   is shown in Figure 2.

Integral action

It can be shown [6] that with the special choice of environmental model (eq. 3) the control system will work as a multivariable proportional - plus - derivative - plus - integral controller. The integral action is very important in a multivariable system.

Primarily it eliminates the steady state offsets which arise when proportional control alone is used on systems subject to constant process disturbances. In this case it will also compensate for some of the errors which arise because of using the approximized model (linear) in the design of the control system. In Figure 7, there are shown responses with and without the environmental model. The offset is   clearly indicated.

In [6] there is shown that the assumed covariance of the environment exitation determines the way in which $\hat{x}_2(k)$ will track $\underline{x}_2(k)$, since K_2 determines the reset time for tracking $x_2(k)$ in the estimator. It is always difficult to assume reasonable values for the environment exitations, and therefore we have used a modal method to determine K_2. Thus we specify in advance the desirable reset time in the controller. It is reasonable to assume that the process estimator is considerably faster than the environment estimator. If H is the specified eigenvaluematrix (with diagonal elements only) for the environment, we find that

$$K_2 = (I - H)(D(I- \Phi + \Phi K_1D)\theta)^{-1}$$

K_1 is determined from the equation for optimal estimation. A necessary condition for $(D(I - \Phi+\Phi K_1D)\theta)^{-1}$ to exist is that the number of environmental states is assumed to be equal to the number of measurements,

m = p.

If m < p the environmental model is not observable,

Alternative solution

The same integral action is produced by augmenting the state vector with the set point vector $\underline{x}_3(k)$ and the use of feedback control from this state vector (7), (8).

$$\underline{x}_3(k+1)=\underline{x}_3(k)- \underline{y}(k) + \underline{r}_{ref}(k) \qquad (21)$$

A schematic representation of this control system is given in Figure 3. Now

$$\underline{x} = \begin{bmatrix} \underline{x}_1 \\ \hline \underline{x}_3 \end{bmatrix}$$

and the performance index could now be:

$$J_2 = \tfrac{1}{2}\sum_{k=0}^{\infty} \left[(\underline{x}(k)-\underline{x}_d)^T Q(\underline{x}(k)-\underline{x}_d) + \underline{u}(k)^T P\underline{u}(k) + \right.$$
$$\left. (\underline{r}(k) - \underline{r}_{ref}(k))^T Q_2(\underline{r}(k)-\underline{r}_{ref}(k)) \right]$$

The feedback - feedforward matrices are given in appendix A2.

The weighting elements for the augmented states must be carefully chosen, so that their dynamics do not influence the main dynamic behaviour. This can be examined by studying the eigenvalues in the closed loop ($\Phi + \Delta G_1$) with and without the set point vector included.

In (9) the control system is designed in detail and the strategies used in the following examples are based on this report.

2. REAL TIME SIMULATION

The real time simulation system

Testing of the multivariable control system is performed in the laboratory as indicated in Figure 4. Two digital process computers work together. By digital simulation, one of them serves as the process, while the other is doing the functions of the multivariable controller. (10), (11), (12). The interface between the computers are bidirectional and operates on a voltage analog basis. The digital/analog (D/A) converters have 8 bits which gives a maximum error of 0, 2% in the complete dynamic range. The simulation works in real time. Signals may be registered either on a CRT display or on strip chart recorders.

The following signals are transmitted from the "process":

1.   The drum pressure (y_1).

2.   The steam temperature (y_2).

3.   The water level (y_3).

To keep these process variabels constant, the following control loops are activated:

1.   The oil flow control (u_1).

2.   The feedwater flow control (u_2).

3.   The by-pass control valve (u_3).

Process variables in the boiler environment can be simulated by means of potensiometers generating voltage analog signals. White and coloured noise-signals may be generated either analog or by digital means.

The real time simulation is conducted by means of a third order Runge-Kutta method (stepwise integration). The 12th order nonlinear model is implemented.

Verifying the control system by real time simulation

With the all digital real time simulation system it is possible to examin every detail, and probable action of the control system. The control system design procedure can be described as in Figure 5. Matrices for the estimation and the feed-back control are designed off-line. Then the control system is implemented on the real time simulation system for testing. In this way one goes back and fort between the off-line large

computers, and the real time system.

The design will then converge towards a final solution for the control system which is acceptable both to boiler makers and to the personnel operating the ship.

Some of the real time simulation tests are the following:

The stability of the control system with respect to:

- Changes in the load (steam flow to the turbine)

- Changes of measurable process disturbances such as air ratio, feedwater temperature etc.

- Unmeasurable disturbances from white and coloured noise sources such as random noise, digital noise and rolling and pitching of the ship (which will influence the water level measurement).

- Normal changes of the process as a function of time such as gradual wear of components.

- The static and dynamic limitations of the actuators such as upper and lower delivery limits and maximum change of delivery per sample.

The integrity of the control system with respect to probable errors as:

- Loss of important measurements.

- Loss of the degree of controllability of the process (an actuator might be shut off or locked in fixed positions).

- Abnormal changes of the process such as breakdown of components.

In this manner one is using the real time simulation facility as a tool in multivariable control systems design.

Simulation results

Several tests have already been performed. Experiences and results gained are of significant value in the further work to improve the quality of the control system.

Figure 6 shows a typical manoeuvre. The steam flow from the boiler is suddenly increased from 17, 5 kg/s to 26, 5 kg/s.

- Steam temperature is temporarily decreasing.

- The by-pass valve is opened, increasing the cooling of steam.

- The drum pressure is decreasing,

but this is taken care of by an increasing oil flow.

Even if the steam flow is increasing, the water level in drum paradoxically is increasing too. This is due to the "Swell" phenomena.

To reduce the effects of the "swell", the feedwater flow has to be temporarily decreased before it starts increasing towards the new stable condition. This reasonable and correct feedwater action is due to the fact that the estimator is "knowing" what is going to happen to the process.

Looking at the measurements and control signals as a function of time, it is recognized that they vary in steps. This is due to the sampling and the D/A converting. The steam flow, however, is generated in an analog way and is therefore continuously varying.

It can be seen that within one sampling period a controller can not vary more than permitted by its dynamic limitations.

Figure 7 illustrates the importance of the integral action in the multivariable controller. The responses are due to a step change in the steam flow from 15.9 kg/s to 21.9 kg/s.

Figure 8 shows the result of a manoeuvre where the steam flow suddenly decreases from 26 kg/s to 9 kg/s.

- It is recognized that the by-pass valve is permanently closed. Physically this means that there is no possibility of reducing the cooling of the steam any more by means of the desuperheater. The steam temperature therefore has to decrease.

Figure 9. The steam flow is suddenly increased from 5.5 kg/s to 22 kg/s.

- The by-pass valve has opened and the steam temperature increases to its normal value. The normal control strategy is running again.

- Due to the "swell" phenomena the drum level is increasing. This time, however, it is swelling close to the alarm condition.

- In trying to reduce the effect of the "swell", the feedwater flow is reaching its lower limit. A feedwater flow lower than zero is physical impossible and thus it can not reduce the "swelling" any more.

To reduce the consequences the following can be done:

a) Restrict the permitted variation of steam flow.

b) Insert a level-reference dependent on the steam flow. At a low load condition the level reference should be decreased.

At a high load condition, however, the level references should be increased.

c) At a high load condition it is possible to increase the physical capacity of the feed water system.

Figure 10 shows the responses when the level reference variable is changed from 0 to 50mm.

Two possible ways to verify the stability of the multivariable control system due to process changes are:

a) Vary one or more process parameters as step functions.

b) Generate manoeuvres while one or more process parameters are changed.

The heat transfer coefficient from the secondary superheater tubes to gas is one of many process parameters that may be slowly varying with time. In Figure 11 this coefficient is suddenly decreased to the half of its normal value.

- The steam temperature is temporarily decreasing.

- The by-pass valve position is slowly decreasing towards the new steady state.

- The other variables are slightly influenced.

Figure 12 demonstrates what can happen if an important transmitter suddenly is cut off. In most circumstances a back-up system will replace the missing transmitter, but if not, the following can be done:

a) Insert a new estimator specially made to handle the loss of this transmitter.

b) Just give no correction to the operation estimator from the missing measurement.

Under steady state conditions and strategy b the water level is observed to decrease slowly. $(8 \cdot 10^{-2} \text{mm/s})$.

In Figure 12 the steam flow is suddenly decreased from 26kg/s to 9 kg/s.

- The level shrinks as usual, thus keeping a normal dynamic condition. But after 2 minutes, when the level normally should be about zero again, it now is 30 mm too low. A stationary error is introduced.

- The time for which the process may operate without important transmitters is given by:

a)   The accuracy of the estimator.

b)   The quality of the remaining measurements.

Figure 13 demonstrates what may happen if the fuel oil is suddenly shut off:

-    Wanted fuel oil from the controller is increasing rapidly.

-    Both steam pressure in drum and the steam temperature are decreasing while the drum level is rather constant.

    After 2.5 minutes the drum pressure has decreased about 25 ata and the steam temperature about 75°C.

Advantages of real time simulation

Real time simulation on digital computers has proved to be both effective and flexible.

-    There are few limitations concerning complexity or the size of the process and the controllers.

-    Different functions are executed by separate subprogrammes that are easy to change and exchange with each other.

-    Strategies and parameters of the multivariable controller can be changed on-line.

-    Changes of the process parameters are also easily generated on-line.

An analog interface between the computers gives the following features.

-    Manoeuvres and changed load conditions can most easily be generated by voltage analog signals.

-    Analog signals can easily be registered, displayed and stored by recorders. The graphs may be analysed without further preparation.

-    The A/D and D/A conversion gives a realistic simulation of the digital noise.

-    Loss of a controller or an important measurement is easily simulated by disconnecting one of the analog connection-wires. This gives also realistic test of the alarm system.

-    When the control system is acceptable it is just to disconnect the computer simulating the process, and exchange it with the actual process.

Conclusions

A suboptimal multivariable control system has been designed for a large scale ship boiler. The importance of real time simulation is apparent, and perhaps it is a must, in the design of control system of this complexity based on modern control theory. Special advantages can clearly be seen in using all digital real time simulation. The flexibility of the system, the good repeatability of the process simulation and ease of implementation are specially to be noted.

Since transmitters often are considered as weak points in a ship control system, one should also note the advantage of having an estimator for estimation of state variables. This makes it possible to control the process for a period of time even with important measurements (transmitters) out of order.

REFERENCES:

(1)   Rydland, K., Øyvang, K.; "Mathematical model of a ship boiler system", internal document, The Ship Research Institute of Norway, Trondheim, Norway, 1972.

(2)   Brembo, J.C., "Linearization of a nonlinear ship boiler model", internal document, The Ship Research Institute of Norway, Trondheim, Norway, 1972.

(3)   Davison, E.J., "Simplification of dynamic systems IEEE", Tranc. AC-11 Jan. -66, page 93-101.

(4)   Marshall, S.A., "An approximate method for reducing the order of system control, Dec. - 66, page 642-643.

(5)   Eklund, K., "Linear drum boiler turbine models", Lund Institute of Technology 1970, Sweden.

(6)   Balchen, J.G., Endresen, T., Fjeld, M., Olsen, T., " Multivariable PID Estimation and control in Systems with Biased Disturbances. ", Automatica, May 1973.

(7)   Newell, R.B., Fischer, D.G., "Experimental Evaluation of Optimal, Multivariable Regulatory Controllers with Model-Following Capabilities.", Automatica, Vol. 8 1972.

(8)   Endresen, T., "On the control of linear systems with unknown deterministic disturbances", Division of Autom. Control, Institute of Technology, University of Trondheim, Norway, 1973.

(9)   Tyssø, A., "Design of a Multivariable Controller for a ship boiler system.", internal document, The Ship Research Institute of Norway, Trondheim, Norway, 1973.

(10) "SINTRAN, Users guide", Norsk Data-elektronikk, Oslo, Norway 1971.

(11) Grini, T., "MEAS, An analog input program system for process control. Application manual", SINTEF, div. of Automatic Control, Trondheim, Norway 1972.

(12) Markussen, J.I., "SIMON, A real-time simulator for on-line debugging of control systems. Users guide", SINTEF, div. of Automatic Control, Trondheim, Norway 1972.

APPENDIX

A1. List of process variables,
(In paranthesis the numerical values corresponding to 100% load).

The state vector:

x_1 : entalphy of water in mud drum, 299kcal/kg

x_2 : amount of water in drum, 5000 kg

x_3 : mean value of the density of steam-water mixture in risers, 557 kg/m^3.

x_4 : density of saturated steam, 35 kg/m^3

x_5 : mean tube temperature in riser, 307°C

x_6 : :"   "   "   " primary superheater 331.7°C

x_7 : mean tube temperature in secondary superheater 529.3°C

x_8 : mean tube temperature in desuperheater, 292.7°C

x_9 : mean tube temperature in economiser, 189.8°C

x_{10} : mean tube temperature in air preheater, 160.6°C

x_{11} : Exhaust gas temperature in combustion chamber, 1331.9°C

x_{12} : Composed variable, 16377,2 kg/ms

In the 10th order model x_5 and x_{11} are removed.

The control vector

u_1 : fuel flow, 1.58 kg/s

u_2 : feedwater flow, 21.9 kg/s

u_3 : by-pass valve position, 0.445

The measured disturbance vector

v_1 : excess air, 1.073

v_2 : air temperature, 39°C

v_3 : feedwater temperature, 168°C

v_4 : fuel temperature, 120°C

v_5 : steam flow from sec. superheater: 21.9 kg/s.

The measurement vector

y_1 : steam pressure in drum, 68,5 Ata

y_2 : steam temperature after sec. superheater, 512°C

y_3 : drum liquid level, 0 m

A2. Expressions for the feedback-feedforward matrices G, G_3 and G_4 (The method described in (9)).

$$G = -P_2^{-1} \Delta_2^T \Phi^{-T}(R-Q_3) = M(R-Q_3)$$

$$G_3 = M(N+D^T T^T Q_2) + P_2^{-1} D_B^T T^T Q_2$$

$$G_4 = M \cdot K$$

where

R is the solution of the matrix Riccati equation.

$$Q_3 = D^T F^T Q_2 TD + Q$$

$$Q_2 = P + D_B^T T^T Q_2 TD_B$$

$$N = (\Phi + \Delta G)^T N + (R-Q_3)\Phi^{-1}(I+\Delta P_2^{-1} D_B^T T^T Q_2)$$

$$K = (\Phi_2 + \Delta G)^T K + (R-Q_3)\Phi^{-1}\Omega$$

336

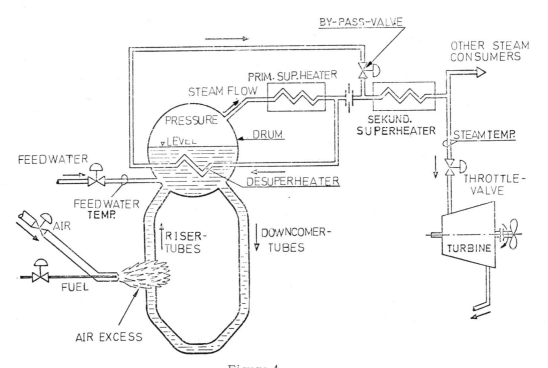

Figure 1.

A simplified boiler system

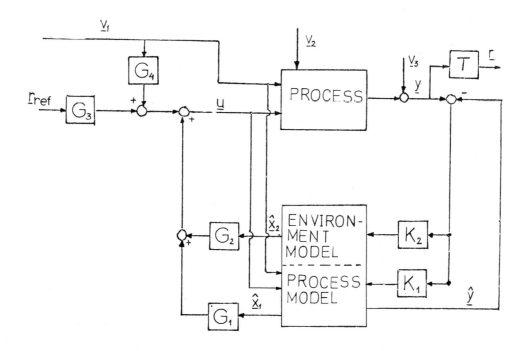

Figure 2.

Structure of a system consisting of process, state estimator and feedback -
feedforward controls.

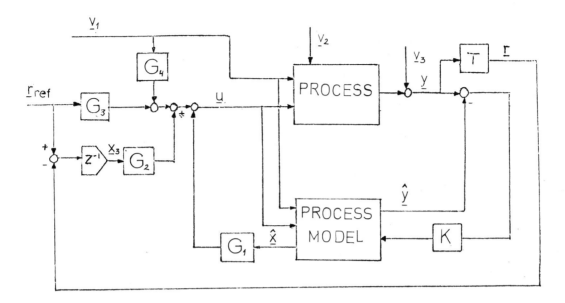

Figure 3.

Integral action by augmenting the state vector with the set point vector.

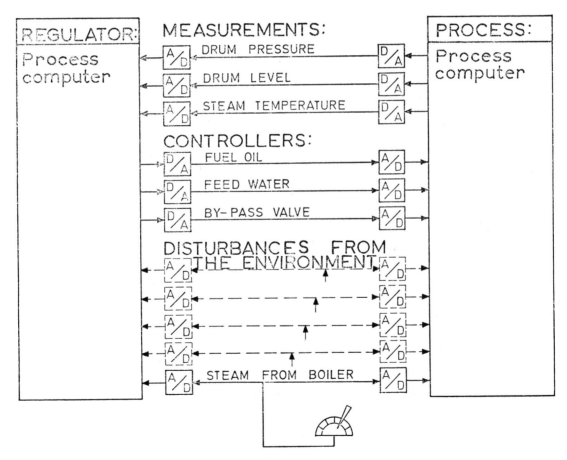

Figure 4.

The two digital process computers simulating process and control system.
The analog bidirectional connections can be seen.

338

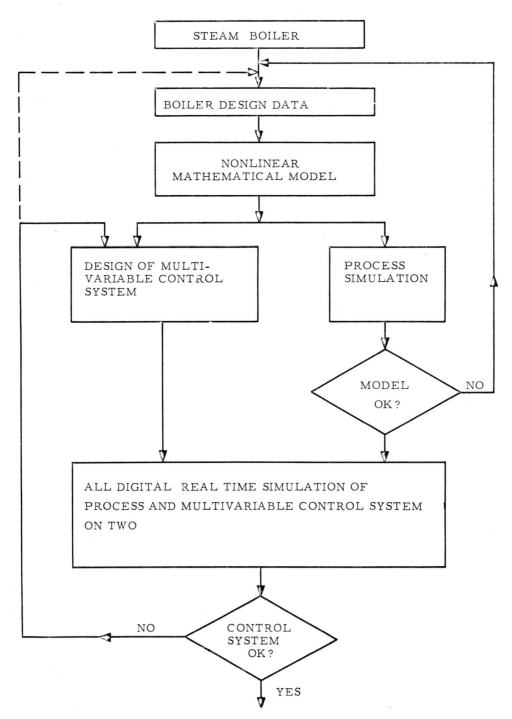

DESIGN AND TESTING OF MODEL AND MULTIVARIABLE CONTROL SYSTEM

Figure 5.

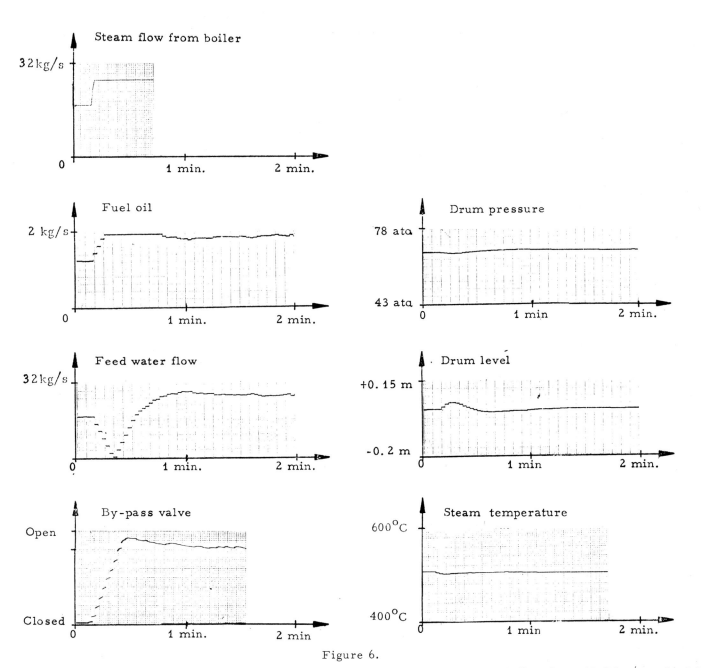

Figure 6.

A typical manoeuvre. The responses are due to a step change in the steam flow from 17.5 kg/s to 26.5 kg/

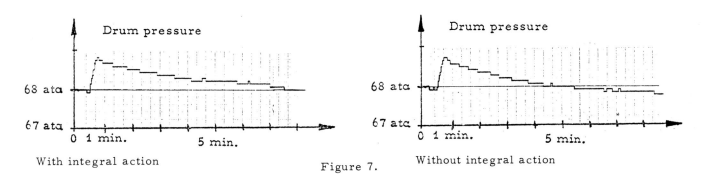

With integral action

Figure 7.

Without integral action

Responses of the drum pressure with and without integral action in the multivariable controller. The responses are due to a step change in the steam flow from 15.9 kg/s to 21.9 kg/s.

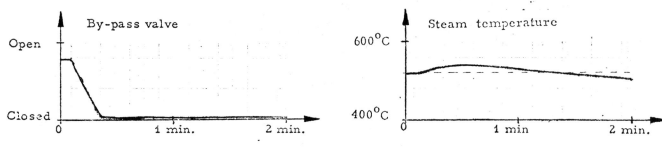

Figure 8.

When the by-pass valve is permanently closed, the steam temperature has to fall. Step change in the steam flow from 26 kg/s to 9 kg/s.

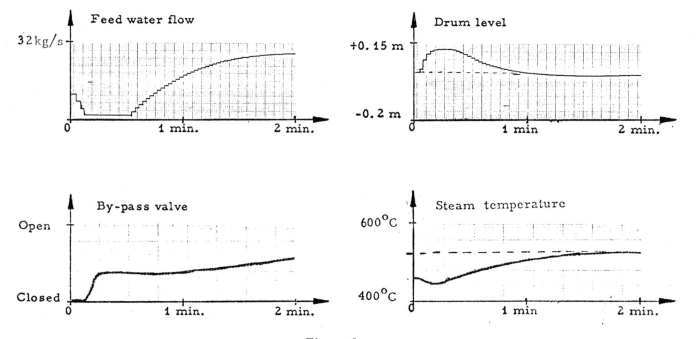

Figure 9.

Step change in the steam from 5.5 kg/s to 22 kg/s.

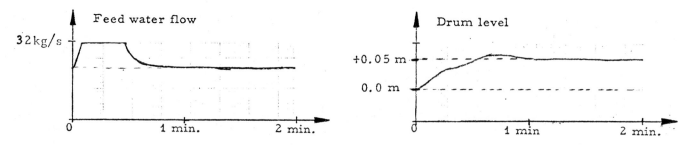

Figure 10.

Responses when the level reference variable is changed from 0 to 50 mm.

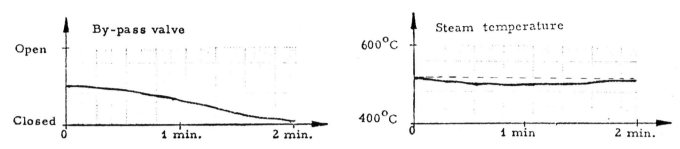

Figure 11.

Responses of a step change in one of the process parameters.

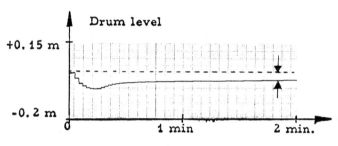

Figure 12.

Step change in the steam flow from 26 kg/s to 9 kg/s,
when the level transmitter is taken out.

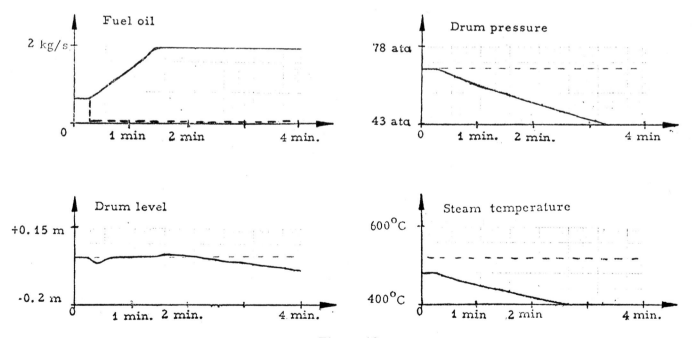

Figure 13.

Responses demonstrating what can happen if the fuel oil delivery is suddenly shut off.

RAYTHEON WATCHSTANDER SYSTEMS
FOR
CONDITION MONITORING OF STEAM TURBINE PLANTS

J.W. Cummings
Program Development Manager
Raytheon Company
Submarine Signal Division
Ocean Systems Center
Portsmouth R.I.
U.S.A.

1. INTRODUCTION

Raytheon's Watchstander Monitoring/Control System was originally developed under a U.S. Maritime Administration contract to provide a means of automatically determining when equipment should be replaced or adjusted. More time at sea with fewer failures and less preventive maintenance are direct benefits. In addition, it also provides the nucleus of a complete shipboard computer system that can be utilized now or at any future time to solve a variety of routine shipboard data-processing needs.

With the Watchstander System, hundreds of sensors located throughout the ship (engineering and cargo spaces, deck areas, etc.) measure such important parameters as temperature, pressure, flow, vibration, etc. This data is automatically collected and fed to a central computer station. Here it is processed and compared to pre-determined tolerances. When data does not agree, visual and audible alarms are sounded. Any or all data is available for immediate review on a cathode ray tube display or on hard copy printout. For review and trend observation, complete records of all stations monitored can be printed out daily or stored on magnetic tape for future use.

The system is designed to run unattended and continuously. If and when data thresholds are exceeded, alarms will be generated, but unless the operator desires more information, the system is returned easily to unattended operation. For other than normal activity, the operator may assume complete control, either manual or computer directed. To improve reliability, a performance monitoring and fault location feature is included. Training to operate the Watchstander System takes about two weeks and is provided by Raytheon.

The heart of the system - the rugged Raytheon 707 Computer - assures at-sea reliability. The computer is designed to full military specifications to maintain high performance levels in the most severe marine environments. Examples of this rugged, reliable design include: redundant circuits to guard against sudden failure; conformal coating to protect against corrosion; EMI shielding to minimize interference; mechanical reinforcing for delicate components; sealed switches to prevent moisture entry; and testing to shock, vibration, and temperature requirements that will exceed any shipboard conditions ever encountered.

And precisely because the 707 Computer is designed for growth, it can also perform a number of other shipboard data-processing chores. Payroll, medical diagnostics, spares inventory, fuel consumption, dock-side maneuvering, cargo control and distribution, and satellite navigation are just a few. Once the Watchstander System is installed, only the addition of software programs and sensors are needed to do routine foreground (real time) and background (delayed analysis) data processing.

The computer's modular construction also permits future expansion of data-processing capability. There's no danger of obsolescense or non-compatibility of elements. Raytheon 707 Computers can be installed independent of the Watchstander System now, or at any time in the future. And, of course, the computer will interface with any existing or future shipboard data-processing system, regardless of type.

The first installation of a Watchstander System for condition monitoring of a steam plant is underway. This paper will discuss the design of the system.

2. SYSTEM DESCRIPTION

The system is comprised of three major equipments: Acquisition Stations, Computer Center, and VIDEC Console.

Information from the pressure, temperature, flow and miscellaneous sensors is acquired, processed and displayed. Acceleration data from vibration sense points is also acquired, separated into frequency bands, processed with plant status information from the non-vibration sensors and displayed. NRT storage of raw vibration data will allow off-line narrow-band analysis.

The acquisition stations will be located throughout the ship in proximity to the equipment and ship's systems being monitored. Each acquisition station will receive inputs from some of the vibration, pressure, temperature, flow, and other sensors. Signal conditioning will convert the sensor outputs to uniform current levels for transmission to the Selector Unit located in the VIDEC console in the engine room. Here the current signals will be received, converted to voltage levels, time division multiplexed, and this raw analog data sent to the computer center on computer command. A programmable gain amplifier will adjust the signal level as required that feeds the filter bank consisting of 29 low pass and 1/3-octave filters covering the range of 1.25 Hz to 5.6 Hz. Outputs from this filter bank or the FM converter will be multiplexed to the analog-to-digital converter (A/D) with the resulting digital data processed and stored in the computer. Digital data received from the A/D converter that is processed and stored in the computer will finally be displayed on the VIDEC console in the engine room. Operator interface with the VIDEC system is via a keyboard and CRT display on the console. Once the computer has acquired the data from the sensors, there are virtually no restrictions on the manipulations that may be performed on it, nor are there any significant limitations on the display formats that may be presented to the operator. In general, the system is easily usable and operable with minimum personnel attention and training and provides a viable adjunct to the existing ship's systems.

In addition, it is possible on operator command for broadband or bandlimited data from any sensor to be recorded in real-time on the analog tape recorder in the computer center.

2.1 ACQUISITION SYSTEM

The acquisition station and selector unit make up the acquisition system. Each station is located near the equipment being monitored. The sensor outputs feed their signal conditioners contained in the acquisition station. Current outputs feed the line receivers located in the selector unit. After current-to-voltage conversion each signal routes to a channel of the 232-channel, solid-state multiplexer (MUXS) in the selector unit. Time division multiplexing now feeds each sensor's analog data to the computer center over a single twisted, shielded-pair cable.

The actual multiplexer is made up of

29 MAMI modules. As necessary, all digital sensor information is converted to analog data by D/A converters prior to entry into the multiplexer. Steady state information from sensors is current to frequency converted prior to feeding the multiplexer. A frequency-to-dc converter in the computer center re-establishes the correct dc level.

The line driver provides adjustable drive gain and a blanaced signal for cable transmission. In this way, maximum common mode noise rejection is possible. Control of MUXS is by digital command from the computer center. A parallel, 16-bit word is sent to the selector unit, stored, and decoded. Decoding activates the multiplexer switching and other control lines. Digital line receivers provide isolation and minimize line noise pickup. It should be noted that use of the MUX system as a transmitter in the engine room rather than as a receiver in the computer room reduces system installation costs.

Power supplies provide the necessary voltages to run the electronics and signal conditioners.

One of the most difficult problems to solve in any large electronic system is EMC (electromagnetic compatibility), i.e. the susceptibility of the system to and the generation by the system of conducted and radiated electrical interference. However, by judicious selection of components and use of correct wiring techniques and enclosures, problems are eliminated. All data transmission whether analog or digital are by twisted shielded pair cable. Single point grounding procedures are utilized throughout the system. Transmission over any distances uses balanced line drivers and receivers.

2.2 COMPUTER CENTER

Preprocessing

Signals from the selector unit analog line driver are received by the line receiver in the computer center. Outputs of the receiver feed a computer-controlled, programmable-gain amplifier. Thus, by program control the correct signal range is supplied to the filter bank. It is composed of a low pass filter (1.25 to 9 Hz) and 28 1/3-octave filters with center frequencies of 10^a where $a = \dfrac{\text{Acoustical Band}}{10}$.

All comply with ANSI performance requirements. Filter outputs as well as broadband unfiltered data feed a multiplexer (MUXI). However S/N ratio requires bandlimiting to a range of 1.25 to 5000 Hz although this range is variable. A frequency-to-dc converter also feeds MUX and re-establishes the dc state of the frequency converted signals from the acquisition stations.

Utilization of MUXI allows use of a single sample and hold (S/H) amplifier and analog-to-digital (A/D) converter insuring sample-to-sample tracking. A settling time of 2.5 usec for the S/H amplifier couples with the A/D conversion time of 18 usec limit the conversion throughput to about 50 KHz. However use of multiple S/H amplifiers, two A/D converters, and a digital multiplexer can provide any throughput desired without significant changes in control speeds. However, at this time, throughputs greater than 50 KHz are not needed. Output of the A/D converter is a parallel, 12-bit binary word including sign yielding a 1-part-in-4096 accuracy (.02%) and a 5 m V resolution. The central processing unit (CPU) accesses the digital data from the A/D converter via the input/out controller (IOC). THis device consists of buffer storage, device select decoding, and appropriate connectors. The procedure used to prepare the broadband analog data for processing is simple filtering. Sampling the bandlimited data at a minimum rate equal to two times the maximum frequency for a period of at least one cycle of the lowest frequency allows extraction of band energy, i.e. computation of rms signal values.

2.3 VIDEC CONSOLE

Operation of the complete VIDEC system is controlled from the VIDEC console located in the engine room and installed adjacent to the COS. All routine operator communications with the computer are by means of a keyboard on the console.

The major items included in the console are a time code generator (digital clock), keyboard and graphic CRT display a control panel including manual override, control, and alarms.

2.4 CLOCK

Time of day in hours, minutes, and seconds as well as day of the year is provided by the time code generator. Digital outputs will feed the computer input bus to provide time information as required by the program and necessary interrupts. All in-line display also informs the operator of the time. Most TCG's do not give a month, day, and year but rather a day number of the year from 1 to 365 (366). A simple subroutine in the computer will do the necessary conversion to month, day, and year desired on the printouts.

In addition, the TCG will supply timing signal to the CPU for program sequence initiation.

2.5 CRT DISPLAY

Any number of horizontal points up to 1024 can be displayed on the display. Hence when an "A" scan presentation is desired with

time as the horizontal axis, the time span of the displayed data is variable depending on sample rate. For example if a broadband data point is generated for display every 1/8 second then a total of 1024 x 1/8 = = 128 seconds can be displayed.

Record of CRT Display

Raytheon provides a unit that will allow permanent retention of the various display pictures presented on the CRT.

2.6 VIDEC SYSTEM CONTROL

Normal operation of the VIDEC System does not require an operator. However, during machinery maintenance, troubleshooting, system evaluation, or machinery repair, it is possible to manually direct the VIDEC System from the console. A control takeover switch must be activated and the various control words initiated from the console to effect the desired switching and control functions. Naturally the computer system will no longer continue data acquisition automatically but is available for display and printout of previously acquired and computer information.

2.7 KEYLOCK

A keylock for the keyboards is required by the RFB to prevent unauthorized tampering with the computer programs. Because of the adverse environment in which this unit will be used, a Plexiglass cover with a lock is added over keyboard assembly to protect the unit. Additionally, to preclude any accidental modifications to the software the file protect capability of the bulk memory is used. All programs are in the disk storage units and not accessible for alteration without releasing the file protect key operated switch. However, any program in core is alterable by keyboard entry. Hence, alarm level changes, deviation alarm overrides, changes in format, etc., can be keyboard modified but when the program is repaged in from bulk the changes are reset to the original values. Alterations to the program in bulk storage is possible by keyboard entry on paper tape with the file protect deactivited.

2.8 ALARMS

Alarms, both visual and audible, will be located on or near (at your option) the console. When an alarm occurs, a red indicator will flash and an adjustable volume klazon will sound. Depressing the appropriate switch will silence the klaxon and keyboard acknowledgement of the flashing indicator will change it to a steady red. Clearing or threshold change of all alarms will illuminate a steady green indicator.

Source of the alarm will be displayed on the CRT and printouts as appropriate will occur on the printer. Keyboard entry will clear the alarm. Simultaneous occurence of several alarms will activate a single indicator and horn but all causes are listed on the CRT. Each individual alarm can be cleared or a master clear generated by keyboard entry. It is also possible for the operator to insert a new temporary threshold for each alarm. This prevents repetitive alarms occurring on an acknowledged problem. Periodic operator determined selectable reset to the original alarm threshold will occur. At some selected time or by operator call, a status of alarm states will be displayed. At this time the watch supervisor could determine which alarm thresholds should be restored to the original value, which could remain changed, and which should be permanently modified. This procedure allows a known condition producing an alarm to be inhibited yet not preventing further alarms if the problem becomes worse.

2.9 COMMUNICATIONS FOR INSTALLATION AND OPERATION

Some communication system between the acquisition stations, computer center, and the VIDEC console should be installed to facilitate setup, test, and use of the VIDEC System. However, it is not a part of the VIDEC System.

2.10 ON-LINE TESTING

The intent of the VIDEC System design is to minimize operator assistance. To insure minimal operator attendance the continual testing of the system's performance during each data gathering cycle is necessary. This is accomplished by injecting a known signal into each acquisition station and processing it in a manner similar to normal sensor data. Comparison of the test signal from each acquisition station to the baseline value will establish the satisfactory performance of the acquisition, transmission, preprocessing electronics, and software.

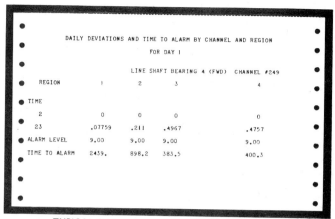

TYPICAL WATCHSTANDER VIOLATION REPORT

DAILY DEVIATIONS AND TIME TO ALARM BY CHANNEL AND REGION FOR DAY 1				
LINE SHAFT BEARING 4 (FWD) CHANNEL #249				
REGION	1	2	3	4
TIME				
2	0	0	0	0
23	.07759	.211	.4967	.4757
ALARM LEVEL	9.00	9.00	9.00	9.00
TIME TO ALARM	2439.	898.2	383.5	400.3

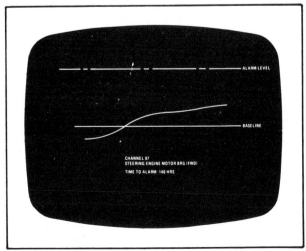

TYPICAL WATCHSTANDER DISPLAY

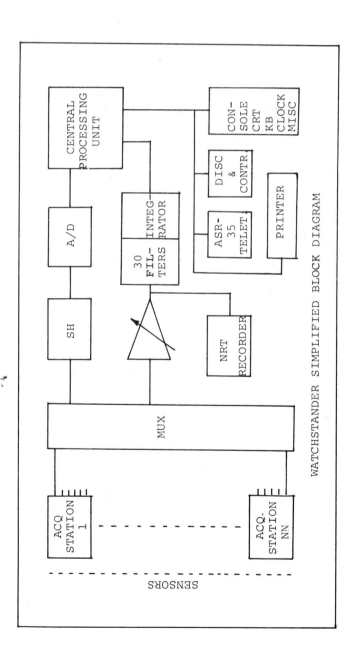

WATCHSTANDER SIMPLIFIED BLOCK DIAGRAM

CONDITION MONITORING OF STEAM TURBINES BY MEASURING EXTRACTION PRESSURES.

Tallak Aas
Project engineer
NORATOM-NORCONTROL A/S
Horten, Norway

ABSTRACT

The paper studies how local flow resistance variations in steam turbine stages affect the pressure distribution at steam extraction points.
Influence of varying extraction flow is considered.
A means of reducing the effect of measuring errors on the computed resistance parameters is demonstrated.

INTRODUCTION

The condition of a steam turbine can be supervised by computing the thermodynamical efficiency of each turbine section from pressure - and temperature measurements at extraction points. The method requires that the steam is in superheated state and is hence inapplicable to the LP-turbine in most cases.

A simpler method for condition monitoring which may be used even in the wet region, is based on a monitoring of the pressure distribution through the turbine. The aim of this paper is to investigate analytically how local flow resistance variations will influence the pressure distribution along the turbine and conversely to estimate flow resistance variations from the pressure distribution at extraction points.

EFFECT OF A DAMAGE IN A TURBINE SECTION ON THE PRESSURE DISTRIBUTION.

Fig. 1a represents a cross-section of an extraction steam turbine. The steam pressure is measured at each extraction point. The turbine stages between extraction point n and n+1 are in the following referred to as "turbine section n". For turbine section n the following relation between flow G, pressure p_n, p_{n+1} and the sectional flow parameter a_n applies, the extraction pipes considered closed for the time being:

$$(1) \quad G^2 = a_n(p_n^2 - p_{n+1}^2)$$

Sections n+1 to n+j-1 are described by the same relation:

$$(2) \quad \begin{aligned} G^2 &= a_{n+1}(p_{n+1}^2 - p_{n+2}^2) \\ G^2 &= a_{n+2}(p_{n+2}^2 - p_{n+3}^2) \\ &\vdots \\ G^2 &= a_{n+j-1}(p_{n+j-1}^2 - p_{n+j}^2) \end{aligned}$$

These j equations give the following recursive formula for the flow between section n and section n+j:

$$(3) \quad G^2 = b_{n,n+j}(p_n^2 - p_{n+1}^2) \qquad j \geqslant 2$$

$$(4) \quad b_{n,n+j}^{-1} = b_{n,n+j-1}^{-1} + a_{n+j-1}^{-1}$$

$$b_{n,n+j} = a_n \qquad j = 1$$

Let sectional pressure ratio, α_n, and flow parameter ratio, θ_n, be defined as:

$$(5) \quad \alpha_n \triangleq \frac{p_{n+1}}{p_n}$$

$$(6) \quad \theta_n \triangleq \frac{a_n}{a_{n+1}}$$

Equation (1) and (2) give:

$$(7) \quad \theta_n = \alpha_n^2 \frac{1 - \alpha_{n+1}^2}{1 - \alpha_n^2}$$

Equation (4) and (6) give after some computation:

$$(8) \quad b_{n,n+j} = \frac{a_n}{1 + \sum_{p=0}^{j-2} \prod_{i=0}^{p} \theta_{n+i}} \qquad j \geqslant 2$$

Assume a damage in section n+s such that the effective flow area of the section is changed by a factor k, see fig. 1b. Nozzle wear results in increased area and k>1, deposits to decreased area and k<1, as an example. The flow parameter of the damaged section, a'_{n+s} is then:

$$(9) \quad a'_{n+s} = k^2 a_{n+s}$$

346

The flow parameter for the combined j turbine sections n, n+1, n+2,...n+j-1 with damage in section n+s, $sb_{n,n+j}$, is from equation (4), (6) and (9) computed to

(10) $$sb_{n,n+j} = \frac{a_n}{1+\sum_{p=0}^{j-2}\prod_{i=0}^{P}\theta_{n+i}+(k^{-2}-1)\prod_{i=0}^{s-1}\theta_{n+i}} \qquad s \geq 1$$

(11) $$sb_{n,n+j} = \frac{a_n}{k^{-2}+\sum_{p=0}^{j-2}\prod_{i=0}^{P}\theta_{n+i}} \qquad s = 0$$

Assume momentarily that the number of turbine sections are unlimited and define:

$$\gamma_n \triangleq \lim_{j\to\infty} b_{n,n+j} \qquad \gamma_{n,s} \triangleq \lim_{j\to\infty} sb_{n,n+j}$$

From equation (8), (10), (11), and (7) it can be shown that

(12) $$\gamma_n = a_n(1-\alpha_n^2)$$

(13) $$\gamma_{n,s} = \frac{a_n(1-\alpha_n^2)}{1+(1-\alpha_n^2)(k^{-2}-1)\prod_{i=0}^{s-1}\theta_{n+i}} \qquad s \geq 1$$

(14) $$\gamma_{n,s} = \frac{a_n(1-\alpha_n^2)}{1+(1-\alpha_n^2)(k^{-2}-1)} \qquad s = 0$$

Further:

$$G^2 = \lim_{j\to\infty} sb_{n,n+j}(p_n^2-p_{n+1}^2) = \gamma_{n,s}\,p_n^2$$

$$): \quad G = \sqrt{\gamma_{n,s}}\,p_n$$

Also define the normalized sectional pressure ratio:

(15) $$\pi_{n,s} \triangleq \frac{\left(\frac{p_{n+1}}{p_n}\right)_{damage\ in\ section\ n+s}}{\left(\frac{p_{n+1}}{p_n}\right)_{no\ damage}}$$

$$G = \sqrt{\gamma_{n,s}}\,p_n = \sqrt{\gamma_{n+1,s-1}}\,p_{n+1}$$

(16) $$): \quad \pi_{n,s} = \frac{1}{\alpha_n}\sqrt{\frac{\gamma_{n,s}}{\gamma_{n+1,s-1}}}$$

Equation (12) - (16) give, noting that $\gamma_{n,s} = \gamma_n$ for s < 0:

(17) $$\pi_{n,s} = \left[\frac{1+(1-\alpha_{n+1}^2)(k^{-2}-1)\prod_{i=1}^{s-1}\theta_{n+i}}{1+(1-\alpha_n^2)(k^{-2}-1)\prod_{i=0}^{s-1}\theta_{n+i}}\right]^{\frac{1}{2}} \qquad s \geq 2$$

(18) $$\pi_{n,s} = \left[\frac{1+(1-\alpha_{n+1}^2)(k^{-2}-1)}{1+(1-\alpha_n^2)(k^{-2}-1)\theta_n}\right]^{\frac{1}{2}} \qquad s = 1$$

(19) $$\pi_{n,s} = \left[1+(1-\alpha_n^2)(k^{-2}-1)\right]^{-\frac{1}{2}} \qquad s = 0$$

(20) $$\pi_{n,s} = 1 \qquad s < 0$$

On assumption that $|k^{-2} - 1| \ll 1$, equation (17) - (19) can be linearized. Equation (17) may then be expressed as

$$\pi_{n,s} = 1 - \frac{1}{2}(k^{-2}-1)\left((1-\alpha_{n+1}^2)\prod_{i=1}^{s-1}\theta_{n+i}-(1-\alpha_n^2)\prod_{i=0}^{s-1}\theta_{n+i}\right)$$

By means of equation (7) one finds that

$$(1-\alpha_n^2)\prod_{i=0}^{s-1}\theta_{n+i} = (1-\alpha_{n+s}^2)\prod_{i=0}^{s-1}\alpha_{n+i}^2$$

$$(1-\alpha_{n+1}^2)\prod_{i=1}^{s-1}\theta_{n+i} = (1-\alpha_{n+s}^2)\prod_{i=1}^{s-1}\alpha_{n+i}^2$$

Define

$$\Delta\pi_{n,s} \triangleq \pi_{n,s}-1 \quad , \qquad \Delta k \triangleq k-1$$

giving:

(21) $$\Delta\pi_{n,s} = -\Delta k(1-\alpha_n^2)\prod_{i=1}^{s-1}\alpha_{n+i}^2(1-\alpha_{n+s}^2) \qquad s \geq 2$$

(22) $$\Delta\pi_{n,s} = -\Delta k(1-\alpha_n^2)(1-\alpha_{n+1}^2) \qquad s = 1$$

(23) $$\Delta\pi_{n,s} = \Delta k(1-\alpha_n^2) \qquad s = 0$$

EFFECT OF VARYING EXTRACTION FLOW ON THE PRESSURE DISTRIBUTION

Assume that the steam flow g . G is extracted between section n+s and n+s+1 as indicated on fig. 1b. How will this extraction change the pressure ratios?
The following equations apply:

(24) $$G^2 = a_n(p_n^2-p_{n+1}^2)$$
$$\vdots$$
$$G^2 = a_{n+s}(p_{n+s}^2-p_{n+s+1}^2)$$
$$G^2 = a'_{n+s+1}(p_{n+s+1}^2-p_{n+s+2}^2)$$
$$G^2 = a'_{n+s+2}(p_{n+s+2}^2-p_{n+s+3}^2)$$
$$\vdots$$

where:

(25) $$a'_{n+q} \triangleq a_{n+q}(1-g)^{-2} \qquad q \geq s+1$$

The resulting flow parameter for flow between section n and n+j with steam extraction after section n+s can from equation (4), (6), (24), and (25) be computed as:

(26) $$sb'_{n,n+j} = \frac{a_n}{1+\sum_{p=0}^{s-1}\prod_{i=0}^{P}\theta_{n+i}+(1-g)^2\prod_{i=0}^{s}\theta_{n+i}\left(1+\sum_{p=1}^{j-s-2}\prod_{i=1}^{P}\theta_{n+s+i}\right)}$$

(27) $$sb'_{n,n+j} = \frac{a_n}{1+(1-g)^2\sum_{p=0}^{j-2}\prod_{i=0}^{P}\theta_{n+i}} \qquad s = 0$$

(28) $$sb'_{n,n+j} = \frac{b_{n,n+j}}{(1-g)^2} \qquad s < 0$$

Assuming again an unlimited number of turbine sections:

$$\gamma'_{n,s} \triangleq \lim_{j \to \infty} {}_s b'_{n,n+j}$$

Equation (7) and (26) - (28) give,

$$(29) \qquad \gamma'_{n,s} = \frac{a_n(1-\alpha_n^2)}{1 + \prod_{i=0}^{s} \alpha_{n+i}^2 ((1-g)^2 - 1)} \qquad s \geq 0$$

$$(30) \qquad \gamma'_{n,s} = \frac{a_n(1-\alpha_n^2)}{(1-g)^2} \qquad s < 0$$

The normalized pressure ratio is now defined as:

$$\pi'_{n,s} \triangleq \frac{\left(\frac{p_{n+1}}{p_n}\right)_{\text{steam extr. after section } n+s}}{\left(\frac{p_{n+1}}{p_n}\right)_{\text{no steam extraction}}} = \frac{1}{\alpha_n} \sqrt{\frac{\gamma'_{n,s}}{\gamma'_{n+1,s-1}}}$$

From equation (29) and (30):

$$(31) \qquad \pi'_{n,s} = \left[\frac{1 + ((1-g)^2 - 1)\prod_{i=1}^{s} \alpha_{n+i}^2}{1 + ((1-g)^2 - 1)\prod_{i=0}^{s} \alpha_{n+i}^2} \right]^{\frac{1}{2}} \qquad s \geq 1$$

$$(32) \qquad \pi'_{n,s} = \left[\frac{(1-g)^2}{1 + ((1-g)^2 - 1)\alpha_n^2} \right]^{\frac{1}{2}} \qquad s = 0$$

Assuming $|g| \ll 1$, equation (31) and (32) can be linearized:

$$(33) \qquad \Delta\pi'_{n,s} = -g(1-\alpha_n^2)\prod_{i=1}^{s} \alpha_{n+i}^2 \qquad s \geq 1$$

$$(34) \qquad \Delta\pi'_{n,s} = -g(1-\alpha_n^2) \qquad s = 0$$

$$\Delta\pi'_{n,s} \triangleq \pi'_{n,s} - 1$$

Turbine with Constant Extraction Pressure Ratios. Example.

Consider a turbine where $\alpha_j = \alpha$ for all j, damaged in section $n+s$ so that the effective flow area of section $n+s$ has increased relatively by the amount Δk. The pressure ratio deviations caused thereby is from equation (21) - (23) found as:

$$(35) \qquad \Delta\pi_{n,s} = -\Delta k \alpha^{2(s-1)}(1-\alpha^2) \qquad s \geq 1$$

$$(36) \qquad \Delta\pi_{n,s} = \Delta k(1-\alpha^2) \qquad s = 0$$

Increased steam extraction between section $n+s$ and $n+s+1$ will according to (33) and (34) cause the following pressure ratio deviations:

$$(37) \qquad \Delta\pi'_{n,s} = -g\alpha^{2s}(1-\alpha^2) \qquad s \geq 0$$

Fig. 2 shows how a damage in one turbine section is influencing the pressure ratio of the damaged section and the preceeding ones. An effective flow area increase of 10% is assumed in section 1 and the corresponding deviations in pressure ratio is given for different normal extraction pressure ratios. All sections where the pressure deviation is more than 1% of maximum deviation are included in the drawing. According to this criterion, 8 sections are affected by the damage when $\alpha = 0.75$, (a), decreasing to 4 when $\alpha = 0.25$, (c). (All sections down stream the damaged one have unchanged pressure ratios).
Practical extraction pressure ratios for typical marine turbines are in the range 0.25 - 0.75.

Numerical computations indicate that the linearization resulting in equation (21) and (33) is quite accurate for flow area deviations up to 20%, when α is in the order of 0.5 or less. The effect of simultaneous flow area changes in different sections can then be found by superposition: Fig. 3 shows 4 different pressure deviation patterns and the corresponding assumed flow area changes (dotted line), for $\alpha = 0.5$. It is evident that the interpretation of an observed pressure ratio deviation distribution in terms of flow area changes calls for considerable caution.

The consequence of varying extraction flow on the pressure distribution is indicated on fig. 4: The extraction flow after turbine section 1 is reduced by 10% and the deviation on the sectional pressure ratios is computed. For $\alpha = 0.25 - 0.50$ the effect can be traced 2 - 3 sections ahead of the disturbance.

COMPUTATION OF SECTIONAL FLOW AREA VARIATIONS FROM MEASURED EXTRACTION PRESSURES.

If the variations in the effective flow areas of the various turbine sections, or the variations in steam extraction, are small, say less than 20%, the effect on the pressure distribution can be found by superposing the individual effects from each section. Assume that the m sections $n, n+1, \ldots\ldots n+m-1$ of the "semiinfinite" turbine shown on fig. 1c are to be monitored. Let variation in flow area and extraction flow of the typical section $n+j$ be denoted by Δk_{n+j} and g_{n+j} respectively. From equation (21) and (33) the deviation in pressure ratio for section $n+j$ due to Δk_{n+q} and g_{n+q} is given by:

$$(38) \qquad \begin{aligned} \Delta\pi_{n+j} = & -\Delta k_{n+q}(1-\alpha_{n+j}^2)\prod_{i=1}^{q-j-1} \alpha_{n+j+i}^2 (1-\alpha_{n+q}^2) \\ & -g_{n+q}(1-\alpha_{n+j}^2)\prod_{i=1}^{q-j-1} \alpha_{n+j+i}^2 \end{aligned}$$

Adding up the contribution from all sections n+q, q = j+1, j+2,.....m-1, for j = 0, 1, 2....m-1, one arrives at the following matrix equation:

$$(39) \quad \Delta \underline{\pi}_n = A \Delta \underline{k}_n - B \underline{g}_n$$

where

$$\Delta \underline{\pi}_n \triangleq \begin{bmatrix} \Delta \pi_n \\ \Delta \pi_{n+1} \\ \vdots \\ \Delta \pi_{n+m-1} \end{bmatrix} \quad \Delta \underline{k}_n \triangleq \begin{bmatrix} \Delta k_n \\ \Delta k_{n+1} \\ \vdots \\ \Delta k_{n+m-1} \end{bmatrix} \quad \underline{g}_n \triangleq \begin{bmatrix} g_n \\ g_{n+1} \\ \vdots \\ g_{n+m-1} \end{bmatrix}$$

$$A \triangleq \begin{bmatrix} (1-\alpha_n^2) & -(1-\alpha_n^2)(1-\alpha_{n+1}^2) & -(1-\alpha_n^2)\alpha_{n+1}^2(1-\alpha_{n+2}^2) & \cdots \\ 0 & (1-\alpha_{n+1}^2) & -(1-\alpha_{n+1}^2)(1-\alpha_{n+2}^2) & \cdots \\ 0 & 0 & (1-\alpha_{n+2}^2) & \cdots \\ 0 & 0 & 0 & \cdots \\ \vdots & \vdots & \vdots & \vdots \\ 0 & 0 & 0 & \cdots (1-\alpha_{n+m-1}^2) \end{bmatrix}$$

$$B \triangleq \begin{bmatrix} (1-\alpha_n^2) & (1-\alpha_n^2)\alpha_{n+1}^2 & (1-\alpha_n^2)\alpha_{n+1}^2\alpha_{n+2}^2 & \cdots \\ 0 & (1-\alpha_{n+1}^2) & (1-\alpha_{n+1}^2)\alpha_{n+2}^2 & \cdots \\ 0 & 0 & (1-\alpha_{n+2}^2) & \cdots \\ 0 & 0 & 0 & \cdots \\ \vdots & \vdots & \vdots & \vdots \\ 0 & 0 & 0 & \cdots (1-\alpha_{n+m-1}^2) \end{bmatrix}$$

The diagonal "area coeffisient matrix", A, can be inverted and equation (39) solved for the pressure deviation vector:

$$(40) \quad \Delta \underline{k}_n = A^{-1} \Delta \underline{\pi}_n + A^{-1} B \underline{g}_n$$

The inverse of matrix A can be shown to be:

$$A^{-1} = \begin{bmatrix} \frac{1}{1-\alpha_n^2} & 1 & 1 & 1 \cdots 1 \\ 0 & \frac{1}{1-\alpha_{n+1}^2} & 1 & 1 \cdots 1 \\ 0 & 0 & \frac{1}{1-\alpha_{n+2}^2} & 1 \cdots 1 \\ 0 & 0 & 0 & \vdots \\ \vdots & \vdots & \vdots & \frac{1}{1-\alpha_{n+m-1}^2} \\ 0 & 0 & 0 & \end{bmatrix}$$

$$A^{-1}B = \begin{bmatrix} 1 & 1 & 1 & 1 \cdots 1 \\ 0 & 1 & 1 & 1 \cdots 1 \\ 0 & 0 & 1 & 1 \cdots 1 \\ 0 & 0 & 0 & 1 \cdots 1 \\ \vdots & \vdots & \vdots & \vdots \\ 0 & 0 & 0 & 0 \cdots 1 \end{bmatrix}$$

According to this, the effective flow area variation of section n+j can be expressed as:

$$(41) \quad \Delta k_{n+j} = \frac{1}{1-\alpha_{n+j}^2} \Delta \pi_{n+j} + g_{n+j} + \sum_{i=j+1}^{m-1}(\Delta \pi_{n+i} + g_{n+i})$$

EFFECT OF THE CONDENSER ON THE PRESSURE RATIO DISTRIBUTION.

Assume that the semiinfinite turbine considered so far, is terminated after section n+m-1 and that a condenser is substituted for section n+m and the following. The influence of the condenser, or any other turbine termination, can then be regarded as originating from a change in flow area of section n+m. The formal pressure ratio deviation in this "condenser section" can for small variations be written as:

$$(42) \quad \Delta \pi_{n+m} = \left(\frac{\Delta p_{n+m+1}}{p_{n+m+1}} - \frac{\Delta p_{n+m}}{p_{n+m}} \right) \triangleq g_c - \frac{\Delta p_c}{p_c}$$

g_c = relative variation in total steam flow to the condenser

Δp_c = condenser pressure deviation from normal

The effect of the condenser on the computed flow areas can then be compensated for by, in equation (41), adding the term $\Delta \pi_{n+m}$.

The Stodola formula (1) applies for subsonic flow through the turbine stages. In sonic or supersonic stages the flow does not depend on the pressure after the stage. As the flow in one or more of the stages constituting a turbine section approaches sonic flow, the effective α-ratio therefore will diminish and finally reach zero at sonic flow, making the influence of flow area variation more and more "short-ranged".

Often the last turbine stage(s) before the condenser is (are) made supersonic. This virtually isolates the preceeding subsonic stages from the influence of the condenser. Equation (41) can then be applied with no correction, with section n+m-1 meaning the last section before the supersonic one.

In the following, variations in extraction flows are neglected. For the small pressure variations in question:

$$(43) \quad \Delta \pi_{n+j} = \frac{\Delta p_{n+j+1}}{p_{n+j+1}} - \frac{\Delta p_{n+j}}{p_{n+j}}$$

For a "sonically" terminated turbine, equation (41) and (43) give

$$(44) \quad \Delta k_{n+j} = \frac{1}{1-\alpha_{n+j}^2} \cdot \frac{\Delta p_{n+j}}{p_{n+j}} + \frac{\alpha_{n+j}^2}{1-\alpha_{n+j}^2} \cdot \frac{\Delta p_{n+j+1}}{p_{n+j+1}} + \frac{\Delta p_{n+m}}{p_{n+m}}$$

For a "subsonically" terminated or "condenser" terminated turbine, equation (41) - (43) give

$$(45) \quad \Delta k_{n+j} = \frac{1}{1-\alpha_{n+j}^2} \cdot \frac{\Delta p_{n+j}}{p_{n+j}} + \frac{\alpha_{n+i}^2}{1-\alpha_{n+j}^2} \cdot \frac{\Delta p_{n+j+1}}{p_{n+j+1}} + g_c$$

Regard once more the basic equation (1):

$$G^2 = a_{n+j}(p_{n+j}^2 - p_{n+j+i}^2)$$

Linearization gives, writing

$$\frac{\Delta a_{n+j}}{2 a_{n+j}} = \Delta k_{n+j} \qquad \frac{\Delta G}{G} = g_c$$

equation (45) directly.

I.e. including the effect of the condenser, leads to the highly undesirable steam flow measurement! In equation (44) the flow measurement is substituted by a pressure measurement at the last section.

Sensitivity to Measurement Errors. Example.

All measured variables are considered to be independent, stochastic variables, normally distributed, with standard deviation 1 and 2.5% for pressure and flow respectively. For a pressure ratio of 0.5, equation (44) gives the following standard deviation in computed flow area:

$$\sigma_k \triangleq (Var \Delta k_{n+j})^{\frac{1}{2}} = (1.33^2 + 0.33^2 + 1.0^2)^{\frac{1}{2}} = 1.70\%$$

Equation (45) gives:

$$\sigma_k = (1.33^2 + 0.33^2 + 2.5^2)^{\frac{1}{2}} = 2.85\%$$

DATA PROCESSING TECHNIQUE FOR REDUCING THE INFLUENCE OF AN INACCURATE FLOW MEASUREMENT

The influence of varying steam flow on the extraction pressure ratios is most severe at the turbine end but diminishes rapidly up the steam flow as indicated by fig. 4. This fact suggests the following approximate formula for the flow area, to reduce the influence of pressure deviations of distant sections:

$$(46) \quad \Delta \hat{k}_{n+j} = \frac{1}{1-\alpha_{n+j}^\epsilon} \Delta \pi_{n+j} + g_{n+j} + \sum_{i=1}^{m-j} \epsilon^i (\Delta \pi_{n+j+i} + g_{n+j+i})$$

ϵ is a weight factor to be chosen less than one. The sensitivity to main flow measurement errors is now reduced by ϵ^{m-j}, m-j being the number of turbine sections between the section under consideration and the condenser. The systematic error which is hereby introduced is found as:

$$(47) \quad \Delta \Delta k_{n+j} = \sum_{i=1}^{m-j} (1-\epsilon^i)(\Delta \pi_{n+j+i} + g_{n+j+i})$$

where:

$$\Delta \Delta \hat{k}_{n+j} \triangleq \Delta k_{n+j} - \Delta \hat{k}_{n+j}$$

Let $e_{n,s}$ denote the error in $\Delta \hat{k}_n$ due to a unit flow area change in section n+s. Assuming that all extraction pressure ratios are equal, equation (47) and (21) give after some computation:

$$(48) \quad e_{n,s} = (1-\epsilon)(1-\alpha^2)(\epsilon^s - \alpha^{2s})(\epsilon - \alpha^2)^{-1} \quad s \geq 0$$

Similarly the relative error in $\Delta \hat{k}_n$ due to extraction flow variation after section n+s, e'_{n+s}, is found from equation (47) and (33) as:

$$e'_{n,s} = \frac{\alpha^2}{1-\alpha^2} e_{n,s}$$

Total error can be written as:

$$(50) \quad \Delta \Delta k_n = \sum_{s=1}^{m-1} e_{n,s}\left(\Delta k_{n+s} + \frac{\alpha^2}{1-\alpha^2} g_{n+s}\right)$$

Fig. 5 shows $e_{n,s}$ for different combinations of ϵ, α and s, s being indicated by the horisontal number. The systematic error in $\Delta \hat{k}_n$ is greatest from nabouring turbine sections, but diminishes fairly rapidly as the distance between the sections in question increases.

Between the first section of the HP-turbine and the condenser there will be 5-6 sections for a typical marine turbine installation, the HP- and LP-turbine being regarded as one.

Assuming 5 sections, the effect of an error in the main steam flow measurement on section 1 would be reduced by a factor given by:

$$f = \epsilon^m \qquad m = 5$$

$$\epsilon = 0.9 \quad f = 0.591$$

$$\epsilon = 0.7 \quad f = 0.168$$

$$\epsilon = 0.5 \quad f = 0.032$$

Referring again to fig. 5, $\epsilon = 0.7 - 0.9$ appears to offer a reasonable compromize between accuracy and sensibility to distant measurement errors.

SUMMARY AND CONCLUSIONS

The sectional pressure ratio exhibits several features making it suitable as an indicator for condition monitoring purposes:

1. It can be used for both HP- and LP-
   turbine sections.
2. It is easy to measure accurately.
3. It is fairly independent of total steam
   flow.

A damage in one section affects in principle the pressure ratio of all the preceeding sections, but the influence is
rapidly diminishing in magnitude with the
distance from the damage. None of the
successive sections are affected, if the
total steam flow is kept constant or the
influence of the condenser can be neglected. It is necessary to correct for total
steam flow for sections near the exhaust
end of the turbine, and it is also generally
necessary to compensate for varying extraction flow.

FIGURE 1 CROSS SECTION OF TURBINE

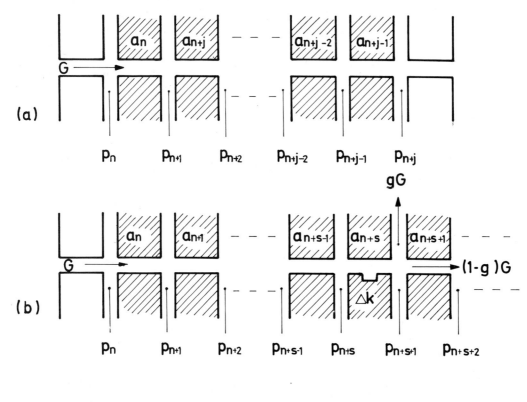

(a)

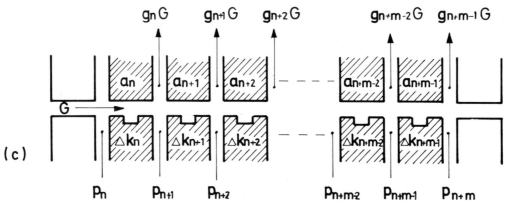

(b)

(c)

FIGURE 2. EFFECT OF INCREASED SECTIONAL FLOW AREA

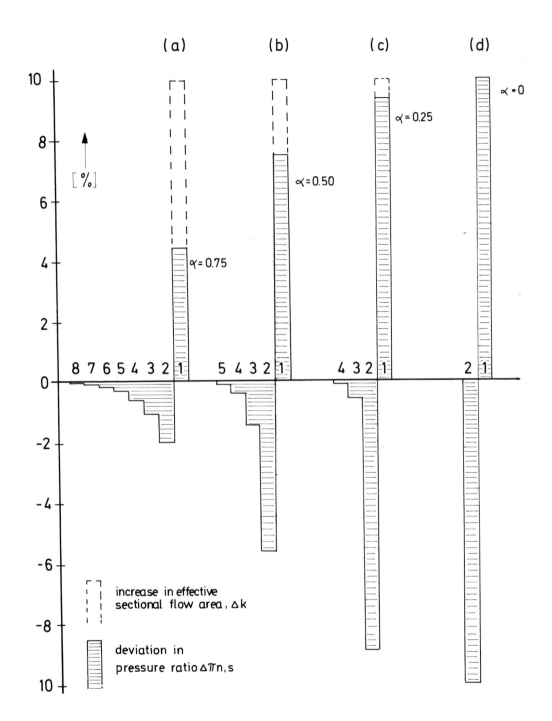

FIGURE 3. PRESSURE DEVIATION PATTERNS, α-0 5

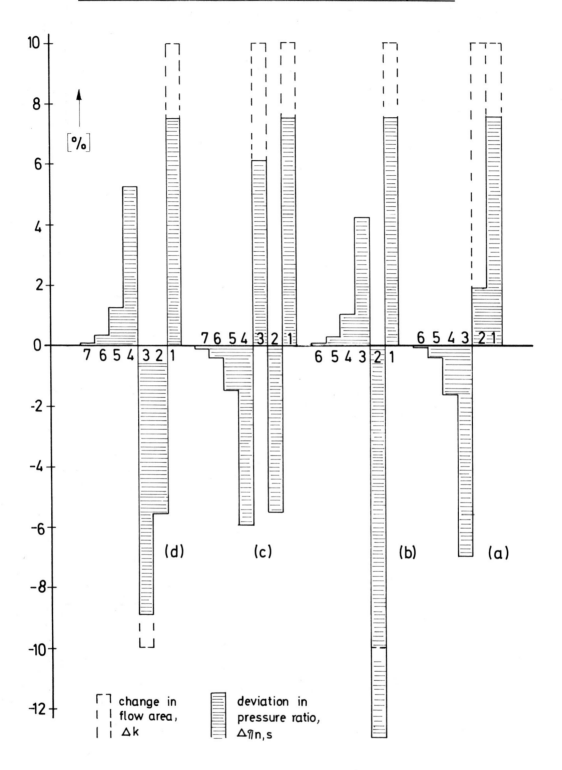

FIGUR 4 EFFECT OF REDUSED EXTRACTION FLOW

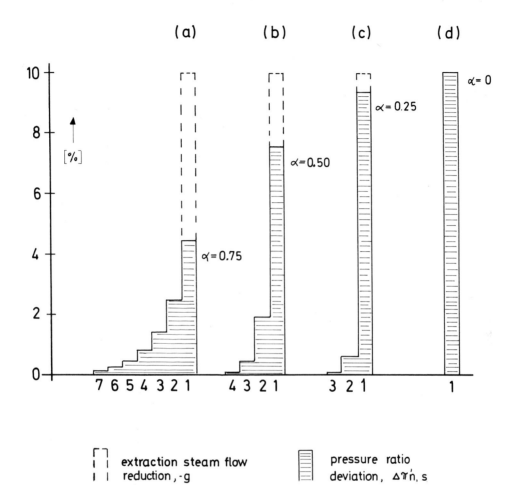

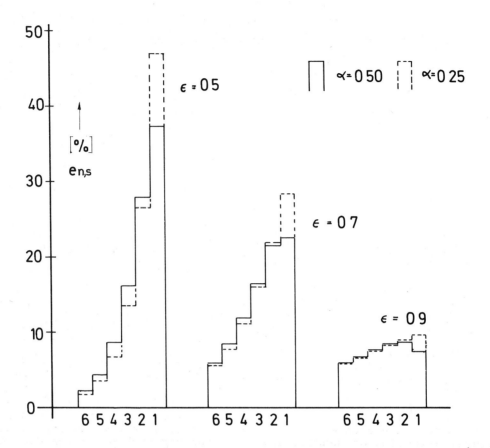

FIGURE 5. ERROR FUNCTION $e_{n,s}$

EXPERIENCE WITH ADVANCED INSTRUMENTATION
ON LARGE BORE ENGINES

Ørjan Steen

NORSK A/S PHILIPS
Oslo, Norway

ABSTRACT

The author has been engaged in design, installation, commissioning, and subsequent operation of a ship automation system with advanced instrumentation. The paper deals with the instrumentation as such, without entering into details of the end use of this instrumentation.

The instrumentation was installed in a motor tanker, and much thought was given to the planning of locating and securing components, selecting cable runs, screening and grounding methods. Experience shows that preparing and working according to such plans pay off in reduced electrical noise problems. Selection of sensors and other components has been found to be a tricky business. The severity of the ship environment can be misjudged. While temperature and vibration problems are at least expected, if not fully understood, the hazards of climbing crew members and liberal use of high pressure cleaning may be surprises.

The instrumentation is considered overall successful, However, the paper points out some mistakes that were made. Good practice and well considered component selection help to reduce mistakes, but there are cases where components will not stand up to all requirements of the specification at the same time. These cases can hardly be avoided except through experience.

INTRODUCTION

Early in 1970 Norsk A/S Philips and A/S Sig. Bergesen d.y. & Co., after a prestudy of 18 months, agreed to install a computer in one of the shipowner's large tankers. The prestudy, done by a project group consisting of engineers from both participating firms, had pointed out 12-13 different applications that through computerization were likely either to increase the profitability or the safety of the ship. Some of these applications are presented in other papers at this symposium.

DESCRIPTION

These applications were to make use of data from all over the ship, which, paranthetically speaking, is 300 m long and 40 m high, and it was decided to have one comparatively large computer serving all the applications. Against this background it was easy to foresee that the environment could produce problems in the system in general and in the instrumentation in particular. After having studied the vibrations in the superstructure of a sailing sistership, it was decided to weld the computer to the hull in a cabin on the poop-deck in the office suite. Although this cabin is placed far aft, it is pretty close to what might be called the center of gravity of both human and technical activity in the ship. More than 90% of the instrumentation for the system is located in the engine room, and there mainly on the large 8RND105 Sulzer diesel engine. The distance from the engine to the computer measured along the cable run is 62 m, and the "Instrumentation Division" of the project group - which for the occasion was reinforced by two consultants - found that each signal had to be amplified as close to the transducers as possible. Accordingly, a suitable amplifier system was designed. The best solution to the location problem was to install the amplifiers in the engine control room which has its separate air-condition unit.

In spite of very short time available (the ship was to leave the yard in November 1970) much time was spent in studying literature on ship instrumentation, but with rather disappointing results. Our final impression was "if you buy the best and most expensive, you are likely to have a system working for maximum half a year".

As the main application in the engine room, "Supervision and Predictive Maintenance of Main Engine" in this special development project needed at least six months of continuous data acquisition to observe the trends in wear and tear, this conclusion was rather shocking, but made the project even more challenging to this group of "Instrumaniacs". A thorough analysis of all applications concerned showed that the input/output equipment would contain 208 analogue, 240 digital and 16 counter input channels plus 16 digital and 4 analogue output channels.

Beside the problems of selecting suitable transducers capable of surviving the vibrations, temperatures, mechanical stresses, and the salty, oilfilled atmosphere and still have an extreme long-time stability, the main problem was how to avoid electrical noise.

TRANSDUCERS

Some of the parameters needed in the system had never been measured with any success before, except in laboratories or testbeds with rather complicated equipment. Since easy maintenance and dependable operation is a "must" in ships, several new solutions had to be worked out.

One example is the cylinder combustion pressure which contains a multitude of information about the condition of the engine when measured continuously and accurately, but neither the accuracy nor the continuity are easy obtainable when the pressure varies from 1,5 kp/cm^2 to 85 kp/cm^2 and the temperature from 60-70^{0}C to 2000^{0}C two times per second. Furthermore, the exhaust gases contain corrosive components such as sulfuric acid.

The solution - which is now patented - is shown in Figure 1. The transducer itself (A) is located outside the combustion chamber (B) where the temperatures are moderate (50-70^{0}C). The hole through the cylinder liner (D) is continuously filled with lubricating oil, which is pressed through the tube (E) and the non-return valve (F). The lubricating oil that tends to coke at (C) during combustion, is forced into the combustion chamber by the new oil when the combustion pressure is low.

This oil string is for measurement purposes practically incompressible and transmits the pressure accurately to the transducer. The accuracy is destroyed if the outlet of the oilduct is not at the highest point in the system, so that air or gas in the oil will disappear. The presence of air or gas which are compressible

will cause pressure oscillations which will give incorrect readings.

In using this system the problem was reduced to finding a suitable transducer that could take at least 10^8 load changes and fulfil the other specifications. A well-known Swedish manufacturer was willing to give a guarantee on one of his strain-gauge transducers. Only one of these transducers have failed in 2½ years of continuous use, which we regard as being very good.

However, it was the oil channel and not the transducer that was doomed beforehand by several diesel engine experts. It was thought for sure that it would coke up within a few minutes! Two of the channels did in fact coke up after four months' operation due to water leakage in the engine. Then, after another year five of the channels closed up within a short time. This time the reason was deposits and additives in the lubricating oil together with small grains of sand that prevented the non-return valve from functioning properly. This caused the oil to leak back through the valve. Accordingly the hot exhaust gases would get into the channel and gradually coke would form. By regularily (every six months) cleaning the valves, this is no longer a problem.

Another interesting transducer in the field of diesel engine supervision is the so-called "Cylinder Wear Sensor". It was originally developed to check the condition of the piston rings, but at least in this engine it is doing a better job of even more interest in detecting wear in the cylinder liner, i.e. how much the liner has worn since new. This, in turn, makes it possible to tell something about the wear rate in the future, and this is one of the aspects of the application"Predictive Maintenance".

The principle of this transducer is similar to that of the inductive proximity sensors. The flux in a ferrite core in an AC driven coil will change when metal of varying magnetic properties passes "the face" of transducer, or if the distance between the metal and the sensor changes. Figure 2 shows the mounting of the sensor (A) in the cylinder liner (B) and the signal occurring when the piston (C) passes upwards. The peaks are the piston rings which are closer to the liner wall - and the transducer - than the piston. The negative peaks come from the so-called wear-rings made of bronze. Furthermore, it is possible to say that the third ring is either defect or is partly coated with copper or that a ring joint is just passing the transducer on its turning around the piston. The speed at which these piston rings are turning around the

piston is varying greatly depending upon
the condition of the rings, the load and
speed of the engine, the amount of lubricating oil etc. On this type of engines the
rings always seem to break (whenever these
failures occur) near the joints. As the
turning speed varies it is difficult to
say whether the lack of a peak is an abnormal or a normal situation. However,
piston ring failures are also detected in
other ways and, as mentioned before, this
sensor is useful in detecting wear of the
cylinder liner. The DC-level of the signal
at A and B contains this information (of
wear). When the ship is rolling, this level will vary. The computer reads these
levels and stores the maximum and minimum
distance between piston and liner.

Figure 3 shows the movement of the piston
within the liner. A point P on the piston
will move as indicated on Figure 3b when
the liner is new, and as indicated on Figure 3c when it is worn.

Another important parameter in diesel engines is the fuel oil pressure. In addition to the information about the pressure and amount of fuel oil injected, this
measurement also gives the timing and duration of the fuel oil injection. However,
there is nothing special in this measurement of pressure, except for the relatively high pressure, and it would not have
been mentioned unless the title of this
paper had not contained the word "experience". Because this is what this transducer has given us - besides trouble.

The original specifications for this transducer were a pressure range of 0-2000 kp/
cm^2 (due to expected pressure transients
up to 1000 kp/cm^2 and general instrumentation caution), temperature range 50-
120^{0}C (fuel oil temperatures are 90-100^0
C), and a life expectancy of at least 10^8
load changes.

This means about 2 years of operation on
this diesel engine, but as no one was willing to give a warranty of more than 12
months, we had to renounce on that point.
Anyway, we procured the transducers that
seemed to be the best on the market at
that time. After approximately four months
two more became "silent". The manufacturer
rejected our guarantee claim and told us
after an investigation not to use the
transducer outside its temperature specifications.

However, the lubricating oil temperature
is closely regulated and the engine log
showed that the temperature had never exceeded 115^{0}C, which is the alarm limit.

The problem, therefore, seemed unsolvable
and started to become expensive as these
sensors continued to break down. Two other

types of sensors were tried, but the result was unsatisfactory. The only possible
explanation seemed to be some kind of self-
heating within the transducer. To prove
this theory one sensor was equipped with
thermocouples as shown on Figure 4, and
installed. The temperatures at point B
increased rapidly and became higher than
in point A which again was higher than
the oil temperature (at C)!

Then after having checked the compressi-
bility of the fuel oil - which is rather
high at this pressure - it was quite
clear that the "dead volume" in the transducer, i.e. the amount of oil, was too
large. When exposed to approx. 110 load
changes between 5 and 7-800 kp/cm^2 per
minute, the oil - which in the cylinder
pressure case could be regarded as incompressible - compresses about 6%. The
work done on the oil causes a temperature rise in the relatively thin walled
sensing element. This heat has rather
small possibilities of escaping due to
the isolation effect of stationary air
between the element and the outer wall of
the transducers and the small square area
of element at A.

Due to this unfortunate construction of
the transducer it is not fit for use when
exposed to rapidly changing loads in compressible media and accordingly it is not
standing up to its specifications.

However, this weakness in construction is
easily corrected in at least two ways
which we have suggested to the manufacturer. The first one is to decrease the
"dead volume" and the other one is to
fill the transducer with some kind of material suited for heat transfer.

SIGNAL TRANSMISSION AND CONDITIONING

Measuring the parameters accurately is
just one part of the problem. The information must be received by the user (i.e.
the computer) in such a way that the data
can be trusted. There are many factors
that make this complicated. Two of the
most important are the multitude of data
and the noise. The noise because it de-
stroys the signal, and the multitude of
data because of the inherent tendency to
drown the relevant information in the
irrelevant. Most dynamic, or rapidly
varying signals are burdened with both
phenomena, while the static, or slowly
varying signals do not contain "too
much" information and accordingly they
are only subject to noise.

1. Noise.

    These problems were given close att-
    ention from the early beginning of
    the project, and up to now this

seems to have payed off very well. A ship's hull, mainly consisting of steel, is considered to be the ideal earth by all suppliers of electrical ship's gear. But since everyone thinks like that, whether they deal with mV og kV, AC or DC equipment, problems must occur. The hull is often so "crowded" by wild currents that you may wonder why one should bother with cables for lighting etc. at all. The noise caused by this grounding practice is annoying, but can be avoided by applying old- but often neglected - principles in instrumentation and measuring techniques. There exist a number of theories on the grounding problems and most of them have that in common that they are all right if they are consistently practiced. Accordingly, the author will drop the discussion of which one is best and give a brief description of this actual system.

Each channel from the transducer to the central computer is in principle as shown on Figure 5. The transducers (A), junction boxes (B) and amplifiers (C) are placed all over the ship while the filters (D), signal conditioning units (E), multiplexers (F) and A/D converters (G) are in the computer rack.

From the sensors to the junction boxes most cables originally were equipped with flexible metal hoses (to protect the cables from mechanical damage), and the cable entrys in the boxes and the transducers were sealed with ordinary sealing compound. From the junction boxes to the amplifiers, which brings the signal up to a higher DC-level (1-10v), and further on to the computer room, newly developed marine multi-core, copper braided cables with individually twisted pairs are installed. To the greatest possible extent the cables are installed according to the following instructions which were distributed to all workers concerned on the yard:

a. All AC mains cables, including those for the computer, and signalling cables must be separated. If two cables are running paralell for more than 2 m, the minimum distance between the two types of cables must be at least 0,4 m. Crossovers that bring power and signal cables in close proximity to each other should be made at right angles, and the distance should be at least 0,25 meter.

b. Multicore cables carrying mV-signals are going to have separate conduits and the length should be kept as short as possible.

c. All signalling cables must be kept at least 2 m away from the following noise generation equipment, unless there are steel bulkheads in between:

- Static and rotating converters.
- Transformators.
- Fluorecent tubes.
- Radio stations.

d. All braids are to be connected in one point in the computer room. That means that the braids should be treated as an isolated conductor in all junction boxes. Special care should be taken when dismantling the cables in the junction box cable entry.

These precautions have kept the system relatively free of capacitive and inductive interference directly to the cables, and the worst thing that might happen is direct insulation break at the transducer. This will cause a ground loop, and depending upon the potential difference in the "earthing" points the signal will more or less disappear in noise. If this potential difference is too high it will even cause damage of the electronics. Accordingly a good half of the input channels are protected against overvoltage up to 230 volts. When a cable braid accidently is grounded somewhere in the system, it is not that critical, but due to the noise transmitted through the cable capacitance the signal/noise ratio will deteriorate. In ships, and particularly in diesel powered ships, everything is constantly vibrating, and shields will sooner or later be grounded. Therefore it is of extreme importance to have connections etc. which make it easy to disconnect the cables and check the insulation.

As it was stated before, many thoughts were given to the installation work, and experience was gathered from everywhere. However, there was not much experience on the market at that time when we wanted to design an instrumentation system comprising high accuracy and long-time stability in ships. On the electronic side the problem was solved in a rather traditional way by demanding better (and more expensive) components (amplifiers, resistors etc.) with better specifications. The logical consequence of this was to make the rest of the system, for example the cable connections, as insensible as possible to environmental changes. Accordingly, plugs were banned on the transducers and the connections in the isothermal junction boxes in the engine room were soldered.

2. Experience.

Installation experiences were excellent but during the last busy hours at the yard we learned that the steel armoured flexible hoses looked too solid and were used for climbing, while other cables not that thrustworthy looking were handled with utmost care. So experience number one is: Your equipment must look weak, but be strong.

Later on we have experienced that flexible hoses are not at all the perfect solution to the problems of mechanical and chemical deterioration of flexible cables. Besides being cable conduits, they are also water, oil and chemical conduits both outside and - when leaky - inside, which means that either the transducer and/or the junction box becomes damaged.

Then after a couple of months we experienced that cleaning of engines etc. is no longer a purely manual operation. It is "automated" by means of chemicals sprayed on the bulk heads, motors, engine, cables and junction boxes.

Unfortunately, these chemicals are not as harmless as they are said to be, and when the spray gun is pointed to a junction box or a flexible hose, the fluid often penetrates into it. Besides, some of the chemicals will destroy the sealing compound commonly used at cable entrys and clear the way for oil, water etc.

The next thing to be experienced was that it was a failure to omit the plug connectors on the transducers. It may seem ridiculous - when looking back - but in trying to get a theoretically perfect instrumentation system we forgot that most engine parts have a rather high repair and overhaul frequency, and this demand a very quick and easy dismounting of all sensors etc. Besides being time consuming, soldering small wires on a vibrating hot engine is more than inconvenient, and the connecting plugs which were rapidly installed are very much appreciated.

To conclude, the practical demands have changed "the transducer end" of the instrumentation system considerably while the central parts are more or less unchanged.

Briefly, the sensors to-day are connected to the cables via connectors especially treated to keep the connector pins unaffected of environmental influence.

The flexible armoured hoses are omitted and new flexible cables of an oil and chemical resistant steel braided type with a rather poor appearance are installed. This trick has worked, no one has climbed them yet. As sealing compounds in transducers and boxes a special type of silicon-rubber has proven excellent and has resisted all attacks by an unfriendly environment. The soldered connection in the isothermal boxes are still there, but will not appear in other systems.

From what is said above it might be concluded that the failures mentioned have caused much trouble, but fortunately there have been at least two engineers on board continuously on this trial ship, and they have taken immediate action when these malfunctions appeared and accordingly nothing really serious has happened.

3. Signal Conditioning.

In spite of all these precautions noise has appeared on some of the signals, but this is high frequency noise and is easy eliminated with simple low pass filters or by digital (software) filtering in the computer. However, it is well known that dynamic signals cannot be filtered too heavily without loosing information. In addition, the sampling frequency must be sufficiently high, in order not to overlook information, but not too high in order not to overload the computer or fill the memory with superfluous data.

This may be exemplified by considering the signal from one of the so-called scuffing detectors. Those pulses have a duration of about 1 ms and accordingly the sampling frequency should exceed 1 kHz to be sure to "hit" each puls. If the amplitude is of importance, and if there are four sensors per sylinder, the frequency should be at least 40 kHz Here the solution is obvious, the number of pulses exceeding a threshold are counted, and the content of the counters is fed into the computer at fixed intervals.

Similar reasoning is valid for the pressure signal on Figure 6. Among other things, the peak value and the area of the curve between the points t_1 and t_2

$$A = \int_{t_1}^{t_2} f(p)\,dt$$

is of importance.

In this case special electronics which directly give the peak value and the integral as analogue DC voltages (and store them until the computer can "read" them),were developed.

The alternative to this technique is letting the computer sample, and then compare the signals sufficiently frequently to be sure to hit the peak value. According to information theory the sampling frequency should then be at least twice the highest frequency represented in the signal, and as in the previous example, this will lead to overloading of the computer.

This kind of signal conditioning, known as pre-processing, has been a success in this system and will be extended in systems now under development in our laboratories. The method will be of increasing importance in the future when the demands for information grow, the instrumentation systems become even more comprehensive, and the multitude of data more difficult to handle.

To achieve the best results, all the information i.e. the signals, must be analyzed in advance to find which parts thereof are useful. Then the signals must be filtered to leave out the unnecessary parts as early as possible. Otherwise this dead information will load the system and prevent the computer from working optimally.

RELIABILITY

This presentation, which is too brief to give a real impression of the instrumentation system in M/T "BERGE FISTER", might leave the impression that we have had nothing but trouble, but that is not so. In fact we have had 39 instrumentation failures or malfunctions counted from January the 1st 1971 which is the date at which the installation was finished. This number includes all the fuel oil pressure gauges and all cases of coking in the holes of the cylinder pressure measuring systems. If those failures are

counted for as a total of one, the remaining 15 failures give an MTBF (Mean Time Before Failure) of $4 \cdot 28 \cdot 10^6$ hours per transducer (200 transducers).

However, the MTTR (Mean Time To Repair) is not as favourable as the MTBF. The repair-time in itself is not too long, as the defect transducers normally are replaced, but usually replacing cannot take place until the main engine has stopped. One trip from Persian Gulf to Europe takes 30-35 days and the MTTR per transducer will be about 350 hours.

In turn this leads to a rather poor availability, defined as

$$A = \frac{MTBF}{MTBF + MTTR}$$

However, this is clearly not the availability of the total system, and the software system is prepared to handle these situations. Whenever a transducer fails, either an average value of the parameter is inserted or the average of the same parameter for the other cylinders is used.

A far more interesting subject is the availability of the total instrumentation system, but so far we have had no failures putting the complete system out of work, and we therefore cannot give any figures for this.

CONCLUSION

However, one has both hard times and good times on board a ship and to colleagues in the same position I would like to give this advice which might sound humoristic, but is meant seriously:

Use your common sense and never doubt Ohm's law.

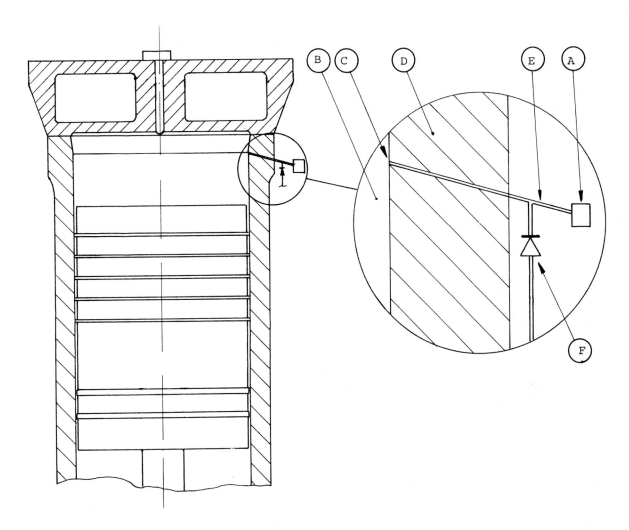

FIG. 1

364

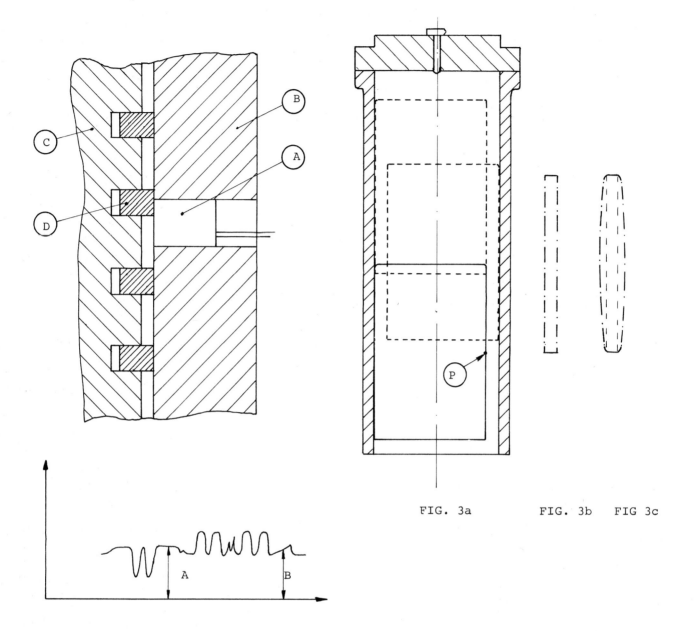

FIG. 2

FIG. 3a   FIG. 3b   FIG 3c

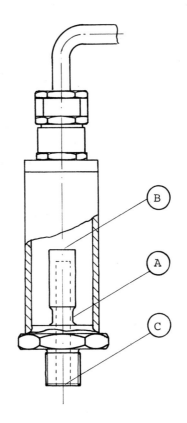

FIG. 4

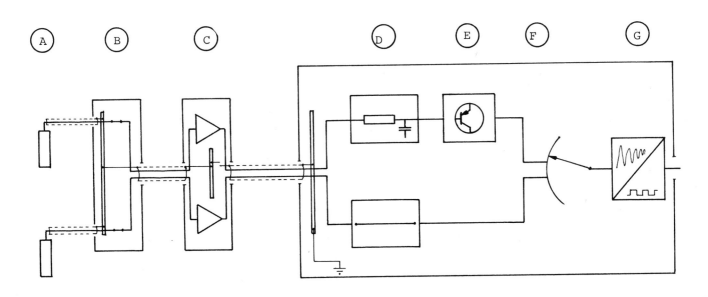

FIG. 5

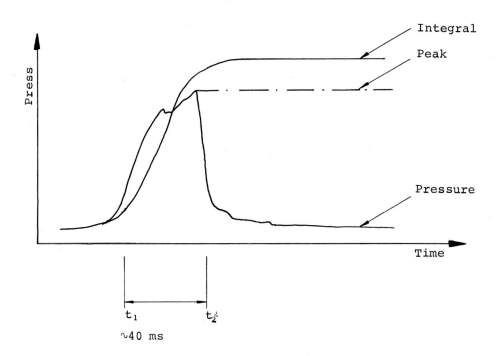

FIG. 6

ENGINE TESTING BY MINICOMPUTER

Ernst Jonsson
SAAB-SCANIA AB
Missiles and Electronics Section
Electronics Development
Gothenburg, Sweden

ABSTRACTS

Long term testing is one part in engine development work. The use of digital computers in such
a test facility has shown great benefits in time-
saving, and accuracy of setting and measurement
of test parameters. A large number of readings
can be recorded simultaneously. They are mathematically processed and the results presented.
Due to the fact that no human operation is involved in this chain there are practically no
errors in the system.

It is also possible to use the computer itself
as the controller and monitor of the various
engine parameters.

INTRODUCTION

This paper gives a short description of a mini-
computer system built by SAAB-SCANIA AB, Missiles
and Electronics Section, Gothenburg, and installed at the Central Laboratory of SAAB-SCANIA,
Car and Truck Division, Södertälje, Sweden.

The system is today (July 1973), since one and
a half year, running three test stands for
diesel- and petrol engines in endurance test.

The system:

- controls the test engines according to test
  programs with varying speed and load
- monitors the engines to prevent damage
- collects data
- makes computations
- records collected and calculated data

This system is one application of SAAB-SCANIA:s
general minicomputer system, SYSTEM 330.

GENERAL

The test engine is run for weeks (months) under
conditions representing a forced form of real
operation, i.e. varying speed and load.

Control of the engine is possible in two major
modes, manual and automatic. After manual start
and warming up in manual mode the operator initiates the automatic mode. In the automatic mode
the engine is run in several program phases,
stated in beforehand, with respect to the control of the brake and the throttle. The program
is cyclic and runs without break or manual
intervention.

Measurements of speed, torque, temperatures,
pressures, fuel and oil consumption etc. are made
continuously.

Computation is made at the end of each program
phase, for example specific fuel consumption.

Registration is done of all data of interest,
measured as well as computed.

Monitoring is another very important feature
meaning that speed, torque, temperatures, pressures etc. must not exceed preset upper or lower
limits. These limits are different for the different program phases. Exceeding the limit means
that the engine may be damaged and must immediately be stopped. Afterwards it is easy to see
what was the cause.

Visual readings of momentary data are presented
on displays and pointing instruments. It is also
easy to see in which mode and program phase the
equipment is just working.

The engine is installed in a test bed with shaft-
coupling to a water dynamometer. A torque transducer is connected to the lever arm on the dynamometer.

Water for cooling the engine is supplied from a
big reservoir to which the returning water also
is led. Thermocouples are used for temperature
measurement of in- and outgoing water.

A volumetric technique is used to measure fuel
consumption. The engine takes the fuel from a
small container. Each time the container is empty
it is refilled with certain fuel and an electrical
impulse is sent.

The oil consumption is measured in a similar manner.

Blow-by, which is the flow of gases passing the

pistons into the crankcase, is measured with a special instrument giving one electrical impulse per litre passed gas.

The throttle lever is connected to an electric servo motor with feedback potentiometer.

Engine speed is represented by electrical pulses.

A special servo system controls the dynamometer to keep the desired speed.

Several thermocouples are connected to the engine for temperature measurements.

The exhaust-gas may be taken to a gas analyser.

COMPUTER SYSTEM

The principal configuration of the system is shown i figure 1.

The system is today running three engine test beds and includes:

- one central unit, the COMPUTER STAND
- for each test bed one control and interface unit, CONTROL STANDS L5, L6 and L7.

With the same central unit the system can be expanded up to six test beds.

The mechanical configuration is shown in figure 2.

The computer stand includes:

- computer VARIAN 620/L with 8k words of core memory
- fast tape reader for program feeding
- one terminal assembly, TERMINAL D, interfacing all analogue inputs from the test beds
- cold junction for all thermocouples

Close to the computer stand is placed one Teletype ASR 33, TTY, for the input of system changes information, for example program listing, parameter changing etc.

The control stands include each:

- operators control panels, figures 3-6
- one terminal-330 assembly, TERMINAL L5, L6, L7 resp., interfacing all digital signals in and out and all analogue signals out
- servos holding the process
- power supplies, fans etc.

Close to each control stand is placed one typewriter IBM Selectric for printout of test results.

The computer communicates with all terminal-330-assemblies via in/out-bus PDB, Primary Data Bus. The PDB may have a length of up to 200 metres by cable and for longer distances modem technique is used.

Computer

The computer is VARIAN 620/L including:

- Central Processing unit
- Core Memory, 8k words
- Maximum storage, 32k words
- Word length, 16 bits
- Storage cycle, 1.8 µs
- Addition time, 3.6 µs
- Real-time clock
- Power fail-safe
- Priority interrupt unit
- Multiplication/division unit

Program

The system includes complete program for engine testing.

The program is made up of:

- A Real-Time Monitor program (RTM) which supervises all activities in the system and controls the co-operation of the various subprograms
- Users Applications Program specially designed for this particular task. The different parts of this program are listed below.
- Standard functions, arithmetic functions, mathematical functions etc.
- Test program, a special program for checking instructions, storage and peripheral units.

All programs are of a modular design, which means that program sections can be inserted or deleted without influencing the rest of the program.

Users applications programs

The program specially designed for this application is named the Users Applications Program. This program has been written by the contractor as a part of the development work for this specific system and they include:

- reading the operators control panels, keyboard, switches etc.
- commanding the operators panels, signalling lamps, displays, instruments
- controlling the program phases, (ten automatic steps and one manual step)
- feeding set-points to servos
- feeding commands (on/off) to the test bed
- measuring signals from the test bed (speed, consumptions, temperatures etc.)
- checking upper and lower limit values
- computation of mean values
- computation of sum totals
- computation of specific consumptions
- editing of typewriter printouts.

Terminal system

As mentioned the complete terminal system consists of four 330-terminal assemblies located at four different places.

The Primary Data Bus, PDB, constitutes the communication link between the computer and the terminal assemblies. The PDB is double-directional and transmitts information in parallell-digital form with parity check, giving a very reliable data transmission over long distances in locations having severe environmental disturbances.

In the terminal assembly the PDB is converted to
a general terminal bus system, T-BUS, also
double-directional, digital and analogue. (Always
the same T-BUS in all terminal assemblies).

To the T-BUS is connected all the interface
needed in the form of modular plug-in printed
circuit boards giving desired number of digital
and analogue, in- and output channels.

One terminal assembly can house any number of
plug in boards up to 21, and any combination of
modular boards belonging to the SYSTEM 330 series
is possible.

Instead of having special central multiplexers
we have split up and moved the multiplexing function to each individual modular board. No relays
are used. Whenever one needs an expansion of the
system, say some more analogue inputs, one only
plugs in one or more modular boards - no wiring
no soldering - and the multiplexing function
comes automatically. The computer simply points
out terminal assembly number X, modular board
number Y, channel number Z and transfers data
in or out.

From the back end of the circuit boards plug-in
modular cables connect the circuit boards to an
in/out connection board (placed inside the wall
of the stand) to which also the external cables
are connected.

Today we all know about the very excellent reliability of the minicomputer. All the interface
boards placed in the terminal assemblies are built
up along the same principles and exactly the same
components are used as in the minicomputer itself.
In this way most of the total system is given
highest possible reliability.

System Operation

After the program via paper tape is fed into the
computer the system is ready for work.

The program sequence consisting of ten steps is
stored in the computer memory. Actual parameters
for each step are fed in via a keyboard and
corresponding display placed on the control
panel PARAMETER SETTINGS.

On the control panel PROGRAM STEPS the computer
shows the step just working by lighting corresponding signal lamp.

Printouts on the typewriters are done:

- automatic at the end of each program step
- automatic when limit values are exceeded
- operator initiated when desired

The computer edits the printout, turns page etc.
The three control stands are working completely
independent of each other and may be regarded as
three separate units giving the operators full
freedom of individual testing.

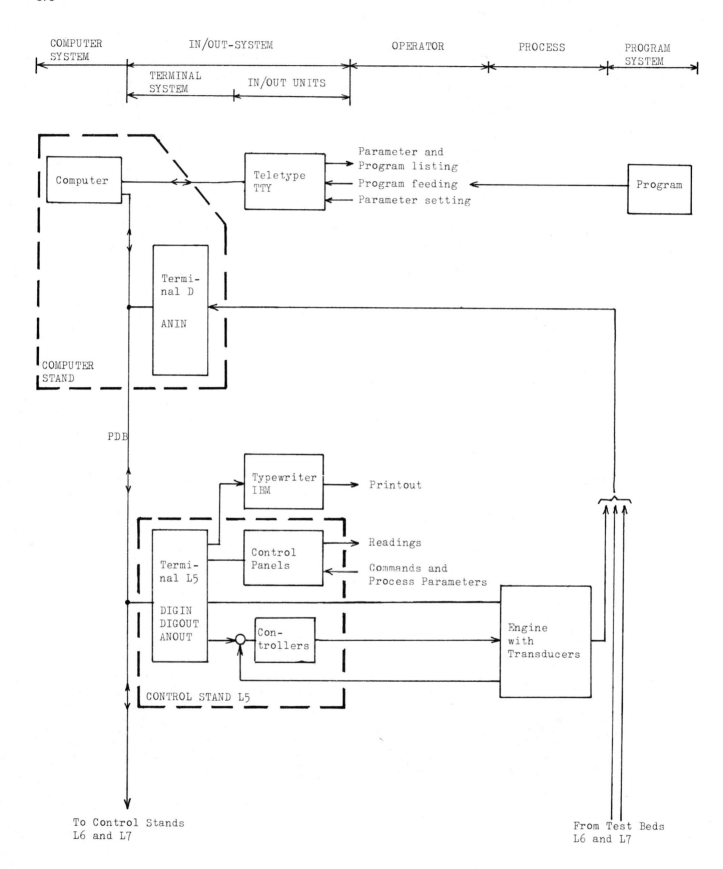

Figure 1. Block diagram

Figure 2. Mechanical configuration

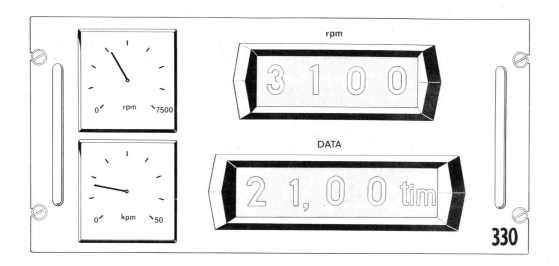

Figure 3.   Control panel DISPLAYS

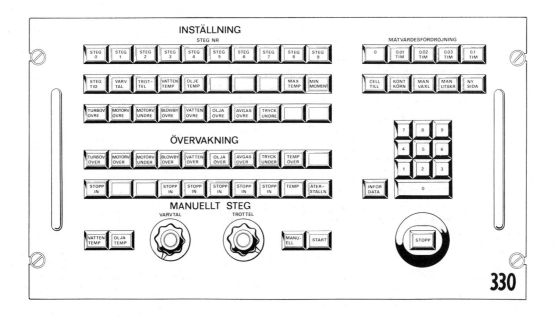

Figure 4.   Control panel PARAMETER SETTINGS

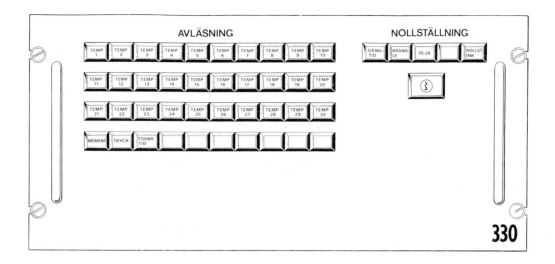

Figure 5.   Control panel READINGS

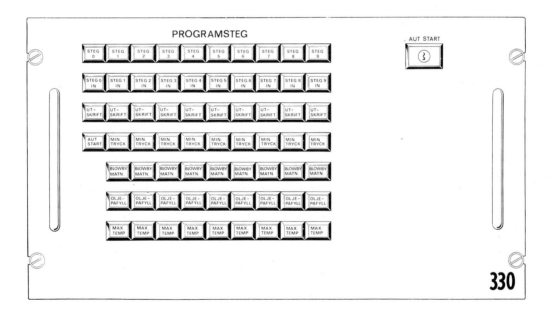

Figure 6.   Control panel PROGRAM STEPS

MACHINERY ALARM SYSTEMS FOR SHIPS OPERATED WITH
UNATTENDED MACHINERY SPACES.

Ir.W.de Jong C.Eng.M.I.E.E.
Lloyd's Register of Shipping
Rotterdam.

ABSTRACT.

This paper is intended to underline the importance of alarm systems for the safety of ships operated with unattended machinery spaces. Basic requirements for these systems are listed and a machinery alarm system philosophy is explained.
Attention is given to system design, sensors, installation and testing. Reference is made to decentralized machinery alarm systems.

INTRODUCTION.

The primary task of the engineering staff on ships with conventional machinery spaces is watchkeeping. Running machinery has to be controlled and supervised and adequate steps have to be taken when engineering variables move out of control or when telegraph orders are given. Such watchkeeping requires the continuous attention of engineers to check meters, gauge glasses and other equipment scattered around the machinery spaces. For an engineer accustomed to ships now being designed and built it is difficult to realize that this supervision task can be satisfactorily carried out without the aid of automatic control, alarm and safety shut-down systems.
On ships with conventional machinery this task could be effectively and satisfactorily performed because of:
a) comparatively simple machinery.
b) an extensive engineering staff per watch.
c) admirable devotion of the engineering staff.
As all of us know a revolutionary development has taken place during the last 15 years or so in the design and operation of our ships.
Machinery installations became more complicated, power outputs increased, equipment is run closer to physical limits, instrumentation, remote and automatic control systems have been installed and engineroom staffs were strongly reduced.
On many new and existing ships this leads to the introduction of unattended enginerooms.
This development had a marked effect on the work of the ship's engineers. Their task shifted gradually to operational, maintenance and repair duties. This change of watchkeeping practice could only be successful where the supervisory work was taken over by suitable alarm and instrumentation systems.

It is apparent that the effective functioning and reliability of such installations are of utmost importance for the safety of the ship and the machinery. The purpose of this paper is to list basic requirements and features of these systems and to explain a machinery alarm system philosophy. It may be mentioned that the ideas explained in this paper are primarily intended for "bread and butter" ships, i.e. comparatively simple ships, built for commercial shipowners who wish a ship for an acceptable price, without superfluous equipment, but on the other hand with effective protection for the installed machinery and suitable to be operated with an unattended engineroom.
It may be realized that also now still many ships are built which are designed to be operated with attended enginerooms. The great majority of these ships is also equipped with more or less extensive machinery alarm systems in order to provide proper protection for the machinery and because also on these ships the engineroom staffs will be much smaller than was normal on the really conventional ships.
It is hoped that the contents of this paper could also be of value when designing alarm installations for such ships.

GENERAL.

Already a long time before ship's operators thought of the concept of an unattended engineroom, machinery alarm installations were fitted on some ships to assist engineers in their watchkeeping routine and to give warning when a few, but very important variables exceeded safe values.
Usually those panels were fitted close to the machinery manoeuvring position, i.e. the place where the watchkeeping engineer was expected to be.
There is quite some difference between those early machinery alarm installations and the alarm systems now being fitted. Whilst the first were merely intended to <u>assist</u> engineers on watch, the latter in fact <u>replace</u> the engineers, at least in so far as supervision of the machinery plant is concerned.
The terminology included in the "Standardization Code for Trials and Testing of New Ships" issued by the "Association of Ship Technical

Societies in Norway" describes short and concise the function of an alarm system as follows: "Detects an abnormal condition and gives acoustic and visual warning".

In order to perform this function satisfactorily the following basic problems have to be solved:

a) which machinery variables have to be alarmed.

b) what sensors have to be used to measure the variables and to trigger the alarm system when preset levels are exceeded.

c) how has the alarm circuit to be designed in order to process the alarm signals effectively and to avoid as much as possible harmful effects of internal and external system faults (fail-safe characteristics)

d) where should the alarm signal sound and flash and who is expected to react on it.

The first question cannot be solved by the designer of the alarm system but should finally be decided by the designer of the overall machinery installation.

The items b) and c) are technical problems within the scope of this paper.

Item d) is of operational nature and perhaps the most interesting of all.

Before dealing in detail with this last problem it may be noted that although the alarm system detects abnormal conditions, the occurrence of a machinery alarm on a ship with an unattended engineroom could be considered as a normal situation. Experience on many ships now being operated on this way learns that an average of one alarm per 48 hours is not unusual. It is therefore understandable that the ship's staff will consider the occurrence of an alarm as a normal situation and this should be borne in mind when designing the alarm system and particularly when specifying repeat alarms in accomodation and navigating bridge areas. It is also for this reason that some ship operators are reluctant to refer to "machinery alarm systems" but prefer the wording "monitoring and supervisory systems", in this way the use of the term alarm systems restricting to the real alarm conditions like CO_2 alarm, general alarm, fire alarm, etc.

The following basic points may be considered when deciding where and how to present the machinery alarm signals on ships operated with an unattended engineroom:

a) alarms should only alert engineer(s) who is (are) expected to take action.

b) final acknowledgement of an alarm should only be possible where the kind and extent of the deviation can be determined and where corrective steps can be taken.

c) no alarms should be given to staff who can or should not take any corrective action and who cannot determine the exact cause of the alarm.

d) an effective system should be provided enabling the engineer called to the engineroom by an alarm to ask for assistance from other engineers.

e) additional alarms should be given at proper locations, e.g. navigating bridge and

engineers alleyway, when after a predetermined period of time e.g. 5 minutes, an alarm has not been acknowledged by the responsible engineer.

f) arrangements should be provided to protect the well-being of an engineer attending the engineroom on its own for e.g. dealing with an alarm condition (patrol alarm or engineers safety system).

g) alarm signals should be presented on the navigating bridge for conditions directly affecting the propulsion power (e.g. alarm conditions which could lead to shut-downs) or when the navigating officer is requested to take action (e.g. request for slow-down or shut-down).

h) only real alarm conditions should be presented. When machinery has been stopped on purpose, the concerning alarms should be inhibited.

Most of the above points are evident but some need perhaps further explanation. Compliance with item c) would mean for example that machinery alarms are not directly indicated on the navigating bridge, as the bridge officer is neither expected nor in a position to take any action. It would unnecessarily divert his attention from his own duties and could perhaps lead to lack of interest at the moment an alarm would sound which would really need his immediate attention and action.

Item d) is self-explanatory but very important and a telephone connection should not be considered sufficient for this purpose. Such an engineers call system proves its value when a few important alarms occur about simultaneously or when a major fault caused the alarm to sound.

Item e) is an essential alarm in the above outlined alarm systems concept, as in this concept in principle only one man is warned when an alarm condition occurs. The possibility that this man does not or cannot properly react on the alarm has to be taken into account.

Item f) is based on the same principle: it is unwise to entrust the ship's installation to one man only, particularly not when this man has to work in an engineroom with numerous staircases, running machinery, etc. Arrangements should be made to monitor the well-being of this man, either by an alarm system which has to be reset at predetermined intervals (e.g. each 30 minutes) or by the use of a walkie-talkie or a similar direct communication system between the engineer down in the engineroom and the navigating bridge staff. Such arrangement would as well be in the interest of the engineer as of the ship. It is thought that such patrol alarm or engineers safety system should be provided on all ships operated with a one man engineroom watch.

The above considerations are primarily intended for larger ships with considerable propulsion power and do not necessarily apply to ships like coasters, tugs and similar ships.

SYSTEM DESIGN.

When specifying an alarm system the first major choice to be made is the choice between a system with analogue inputs and one with on/off (switch-type) inputs.

When analogue inputs are selected a more comprehensive system can be made, combining alarming with read-out of measured variables on scale meters or in digital form.

Systems using analogue inputs have certain advantages:
a) direct read-out of variables.
b) constant check on the functioning of the system, including the sensing device and its connections.
c) easy testing of the alarm circuits by e.g. adjusting the alarm setpoint values to values obtained during normal operation.

The above applies particularly to those variables for which simple and reliable analogue sensing devices are available such as for temperatures. It is understandable that for other variables, particularly levels, many shipowners still prefer to use switch-type sensors. It may however be expected that within some years most ships will be provided with combined monitoring and alarm systems based on analogue inputs.

The use of analogue sensing devices also offers the possibility to extend the system with datalogging facilities but it is mostly hard to see any real advantage in this addition, except of course for ships with cargo refrigeration installations when temperature logging is required. Quite a few shipowners found out that the datalogger sheets filled a lot of space in their filing system but that they did not find it worthwhile to devote time of their technical staff to process all the required information.

The same reasoning applies to some extent to the usefulnes of alarm printers fitted in conjunction with alarminstallations. It is sufficient when ship's engineers regularly, e.g. per voyage, send a report of alarms occurred during a certain period. Such reports do not need decoding and more-important for the Owner's staff, can contain additional useful information such as cause of alarm, ship's conditions at the moment of the fault and other information which cannot be logged by a datalogger or an alarmprinter. Figure 1 shows a translated report containing alarms occurred during a round voyage of m.s. "TRIDENT ROTTERDAM" operated by Messrs. Koninklijke Nederlandsche Stoomboot Maatschappij N.V. in their service between Western Europe and the Caribbean. This ship is a modern cargoliner of about 10.000 tons d.w., propelled by a 16.000 hp diesel engine and equipped for operation with an unattended engineroom. Alarm lights are usually presented on centralized control panels, together with remote metering and control devices. The arrangement of the alarm signalling lamps in conjunction with the other instruments and devices is important. The engineer should be able to determine at a glance which alarm has operated and the actual value of the concerning variable. All alarm lights should have the same colour significance and controls and displayed data should be arranged in functional groups. When alarms are indicated and analysis of the alarm situation is necessary before any action can

be decided upon the engineer must have a clear picture in his mind of the plant lay-out. When this is difficult a mimic diagram showing the alarm points in relation to the plant may be of value. This cannot so easily be arranged when using alarm systems of the annunciator type with several alarm modules grouped together in one chassis. However if the alarm presentation is made up of a number of group chassis each containing not more than 6-8 annunciators, also this system can be arranged to give an acceptable lay-out.

The usual and minimum alarm sequence is as follows:
no fault: all lamps dark and horns silent.
fault: : flashing lamps, horns sounding.
fault acknowledged: steady lamps, horns silent.
fault rectified: all lamps dark and horns silent.
For alarm systems with many alarmpoints it is advisable to arrange for separate acknowledge push-buttons for the flashing lamps and audible alarm circuits. This enables the engineer to acknowledge directly the audible alarm and to look quietly for the flashing alarmlamp. For machinery systems where one alarm condition could quickly lead to subsequent alarms it is worthwile to consider the provision of an alarm system with possibility to indicate first failures, in order that the initial cause of the fault condition can be easily traced. This could e.g. apply to complex steam propulsion installations. Alternatively in such cases the use of event recorders or alarmprinters could be useful.

Alarm systems should be designed so that a fleeting alarm i.e. an alarm condition of short duration which has disappeared before being acknowledged, is locked-in. However false alarms should be avoided as much as possible. It is therefore necessary to have a minimum delay in the order of 0.2 to 1 sec. on all alarm channel inputs. This prevents false alarms due to transient phenomena as sensor contact bouncing, pressure waves in protected pressure systems or electromagnetic interference from other systems. This also enables in most cases the use of unscreened cables to connect the sensing devices with the alarm processing unit.

In addition to this minimum delay certain alarms need to have much longer delays, like e.g. level alarms.

Although the alarm system as a whole may operate with an average of one alarm per 48 hours, it must be realized that many individual alarm circuits are hardly ever asked to function. When however, the concerning variable protected by such an individual alarm circuit, moves outside its safe limits, it may be of crucial importance that at that moment the alarm circuit is in a healthy condition and able to sound the alarm. To achieve this the following two points cannot be stressed enough:
a) Alarm installations, including the individual sensing devices, need regular and proper testing.
b) The design of the system should ensure as much as possible failsafe characteristics.
Point a) will be dealt with in a further section of this paper whilst concerning b) the

following is noted.

Faults which could disturb the correct functioning of an installation might be split up in external faults and internal faults. The external faults may be broken wiring, loose connections, earthfaults, short-circuited wiring, defective sensing devices, etc. The internal faults may be defective transistors, integrated circuits or relays, broken connections on printed circuit-cards, defective plug-in contacts, etc. Preferably all such faults should lead to a safe situation, either directly being indicated or not preventing the alarm to sound when the variables require so. In practice this can never be achieved completely. However attempts should at least be made to restrict the harmful affects of most likely faults. In respect of failsafe characteristics systems using analogue inputs are in principle better than systems with on/off inputs. The analogue inputs are also used for measuring purposes and consequently a considerable part of the circuitry is automatically tested when measurements are made. Analogue systems with high and low alarm setpoint on their channels indicate both short-circuited and interrupted wiring to the sensors as alarm conditions. More elaborate systems of this kind are provided with current detecting circuits checking the continuous output of sensors and part of the sensor output processing circuitry. Such current detecting circuits could also be used to check continuously the connections between the main alarm panel in the engineroom and the repeater panels elsewhere in the ship, e.g. engineers accomodation. These current detecting circuit(s) can indicate defective installation and systems power failure. As far as failsafe characteristics are concerned it must be admitted that, compared with systems with analogue inputs, systems using on/off type sensors such as pressure and temperature switches, are rather primitive. It is generally considered that the use of normally closed sensor loops is required for such systems. In this way at least all circuit interruptions trigger the alarm enabling the ship's staff to rectify the fault. Sensing devices are usually located at very unfavourable locations and it is possible that due to e.g. moisture a more or less conductive path is developed between its terminals. The alarm circuit should preferably be so designed that the closed loop current cannot easily be maintained over this path, preventing the alarm to operate when the sensor contacts open. To some extent this may be avoided by using a rather high closed loop current, which will only be maintained when the resistance between the terminals is sufficiently low, e.g. below 500 ohms. Such provisions can of course never guard against a fully shorted sensor.

Earthfaults are in many alarm installations the most dangerous faults. When the alarm is electrically isolated from earth, the first earthfault will in general not cause any harm. However the second earthfault could do damage to a good part of the installation, cause spurious alarms or prevent alarms to operate. When the alarm system is not isolated but connected to earth, e.g. through its supply system, the first earthfault in the system could have similar effects. Earthfaults are most likely to occur in the sensor circuits, in repeat alarm panels and in similar outgoing circuits. It is often very difficult and time consuming to trace such earthfaults.

The following measures could be taken to restrict the effect of earthfaults:

a) Isolate the system electrically from other ship's systems. This means that e.g. the supply for the alarm system should not be directly taken from a battery system also used for the supply of other services.

b) If a complete isolated system is used earthfault indication may be provided to indicate the first earthfault.

c) To provide means of separation between the sensor inputs and the alarm processing circuits. This could e.g. be done by the use of miniature relays or reed relays in the input circuits or by the use of photo-transistors as opto-isolators between the input and processing circuits.

d) To arrange for suitable subdivision of the alarm installation in a number of groups, each with its own protection against earthfaults.

Besides short-circuits and earthfaults in sensor and similar circuits, consideration should be given to the effect of short-circuit faults in alarm lamp circuits. In view of the size and type of the concerning lampholders such faults can sometimes easily occur e.g. when lamps are replaced, and should not render the audible alarm inoperative when an alarmcondition occurs on the concerning channel.

The engineroom staff should be able to distinguish between various kind of alarms such as: machinery alarm, general alarm, fire alarm, CO_2 alarm, engine telegraph and often a few different telephone system. It is possible, but rather impracticable to arrange different audible signals for all those systems. An attractive way to avoid this multiplicity of aural signals is the use of luminous call panels in conjunction with one audible alarm. A few of such luminous call panels can be scattered around the engineroom and when the engineer's attention is drawn by the audible signal, he can distinguish on the luminous call panel which system is involved. Audible alarms may also be replaced or supplemented by rotating beam lights. If only rotating beam lights are used it may be noted that due to the lay-out of most enginerooms many of those lights have to be used to ascertain that the lights are automatically seen from all possible locations. Particularly in enginerooms with a high noise level, such as on ships with medium speed engines, it will be worthwile to consider the use of these rotating beam lights. CO_2 alarm signals should not be combined with other alarms and it cannot be stressed enough that these signals should be easily distinguishable from other alarm signals. Owners should try to standardize the audible signals used on ships of their fleet to avoid wrong reaction in emergencies. The selection of a good power supply arrangement is of prime importance for

a good functioning of an alarm system. Voltage
transients caused in the ship's main electrical
supply system by switching operations, heavy
load rushes or short-circuits and earthfaults
should not unduly influence the operation of
the alarm system.
A preferred power supply arrangement may consist of a transformer rectifier supplied from
the mains and provided with its own battery
of sufficient capacity to supply power for a
period of e.g. 30 minutes. Under normal conditions the system is supplied from the mains
with the battery being kept under charge, whilst
at mains power failure the battery takes over
without interruption and without loss of alarm
memory. As the load asked by the modern solid-
state alarm systems is limited, a small size
battery is usually sufficient. In view of
maintenance it might be advantageous to use
totally enclosed batteries for this purpose.
Failure of the power supply to the alarm installation should be properly alarmed, i.e.
should be brought to the attention of the
duty officer without delay. A reliable power
source has to be available for this purpose,
e.g. the ship's emergency batteries if fitted. This alarm should also indicate loss of
power in subdivided circuits of the alarm
system, each protected by individual fuses,and
loss of power to horn and rotating beam light
circuits when not supplied from the common
alarm systems supply. When a battery is used
for supply purposes an alarm should sound at
low battery voltage, indicating charging failure, battery overload or poor battery condition.
It may finally be noted that for obvious reasons
alarm systems are not to combined with machinery
control and safety shut-down systems. In some
instances however this rule cannot be complied
with e.g. where sensing devices have to be
shared by the shut-down and alarm system. This
might be the case for sensors monitoring vibrations, overspeed or axial displacements.

SENSING DEVICES.

The sensor is the primary element in an alarm
system and often considered to be the weakest
link of the chain. If reliable alarm indication
is to be achieved over a long period of time
sensors should give stable and repeatable performance under the unfavourable machinery space
conditions. Practice has shown in many cases
that not all sensors are able to stand up to
this basic requirement. Failures have occurred
due to vibrations, corrosion, ingress of water,
broken connections, etc. For use in alarm systems it is often of more importance that sensors are robust than very accurate. It is
essential that a sensor operates: usually not
whether at 85 or 86°C. For most applications
in alarm systems it will be sufficient when
the performance of switch-type sensors, such
as temperature and pressure switches, complies
with the following figures:
a) Repeatability of actuation and reset values
   within ± 1½% of instrument range.
b) Accuracy of scale calibration within ± 3%
   of instrument range.
c) Accuracy of sensors with fixed settings

within ± 3% of set value.
The switching differential i.e. the difference
between actuation and reset value, should be
sufficiently large to avoid nuisance alarms
due to the measured value of the protected
variable rising and falling around the sensor
set point.
Sensors should have a fast response to changes
in the measured variable, particularly where
scanning alarm systems are used.
It is convenient that sensors of some alarmpoints, such as diesel engine alarms, have
easily adjusted setpoints, as operating levels
cannot always be accurately predicted and re-
adjusting might be necessary during commissioning and initial operation. When selecting
or specifying sensors it might be necessary
to consider the following points:
- range of control point setting.
- accuracy of control point setting and scale
  calibration.
- repeatability of switch action.
- range of switching differential setting.
- maximum and minimum temperature of process
  fluids.
- maximum pressure or vacuum over range.
- corrosion resistance of material in view of
  process fluids.
- mounting, installation and connection facilities.
- contact action and contact rating.
- recommended time between inspection or cali-
  brations.
- effect of vibration and ambient temperature
  upon switching differential and set point.
- response time.
- mechanical protection and type of enclosure.
- results of environmental tests and possible
  other type tests carried out, such as long
  life test, temperature shock test, overpressure test, intrinsic safety test.

However good a sensor may be, satisfactory results will only be obtained when it has been
properly mounted and connected. Good workman-
ship is of utmost importance in this respect.
Where possible, sensors should not be placed
on engines, compressors and similar machinery
liable to give strong vibrations. This applies
particularly to sensors provided with switching
devices or other moving parts. It may further
be remembered that engines are dismantled for
repairs and overhauls and at these occasions
sensors and connecting cables might easily be
damaged. Sensor cables should be mechanically
robust, flexible and provided with an oilre-
sisting sheath. In order to reduce the risk
of having earthfaults it is recommended to
avoid the use of screened cable whenever possible. Cable conductors should not be less
than 0.5 sq. mm. Terminalboxes are to be watertight, including the cable entries and this
point cannot be stressed enough. Sensors should
be effectively immersed in the medium being
monitored and should be sited so that the sensor output is a realistic measure of the condition of the variable.

TESTING.

Fortunately it can be said that many machinery

alarms are never asked to function because their variables monitored stay within safe limits. Other alarms operate at long intervals; only a few operate regularly. But at the moment that whichsoever variable exceeds safe limits, we must be sure that its alarm channel operates correctly. It could be of crucial importance for the safety of the ship or her engine. It has been argued before that to achieve this the installation must be well designed and constructed. And although this is very important it is not sufficient. It is equally important that the alarm system and associated systems are very regularly completely tested. The initial testing of the alarm system is carried out when the ship is being commissioned i.e. during the last week(s) before seatrials and delivery. At that stage enginerooms are usually overcrowded with fitters, painters, electricians and other workers making last minute arrangements. It is probably true to say that many yards look more or less panic-stricken at that time, with overstressed managers fighting to make the scheduled trial and delivery date. It is evident that under such circumstances the conditions for proper testing of such delicate equipment as alarm and monitoring systems are not very good. And yet those installations should be properly and realistically tested. Testing may not be limited to simulating of alarm conditions, e.g. by interrupting closed loop sensor circuits, but pressures, temperatures and other variables should be raised or lowered to operate sensors at correct levels. The following measures might be taken to facilitate testing:

a) To take due account of testing possibilities when selecting and installing sensors, e.g. temperature sensors should be fitted in pockets from which they may easily be removed for testing in a portable test unit. Similarly when pressure sensors are provided with test connections they may easily be tested with a portable pressure testing unit.

b) To provide adequate testing equipment such as portable temperature and pressure testing units.

c) To make a proper test schedule, containing sufficient information and being logically arranged. An example of such testing schedule is shown in fig. 2.

d) To use analogue sensors where possible, particularly for temperatures.

More detailed information concerning testing of alarm installations may be found in the "Standardization Code for Trials and Testing of New Ships" mentioned earlier in this paper. After the ship has been commissioned testing of the alarm installation should be repeated regularly. For this purpose it is essential that a good schedule is on board, with up-to-date information concerning selected alarm levels and tailor made for the concerning machinery plant. Intervals between testing should be specified by the Owner and where applicable by the Authorities responsible for the issue of certificates allowing unattended machinery space operation. The Netherlands Shipping Inspectorate requires e.g. that testing is carried at 4 months intervals and recorded by the ship's staff in a check list specially issued for this purpose.

DECENTRALIZED ALARM SYSTEMS.

All machinery alarm signals are usually led to a controlpanel located in a central controlroom or centrally placed open in the engineroom. This panel contains besides the machinery alarm presentation, various machinery controls, remote gauges and other remote monitoring devices. The Royal Interocean Lines (Koninklijke Java-China Paketvaart Lijnen N.V.) applied on 4 ships of their fleet a different concept. The m.s. " STRAAT NASSAU " and her 3 sisterships built in 1971/2 for operation with an unattended engineroom have been provided with a decentralized alarm system. The layout of this system and some of its panels are shown on figures 3,4 and 5. The system may be described as follows. Three "Group Monitoring Panels" have been fitted in the engineroom, one near the engineroom entrance, one on D-deck and one on floor level. A total of 17 "Local Panels" have been fitted at various locations in the engineroom. Each "Local Panel" monitors a specific engineroom plant or a main engine subsystem. When the duty engineer is summoned to the engineroom for an alarm, he can distinguish on the "Group Monitoring Panel" near the engineroom entrance which plant or subsystem is involved and to which "Local Panel" he should go. On the "Local Panel" the kind of deviation can be determined and only there the alarm can be acknowledged. The "Local Panels" are strategically situated near the controls and gauges of the subject system and adequate action can be taken rapidly. In case the engineroom is not unattended, the "Group Monitoring Panels" at D-deck and engineroom floor serve in case of an alarm to indicate which "Local Panel" is involved. Failures which could directly affect propulsion are presented on the navigating bridge. When an engineer called to the engineroom for an alarm acknowledges this alarm, he automatically switches on the "Engineers Safety Alarm" system. This patrol alarm system needs resetting every 30 minutes and in case the engineer fails to do so, an alarm is energized at the Chief Engineer and on the navigating bridge. This system can also be switched on manually when an engineer enters the engineroom and switched off when he leaves. When an alarm is not acknowledged at its "Local Panel" within a predetermined time a "General Engineer Alarm" system is energized, sounding bells in the engineers accomodation. This alarm can also be triggered at the Group Monitoring Panels when an engineer needs assistance and has no time to telephone one of his fellow engineers. The alarm system to summon the duty engineer is an interesting system on its own. The summon alarm signal is led to socket outlets installed in all officers cabins, messroom, salon, etc. The socket outlets are wired in parallel and the duty engineer has a plug provided with a bell. He can plug the alarm unit in the socket outlet of the cabin or place where he wishes to spend his time and when an alarm occurs the bell will warn him.

This system provides great flexibility for the
duty engineer without annoying anybody else.
The datalogger showed on the general layout is
used for recording refrigerated cargo and liquid cargo temperatures and main- and auxiliary
engines output. It is evident that the price
of a decentralized alarm system as described
above is appreciably higher than of a comparable centralized alarm system. It is equally
evident that such an alarm system concept is
only part of a greater concept, involving the
whole design of the automation and monitoring
of a machinery plant. In such a concept the
machinery installation is built up from independent, separate "units", each provided with
own control equipment and offering to the
engineroom staff a clear arrangement for operation, maintenance and repairs. No central
control panel with remote controls and remote
monitoring equipment needs to be provided and
considerable savings can be made in this area.
For diesel driven ships this design concept
might be attractive, as well from an operational as from an economical viewpoint. For
turbine driven ships with complex steamplants
and many interdependent subsystems and sub-
loops a centralized system is perhaps better
at this stage.

CONCLUSION.

It is hoped that the foregoing will contribute
to a better understanding of the specific
requirements and design concept applicable to
alarm systems for unattended machinery spaces.
It may be expected that in the future a con-
tinuing trend will be seen to systems using
analogue sensors and provided with read-out
facilities. Perhaps alarm lamps will disappear
altogether and be replaced by automatic read-
out of a variable and its value when in alarm
state. On ships designed for real unattended
engineroom operation a shift may perhaps be
seen from centralized to decentralized systems.
More attention has to be paid to testing, particularly to regular routine testing whilst
the ship is in service.

ACKNOWLEDGEMENT.

The following Companies are gratefully thanked
for their cooperation when preparing this paper
and for the permission to reproduce their drawings and illustrations:

N.V. C.S.I. Instrumentatie voor Meet - en Regel-
techniek.
N.V. Koninklijke Nederlandsche Stoomboot Mij.
N.V. Nederlandsche Dok & Scheepsbouw Mij.
N.V. Royal Interocean Lines.

REFERENCES.

Dipl. Ing. Hansjörg Klante:
"Probleme beim Entwurf und Betrieb von Auto-
matische Schiffsmaschinenanlagen"
Schiff und Hafen, Haft 12/1971.

"Association of Ship Technical Societies in
Norway"
"Standardization Code for Trials and Testing
of New Ships".

m.v. " TRIDENT ROTTERDAM "   VOYAGE 11.

Alarms which occurred at sea whilst engineroom was unattended.

<u>OUTWARD BOUND</u>   engineroom unattended 29-5-1972 to 4-6-1972

Date and time	Alarm	Cause
29.5 02.15	exhaust gas boiler high water level.	rolling ship, bad weather.
18.35	evaporator	salinity too high.
30.5 04.00	bilge alarm	lub. oil cooler aux. engine 2, leakage in watercircuit.
4.6 03.10	aux. boiler high water level.	solenoid valve in boiler water supply defective, caused continuous water supply.

<u>HOME BOUND</u>   engineroom unattended 17-6-1972 to 23-6-1972.

18.6 03.10	refrigerated cargo hold 1 temperature bananas too high	alarm temperature switch wrongly adjusted.
19.6 12.15	evaporator	salinity too high
20.6 02.30	low fuel oil pressure for main engine.	irregular pressure in low pressure fuel oil system, presumably due to too much gas in fuel oil bunkered in Maracaibo.
21.6 04.10	low fuel oil pressure for main engine.	as above.
07.00	high temperature domestic refrigerated stores.	doors open for cleaning.
22.6 01.10	bilge alarm	leakage seawater pipe lub. oil cooler aux. engine 2. temporarily repaired.
07.20	bilge alarm	as above
12.20	low pressure fuel valve coolingwater.	defective pressure switch.

FIG. 1

ALARMS OCCURRED DURING A VOYAGE OF

m.v. " TRIDENT ROTTERDAM "

NED. DOK en SCHEEPS-BOUW MIJ. v.o.f. AMSTERDAM	ORDER: 01854. MACH.: VESSEL:	SECTION: PAGE:
DATE:		

Turbo Alternator. Safety Devices and Alarms

	Item.	Setpoint.	Actual.	High.	Low.	Press.		Temp.	Flow.	Speed.	Level.	Alarm.	Shutdown.	Stop.	Start.		DATE.	YARD.	OWNER.	CLASS.
Overspeed.		1360.		X						X			X			Mach.				
,,	S[illegible]3.	1330.		X						X		X								
Lub.oil.	PA.754.	0,35			X	X						X								
H.P. Bearing.	TIA.760.	77		X				X				X								
,,	TS.1692.	82.		X				X					X							
L.P. Bearing.	TIA.762.	77.		X				X				X								
,,	TS.1693.	84.		X				X					X							
Pinion. Aft. Bearing.	TIA.766.	77.		X				X				X								
,, Fwd. ,,	TIA.768.	77.		X				X				X								
Wheel Bearing. Aft.	TIA.770.	77.		X				X				X								
,, ,, Fwd.	TIA.772.	77.		X				X				X								
Generator Bearing. Aft.	TIA.774.	77.		X				X				X								
,, ,, Fwd.	TIA.777.	77.		X				X				X								
Lub.oil. After cooler.	TIA.750.	49.		X				X				X								
Lub.oil.	PS.757.	0,3.			X	X							X							
Lub.oil. Pump.	PS.755.	0,4.			X	X									X					
Governor lub.oil. Pump.	PS.756.	0,4.			X	X									X					
,, ,,	PA.758.	0,3.			X	X						X								
Turning Gear.	XS.773.												X							
Back pressure.	PS.2421.	0,7.		X		X							X							
Sump.	LA.744.	150.			X						X	X								
,,	LA.745.	150.		X							X	X								
Air cooler leakage. Generator.	[illegible]203.			X							X	X								
,, ,, ,,	TIA.20[illegible].	70.		X				X				X								
Glandsteam.	PA.2811.	[illegible],1.			X	X						X								

FIG. 2.

EXAMPLE OF TEST SCHEDULE FOR SAFETY DEVICES AND ALARMS.

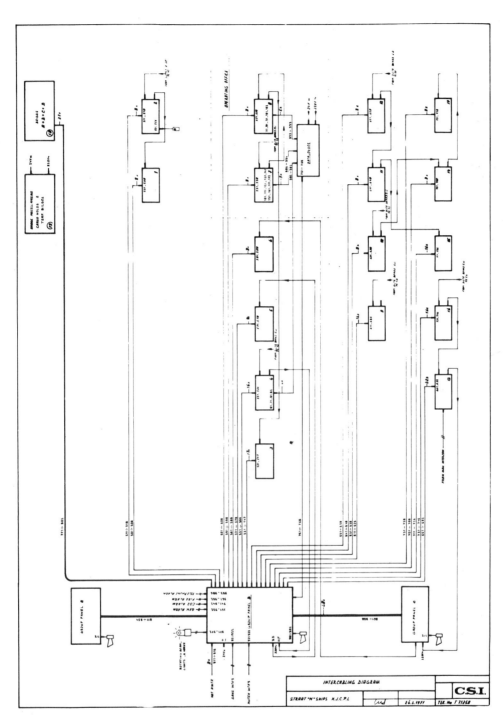

FIG. 3

GENERAL LAYOUT OF DECENTRALIZED
ALARM SYSTEM, SHOWING GROUP
MONITORING PANELS AND LOCAL PANELS.

384

FIG. 4

PHOTOGRAPH SHOWING LOCAL PANEL Nr.15
INSTALLED ÍN THE ENGINEROOM.

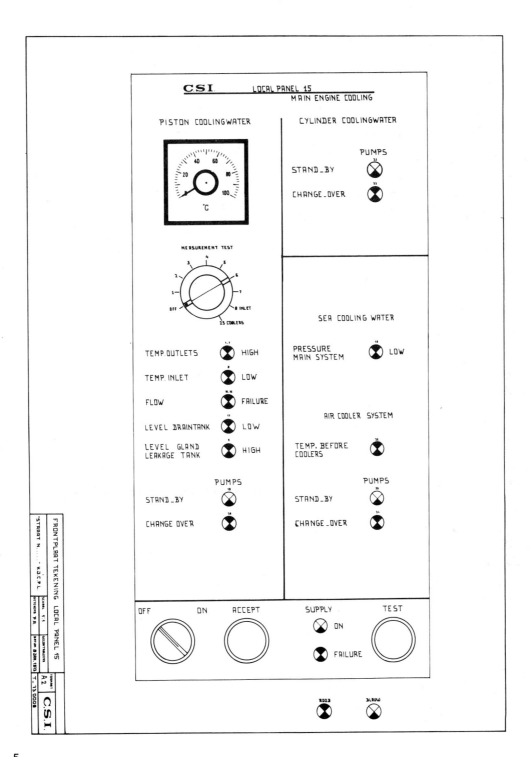

FIG. 5

FRONT OF LOCAL PANEL NR. 15

RESISTANCE THERMOMETERS AND THERMOCOUPLE ASSEMBLIES
FOR SHIP AUTOMATION

Fritz Schwarz
Degussa
Hanau, Germany

Joachim Scholz
Degussa
Hanau, Germany

ABSTRACT

Special standards are required for temperature sensors in the field of ship automation. Typical positions for the application of these sensors are mentioned and basic precautions to maintain the necessary accuracy and reliability are discussed. A selection of proved sensor designs is described and performance data given. Special consideration is given to exhaust gas temperature sensors for Diesel-engines.

1. INTRODUCTION

The use of mechanical operated temperature-measurement devices is more and more limited by the application of electronic measuring and warning systems in ships. Those systems have been proved in practice for years and showed satisfying performance.

In combination with those nowadays reliable systems sensors with a high degree of reliability are needed. For the monitoring of temperatures special designs of resistance thermometers and thermocouples are used. The output of these electrical thermometers is capable for transmission over far distances so that centralized control- and monitoring units are possible.

The advantages of those systems are obvious: The readings are not influenced by subjective errors, the transmission of informations can not be delayed and the necessary reactions can be initiated instantaneously and in most cases automatically.

The praxis of ship automation shows that special high standards are to be set for the systems as well as for the sensors, because of the severe working conditions on ships and the extraordinary requirements for reliability in this field of application.

2. MEASURING POINTS

There is a plurality of equipments on ships to be monitored in respect of temperature in order to avoid expensive damages. Typical positions for the application of temperature sensors are:

2.1 Engines and Power Transmission

Diesel main and auxiliary engines and exhaust gas ducts.

Gas- and steam turbines.

Boilers, steam- and cooling-water-ducts.

Oil- and lubricating-systems.

Stern-bearings.

2.2 Refrigeration Systems

Compressors.

Brine-lines.

Containers.

2.3 Storerooms

Room-temperature.

Air ductings to and from storerooms.

Skin temperatures of liquid-gas-tanks.

2.4 Products

Fruit, meat, grain, liquid-gas.

For all these positions special resistance thermometers and thermocouples have been developed. The special requirements are considered by their design and material selection.

3. BASIC PRINCIPLES OF MEASUREMENT

3.1 Thermocouples

Thermocouples are generating an electromotive force (Emf) between the junction point of two dissimilar metals and their open ends in case of a temperature difference between these two points. The magnitude of the Emf depends upon the selected material combination and the temperature difference between the junction point (hot junction) and the open ends (cold junction or reference junction). For the purpose of temperature measurement the temperature of the reference junction (reference temperature) has to be known and constant.

The main guidelines for the selection of thermocouple materials are:

High differential Emf (μV/°C), good linearity of the Emf-temperature characteristic, constance of calibration over long times, good reproduceability of alloys in mass-production, high melting points and good oxidation resistance.

The most common combinations have been standardized in various national standards in respect to basic values and tolerances.

In the field of marine applications the combinations Ni-Cr/Ni-Al or Fe/Cu-Ni are preferred, for cryogenic temperatures Cu/Cu-Ni as well.

In many cases it is difficult to keep the reference junction at constant temperatures. In this case the junction has to be located at a place with constant room-temperature or within a cold junction compensator. For the connection between thermocouple and cold junction compensating cables are used. The leads of those cables are made of special alloys having the same Emf-temperature characteristic up to 100 °C or 200 °C respectively.

The sensitivity of thermocouples is small compared with resistance thermometers. An average value for base metal thermocouples is 40 μV/°C. Corresponding values for platinum resistance thermometers are 4000 μV/°C and for semiconductor thermometers 400 m$\textbf{V}$/°C. But thermocouples have some significant advantages so that they cannot be replaced by resistance thermometers in any case.

3.2 Resistance Thermometers

Resistance thermometers utilize the effect of change in resistivity by temperature. Metals show an increase of resistivity with increasing temperatures (positive temperature coefficient, ptc). Semiconductor thermometers have generally a negativ temperature coefficient (ntc) in some cases ptc as well.

A rough characterisation of sensitivity of metal resistance thermometers is the temperature coefficient between 0 °C and 100 °C. Metals have in general a nonlinear characteristic but have better linearity than semiconductors.

The temperature coefficient of pure metals is in general higher than of alloys, therefore pure platinum, nickel or copper is used for resistance thermometers.

Though semiconductors have a temperature coefficient some orders of magnitude higher than metals their application is limited by narrow temperature ranges, high nonlinearity,

low stability and wide production tolerances.

Platinum resistance thermometers are operated in the range of -250 to +850 °C, sometimes up to 1000 °C. Nickel is used in the range of -60 to +150 °C, sometimes up to 250 °C, copper is used from -60 to +150 °C. Semiconductors are known for temperature ranges between -270 to +1000 °C, but the maximum range of one type is not more than 250 °C. For the reason of temperature range, stability and accuracy platinum is the most common material for resistance thermometers. In the field of industrial temperature measurement the platinum wires for resistance thermometers are encapsulated or embedded in glass or ceramic insulation materials to give a good mechanical support and protection against environmental influences.

There are various national standards for platinum, nickel and copper resistance thermometers. For platinum more than 80 % of the elements used all over the world have a nominal resistance of 100 Ω and a temperature coefficient of 3,85 x 10^{-3}/°C.

For industrial temperature measurement especially under severe environmental conditions the resistance element with its connection leads has to be supported and protected to give satisfying endurability.

4. SOURCES OF ERRORS IN INDICATION

With electrical thermometers as well as with mechanical operated systems or filled systems it is necessary that some basic requirements have to be met to assure appropriate measuring accuracy. In the following section the electrical aspects of these requirements are discussed.

4.1 Thermocouples

4.1.1 Insulation Resistance

The error created by insufficient insulation resistance between the two legs of the thermocouple can be calculated by the following equation:

$$f_{rel} = \frac{U - E}{E} \times 100 \ (\%) = - \frac{1}{1 + \frac{R_{Ins}}{R_L}} \times 100 \ (\%)$$

with

E   = Electromotive force at the hot junction of thermocouple.

U   = Voltage at the terminals of the measuring instrument.

R_L = Internal resistance of the thermocouple.

R_{Ins} = Insulation resistance between the two legs of the thermocouple. (Can only be measured with an open hot junction.)

This equation is valid only under the assumtion

of a zero-current measurement (compensating method or high input resistance of instrument) and a constant and known reference temperature. The error is always negativ, i.e. the lower the insulation resistance is in comparison to the internal resistance, the lower is the measured voltage U. The insulation resistance acts as a ballast resistor parallel to the Emf.

4.1.2 Correct Selection and Polarity of compensation and extension leads

The use of incorrect compensation leads and/or in wrong polarity leads to significant errors. Table I shows the amounts of error with a temperature difference between the junction thermocouple-compensation leads and the reference junction of 50 °C.

Thermo-couple	Compensating leads for	Polarity	Error in indication $\approx$ (°C)
Fe/Cu-Ni	Ni-Cr/Ni-Al	correct	− 10
	Pt-Rh/Pt	"	− 40
Ni-Cr/Ni-Al	Fe/Cu-Ni	correct	+ 20
	Pt-Rh/Pt	"	− 40
Pt-Rh/Pt	Fe/Cu-Ni	correct	+210
	Ni-Cr/Ni-Al	"	+150
Fe/Cu-Ni	Ni-Cr/Ni-Al	incorrect	− 80
	Pt-Rh/Pt	"	− 50
Ni-Cr/Ni-Al	Fe/Cu-Ni	incorrect	−110
	Pt-Rh/Pt	"	− 60
Pt-Rh/Pt	Fe/Cu-Ni	incorrect	−280
	Ni-Cr/Ni-Al	"	−220

4.1.3 Controlled Reference Temperatures

The reference junction can be located within a small temperature-controlled room. This room can either be heated or refrigerated. With the heated oven version the reference temperature has to be heigher than the maximum room temperature. For industrial purposes this temperature is 50 °C for general. With the refrigeration method the temperature is 0 °C.

Another possibility is the electrical bridge method:

This method usually employs a self-compensating electrical bridge network. This system incorporates a temperature sensitive resistance element which is in one leg of the bridge network and thermally integrated with the cold junction. The bridge is usually energized from a stable d.c. power source. The output voltage

is proportional to the unbalance created between the pre-set equivalent reference temperature and the hot junction. In this system, the reference temperature may be chosen within a wide range.

Are controlled reference temperatures not available, the influence of the actual cold junction temperature may be corrected by means of the following equation:

$$f_v = c(t_r - t_v)$$

f_v = Error in °C.

t_v = Actual cold junction temperatur measured with a mercury thermometer for instance.

t_r = Reference temperature to which the reference table is referred or the measuring instrument is adjusted.

c = Correction factor depending upon the type of thermocouple and the temperature range. For most cases it is sufficient to select a factor of 1 for base-metal and 0.5 for precious-metal thermocouples.

4.1.4 Errors Created by Electrical or Magnetic Pick-up

Those errors have to be considered especially in combination with measuring instruments in corporating electronic amplifiers and with digital computers. Those errors can be avoided by sufficient guarding of thermocouples, compensating- and connection-cables. This guarding is made by metal braidings or foils. Additional to this it is recommended to twist the single leads of a cable with at least 20 turns per meter.

4.2 Resistance Thermometers

4.2.1 Besides the accuracy of the resistance element itself — which is not to be discussed here — the most important source of errors is the insulation resistance. The requirements for insulation resistance with resistance thermometers are in general higher than with thermocouples. The total resistance of the resistance thermometer consists of the temperature dependent resistance of the element and the insulation resistances of the internal connection leads and the connection cable according to the equation:

$$\frac{1}{R_T} = \frac{1}{R_e} + \frac{1}{R_{i1}} + \frac{1}{R_{i2}} + \frac{1}{R_{in}}$$

with

R_T = Total resistance.

R_e = Resistance of the element.

$R_i \ldots$ = Insulation resistances.

It is recommended that the total insulation resistance in a 100 Ω-resistance thermometer should not be less than 100 MΩ.

4.2.2 An exact balancing of the resistances of the connection leads is very important as well. The connection leads are resistors in series to the element. In the 2-wire connection they have to be considered in the reading of the instrument. Most instruments have an internal correction for a fixed value of connection-lead resistance. A balance resistor representing the difference between the fixed value of the instrument and the actual connection lead resistance has to be inserted into the measuring circuit. As the connection lead itself has a temperature coefficient it is necessary for the connection lead resistance to be limited. Where a high length of connection cable is required or where it is exposed to high temperatures and high temperature variations a 3-wire or 4-wire connection or 2-wire connection with compensating loop is recommended to eliminate the influence of the resistance variations of the connection cables.

If high accuracies are required, for instance with temperature measurements in refrigerated cargos these connections are necessary even for shorter lengths of cables.

5. DESIGN OF RESISTANCE THERMOMETERS AND THERMOCOUPLES FOR VARIOUS APPLICATIONS

5.1 For Temperature Measurements in Products of Refrigerator- or Fruit-Ships

By careful multipoint monitoring of temperatures in products local temperature rises or insufficient refrigeration can be detected. This is necessary to avoid waiste of products or self-ignition of grain for instance. These sensors are affected by severe mechanical working conditions. So they have to be of robust design and 100 % water-proof. Figure 3 shows two service-proved embodiments of sensors for temperature measurements within the cargo. One type is to be placed within bulk material or between solid pieces or boxes. The other type has the element located at the tip of a solid needle and is to be inserted into products as meat or fruits. In respect to the required accuracies for this application ($+ 0,10$ °C in a temperature range of -20 to $+20$ °C) only resistance thermometers in a special grade can be used. The elements (Pt 100 Ω or 2 x 100 Ω) are housed within metal sheaths. In one case this sheath is covered completely by a solid layer of rubber. This insures a water-proof encapsulation and gives a suitable mechanical rigidity. In the case of the insertion type only the handle of the thermometer is covered by rubber. For these sensors often cable lengths up to 15 m are required. Therefore it is necessary to provide the sensors with 4-wire, 3-wire or 2-wire connection with compensating loop.

To avoid a measurable self heating of the sensors the power-dissipation has to be limited. The recommended maximum current is 3 mA.

5.2 Resistance Thermometers for the Measurement of Air Temperatures in Storage Rooms or Air Ducts

The temperature control of the cargo is closely connected to a good control of air temperature in the storage rooms. Sensors for this application are not only required to have a high grade of accuracy but also a very low response time to achieve a good control performance.

This leads to designs of resistance thermometers whose elements are exposed to the air directly or covered by a very thin sheath only.

Fig. 4 shows two embodiments of those sensors, one type having a perforated protection tube which is suitable for temperature measurements within air ducts. The design allows for a variation of insertion length in the range of 75 and 150 mm. The mounting thread has the size of R 1/2".

The other type is designed for wall-mounting in the storage rooms.

Inspite of the poor conditions for heat transmission in this application these sensors have a response time $T_{0,2} = 10$ sec or a time constant of 40 sec.

The selected materials (stainless steels, seawater resistant bronze or suitable surface protections) assure a sufficient corrosion resistance for the given working and storage conditions.

The accuracy is equivalent to the types for in-cargo-measurement, as well as the precautions to assure this accuracy as there are kind of connection, maximum current.

5.3 Sensors for the Temperature Measurement in Refrigeration-, Cooling-Water-, Oil- and Lubricating Systems

For this application small and rigid types of resistance thermometers or thermocouples are used. Fig. 5 shows two preferred embodiments for this field. The sensors consist of a protection tube with a mounting thread R 1/2" and have insertion lengths between 50 and 250 mm and - what is a strict requirement for this application - have exchangeable inserts. One type has its connection cable undetachable fixed to the inset, the other type has terminals within an aluminium connection head which allows a removal of the connection cable. The fixed cable has the advantage of higher vibration and corrosion resistance, what means better reliability but the cable length has to be prespecified.

The termination of the cable within the connection head and the sealing of the head has to be made carefully by skilled personal.

Besides conventional screw-type terminals nowadays corrosion resistant plug-type terminals as known from aircraft- and automobil-production are used.

The selected materials for protecting tubes, bronzes or stainless steel for instance are corrosion resistant in sea-water, refrigerants, oil and boiler water. The small dimensions and the good heat transmission behaviour of the thermometers give time constants in water for resistance thermometers of 35 sec and for thermocouples of 25 sec.

The maximum current for resistance thermometers is 10 to 15 mA.

These figures show the excellent performance of these sensor for control purposes.

5.4 Another important application is the monitoring of bearing temperatures in the field of mechanical power-transmission, especially the stern-bearings. The unapproachable location of this measuring point forces an excessive reliability of the sensors as an exchange is not possible without removing important parts of the transmission system. For this purpose resistance thermometers are used as well as thermocouples. Both types are either mineral insulated thermocouples or mineral insulated cables. The outside diameter is 3 mm in general, at the tip a resistance thermometer element or the hot junction of the thermocouple is located. These sensors are flexible or bendable over the whole length so that they can be formed to any suitable shape and such can easily be mounted within the bearing structure. Sometimes they have to be led through the oil reservoir by means of pressure tight screwings. The sheath is stainless steel, the internal leads for resistance thermometers are made of materials with extremely low temperature coefficient. The actual resistance of the internal leads is very accurate measured during production and labeled to each thermometer, so that an accurate correction is possible.

5.5 Sensors with similar dimensions and identical design are used as well for temperature measurements within liquid-gas tanks or for the monitoring of wall temperatures of these tanks. The sensors often have lengths of more than 30 m. Sometimes a penetration through the tank cover is necessary. For this purpose swage-lock screwings made of stainless steels gave best results. With this screwings it is possible to have a multitude of pressure tight penetrations on a relative small area. To fix the elements at the tank walls special supporting elements are used. With the extraordinary length of the sensors it is recommended for thermocouples to use measuring instruments with the zero-current method and for resistance thermometers a 4- or 3-wire connection.

The mineral insulated cables should be installed parallel to the internal structures or walls of the tanks with a minimum distance to avoid wear of the cables due to vibrations generated by the fluid movements.

5.6 Exhaust Gas Temperature Measurement in Diesel-engines

Concerning the reliability of sensors this is the most critical temperature measurement in the field of marine applications.

5.6.1 Working Conditions

Sensors for this application (resistance thermometers and thermocouples) are operated under the most severe environmental conditions which have to be considered by their design.

5.6.1.1 Temperature Conditions

Maximum working temperatures are about 750 °C, what requires the selection of heat resistant materials. During the start operation of the engine the sensors are subjected to thermal shocks what may lead to significant stress gradiants within the structure of the sensor.

5.6.1.2 Vibration

The gas flow at the position of the sensor (behind the outlet valve or -slot) is intermittant with very rapid changes in velocity and pressure. The magnitude of the vibration- or shock-stresses depends upon the design of the engine and the speed of rotation. In 4-stroke engines the stresses on the sensor are higher than in 2-stroke engines in general. In high-speed auxiliary engines the stresses are higher than in low-speed main engines, but in some cases it has been found that in low-speed engines - especially during start or reverse operations - damages of sensors occured.

The mounting position of the sensor is of special significance for the vibration- or shock stresses. Nowadays the sensors are mounted transvers to the flow direction. This may be the best solution concerning the engine design, but it leads to maximum vibration stresses. If it was possible to insert the stem of the sensor mainly parallel to the flow direction the main part of the problems could be avoided.

The determination of the actual accelerations at the sensors tip during operation is a severe problem and not yet been solved sufficiently.

From literature and other communications acceleration peak values up to 200 g are known, but not yet ascertained. Because of this incertainity the ship classification companies up to now were not able to give generally valid test specifications for exhaust gas temperature sensors.

5.6.1.3 The protection tubes of the sensors are subjected to corrosion- and erosion-attack, giving special requirements to material selection.

5.6.1.4 All parts of the sensor outside the gas duct as connection cables and connection heads may be subjected to severe radiant heating from hot engine parts.

5.6.1.5 Furthermore all outside parts of the sensors are subjected to chemical attacks by fuel, oil or detergents.

5.6.2 Design

In Fig. 6 are some proved types of exhaust gas temperature sensors shown. They are produced as thermocouples and resistance thermometers without changes in the external dimensions. Exchangeable insets have been proved to be preferable. One type has a mounting thread of R 1/2" and a maximum insertion length of 100 mm, another type has R 3/4" and a maximum insertion length of 160 mm. For both types pockets are made either with fixed or various insertion length. A third type has a weld-in pocket with prolonged lagging length for use in main steam pipes of steam turbines. With the first two types nearly all Diesel-engines can be equiped.

All cable connections are not detachable to achieve a better vibration resistance. The connection cables can be either stranded wires with PTFE-insulation and outer metal braiding or mineral insulated cable with stainless steel sheath. Mineral insulated cables have higher temperature resistance, are entirely moisture proof and corrosion resistant. This is of importance whenever the cables are subjected to extraordinary environments, for instance behind radiation shields. PTFE cables have working temperatures up to 250 °C and have sufficient corrosion resistance for most cases of applications. They are more flexible than mineral insulated cables and have therefore higher vibration resistance and they are more economic. However it must be considered that a moisture proof sealing between PTFE cable and the sensor especially under the severe environmental conditions on marine engines may cause some difficulties.

The internal design of the sensors assures that the insets are able to endure thermal strains without damage and do not lift from the bottom of the pocket bore even under the maximum longitudinal accelerations.

5.6.3 Reliability Tests

The actual working conditions in respect to vibration and shock can not be reproduced in laboratory even if they were known. However to achieve comparable criterions for the reliability of those sensors tests with sinussodial vibrations are conducted. With mechanical agitated test devices it is not possible to reach the accelerations and frequencies to damage the sensors. Therefore the tests only can be conducted with electromagnetic agitated devices or "shakers". With these devices frequencies up to 10.000 cps and accelerations up to 300 g are reached. For the testing of exhaust gas temperature sensors a frequency of 2500 cps has proven to be reasonable. At this frequency it is possible to agitate the mass of the sensor to accelerations up to 200 g. During test the sensor is heated by an electrical heated furnace. A test temperature 120 % of the maximum working temperature is chosen.

For the test the sensor is fixed to a rigid jig at its mounting thread. The jig is agitated by the shaker.

Tests with resistance thermometers showed a survival probability of about 50 % with 720 °C, 100 g, 2500 cps and 3 h test duration.

With 720 °C, 80 g, 2500 cps and 3 h duration a survival probability of 100 % was reached.

The cause of damage in all cases was an open circuit within the inset.

With thermocouples up to now it was not possible to cause any damage under the given test conditions.

392

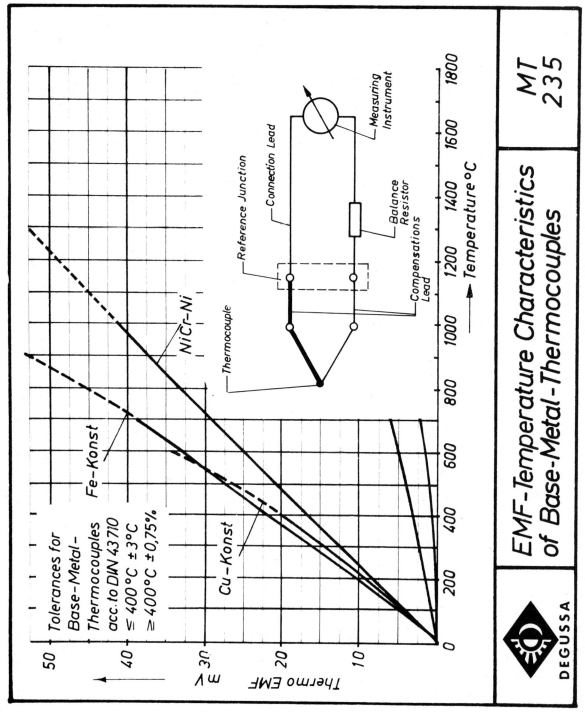

Fig. 1

EMF-Temperature Characteristics of Base-Metal-Thermocouples

MT 235

DEGUSSA

393

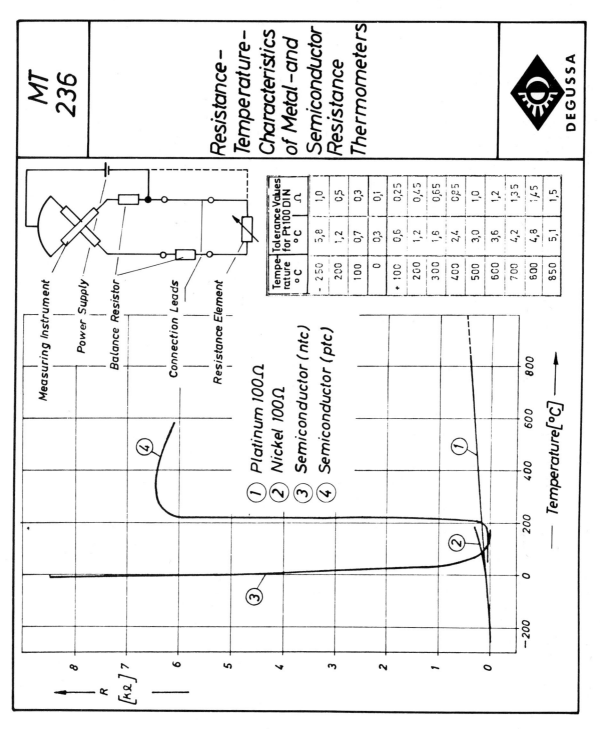

Tempe-rature °C	Tolerance Values for Pt100 DIN °C	Ω
− 250	5,8	1,0
200	1,2	0,5
100	0,7	0,3
0	0,3	0,1
+ 100	0,6	0,25
200	1,2	0,45
300	1,6	0,65
400	2,4	0,85
500	3,0	1,0
600	3,6	1,2
700	4,2	1,35
800	4,8	1,45
850	5,1	1,5

MT 236

Resistance–Temperature–Characteristics of Metal–and Semiconductor Resistance Thermometers

DEGUSSA

Measuring Instrument
Power Supply
Balance Resistor
Connection Leads
Resistance Element

① Platinum 100Ω
② Nickel 100Ω
③ Semiconductor (ntc)
④ Semiconductor (ptc)

— Temperature [°C] —

R [kΩ]

Fig. 2

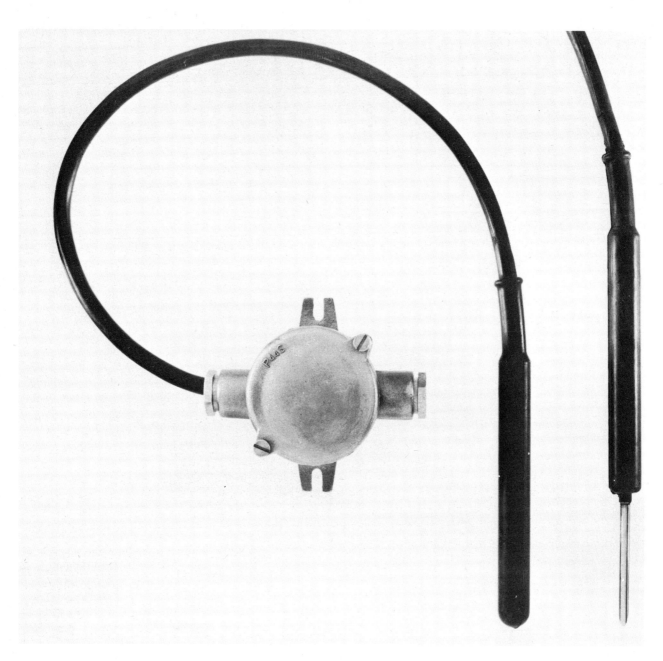

Fig. 3:   Resistance Thermometer for Temperature Measurements
within the Cargo

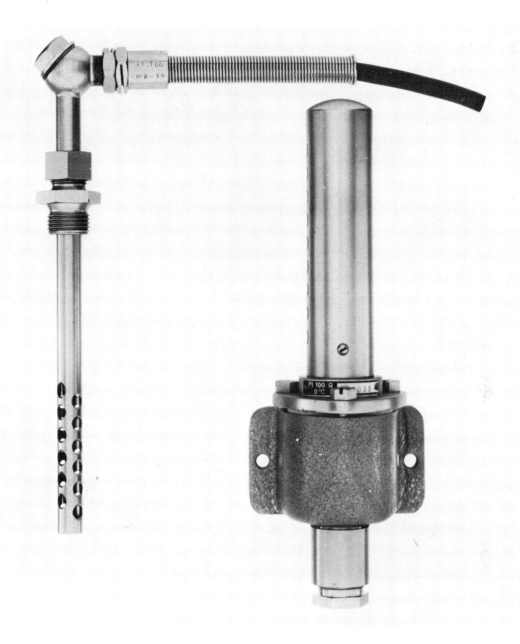

Fig. 4:   Resistance Thermometers for Temperature Measurements
           in Storerooms and Air Ducts

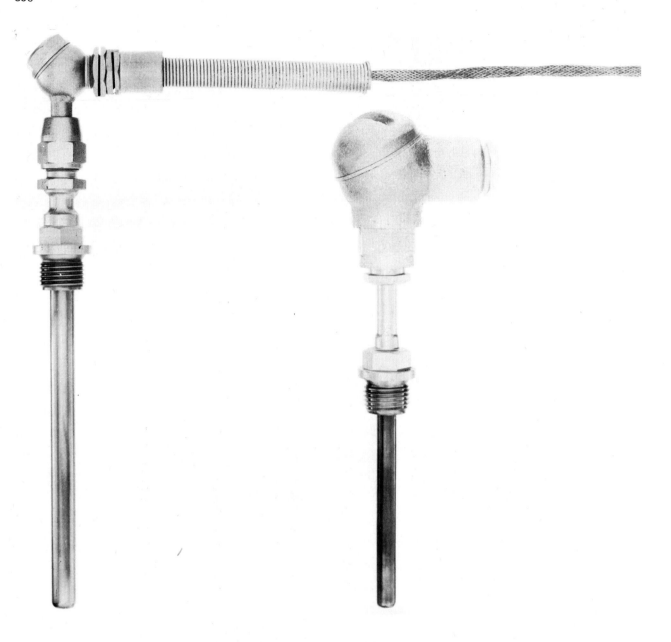

Fig. 5: Resistance Thermometers or Thermocouples for Temperature
         Measurements in Refrigeration-, Cooling-Water-, Oil-
         and Lubricating Systems

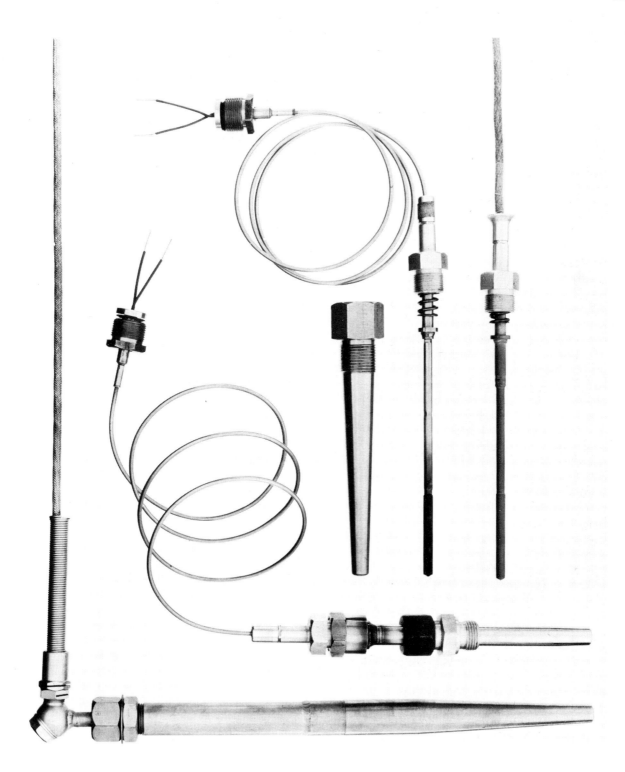

Fig. 6: Resistance Thermometers and Thermocouples for Exhaust
Gas Temperature Measurements in Diesel-Engines

COMPUTERIZED CARGO HANDLING ON LARGE TANKERS

L Sten, M El Eng
Kockums Mekaniska Verkstads AB
Malmoe   Sweden

INTRODUCTION

Transportation of oil and other liquids has grown rapidly during the last years due to the increasing demands for energy in industrialized countries. The units for transportation have grown continuously. Today leading ship-yards of the world are producing very large crude oil carriers (VLCC) with transport capacities exceeding a quarter of a million tons. The trend is pointing towards vessels with transport capacities of up to one million ton deadweight.

Ships of this size become difficult and intricate to handle. Every precaution must be taken to prevent disasters such as oil pollution.

The cargo handling automation is specific for each ship. The type of cargo, the type of ship and the type of harbour affect distinctly the automation equipment design.

During the cargo handling the ship cannot be regarded as an autonomous unit - the ship is dependent on harbour facilities and jurisdiction. These seem to be the main reasons for the present focussing on Engine Room and Bridge automation.

There are, however, outstanding advantages to be gained by automation of cargo handling activities.

Some important features are:-

(i)   Improved safety for ship, crew, cargo and environment,
(ii) Time savings in port,
(iii) Only a few persons required for cargo-handling.

Centralized control and monitoring from a Cargo Control Room is well known. Remote level readings, remote cargo pump control are implemented in the majority of modern VLCC's built today.

The Cargo-Handling System in the 'Sea Sovereign'

The Swedish turbine tanker 'Sea Sovereign' is one example of a ship with a fully automated cargo-handling system. The system is part of a ship-borne process computer project work sponsored by the Swedish Ship Research Foundation (SSF).

The development work was carried out by Kockums Mekaniska Verkstads AB in Malmö. The 'Sea Sovereign', a 210,000 ton crude carrier was built by Kockums and delivered to the Salén Shipping Co in Stockholm in November 1969. The computer system has been in use since her maiden voyage.

The first automated loading of the ship was carried out in the Persian Gulf in 1970, using a program designed to load and discharge cargo of one gravity in a set sequence.

It was quickly discovered that the ship normally would carry cargo of one gravity only was an incorrect assumption. More than 50 percent of the voyages entailed two or three types of cargo. During these voyages, the system could not be used to full advantage.

The program was expanded in 1972 to allow four different types of cargo. The ship was loaded by this system in December 1972.

System Description

A Control Data 1700 process computer with a 28 k core memory is used on board the 'Sea Sovereign'. The computer equipment is installed in the Engine Control Room and connected to typewriters in the Cargo Control Room and in the Wheelhouse.

The tank lay-out of the 'Sea Sovereign' is shown in Figure 1.

The computer reads the levels from 25 cargo, ballast and bunker tanks. It can automatically control 52 hydraulic valves and senses the position of further 86 manually operated valves. New positions of these valves can be ordered via a typewriter or by the program. Four cargo pumps are controlled and the pumping is optimized by the computer.

During the cargo-handling the computer controls the levels in each individual tank. On reaching the set ullage value in a tank, the valve to this tank is closed automatically.

The cargo-handling program is built up in modules, see Figure 2. Every module works independent of other programs.

There are possibilities to off-set the action of the computer and perform parts of the cargo-handling manually. If a certain component, for instance a valve, should not work satisfactorily, the operator can control such a component manually.

The conditions are monitored by a specific program which controls to which extent every tank shall be discharged or loaded. The supervision program can order changes of valve positions and of pump speeds.

It should be strongly emphasized that the computer will assist the crew when loading and discharging the ship. Naturally the Master is still responsible for the cargo-handling, but the computer warrants a rapid and safe operation.

Computer-Controlled Pumping

Each of the four cargo pumps on board the 'Sea Sovereign' has a capacity of 4,500 cubic meter/hour when operated on the top of the pump characteristic without cavitation.

The computer controls the pump speeds by means of a programmed proportional and integrating control. Appropriate pump speeds can be set either by the program or by the operator.

The computer also controls the discharge valves on the pressure side of the pumps, thus decreasing the risk of cavitation.

The hazardous moment occurs at stripping when air may enter the pipe system and ruin the pumps. To prevent this separators are installed ahead of the pumps. Separator level signals are used to govern the position of the discharge valve.

Level Gauging - the Most Critical Subsystem

As a rule, the most difficult problem to solve is level gauging. The levels in critical tanks shall be measured with:-

(i) Good accuracy,
(ii) Good reliability.

It is highly essential that the information regarding each tank level is correct. During a topping-up sequence this is a necessity. Over-filling could mean disaster. To prevent this, an accuracy of one or two inches would be sufficient.

In order to calculate satisfactorily volume and weight of the contents in each tank the accuracy must be enhanced. Each inch might mean a weight error of about 50 ton. These errors will of course affect the stress calculations and the trim calculation. Errors of the order of one inch might be tolerated.

The level gauging system must be highly reliable. If there is a level reading error this must be indicated immediately. The 'Sea Sovereign' computer program is capable of continuously monitoring the level gauging system, giving alarm in case of a suspected failure.

Even if the indication of level gauging errors with the computer system has proved very useful, no effort should be saved to choose the best level gauging system. Critical tanks should have redundant level gauges. The system should also be able to read levels when at sea during tank washing and ballast handling.

On-Line Stress Calculations

Improper cargo distribution may damage the vessel seriously. Stresses are most severe in rough weather with heavy seas such that the distance between wave-crests is about equal to the ship's length. If the ship is imperfectly loaded, severe shear forces and bending moments are likely to occur in calm weather also.

The hull is designed to withstand certain stresses. If the ship is unsuitable loaded, exceptional stresses can cause cracks in the hull. In extreme cases the ship may break in two. Improper loading will in any case shorten the life of the ship.

Hence it is most essential to calculate shear forces and bending moments in the hull correctly.

The stresses can be continuously and automatically calculated by the cargo-handling computer.

The characteristics of the ship is programmed into the computer. Levels which change during the cargo-handling can be obtained by means of the process input acquisition program.

The levels are transformed to volume and by multiplication of the specific gravity at the actual temperature, the weight in each tank is obtained.

Weight of stores, fresh water, lubrication oil etc, which do not change during the cargo-handling, can be fed in by means of the general communication unit.

Using this information, buoyance and trim is calculated.

The measured draft and trim is compared with the theoretical figures and an unacceptable difference causes alarm.

The shear forces are obtained by integrating the load distribution, and the bending moments are obtained by integrating the shear forces.

An unpermissible shear force or bending moment will also cause an alarm and action may be taken by the operator.

The results from the stress calculations can be typed out on the typewriter whenever the operator wishes. Program outputs are shown in Figure 3.

The stresses can also be displayed on instruments showing the operator, for instance, if any of the stresses is increasing rapidly, thus enabling him to take the necessary action.

Automatic Trim and List Control

During loading and discharging the trim must be
kept within certain limits. On emptying the tanks
the ship shall normally be trimmed by the stern
because the suction pipes are placed in the aft
ends of the cargo tanks. The loaded ship shall
often be trimmed at even keel and with no list.

The computer program is designed to take care of
these cases.

Loading and Discharging Simulation

The operator decides the boundary conditions for
loading or discharging and feeds these into the
computer by means of a conversational program.
The computer checks the conditions for inconsisten-
cy and prepares the program. If required, the
operator can simulate the loading/discharging
process in a time scale speeded up ten times and
off-line the process. The computer will run
through the programs and print out which valves
will be opened or closed.

On exceeding the set limits for stresses and
draught, an alarm is given. Thus the operator
can follow the program and train himself in
handling the system.

Experiencies from the Try-Out Phase

The cargo-handling system on board the 'Sea
Sovereign' has been in use since 1970. The ship
has been loaded and discharged by computer control
approximately 15 times.

The average saving of time amounts to 2 hours per
loading and discharging compared to conventional
centralized cargo-handling.

The saving of time is due to swift topping-up of
the tanks and to rapid and efficient pumping.

At the end of the loading virtually all tanks will
be full simultaneously. The First Officer will
therefore slow down the flow of oil from ashore in
order to be able to top-up one tank at a time.
The computer can top-up all the tanks simultaneously. Automatic alarm at suspected level gauge
failures improves the safety.

Another benefit is that the system permits the
simulation of loading and discharging during the
voyage tand to check intermediate results of
stresses and trim. This means also possibilities
for the operator to handle the equipment without
danger.

The saving of time when discharging depends mainly
on optimized cargo-pump control and more efficient
stripping of the tanks.

Topping-up accuracy, continuous control of
critical valves and continuous stress calculations all aim towards improved safety for ship
and environment.

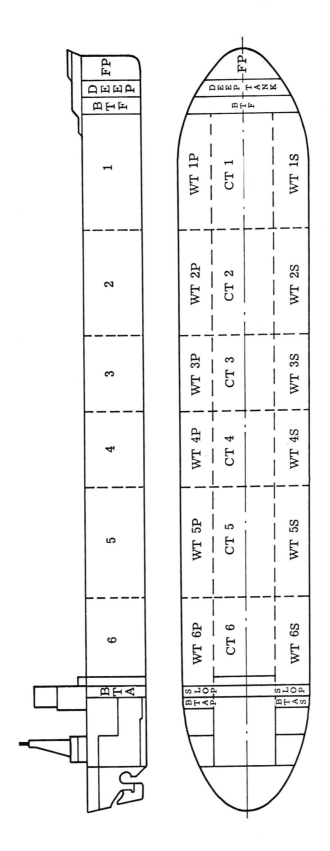

FIGURE 1   TANK LAY-OUT FOR T T SEA SOVEREIGN

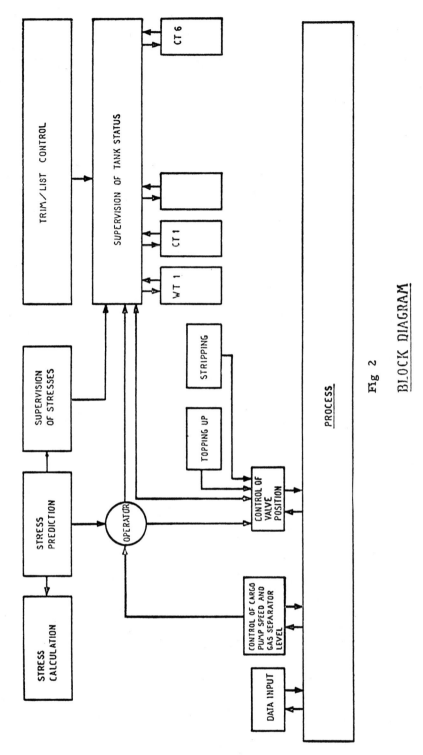

Fig 2

BLOCK DIAGRAM

COMPUTERISED CARGO HANDLING WITH DIFFERENTIATED CARGO

KOCKUMS

MEKANISKA VERKSTADS AB MALMÖ · SWEDEN

Our Dept. and contactman

Document

Date

Page No.

Reference of document
633 H 698

Addressee/Subject

Figure 3. Stress Calculation Output

11.52 Stress Calculation

Sect	Shear Force		Bend Moment	
Nr	LT	Perc	LT M	Perc
3	-8944	-95	-95100	-42
4	-3651	-37	-289100	-72
5	-1157	-10	-332300	-70
6	2913	35	-307500	-65
7	5022	55	-185300	-39
8	-5059	-44	-185900	-39
9	-1377	-13	-268500	-57
10	2111	20	-260900	-65
11	6527	62	-61400	-26

Draft   57.3   Feet Fore 63.9 Feet Aft

Trim   6.6 feet

DW   207997 LT

11.53 Load Condition

Tank	Volume	Weight	Type
	US BBL	LT	
WT2P	88780	11715	01
WT2S	88440	11670	01
WT5P	91080	12018	01
WT5S	91030	12011	01
WT3P	1580	260	BA
WT3S	2560	420	BA
CT3	108570	14613	02
CT5	159660	21488	02
CT6	108720	14633	02
WT1P	86840	11688	02
WT1S	86210	11603	02
CT1	129650	17108	01
CT2	162420	21432	01
WT6P	50960	6725	01
WT6S	50940	6723	01
BTF	930	153	BA
BTAC	00	0	BA
BTAP	90	15	BA
BTAS	90	15	BA
CT4	206520	27794	02
DEEP	14740	2163	BU
BUAP	9970	1465	BU
BUAS	9970	1465	BU
SLPP	1720	232	02
SLPS	150	21	02

DRAFT   57.4 Feet Fore   63.9 Feet Aft
TRIM   6.5 Feet
DW   208041 LT

WHAT ARE THE BENEFITS
OF COMPUTERIZED LOAD CALCULATION ?

R.T. Karlsen

NORSK A/S PHILIPS
Oslo, Norway

ABSTRACT

The safety of a ship is dependent upon proper distribution of the cargo. Load planning is therefore an important task for
ship officers. However, it can be a time
consuming task, and various aids for speed-
ing up and simplifying the operation have
been devised.

The paper discusses the benefits that are
attainable when applying the most recent
device, the computerized load calculator,
to load planning on tankers.

INTRODUCTION

In the early days of oil transport at sea
the oil was carried in barrels and cans on
board ordinary cargo vessels. Later on the
specially designed tanker came into use.
Since then the construction of these ships
has undergone a rapid progress.

To meet the world's demand for oil, the
size of these ships has constantly been
increased towards the mammoth tankers of
to-day.

As experience indicates that hull damage
or loss of ship are closely related to the
distribution of cargo, it is an absolute
necessity that the persons operating these
ships have extensive knowledge of how to
distribute the load. Because of uneven
distribution of forces caused by displacement and the weight of ship and cargo at
various points along the hull, severe
stresses may occur. These stresses are
caused by shear forces and bending moments. They are induced in calm waters,
and naturally they may become greater in
heavy seas.

Rapid loading is essential for economic
reasons. Then - without carrying out the
lengthy calculations required to ascertain an acceptable load distribution, how
can the ship officers determine which is
the most suitable load distribution in a
specific case ?

AVAILABLE AIDS FOR LOAD/STRESS CALCU-
LATIONS

There is a selection of practical aids in
solving the problem of load distribution.
There are various manual calculators, and
more recently computerized calculators.

The object of this paper is to discuss
the benefits of the latter type of calculator. These benefits will in practice be
relative to benefits achieved by devices
of the former type and at least a brief
look at the capabilities of manual load
calculators must be included.

Today's conventional load calculators are
built on an analogue principle, and may
be electrical or mechanical. The fixed
data concerning the construction of the
ship are permanently stored in the calculator. The operator supplies the variable
data, i.e. the cargo weight proposed for
each tank by positioning the input controls. By adjusting other controls the
operator now can read various information
of the loading condition. The main object
of these calculators is to determine hull
stresses. Hence, shear forces and bending
moments can be read, also draught and
trim. Beyond that, the various types
differ.

Without detracting from the value of these
calculators, it is evident that they have
limitations. For practical reasons, the
number of sections into which the ship is
divided, must be limited, which influences
the accuracy of stress computations. The
accuracy of input and output data depends
upon the operator's exactness when reading the various scales.

The ease of operation will vary with the
complexity of the device so that a type
with many worthwhile features is too time-
consuming for a busy loading officer. This
is connected with the inability of the de-

vice to store a situation and accept modifications to it. Some simpler devices appear to have the necessary flexibility in this respect, but fall short in total facilities.

In order to approach a computerized version of this instrument, we shall take a short glance on a general routine which is followed by the cargo officer when he is planning the loading of his ship. The load plan will vary from ship to ship, depending upon the type of charter, but in general the course of action shown in Figure 1, is followed.

POSSIBLE NEW METHODS

Turning to a computerized load calculator system, it seems necessary to distinguish between:

- On-line control of load/unload process
- Off-line load calculation

On-line remote control of cargo oil handling has been adopted by some ships.

In such a system the valve operation and pump control for cargo oil handling are automated. All tank levels, the position of valves, discharge pressures of cargo and stripping pumps are monitored in a centralized control room. All information is fed to the computer which decides the action to be taken, hence gives the output commands to the control devices.

This kind of direct control of loading/unloading is considered the coming thing. However, it calls for a comprehensive instrumentation, some of which particularily accurate level sensors are under development. It also requires a standard of loading equipment, piping and valves, higher than what is required for manual operation.

The economical aspects of such an installation is beyond the scope of this paper.

We shall here take a look at a computerized load calculator which does not exercise any action upon the load/unload process itself. Our reference is a system designed for load planning on board the M/T "BERGE FISTER".

SYSTEM REQUIREMENTS FOR A COMPUTERIZED LOAD CALCULATOR

Observing the instructions given by the classification society, Det norske Veritas, on how to load and handle the vessel we decided to design a tool for accurate and quick calculation with respect to economy (ullage, speed) and safety (hull stresses). With this in mind we arrived at the following main requirements:

- To handle up to four different types of cargo at the same time,
- To present ullage in each tank with weight as input,
- To present weight of each tank with ullage as input,
- To present the utilization of tank capacity,
- To present draught forward, aft and midship as well as trim modified by computation of total deflection due to bending moments, shear forces and temperature differences between keel and deck.
- To check draught forward against minimum draught to prevent slamming,
- To compute bending moments and shear forces in such a manner that an accurate stress curve can be presented,
- To compute the degree of propeller submersion,
- To check all computed values against given pre-set limits.

In addition to these requirements there was an absolute demand that input to the computer programme was simple and that incorrect data given by the operator should easily be detected and rectified.

Finally, it should be easy to try alternative load distributions and see which effect this would have on the complete load plan.

LOADCHECK

Figure 2 shows the main structure of our computerized load calculator called "LOADCHECK".

The programme LUP, which is operated under control of a real-time monitor, is scheduled for execution on request from the operator. LUP consists of two parts: One part handles the input from the operator, computes and presents ullage, weight and degree of utilization for each load compartment. Required inputs are: Weight or ullage for each tank to be loaded, specific weight, temperature and coefficient of expansion. For the stress computation temperature difference between keel and deck is necessary.

The main supervision routine detects operator commands, checks presence and validity of actual parameters and controls the execution of relevant routines.

The second part, which is the stress-calculator of the system, can now be executed. In this section the forces due to tank content are calculated. Since both draught and trim have to be calculated, an iterative method of calculation is used. The aim is to arrive at acceptable values for the ship's trim moments and free forces. The influence from total hull deflection is also considered.

Furthermore, the computed total shear force is divided between ship side and bulk head, following certain rules given by the classification society.

Finally all computed values are checked against their limit values. Should limit values be exceeded, the operator may at once examine both computed and limit values and further propose a new load distribution. Having once inserted the main input data, one complete cycle of calculation will take only a few seconds.

Figure 3 is an example of operation of LOADCHECK. The formula used in these calcalculator is identical to those used by the classification society when making the original calculations for the ship. It is therefore possible to operate with "true" limit values, rather than the ample tolerances on the safe side which are included in some conventional calculators.

DISCUSSION ON BENEFITS OF COMPUTERIZED LOAD CALCULATORS

The foregoing is a brief presentation of the broad classes of load calculation aids. Each aid has its weak and strong points. Surely, the digital computer is the most expensive aid with which to equip the ship, a fact that is probably more evident than the advantages of the same device as compared to the other methods. The aim of the following is to illustrate the benefits of the computerized load calculators.

The benefits can simply be expressed as speed and accuracy together. Both can be obtained with other methods, but not in such a strong combination.

An adequate combination of speed and accuracy in load calculations will ensure the safety of the ship with regard to hull stresses and will assist in obtaining the highest freight income. These are the benefits we shall dwell upon.

Traditional thinking in load planning of any ship used to be strongly influenced by stability considerations. If the stability of the ship was endangered, the load plan was no good, no matter what else could be said for it. To-day's tanker designers have all but eliminated this problem. The large tanker is stable in all "full load" conditions, and also in ballast conditions although the author will avoid to be categoric on this point.

The interest is now centered on the hull stresses which, if neglected, can seriously damage the vessel, and in extreme cases endanger the crew. With the large cargoes carried, the potential hazard to our environment has become a real worry of unlimited dimensions.

Here again the ship designer has made a contribution to ease the situation. A fully loaded tanker will have stresses of moderate or say permissible, magnitudes. A captain will therefore normally have small problems with a full load of one single grade of oil, loaded in one port and unloaded in another. Nor will he have particular problems during loading or unloading, because he can use the full flexibility of the loading equipment and tank arrangement of the vessel. So, where are the benefits to be gained ?

The answer is: In multigrade cargoes, part cargoes, more than one port of loading and/or unloading, late loading orders or counter orders, late cargo specifications from loading port or incorrect such, draught limitations in port, uneconomic trim, ballasting and trimming during tank cleaning.

Multigrade cargoes will generally mean 2 grades of oil. The quantity of each type will be fixed, and the cargo officer must utilize the tank capacity in such a way that the proper quantity of each type can be carried. This can in some cases be done in more than one way, in other cases it may not be done at all. In all cases it will require a lot of calculations to arrive at an optimum solution. This is a situation where quick calculations pay off. The cargo officer will not be able to calculate a number of alternative load distributions by hand, a computer will. So will other aids, but to a smaller degree.

The loading process may be complicated with more than one type of cargo, because the loading sequence will be affected by the loading equipment both ashore and on board. The hull stresses will have to be checked for a number of intermediate load distributions. The computer can hold the current situation at all times and give quick answer on the alternatives the cargo officer need to have investigated. In these cases the accuracy of a conventional loadicator would be adequate, but the speed of operation would probably not.

Part cargoes will occur when more than one loading or unloading port is specified. There should be less need for quick decisions in these cases than for the part cargoes that will develop during the loading as mentioned above. The time element will then be less important, the interest may be turned to accuracy instead. The point here may be that the cause for the part cargo is a draught limit in one port. Accurate calculations of both draught and trim will be necessary. Trim adjustments by ballasting are not always possible for several reasons.

Part cargoes may cause problems. Severe hull stresses may occur with certain partly loaded conditions. The stresses may be reduced by adding or shifting ballast. Adding ballast may be impossible if the original purpose was to maintain a limited draught as mentioned above. Adding or shifting ballast is also a question of where to put it. A captain is very careful in producing dirty ballast, because he knows that he may have serious difficulties in getting rid of it again. It would at least cause additional tank cleaning, and there are rules for that too.

An accurate load calculator will help in these situations because the resulting stresses may be calculated without the safety margins that are either inherent in or practised with simpler methods. The captain will know with confidence what is necessary to make the ship sea-worthy and in certain border cases what will be important.

Now, it would be naive to imply that tanker load planning is a science where all problems are defined and solved in terms of calculations. The final decisions and the responsibility for the consequences rest with the captain, and his judgement will be influenced by his experience and personality. However, knowing the facts is becoming more essential as profitability is becoming marginal. The case of ballasting can be used to illustrate this. One important information is normally missing, the trim/speed characteristic of the ship. But other relations are better known as they comply with the theory. In general terms:

- Fuel consumption is proportional to $(\text{displacement})^{\frac{2}{3}}$

- Fuel consumption is proportional to $(\text{speed})^3$

While these are familiar thumb rules to the captain, he may not always consider them in terms of percentages gained or lost when he decides the amount of seawater to take in for the ballast voyage. What is likely to take place, is that the chief engineer operates the engine to about the same output for cargo and ballast voyages, and the captain chooses a ballast which he as a seaman believes is right for the ship and the people on it, weather and sea considered.

The object of this little diversion is to point out that there is some information available which is not fully utilized. One inherent benefit of a computerized loadicator is that it can be extended into such areas. It then becomes known as load optimalization, the object of which is to point out the conditions of the economically optimal voyage with safety considerations accounted for.

It is general practice that a tanker leaves the unloading port bound for "Persian Gulf for order". The order will be received on board 2-5 days before arrival in Persian Gulf. The time left before arrival in loading port is then adequate for the necessary load planning, if the orders are final. They are not always. Counter orders can arrive even at the loading pier, and then an efficient load calculator will be most welcome.

After receipt of loading orders follows an exchage of information whereby the particulars of the cargo is learned. The information necessary for load planning is specific gravity and temperature at loading.

If this information should be changed just prior to loading, a new round of calculations will be required, and the cargo officer is again pressed for time.

The trim of the ship has effect on the speed. How much, is one of the most important questions in daily ship operation. It is believed that the speed of a large tanker may vary several tenths of a knot for various and all acceptable trim figures. Why it should be so hard to establish an optimum value, is not evident. Part of the answer is that ships are individuals and the "typical" optimum trim of little value. For the particular ship the trim/speed characteristics is difficult to establish, because the speed is also a function of several other effects which all vary, say hull fouling, engine output, propeller efficiency, mean draught and weather. The data on all these components are accumulated too slowly, and probably too unorganized, to permit an analysis of the trim effect.

Obviously, if the optimum trim is unknown, there is no sense in calculating trim accurately in view of speed. Trim calculations are important, however, in establishing resultant draught, fore and aft. The mean draught is known from the deadweight.

The various arguments mentioned above to illustrate the usefulness of a computerized load calculator are mainly motivated by the speed of operation. This will not lead to increased profits if the cargo officer could somehow handle the situation anyway. We know he does. So the question must be: Will he do it better? We believe he will. A computer will make it possible to try more alternative solutions to a problem in the time available, and it will make it possible to do a proper job out of each alternative.

So far we have not particularily profitted by the high accuracy inherent in a digital computer. For the type of computers which are presently dominating ship-borne EDP, the accuracy is 10 decimal digits in any single number handled.

This accuracy is better than the accuracy of the input data to the computer, and exceeds the accuracy required in the output data from the computer. The important feature is, however, that all calculations in between are performed at this accuracy, which will ensure that what comes out of the computer is just as good as what goes in. This is not true for simpler calculating devices.

This advantage is already being used in as much as the classification society (Det norske Veritas) specifies higher bending moment and shear force limits when stresses are computed with improved accuracy. (The author is not familiar with how much is due to calculations on more hull sections). The practical value of this is that the cargo officer will have a wider choice of load distributions available, which may simplify a loading/unloading sequence, and it may be possible to increase the total cargo carried.

The computerized system can calculate weights from ullage, or vice versa, with high accuracy. However, the popular thought that this knowledge can be used to claim that the cargo is larger than otherwise assumed and thereby increase freight income, is unrealistic. The amount of oil is measured ashore at loading, and this "shore figure" is the official cargo quantity. The value of the accurate weight /ullage calculations lies for instance in checking thermal expansion of the cargo for each zone of the voyage.

Summing up benefits, the overall impression must be that the computerized load calculator will be a valuable aid to the cargo officer, enabling him to do a more thorough job at all times, even when the circumstances force him to make quick decisions.

The necessity of having such an aid may well be discussed, since less expensive devices will solve at least part of the problem. But the situation may get worse. The recommendations on tank size proposed by IMCO will increase the number of cargo tanks on the large tankers, which in turn will increase the amount of work in load planning. Also to the computer this will be an added burden, requiring more memory space and more computing time, neither of which, however, are problems to the operator.

CONCLUSIONS

The importance of good planning for reasons of safety and economy is recognized. The task itself is defined, and the methods of doing it are known to those whose responsibility it is. The remaining large problem is that the circumstances do not always leave time for a proper result to be reached. This shortage can effectively be neutralized by using a computerized load calculator which combines all the necessary accuracy with high operating speed. Other aids will partially solve the problem, but only the digital computer has the capacity for the complete solution.

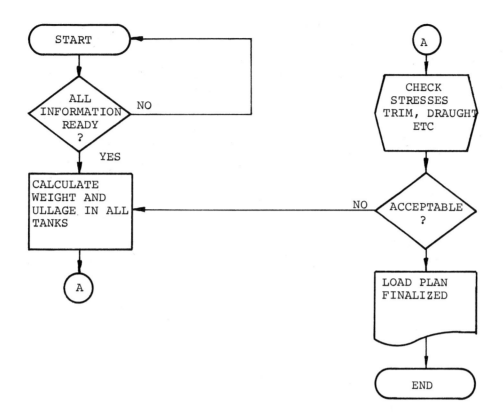

FIGURE 1   GENERALIZED LOAD PLANNING

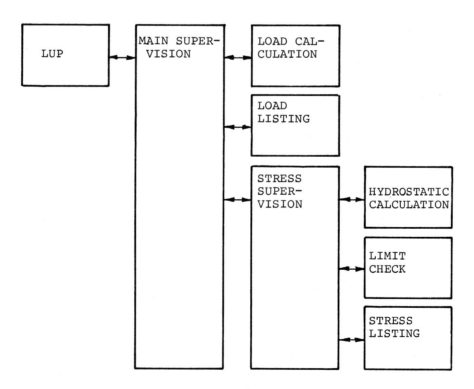

FIGURE 2   LOADCHECK

```
@ RT LUP                              OPERATOR STARTS PROGRAM

LUP STARTS :
 3/ 7-1973 1225

# TYPE 1, 0.85, 0.00044               TWO CARGO OIL GRADES
# TYPE 2, 0.89, 0.00051
# TEMPERATURE 108.                    OIL TEMPERATURE
# SD 1.025                            SEA WATER DENSITY
# DT 10.                              TEMP.DIFF. KEEL/DECK
# 1C WEIGHT 1, 10712.7                LOAD INPUT:
# 3C WEIGHT 1, 11200.                 <TANK NO><WEIGHT/ULLAGE>,
# 6C ULLAGE 2, 2.45                   <TYPE NO>,<TONS/M>
##EXECUTE                             LOAD CALCULATION REQUESTED

OVERFLOW CORRECTION IN TANK 3C        TOO MUCH OIL IN TANK 3C !

##LI0                                 LIST COMMAND

TANK DATA GIVEN FOR LOAD CALCULATIONS

TANK NO.   LOAD TYPE     LOAD      TEMP

   1C          1       10712.70    108.0
   3C          1       11002.50    108.0
   6C          2           2.45    108.0

##LI1

LOAD DATA GIVEN FOR LOAD CALCULATIONS

LOAD TYPE     SP.WT       COEFF. OF EXP.

    1        0.85000        0.000440
    2        0.89000        0.000510

##LI3

TANKS LOADED

TANK NO.   ULLAGE      VOLUME      WEIGHT    % FULL

   1C        1.81     12869.35   10712.70    97.39
   3C        1.00     13217.50   11002.50   100.00
   6C        2.45      9410.12    8174.88    94.88

##LI4

TYPES LOADED

LOAD TYPE     VOLUME       WEIGHT

    1        26086.85     21715.20
    2         9410.12      8174.88

##LI5

TOTAL LOADED

              VOLUME      WEIGHT     % FULL

             35496.96    29890.08     16.76
```

FIGURE 3   EXAMPLE OF OPERATION OF LOADCHECK

```
#*EL                                    STRESS,TRIM AND DRAUGHT
                                        CALCULATIONS REQUESTED

                                        THIS SIMPLE PLAN PRODUCES
                                        ACTUALLY A LARGE NUMBER OF
                                        WARNINGS

                                        TYPICAL STRESS WARNINGS:

BM EXCEEDED HOG-LIMIT AT CROSS SECTION : 5

SHR BULKH. EXC. LIMIT AT CROSS SECTION : 4,3

SHR SHIPS. EXC. LIMIT AT CROSS SECTION : 4,3

DRAUGHT AT FP SHOULD BE INCREASED TO PREVENT SLAMMING !


#*LL1,0

BM COMPUTED
CROSS SECTION       BM

        1              0.0
        2          -5707.60
        3        -110870.31
        4        -187203.69
        5        -396898.31
        6        -572087.31
        7        -604817.00
        8        -561659.00
        9        -502211.00
       10        -411800.00
       11        -341048.00
       12        -154230.00
       13          -9425.00
       14          -7095.00


#*LL3,0                                 EXCERPT OF SHEAR TABLE

SHR BULKH. COMPUTED
CROSS SECTION     SHR

       6,1         -952.43
       6,2         -591.09
       6,3          -49.09
       6,4          332.31

#*LL5

DRAUGHTS:     AVERAGE      MIDSHIP      AP      FP      TRIM BY STERN

               7.13         7.05      8.72    5.71        3.02

#*END

LUP TERMINATES
 3/ 7-1973 1230
```

FIGURE 3   CONTINUED

COMPUTERIZED MONITORING OF

LIQUID CARGO LOADING/UNLOADING

Knut Ellingsen   Alfred Holmberg   Pål Strømme
Project Engineers
N O R C O N T R O L
division of NORATOM-NORCONTROL A/S

INTRODUCTION

This paper describes the method of automatic monitoring of liquid cargo handling
used in the DataTank I system.

DataTank I measures continuously the
draughts and tank contents in order to calculate and check hull stresses, stability,
draughts, cargo weight and total displacement.

The aim is to ensure safe operation of the
ship, thereby excluding damage to the hull
and loss of time due to insufficient loading instructions or neglect on behalf of
the operator.

The paper first establishes the required
standard of measuring and explains how the
requirements have been met in the adopted
arrangement. It goes on to describe the
monitoring system in which the level measuring system is operated from the computer, and the stress and stability analysis program which makes use of the information.

Monitoring of the cargo handling process
is seen as a necessary first step leading
to control of the entire operation from
the computer. It is therefore natural to
consider what problems will be encountered
in planning the optimal load condition and
loading process which is to be implemented
in a completely automatic cargo handling
system.

Finally the problem of assessing the benefits that may be derived from the installation of such equipment and collecting and
analysing data are dealt with in brief.

DEFINING THE MEASURING PROBLEM

The quality of the results depends on the
quality of the input. As the software
treatment of the measured values does not
reduce the accuracy, the sole responsibility rests with the hardware measuring
system.

Environment

The tanks to be measured contain sea water,
crude oil or fuel oil. The horizontal distance between the measuring point and the
control desk may be from 30 to 275 metres,
and the vertical distance between the level
and the desk from 3 to 31 metres. The
deck and pump room area is considered
hazardous for explosions.

The accuracy of the various measurements
should be at least:

- Level measuring, 0-10% level: ± 1‰
                           (of 100% level)
-    "   "   10-90% level: $+1$%
-    "   "   90-100% level: ± 1‰
-    "   "   ballast & fuel: $+1$%
- Specific gravity measuring: ± 1%
- Draught measuring: ± 1%

It should be possible to detect errors in
the equipment outside the cargo control
room from this room, and detection should
preferably be automatic.

Choice of system

Two methods are in use today for remote
measuring of level onboard tankers, float
gauges and the dip tube method.

Float gauges have the advantage that they
indicate levels accurately over the full
range of the tank as long as they work
correctly. The disadvantages of these
systems in connection with a computer
system are:

- They only give information about level;

- They cannot be used in double bottom
  tanks or other tanks that are not accessible from deck;

- Only the electronic part of the installation outside the control room can be
  checked, i.e. it is impossible to establish whether the level signal received
  corresponds to the correct level, as the
  float could be anywhere between the tank

top and the liquid surface.

Correspondingly, the disadvantages and advantages of the dip tube method are:

- The measured pressures, which represent levels, must always be compensated for the density of the liquid;

- The accuracy of the level measuring is not as good as for a float gauge system over the full height of the tank;

- The accuracies of the two systems are, however, comparable over the range that is of particular interest;

- The system can be used for any kind and shape of tank;

- It can be used for draught measuring;

- It is possible to test the entire system centrally (See description of Tube Test);

- The use of a separate level transmitter for 90-100% (and 0-10%) level is an inherent self-check feature for the 0-100% transmitter;

- No electrical or electronic equipment is installed in the hazardous area;

- Remote reading of the actual specific gravity of the liquid is possible once the level in the tank is above 90%.

NORCONTROL's wide experience since 1966 in manufacturing dip tube systems was of course one reason why this type of system was adopted as the level measuring part of DataTank.

SYSTEM CONFIGURATION

The principle of the level measuring for DataTank I is shown in Fig. 1, while the block diagram in Fig. 2 describes the layout of the system in principle. The transmitters are common for all the tanks, and the appropriate measuring tubes are connected by activating solenoid valves.

Basically then, the measuring system consists of dip tubes, a solenoid valve multiplexer, electronic differential pressure transducers, a solid state multiplexer and a 12 bits Analog/Digital converter.

MEASURING ACCURACY

The various sources of error which will affect the measuring accuracy are treated in some detail.

Pressure Drop in Measuring Tubes

As the bubbling air flows through the measuring tubes, a pressure drop will occur.

We know that with a quantity of air of 0.5 l/min. in a tube with inside diameter 9 mm the flow is laminar, and the pressure drop can be calculated from the formula:

$$\Delta p = 32 \frac{L}{D^2} \times v \times \eta$$

If we have

$$L = 200 \text{ m}$$
$$D = 9 \times 10^{-3} \text{ m}$$
$$v = 0.13 \text{ m/sec.}$$
$$\eta = 1.9 \times 10^{-6} \text{ kp sec./m}^2 \text{ (air at } 30^{\circ}\text{C)}$$
$$(R_e \approx 79 \text{ for air of 1 ata and } 30^{\circ}\text{C})$$

then: $\Delta p = 19.6 \text{ kp/m}^2$

which corresponds to:

20 mm Water Gauge (WG)

The pressure drop is proportional to the velocity of the air, i.e. 10% variation in the flow means a 10% variation in the pressure drop.

Therefore high quality air flow regulators are used to control the bubbling air, and the measurements for cargo tanks are differential pressure measurements between two tubes with equal air flows. Thus, inaccuracies due to variation in the flow of air are negligible.

Conditions at the Free End of the Dip Tube

Fig. 3 shows the situation as a bubble of air escapes from the dip tube. The pressure measured in the control room is too large by an amount

$$n = h^1 - h$$

Our investigations have shown, however, that with the values of d, Q and v used in DataTank

$$n < 2.5 \text{ mm}$$

As the tank is 27 500 mm high this error is negligible.

Compensation for Height Difference

The transmitters are positioned approximately 31 m above the bottom of the tanks. The pressure measured by the transmitter is therefore too small by an amount corresponding to the column of air between the transmitter and the free end of the dip tube. This pressure difference can be calculated with the formula (Sears, Thermodynamics, p. 296)

$$P_z = P_o \times e^{-mgz/KT}$$

where

z = height difference
P_z = pressure in height z
m = mass of one molecule
g = 9.81 m/s^2
K = Bolzmann's constant
T = temperature $^{\circ}$K

The resulting values vary from 50 to 100 mm WG, and the necessary corrections are made by DataTank.

Transmitters

NAF electric differential pressure transmitters are used. They have been approved for use onboard ships by Det norske Veritas, following tests in extreme environmental conditions. Their main specifications are:

Accuracy $\pm$ 0.5%
Linearity $\pm$ 0.5%
Temperature
 oefficient 0.02% per $^{\circ}$C

With software calibration (described later) and steady temperature during loading/unloading a measuring accuracy of $\pm$ 0.5% is easily obtained.

Analog/Digital (A/D) - converters and Electronics

Twelve bits A/D converters which are specially designed for ship conditions are used. All parts of the interface equipment are designed to be in accordance with DnV rules and recommendations for automation and instrumentation equipment.

Conclusion on Measuring Accuracy

The upper and lower 10% of the full level in a cargo tank is measured on a separate transmitter (see Fig. 1). Its range is suited to the 10% of the tank level so that 1% accuracy on the measurements are obtained, which means 1 ‰ accuracy on the full level of the tank.

The tank height in this case is 27.5m, 10% of which is 2.75m, 1% accuracy being 27.5 mm. As the pressure drops due to air flow balance, the worst case measuring error for cargo tanks is:

Transmitter: $\pm$ 0.5%	=	13.5 mm
Temperature drift (transmitters) $\pm$ 5°C: $\pm$0.12%	=	3.5 mm
	=	17.0 mm

which is 0.62 ‰, of full tank level.

Correspondingly for ballast tanks:

Transmitter: $\pm$ 0.5%	=	135 mm
Temperature drift $\pm$5°C	=	7 mm
	=	142 mm

which is 0.52% of calibrated range. This is satisfactory for the purpose.

Special Considerations

This measuring system is subject to rather unusual service. It may be out of service for as long as 30 days, and is then switched on for 24 hours. Consequently it was designed to give ultimate short term accuracy. Correction for long term drift is made part of the starting-up procedure. It is assumed that nothing happens to the linearity of the components making up the signal path, while zero and amplification factor may drift.

Transducer Calibration

For correction of each transducer, two points near the ends of its measuring range are needed. When the system is started up, it requests the operator to supply in turn the three different pressures indicated, using the test pressure control valve. For each test pressure the operator reads the exact value on the test pressure mercury manometer and relates the information to the computer via the keyboard.

The two lower pressures and operator readings are then used to compute corrected slope and offset for the signal path from the low pressure transducer pressure input to the A/D output. The two higher pressures are used for the high pressure transducer.

LEVEL MEASURING

Tank Selection

The dip tube pressures are conveyed to the differential pressure transducers via the solenoid valve multiplexer. The valves are operated by the computer, and the different connections which are set up depend on the number of dip tubes in the tank and the level in the tank.

Cross-talk between measurements of different tanks is eliminated by pressuring the central air volume, i.e. transducers and central piping, before every measurement.

Measuring each tank takes less than 3 seconds, without loss of accuracy. If 30 tanks, four draughts, trim and list are measured, the time between two successive measurements of the same tank will be somewhat less than 2 minutes. At times this may be too long, e.g. when topping tanks. The operator may then select tanks for fast sampling, and the measuring sequence is altered as shown in Fig. 5.

Types of Measurements

Levels are measured in four different ways:

1. With one dip tube at the bottom of the tank, e.g. draughts and ballast tanks.

2. With two dip tubes, one at the bottom and one at the top of the tank for gas pressure compensation. This is valuable in tanks which are not vented to the atmosphere or where high filling rates are expected, as the gas pressure may then introduce considerable errors.

3. With three dip tubes, one at the bottom, one at 90% level and one at the top of the tank, for measuring of levels and densities. Cargo tanks are normally equipped with three tubes.

4. Level difference measurements, e.g. trim and list.

Measuring Procedure

Referring to the four groups mentioned above, the measuring procedure is, in each case:

(a) Dip tube pressure is measured against atmospheric pressure. For the lower 10% of the tank level the low pressure transducer is used, and higher levels are measured on the high pressure transducer.

(b) The only difference from (a) is that the pressure from the top dip tube replaces the atmospheric pressure.

(c) The low pressure transducer is used also for the top 10% of the tank level, while the high pressure transducer measures the total pressure in the bottom dip tube. Level and density (γ) are then calculated as follows:

$$\gamma = (H-L)/S$$

$$LEVEL = S + L/\gamma$$

where H = High pressure transducer reading
L = Low pressure transducer reading
S = Distance between bottom and 90% dip tube openings.

(d) Unipolar transducers are used in order to get the best possible accuracy on the level measurements. When measuring trim and list one must therefore be able to cross the dip tube connections to the transducers. This is possible since the transducers give a live-zero output signal. Then readings a little below

zero still make sense, and the multiplexer program is able to switch round the tube connections if the last reading was negative.

Measurement Limits

Measurements are checked against the following limits:

- Instrument limits
- Fixed level limits, full and empty
- Movable level limits, upper and lower
- Level rate limits, highest technically possible filling or emptying rate
- Density limits.

Alarms

Alarms are presented on the alphanumeric display and logged on the teletypewriter. A typical alarm message has the form:

23.40.38 AL013 WING TK1   STARB LE HIGH

SELF-CHECKING FEATURES

Measuring Signal Path

The following conditions result in alarm:

- The readings from the high and low level transducers differ too much when compared

- Long term drift exceeds a pre-set limit

- One of the important system voltages fails. This results in a light emitting diode being lit, and if the system is turned off automatically, this diode remains lit.

Solenoid valves

All the solenoid valves are checked by a computer program every 15 minutes. Broken circuit and driver failure will be detected by this test. In case of failure, the alarm indicates which valve has failed.

Dip tubes

As has been shown, level measuring with dip tubes can be very accurate. The most common causes of deterioration in measuring accuracy are:

- Condensed water vapour in the tubes
- Obstructions built up by dirt
- Leaks caused by mechanical wear or corrosion

In a large conventional system, checking the tubes and purging them with high pressure air takes considerable time. Data-Tank does this job automatically.

The tube test involves measuring test air flows over a time and observing the pressures which occur.

Leaks and obstructions restricting the air
flow are detected this way, and the alarm
system reports which tube is involved and
the type of fault. Moisture in a tube, if
any, is also blown out by a purging air
flow.

Software and Electronic Interface

The data bus between the computer and the
interface is tested for correct transmission
both ways every 5 ms. If the test fails
the interface is turned off.

Software is monitored on three levels:

I)   Administration program running
II)   Measurement program running
III)   Operator communication program
        running.

If one or more fails, a light emitting
diode is lit up, and the interface turned
off.

OPERATOR COMMUNICATION

The operator communicates with the system
via

- The central operating console;
- The analog level display for all tanks;
- The teletypewriter (hard copy logger).

There are also operating facilities for the
level measuring system as a separate back-
up hardware system.

Fig. 4 shows the central DataTank console
which is placed next to the central valve
and pump operation consoles in a convenient
all-in-one arrangement.

Details of the Operation Console

The two digital displays facing the operator are used for:

No. 1: Continuous display of measured
        level and density for up to 14
        selected tanks.

No. 2: Draughts, trim , list total dis-
        placement and cargo, metacentric
        height;
        Alarm display texts;
        Communication texts.

Below the digital displays is the push-
button mimic diagram which is used for:

- Specifying tanks for digital display,
  fast sampling, limit alteration, density
  input

- Flashing the lamp which corresponds to
  the tank measured at the moment.

The remaining push-buttons give the operator
assecc to the "Communication Functions",

Alarm Acknowledge and System on/off. There
is also a numerical keyboard.

The intention has been to make the interaction between the operator and the system
simple and straightforward. Each communication function is clearly defined, and the
entering and operating procedure for each
function is consistent with one basic pattern.

Operating the System

The procedure for starting-up the system
requires:

I)   Specification of density for the
        contents of all the tanks. Once
        the level reaches 90%, the density
        is measured by the system, but ini-
        tially is must be given by the opera-
        tor.

II)   Specification of amounts of bunker
        oil and stores.

III)   Calibration of the pressure trans-
        ducers.

Once this procedure has been completed, the
system works independently. The initial
load condition is printed on the teletypewriter. Later, the load, stability, draught,
trim and stress situation is printed either
periodically or whenever the operator wishes.

Alarms of all kinds are logged automatically.
Changes in the following basic parameters
are also logged:

- Moveable high and low limits,

- Transducer deviation

The system helps the operator judge the
present state of the ship in three ways:

I)   The complete load situation can
        be judged by and large on the ana-
        log level indicators representing
        each tank;

II)   Selected tanks may be studied more
        carefully on the digital display,
        anlog with the stability and trim
        conditions;

III)   Stresses on the hull are logged
        whenever necessary.

STABILITY AND LOAD CALCULATOR (DATALOAD)

General

DataLoad is the largest single part of the
software, occupying some 12K of core space
with mixed assembly and Fortran, formatting
not included.

The program was originally developed in co-operation with A/S Computas, who were able to draw on the knowledge of Det norske Veritas concerning ship strength calculations. The calculating methods therefore bear resemblance to those used in comparable programs in the DnV library, while the communication part and the actual program code is particular to DataLoad.

Application in DataTank

The input from the level measuring system which has to be tackled by DataLoad is somewhat troublesome. For practical reasons the measuring tubes are placed at the aft end of the tanks, in the centre of the tanks athwartships. Therefore, in order to calculate the volume in a tank from the measured level, the trim must be taken into account. But, in irregularly shaped tanks, the variation in volume with varying trim cannot be defined very simply.

However, investigations showed that it would be possible to solve the problem with three sets of curves for each tank. One of level v. volume for zero trim, and one each for fore and aft trim of level v. correction to the volume per unit trim variation. This gives an approximation well within the accuracies required, even at the top and bottom of the tank where the level v. volume curves for varying trim angles are farthest from parallel.

Each time the measuring sequence has been completed, the program calculates total amounts of cargo and displacement for output on the digital display. It goes on to calculate the trim and stability, check the trim against the measured value, and indicate the metacentric height (GM) to the operator.

The trimming procedure is an iteration involving a "model" of the ship, in which each section of the hull is described with curves of volume, centre og buoyancy, waterline area and centre of gravity of the waterline area. The appropriate centre of gravity of the cargo in the section is also calculated, and the resulting trim is that at which buoyancy and weight moments balance.

Next, the shear forces and bending moments at read-out points are calculated, and, integrating the shear forces, the bending moment peak values are established.

In the real-time version an arrangement has been chosen, whereby the three larger values of shear force and bending moment are listed whenever the operator specifies printout, or when one or more of the values exceeds the limit.

OPTIMAL LOAD CONDITION

Optimal Loading/Discharging

This is a minimum time optimizing problem. Transition from one load condition to another specified load condition should take a minimum of time. During the transition period, hull stress limits, stability limits and ship and port capacities must not be exceeded. The problem is finding the optimal trajectory, a problem which in this case has a large number of solutions. Finding a near optimal trajectory does not seem too difficult.

Following our investigations, we do, however, believe that the greatest gain is obtained by monitoring and controlling flows and pressures in pipe systems and cargo pumps and turbines.

Optimal Load Condition

The first step is to set up the criterion for the optimum condition. Actual criteria depend to a certain extent on the conditions of the Charter Party. One may choose between various economic criteria which give maximum profit over a shorter or longer period of time, e.g. per voyage.

Given a criterion for the optimum condition, the next step is to formulate the primary functions which describe all relevant factors and together make up the object function. These factors are:

- Freight income;
- Bunker and port dues;
- Cost relating to crew, stores, insurance, maintenance;
- Capital charges with depreciation.

The importance of some of these factors varies with the terms of the Charter Party, but one must always include factors describing the safety of the ship. Some of these are:

- Danger of oil pollution from temperature expansion because of too small initial ullage;
- Overloading of machinery;
- Stresses on the hull;
- Danger of local damage, e.g. pounding;
- Stability.

The third step is to clarify the relations between these primary functions and the basic functions on which they depend. The most important relations are:

- Freight income varies with speed;
- Bunker cost depends on fuel price and performance;
- Maximum loaded cargo depends on the amount of bunker carried, i.e. performance; bunkering during a voyage means

loss of time but increased cargo capacity;
- The dependence of performance on the condition of the machinery, the speed, draught, trim, fouling and roughness of the hull;
- The increase in power or loss of speed due to wind or wave effects on resistance and propulsive efficiency;
- The condition of the machinery is important for the subsequent wear, and thus maintenance, repairs and depreciation;
- Draught depends on the specific weight of sea water at varying temperatures,
- Restrictions on draught depend on season, load line zone and distance to next zone with different restrictions on draught;
- DataLoad computes these relations: Variation in trim and draught, shear forces and bending moments with varying load distribution.

The fourth step will be to define the relative importance of the primary functions which make up the object function, and assign relative weights according to their importance.

When all data and functions are clearly defined, the optimal load condition will appear by finding the maximum of the object function. The resulting condition covers cargo in each tank, draught, trim, hog/sag, stresses, bunker and speed.

Conclusion on Optimal Loading

In order to obtain the optimal trajectory referred to in the passage on Optimal Loading/Discharging, i.e. find the optimum of the dynamic process, one has to find the minimum of an object function describing stresses and time spent. The initial situation is known, and the final load condition is found by obtaining the optimum of the final condition, as described above.

ECONOMICAL BENEFITS

General

Much as the economical benefits from introducing load monitoring and control systems is by far the most important consideration in deciding their future application, other aspects are also worthy of attention. The most important is perhaps the working conditions of the ship personnel. Disregarding the complexity of the installation, if there is a minimum configuration of monitoring of levels as well as stability and stress, the operator knows that he is within safe limits until the alarm is sounded. This is likely to remove much of the tension which he has been under during transfer operations up till now. It also means that, facing irregularities imposed from ashore or by

conditions onboard, he will be in a position to introduce a makeshift procedure freely and boldly, thereby saving time.

Economic Aspects

When considering the prospects of economic benefits and justification for the various degrees of automation, it may be useful to group the aspects under the headings:

- Loading/Discharging
- Load Planning and Distribution
- Hull Stresses and Damage

So far, comprehensive studies of:

- Operation; Instrumentation; Safety; Crew reduction

in relation to each other and to economy are not available. Following, a brief discussion of each area is given.

Optimal Loading/Discharging

The aim will be to conclude the loading operation in the shortest possible time, with due regard to the limitations imposed by hull stresses, trim and stability, discharging or receiving arrangements ashore, pump capacities and operator capacity.

Experience with automatic oil handling systems onboard ships shows a saving in time of 1 - 4 hours. With a well designed and reliable system, a higher degree of safety is also achieved. A completely automatic system which is fundamentally reliable also makes reduction in crew possible, as one man can handle the entire operation.

The question of lay-out of the cargo handling equipment must be considered together with the automation equipment, also with regard to economy. However, a well designed arrangement for remote manual control will most probably also be suitable for application in automatic control systems.

Load Planning and Distribution

As this has been discussed at some length under the heading of "Optimal Load Conditions" we shall only list the criterion and main parameters here.

Criterion: The most economical combination of load, load distribution, speed and fuel consumption.

Parameters: Charter Party conditions, wanted amount of cargo, cost of fuel oil, harbour conditions (equipment, geographical), load line zones, hull stresses, tides, speed, trim, hog/sag, draught.

In addition, speed as a function of hogging or sagging bending moment and varying trim should be considered, as well as draught variations throughout the trip.

Much work still remains to be done in assessing the relative importance of each parameter.

Hull Stresses and Damage

Damage reports do not normally state reliably the conditions which caused the damage. In order to establish the economic benefits of hull stress monitoring, it is necessary to know more about the direct causes of damage. Work of this kind is in progress under the supervision of Classification Societies.

It is necessary to know what damage is caused by faulty operation during cargo handling, weakness in the hull, rough weather or combinations of these.

One may safely assume that much damage would never have occurred had the officers in charge known more about the forces acting on the ship due to the cargo distribution and the weather. So far intuition has been the only guide. In the context of large modern vessels this is not enough, it must be replaced by facts.

There is more than one way of attacking this problem, but either one is a step in the right direction.

Total Economy

Instrumentation must be considered together with the cost of the ship, operating conditions and size of crew. Evaluation of the merits of cargo handling automation equipment is as yet uncertain. However, experience has already shown that savings of up to 4 hours on the time in port is obtainable. If in addition only a fraction of the time in repair yard or dock is excluded, this could easily mean 2 - 3 days a year. This already makes the equipment very interesting from a financial point of view.

Ultimately, the installation of automatic cargo handling and hull stress monitoring results in smaller crews. Because this means a great deal economically, and because such equipment becomes more essential as skilled ship operators becom less available, we have every faith in the successful completion of these very far-reaching projects in the years to come.

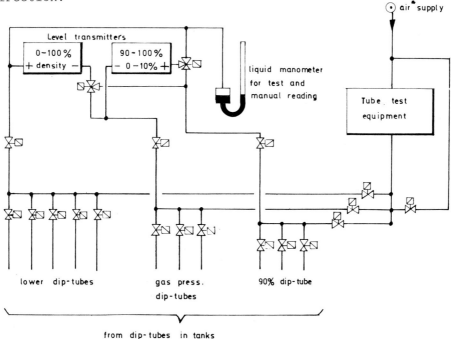

Fig. 1 Principle, Data Tank level measuring

420

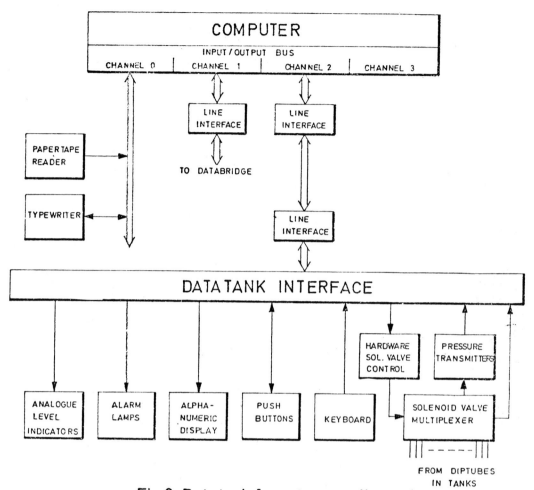

Fig. 2 Datatank I, system configuration

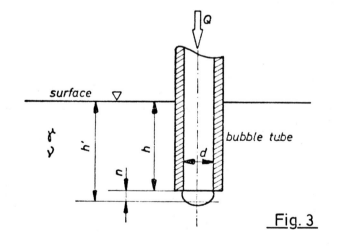

Fig. 3

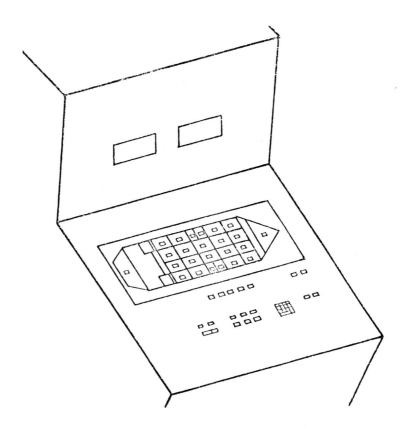

Fig. 4 Operator Communication Console

Normal sequence

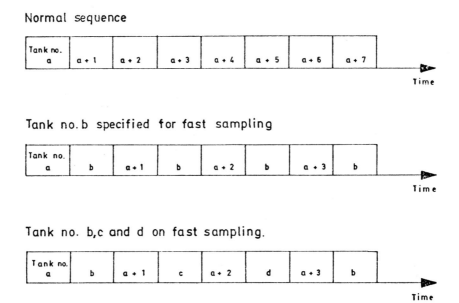

Tank no.b specified for fast sampling

Tank no. b,c and d on fast sampling.

Each box represents adressing and
measuring of the corresponding tank no.

Fig. 5 Measuring sequence

SOME EXPERIENCES IN CARGO OIL AND

WATER BALLAST HANDLING BY SHIPBOARD COMPUTER

Ryuichi Tamura
Yoshiki Okano
Minoru Fujita

KAWASAKI HEAVY INDUSTRIES, LTD.
KOBE, JAPAN

ABSTRACT

A centralized computer system on board a 150,000
DWT ore/oil carrier is composed of cargo oil and
water ballast handling system, navigation system,
medical diagnosis system, etc. Stress is laid on
the description of control and back up techniques
of cargo oil and water ballast handling, which
occupies the largest part of the system.

INTRODUCTION

During the last several years, a number of ships
have been fitted with computers for batch process
or on-line process control. The objects of these
applications are, without doubt, to assure the
operational and maneuvering safety of ships, to
save labour and to improve the working environment
on board, and finally to achieve greater operational economy. In comparison with the computerization
in land-based installations, the progress is rather
slow in severe environmental requirements.
Reliability and economy are the main problems to be
solved, which can be endorsed only by practical
applications on board. This paper describes some
experiences in planning and operating a shipboard
computer system which precedes the coming standardized modules.
In September 1972, M.S. "OHTSUKAWA MARU", a 150,000
DWT ore/oil carrier, was completed in our yard and
was delivered to Kawasaki Kisen Kaisha (K-Line).
The ship is equipped with a centralized computer
system which is composed of the following.

(1) Cargo oil and water ballast control system
(2) Cargo and water ballast calculation system
(3) Astronomical and geographical navigation
     calculation system
(4) Omega navigation system
(5) Ship motion prediction system for ship routing
(6) Medical diagnosis system

Applications are not introduced into the engine
plant in due consideration of economy, as the ship
is equipped with an unmanned engine room certifi-
cate. Items (1) and (2) are described in detail
in this paper, and items (3) - (6) are outlined
hereunder.

Astronomical and geographical navigation system:
This system is to substitute calculations by the
computer for manual calculations by officers.

Data are input manually with ten keys on the operator console in the chart space. The results are
printed by the typewriter adjacent to the console.
Inputs for astronomical navigation program are
estimated position, observed data, correction factors, etc. and outputs are azimuth and intercept.
Geo-navigation program consists of the following
four calculations. Course and distance calculation by the rhumb line sailing, destination calculation by the rhumb line sailing, great circle
distance calculation, and great circle planning
calculation.

Omega navigation system:
Besides a radio direction finder and a Loran receiver, the ship is provided with an Omega receiver,
which is operated manually or coupled to the computer. The calculated position is printed by the
typewriter in the chart space every one hour and at
any time on demand. With this system, automatic
position fixing can be performed on the world-wide
scale and without any restriction in time.

Ship motion prediction system for ship routing:
This system displays predicted values of ship
motions with respect to assumed courses and speed
in a given area, based on prognostic weather maps
received by a facsimile, and provides data for ship
routing to navigators. Inputs are fed by setting
a weather map on a coordinate reading equipment,
reading each isobaric line, shoreline, etc. and
operating a function key board installed in the
computer office. Wind field is estimated from
atmospheric pressure, and wave spectra are calculated as the sum of the wind sea spectra determined from the narrow time-space information and
the swell spectra forecasted from the wide time-
space information. As a result, magnitude of
rolling and pitching is shown as length of lines
on a X-Y plotter for each displayed grid point in
the next day's navigation area.

Medical diagnosis system:
This system is designed to assist the ship's
officer who is in charge of medical treatment in a
vessel with no doctors on board, and deals with
internal treatment and surgery. Basic data prepared in a given format are input by operating the
ten keys in the cargo oil control room, and outputs
are printed by the typewriter. Questions and
answers are repeated until the name of desease and
its treatment are respectively type out in pre-

determined code numbers. Accordingly, a desease number list and its corresponding treatment number list are furnished.

GENERAL DESCRIPTION ON CARGO OIL AND WATER BALLAST CONTROL SYSTEM

In planning the hardware of this system, the first priority was given to the sufficient reliability. A process computer FACOM270-20 of FUJITSU make was adopted, which had achieved steady performances and satisfactory results in land-based processes and on board. CPU and peripheral equipments underwent vibration bench tests and were installed in a carefully stiffened computer room. Some modifications were made for marine use. Magnetic drums were of special design, framings and casings were reinforced, and fixing of parts and wires was made rigid.
An automatic valve control equipment was newly developed to operate valves to any intermediate angle. The other equipments such as sensors and wired logics for pump turbine control are of conventional type. Hardware arrangement is shown in Fig. 1.

Emphasis was laid on safety in control, as it handles inflammable oil or oily water which could cause disaster and pollution. One of the most important sensors is the float type level gauge in the cargo oil tank, which is fitted in duplicate and ensures reliable level detection through relative comparison accordingly. Draft gauges are of float type which are excellent in accuracy. Heel detection is performed not only by an electric heel metre but also by draft gauges amidships.
Attention is paid to the operator consoles and monitoring panel to facilitate operation and watch-keeping in the cargo oil control room.
Various data necessary for the process can be given to the computer only by ten keys, digital switches and push buttons. Input typewriter is located in the computer room and is used only for system maintenance. Output typewriters and the line printer are interchangeable by switches when either of them is out of order. The control system is so designed that the changing over from computer control to manual remote control is available safely and quickly in case of emergency. In order to supply stable electric power for the computer and peripheral equipments, one set of motor-generator is provided in the engine room. In case of power failure, the motor-generator is driven by batteries, which are automatically switched back to ship's power source when recovered. Furthermore, by a fly wheel fitted on the motor-generator, electric power is supplied for 3 seconds during which period memory protection measures are taken by software.

The ship has been engaged in the transport of crude oil from the Persian Gulf to Japan after delivery.

Typical control processes during these voyages are shown in Fig. 2. Control logics are developed so as to stand versatile uses such as multi-parcel oil handling, ballasting in port and at sea and parallel running of two independent control programs.

This control system includes the following six applications.

(1) Cargo oil loading
(2) Cargo oil unloading
(3) Dirty/clean water ballast charging
(4) Dirty/clean water ballast discharging
(5) Pure water ballast charging
(6) Pure water ballast discharging

After delivery of the ship, partial modifications were made in batch process and on-line control programs according to the practical operation results. To facilitate modifying and debugging on board, one magnetic drum was temporarily installed, in which drum utility programs and specially developed debug system were filed. Fig. 3 shows piping diagram.

ANALOGUE INPUT DATA PROCESSING

There are about 100 analogue inputs from level gauges, pump delivery pressure gauges, pump suction pressure gauges, pump revolution metres, manifold pressure gauges, draft gauges, heel metre, etc. These signals are fluctuating by various disturbances and to be smoothed with hardware and/or software filters. Special attention was paid to the smoothing of the level gauge signals, which decide the accuracy of level control while topping up, and by which the flow rate is calculated and pumps are controlled. The largest fluctuation is expected during ballasting and deballasting while the ship is sailing.
In order to solve the problem, experiments were carried out on a tanker engaged in a voyage between the Persian gulf and Japan. Tank level signals, recorded with data recorders, were passed through an A/D converter and were analysed by the spectrum analysis program. Spectral density showed peaks at the ship's rolling frequency, natural lateral and longitudinal frequencies of the liquid motion in the tank, and the natural frequencies of the sensor (Fig. 4). To filter these frequencies and to take out increasing or decreasing level, the arithmetic moving average method was adopted.

$$Y_n = \frac{1}{N} \sum_{i=0}^{N-1} X_{n-i}$$

where X_n is a sampled raw datum in time series, N is a number of datum, Y_n is the smoothed datum. Then the velocity of the level change is calculated by the linear least square method using the average data. The final level is decided after the time lag correction using the velocity.

$$\bar{Y}_n = T V (N-1)/2 + Y_n$$

where T is the sampling interval, V is the velocity $\bar{Y}_n$ is the final level.
Variations are applied to the above principle according to the input stating whether the ship is in port or at sea.
A sample of smoothing is illustrated in Fig. 5. The float type level gauge was chosen for draft and tank level reading considering the accuracy and reliability. The signals from the float gauge consist of a saw-toothed fine signal for 0-100 cm and a linear rough signal for 0-27 m, each from

potentiometres attached to the synchronous receiver. Both rough and fine signals pass through an A/D converter and are synthesized to make a raw level figure.

The other low pass digital filter for other analogue inputs is

$$\bar{Y}_n = (1 - 1/Q)\bar{Y}_{n-1} + Y_n/Q$$

The advantage of this filter is simplicity and versatility only adjusted by Q.

SUPPORT AND BACK UP PROGRAMS

Control data to regulate the process are to be input generally with ten keys before starting the program. Number of these data amounts to around eighty for loading and unloading respectively. Data are typed out and displayed on a projection window when keyed in for confirmation. In addition, for easier and more reliable preparation, standard data for the typical patterns of cargo oil and water ballast handling are filed in the magnetic drum which are shifted to the control data area by a push button. As the process is proceeded by high speed logical calculations, it is very difficult for the operator to follow the rapidly changing phenomena. This is one of the reasons why man-machine communication is important for the computer control. Alarms, notices, and indications are informed by lamps, buzzers and typewriter. Furthermore, three trend recorders are fitted on an auxil. cargo control console for automatic plotting of tank ullages, drafts, trim, heel, manifold pressures, loading/unloading rate, and total liquid capacity in cargo oil tanks. These make the operator to know the transition at a glance.

Data logging is printed by the line printer regularly and at any time at will by operating a push button (Fig. 6).

Many back up procedures are arranged against various abnormalities. Firstly, as preventive measures, inputs are logically checked at program start, and manual preparation works at starting are checked by questionnaire on the typewriter. Manual clearance works at ending are also checked in the same way. Secondly, to discover abnormalities in time, signals from float gauges in cargo oil tanks, fitted in duplicate, are compared at regular intervals. Correlations among signals from draft gauges and heel metre, correlations among signals from delivery and manifold pressure gauges, revolutions, valve strokes, longitudinal strength, etc. are also examined and alarmed when checked out. Thirdly, emergency measures are taken when abnormalities are found. A trouble D/I switch is provided for each sensor and, when switched on, an estimated figure is computed for draft, heel and·pressure, while the normal float gauge is chosen out of the two. Specific back up measures suitable for each process are duly taken as described later.

During loading and unloading, pausing and restarting the process are sometimes necessary according to the land based requirement. Ballasting and deballasting are generally carried out only in the daytime and works are to be paused toward evening and to be restarted in the next morning. "PAUSE" push button is provided for temporarily stopping the process, by which operation pumps are stopped and valves are shut immediately.

Restarting is the same procedure as normal start. "CANCEL" push button is provided for cancelling the program at any intermediate sequence.

PUMP CONTROL

To operate four steam turbine driven vertical pumps (3 x 3,500 m^3/h x 145 mTH cargo oil pump, 1 x 2,500 m^3/h x 35 mTH water ballast pump) at high efficiency all through cargo oil and water ballast handling, revolutions and delivery valves are controlled by pump control programs.

Wired logic modules are provided for the sequential control of warming up, starting, stand-by stopping and complete stopping of pump turbines.

Warming up is of push button command from the control room while starting and stopping are of computer command.

The maximum flow rate for cargo oil pumps is given to the computer with digital switches any time as required. When the flow rate, calculated from the velocities of levels, is less than the limit, the revolution is increased step by step, which is the discrete control. There is a dead zone of dQ under the maximum limit.

$$dQ = (A \cdot dN/N + B)Q$$

where dQ is the breadth of the dead zone, N is the present rpm, dN is the increment of rpm, Q is the present flow rate, A and B are adjustable constants for the stable control. The controllable revolution range of the cargo oil pump (60 - 100 % load) is divided into ten. The digital revolution command is converted to analogue output by D/A converter, and to pneumatic output by E/P converter, and then controls the turbine governor.

The flow rate is also controlled by the delivery valve, the stroke of which is divided into seven. The valve stroke command is expressed in the digital outputs of the binary coded decimal, which are transferred to the valve controller, which applying the compensation for the time lag of the hydraulic oil system, compares the outputs with the present valve stroke signal from the encoder fitted on the valve stroke indicator, and operates the solenoid pilot change-over valve for the hydraulic oil control valve.

In the similar way, the delivery pressure and the manifold pressure are maintained within the limits. The cavitation is one of the most important problems in the pump operation. Unlike the pumping generally seen in the industrial processes, the suction condition considerably varies during unloading. Accordingly the control against cavitation has a great influence upon the efficiency of cargo oil and water ballast handling and the life of the pump. The basic principle is to keep the available net positive suction head greater than the required value. The available NPSH is calculated by the following formula.

$$NPSH_{av} = P_a - P_{vp} + h_s - v^2 \cdot S/2g$$

where Pa is the atmospheric pressure, Pvp is the vapour pressure of the liquid, hs is the suction pressure, v is the suction velocity, S is the specific gravity of the liquid, g is the acceleration of gravity. The vapour pressure of the cargo oil is generally estimated from the curves for typical crude oils plotted against temperature, as the true figure is not always obtainable. Any adjustment is available at the operator console during the control. In order to formulate the required NPSH, shop tests were carried out at the pump makers' test bed. Cavitation points were obtained by keeping the revolution constant and by closing the suction valve up to the point where the delivery pressure fell 3 % below the normal curve. Our operational experiences show that this control is somewhat on the safer side than the manual control of the crew, judging from the vibration and noise of the pump system.

Considerations are also given to those items such as rate up and down, parallel/independent operation, balancing of the boiler load, stripping, etc.

Commands to the revolution and the valve stroke from the various controls are consolidated based on the predetermined priority. Change-over switches for manual mode and computer mode is available any time as necessary.

TRIM, DRAFT AND HEEL CONTROL

During cargo oil loading and unloading, ships must be kept within the proper trim, draft and heel to secure high efficiency, good accuracy of liquid level and safety. Trim and draft are controlled by operating suction valves of forward tanks or aftward tanks, while heel is adjusted by operating suction valves of wing tanks. The valve stroke is divided into four to make each step share approximately equal flow quantity. The objects of the trim control are, during unloading, to make even keel at the early stage to prevent overflowing, to make large trim at the latter stage to procure good pump suction and to minimize residue oil while stripping, and during loading, to make even keel at the latter stage to ensure the accuracy of the topping-up level. For this purpose, several upper and lower trim limits are to be input and the limits are calculated by interpolation. Four control lanes are provided outside of each limit, and each lane corresponds to the valve step. It is the discrete control with hysteresis as shown in Fig. 7. Typical trim curves are given for operators' reference, which were found proper by the use of simulation programs.

The draft control is necessary in the case where the depth of water is comparable to the ship's draft. The control technique is similar to that of the trim control, however, the inputs are the depth of the nearly lowest low water and the tidal amplitudes. The water depth is obtained by sine wave approximation, thereby the valve step is determined based on the control lane above the sea bottom.

In the course of cargo oil handling, the ship is liable to heel to either side due to the unbalance of oil flow caused by the difference of pipeline layout to port and starboard tanks.

The heel control is prepared for the safety and the valve step is determined by the control lane outside of the limit angle. Generally the heel angle has been maintained within ± 0.3 degree during the previous loading and unloading.

As the logics of these controls are different and independent from each other, the final valve step is decided by superposing all requirements when they are in coincidence, or choosing the requirement of higher priority when they are not in coincidence.

The concepts of trim, draft and heel controls are similar and so the logics are assembled into one versatile program, which is used for loading and unloading.

CARGO OIL LOADING CONTROL

This system is to load crude oil fed by gravity or by shore pumps into the ship's tanks safely and in good accuracy, and forms an open loop control since the loading rate is adjusted by the shore operator complying with the request by the ship's operator. After the program start, manual preparation works are to be checked according to the messages on the typewriter, and then tank valves are fully open. "Rate slow" and "Rate full" are requested to the shore operator according to the order from the computer. Figures of loading rate are to be input beforehand, the amount of which is decided by the negotiations among the people concerned. For decreasing the rate, Full-Half-Slow-Stop, previous notices of ten minutes in advance are also given as well as the orders in time, after prediction calculations of filling up sequences. When stopping the loading, an additional notice is given one minute in advance. The calculations are based on the present level velocity and the permissible level velocity varying with ullage which is decided to keep safety and accuracy within the limit. The prediction error largely depends upon the fluctuation of the loading rate, and our records show it is around ± 3 min/10 min. Various control programs are set to run at predetermined intervals.

Normal open control is to keep at least one tank valve fully open in each cargo oil line to protect pipeline from overpressure as required by port regulations.

Vapour speed control is to maintain gas velocity in the vent line within the limit.

Topping up control is as follows. As oil level approaches nearer to the final ullage, the level speed is gradually decreased in order to get accurate signal from the level gauge. The command to shut the valve is transmitted just before the level reaches the final ullage taking account of the level velocity and the time required to shut the valve. The tank level is watched for five minutes after the full shut, and when fluctuation of level is within the permissible range, the tank is defined as finished loading. The last tank(s), which is nominated by an input, is shut at a stand-by level and is reopened when all other tank levels arrive at the final ullage. In the former loading of two-parcel handling, the stop command is given when the last tank level arrives at the final ullage, while in the latter loading, the command is given when the draft arrives at the final draft or when the last tank level arrives at the maximum permissible level which is defined to prevent oil from overflowing. The last tank valve is left open even after the stop command, and after confirming the complete stop of loading and obtaining the approval of the shore operator, and checking the manual clearance work by typewriter messages, all valves are shut by the finishing program. Standard deviation of actual topping up ullages from input ullages has been approximately 1 cm.

In the case where the specific gravity of sea water or crude oil is found to be different from the figures initially input, the final ullage of the last tank or the final draft can be automatically modified by feeding the data with ten keys. One of the important problems during loading is the limit of manifold pressure. To cope with this, the program runs every three seconds to watch the pressure, and when pressure exceeds the input figure, to open the buffer tank-the last tank in stand-by condition and also the other loading tanks if necessary.

Another important problem is overflowing. The back up control is as follows. As the level approaches the final ullage, the tank valve is operated by ±1 step to check the normal movement. As the level arrives at the preset high level, the line is blocked with alarms, shutting the block valve, filling valve and tank valves in the line.

Other back up programs such as watching levels of tanks not in use, checking flow rate, etc. are in service.

Pure water ballast charging or discharging program is generally used simultaneously.

The loading program is so designed as to handle any numbers of parcels with any selected tanks. Segregations in four voyages were 1-parcel at one port, 2-parcel of 30/70%, 35/65% or 45/55% at one or two ports.

Fig. 8 shows the final stage loading plotted by a trend recorder.

CARGO OIL UNLOADING CONTROL

This system is to unload crude oil by ship's pumps from the ship's tanks to the aboveground storage tanks within the limits of maximum rate of flow and the maximum manifold pressure.

The problem to be considered at the initial stage is overflowing. When the ship is trimmed by the stern, the tank levels are rather high, and the unloading rate is slow, the simultaneous opening of all tank valves has a danger of overflowing out of aftward tanks. To cope with this kind of accident, all lines are separated from each other by block valves and levels are lowered one by one to the predetermined ullage. This control is skipped over when levels are low enough, and thereafter all block valves are open and pumps are in parallel operation. After this initial control is over, if a tank happens to come to the high level, the line is to be blocked, all tanks in the line are to be shut and the overflowing tank is to be solely pumped out down to the safe ullage.

At every unloading station, there is a restriction to the chiksan height above the water line. The allowable ship's freeboard is calculated at regular intervals based on the tidal data and an alarm is given when dangerous.

Stripping is carried out in the following sequences by the main pumps fitted with Prima-Vac units.

When the tank level arrives at the lower set level (approx. 1 metre depth), the tank suction valve is shut as stand-by. As the number of open tanks decreases, parallel operation of pumps becomes unfavourable due to the difference of suction condition. When the number of open tanks becomes equal to the number of pumps, the block valves are shut and each pump is operated independently. At the time when all tanks of the line arrive at the lower set level, the foremost tank valve is open to be stripped. Stripping is continued till the level arrives at the minimum set level, and after prescribed minutes, the next tank valve is open. Protection measures are taken for the pump, when the next tank valve is in trouble, by skipping to the tank after next. If the float gauge, which can measure down to 7 cm depth, does not arrive at the minimum set level due to sludges or tarry residues, the sequence is to be proceeded by a time limit defined for each tank. The Prima-Vac unit has its own ability to evacuate air drawn with crude oil, however, it is a fact that time required to evacuate air is proportional to air quantity. In order to make stripping time as short as possible, automatic priming is optionally taken by opening the higher level tank valve when the pump loses suction for more than five minutes. This helps the pump to resume suction within 1-2 minutes by priming the pump and by ejecting air to the stripping tank from the pipe line.

Thus stripping required 10-15 min/tank for the last one metre depth (around 1,000-1,500 m^3/h). Pure water ballast charging or discharging program or clean/dirty water ballast charging program can be used simultaneously.

The unloading program is designed to handle any numbers of parcels with any selected tanks. Segregations in four voyages were 1-parcel at one or two ports, 2-parcel of 35/65% or 45/55% at one or two ports.

DIRTY/CLEAN WATER BALLAST CHARGING AND DISCHARGING CONTROL

This system is to charge or discharge water ballast to or from cargo oil tanks by cargo oil pumps. In loading or unloading ports, either of these programs is used independently, however, while the ship is sailing, both of these are simultaneously used in general.

A specific feature is seen in "water ballast distribution control", which maintains the ballasting ratio of each tank constant all through the process.

$$\text{Ballasting ratio} = \frac{\text{ballasted quantity}}{\text{total ballasting quantity}}$$

$$\dot{=} \frac{\text{present level req'd-initial level}}{\text{final level - initial level}}$$

Tank valves are controlled outside of the dead band which is located around the present level required. It is the intent to change the ship's condition linearly from start to end, on the assumption that the initial and the final conditions (trim, heel, draft, strength) are acceptable and reasonable. The advantages of this control is as follows. (i) When the trims of initial and final conditions are acceptable, the intermediate trim is to be acceptable as it changes linearly.

(ii) Heel is also maintained within the acceptable limit. (iii) Signals from draft gauges and heel metre, which are largely fluctuating among waves, are not used for this control. (iv) Parallel control of charging and discharging is possible by the same concept. (v) Input form is simple. One set of digital switches is provided for the input of charging and discharging rates respectively. Ballast discharging programs are almost in common with unloading programs except the former enables to deballast down to any intermediate ullages. Overflow prevention measures during ballast charging are similar to those of cargo oil loading.

PURE WATER BALLAST CHARGING AND DISCHARGING CONTROL

This system is to charge or discharge water ballast by the water ballast pump fitted with a Prima-Vac unit to or from exclusive water ballast tanks. When the system is used in parallel with unloading programs, heel is controlled simultaneously with water ballast wing tanks. Charging and discharging by gravity is optional and is switched to pumping operation when the flow rate becomes less than the rated capacity of the pump. Discharging to any intermediate ullage or to stripping is available.

CARGO AND WATER BALLAST CALCULATION SYSTEM

This system consists of three programs, loading scheme calculation, longitudinal strength calculation and stowage report printing programs, which are used independently or in parallel with control programs.
Loading scheme results, adjusting trim by fuel oil tanks or cargo oil tanks if necessary, are printed by the line printer with longitudinal strength calculations (bending moment, shearing force and deflection at 12 main stations). As the load is input by the form of weight as well as ullage or volume, planning for ore loading is also possible.
On-line strength calculations are carried out during cargo oil and water ballast control and results are printed on the data logging sheet. When the results are abnormal, the operator is alarmed.
The stowage report is an official report based on the ullages and oil characteristics manually measured by ship's personnel, which is printed by the line printer as many sheets as required.

SIMULATION TESTS

As the shipbuilding schedule was tightly made not to allow long term trial operations, it was necessary to carry out simulation tests as a debug aid at our research laboratory. A simulator was built up with four analogue computers and a provisional cargo oil control console, and was coupled to the ship's computer system via interfacers.
Programs for analogue computers were set up based on formulated ship's process models. These models consist of pumping plant module and ship's hydrostatic module. The former is composed of

simultaneous equations dealing with balance of pressure and flow quantity at every cross point in the piping network taking account of pump characteristics and tank levels. The latter is composed of hydrostatic calculation formulas to obtain ship's drafts and heel summing up the weight in tanks. Tested items are as follows.
(1) Confirmation test of single process
    Each single process of loading (LD), unloading (UL), D/C ballast charging (BC), D/C ballast discharging (BD), pure ballast charging (PC), and pure ballast discharging (PD) were tested independently.
(2) Confirmation test of dual process
    Combinations of LD/PD, LD/PC, UL/PC, UL/PD, UL/BC, BC/BD, BC/PC, BC/PD, BD/PC, BD/PD with Omega program and other batch calculation programs in parallel were tested to check relative interferences and control interval which is restricted by calculation speed.
(3) Confirmation of dynamic characteristics
    Control constants were adjusted to perform stable control.
(4) Back up procedure test
    Abnormal conditions such as sensor trouble, valve trouble, pump trouble, overflowing, etc. were intentionally made and back up procedures were confirmed.
(5) Training of crew
    As all simulation tests were carried out in real time, ship's crew attended to learn how to operate the system.

CONCLUSION

After the confirmation sea trials for about one month, the ship has been engaged in tanker service between the Persian Gulf and Japan. Partial modifications were effected after practical handling of crude oil. Loading programs have proven their merits in a windy port where drafts and levels were unable to be measured manually, finishing complete computer control in good accuracy. Unloading programs have shown high efficiency notably shortening stripping period. Data logging is favourably commented among the crew beyond our expectation, and even shore people often make use of it.
Various kinds of minor failures have been experienced and repaired on board except for a typewriter, a pressure gauge and a stabilizing voltage regulator which were renewed. Most of these failures are deemed to have occured due to insufficient aging and so the number of troubles has been decreasing. Lists of failures including every trifle cases, such as failure of lamps and leakage of gauge piping, are being compiled and analysed in pursuit of reliable system.
Preparing of input data and operations have been generally taken by officers, however, ratings are gradually taking the part especially in ballast handling. There is another problem left behind, which is the training of the new crew when shifting.
Tracing of operational problems will be continued for about one year after delivery and final evaluation will be made thereafter.

428

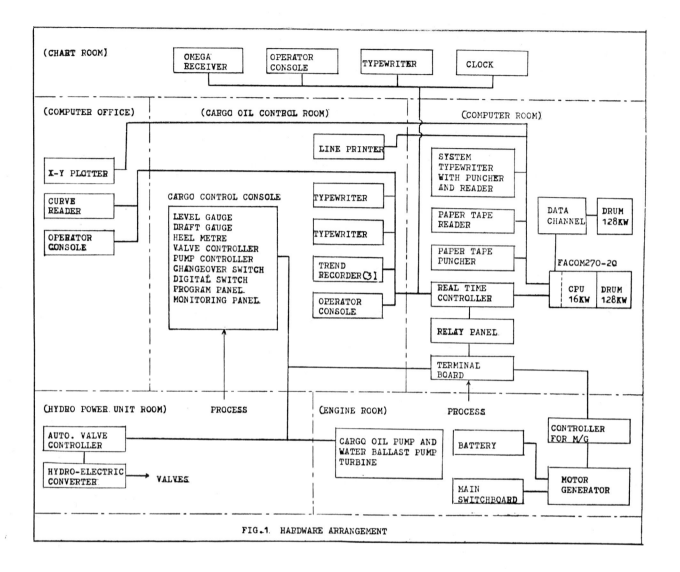

FIG.1. HARDWARE ARRANGEMENT

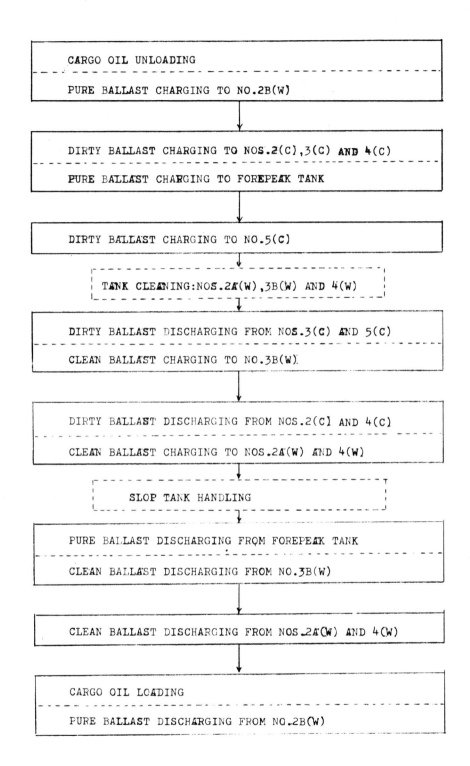

FIG.2 GENERAL CONTROL PROCEDURE IN ONE VOYAGE

430

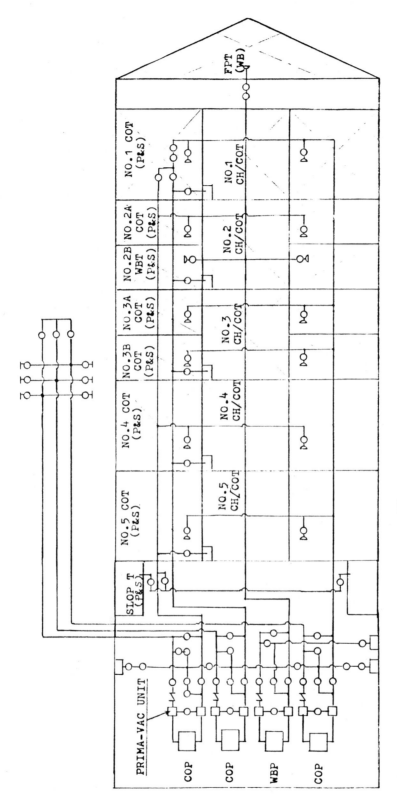

FIG.3 PIPING DIAGRAM

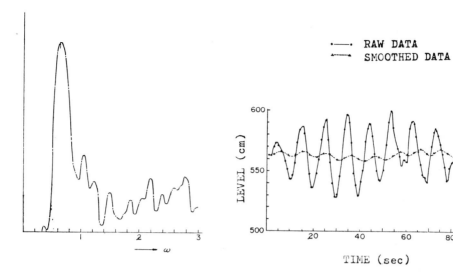

RAW DATA
SMOOTHED DATA

FIG.4 SPECTRAL DENSITY OF
LEVEL GAUGE SIGNAL

FIG.5 SMOOTHING OF LEVEL BY
ARITHMETIC MOVING AVERAGE

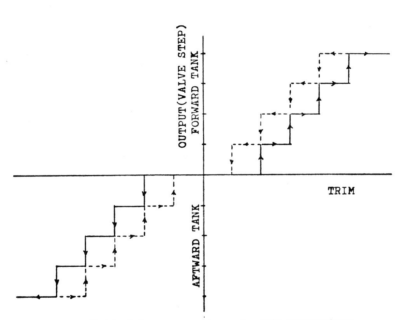

FIG.7 DISCRETE TRIM CONTROL WITH HYSTERESIS

/---- M.S. :OHTSUKAWA MARU: ::K:: LINE ----

(VOY.NO.) 2 (DATE AND TIME) 1972, 11.24, 12.40 (OPERATION) UL PC

	(FORE)	(MEAN)	(AFT)	(PORT)	(MEAN)	(STBD)
DRAFT (M)	4.96	8.81	12.66	8.90	8.87	8.85
DEFLECTION(M)	0.06 SAG					
TRIM (M)	7.70 B/S					
HEEL (DEG)	0.05 S					

	(1 P)	(1 S)	(1 C)	(2AP)	(2AS)	(2 C)	(3AP)	(3AS)	(3BP)	(3BS)	(3 C)
ULLAGE (M)	18.92	19.16	20.73	18.49	18.52	19.86	17.81	17.77	17.50	17.48	19.16
Q.IN TANK(KL)	3015	2899	2224	2216	2208	3143	2418	2429	1995	2000	3499
VALVE STEP	3/4	4/4	4/4	3/4	4/4	4/4	3/4	4/4	3/4	4/4	4/4
KIND OF CONT.	12	13	13	12	13	13	12	13	12	13	13
FINISH											

	(4 P)	(4 S)	(4 C)	(5 P)	(5 S)	(5 C)	(SLP P)	(SLP S)	(FPT)	(2WB P)	(2WB S)
ULLAGE (M)	13.36	11.66	16.84	14.39	16.16	16.66	15.65	15.64	26.11	21.16	22.19
Q.IN TANK(KL)	6628	7446	5337	4325	3644	5317	261	262	16	1133	883
VALVE STEP	2/4	3/4	3/4	2/4	3/4	3/4	4/4	4/4	0/4	4/4	3/4
KIND OF CONT.	10	11	11	10	11	11	13	13	0	13	12
FINISH									NU		

	(NO.1 C.O.P.)	(NO.2 C.O.P.)	(NO.2 C.O.P.)	(NO.3 C.O.P.)	(W. B. P.)
REVOLUTION	957 RPM	971 RPM	962 RPM	857 RPM	
SUCT.PRESS.	0.1 KG/SQ.CM	0.2 KG/SQ.CM	0.2 KG/SQ.CM	-0.2 KG/SQ.CM	
DEL.PRESS.	7.7 KG/SQ.CM	8.3 KG/SQ.CM	7.8 KG/SQ.CM	1.9 KG/SQ.CM	
DEL.Q.	3336 KL/H	3336 KL/H	3336 KL/H	3463 KL/H	
DEL.V.STEP	7/7	7/7	7/7	7/7	
KIND OF CONT.	3. 3	3. 3	3. 3	3. 3	

MANIFOLD PRESS. (NO.1 LINE) 6.0 KG/SQ.CM (NO.2 LINE) 5.5 KG/SQ.CM (NO.3 LINE) 5.4 KG/SQ.CM

	(TOTAL Q)	(CHARGE Q)	(DISCH. Q)	(BALANCE Q)	(AVERAGE RATE)	(LATEST 1 HR RATE)	(PRESENT RATE)
CARGO OIL	176139 KL	0 KL	114864 KL	61275 KL	6431 KL/H	10171 KL/H	10085 KL/H
BAL.CHARGE	0 KL	0 KL	0 KL				
BAL.DISCH.	0 KL	0 KL	0 KL				
P.BALLAST	9348 KL	1975 KL	7372 KL				

TOTAL HOUR FROM COMMENCEMENT 17 HR 50 MIN.

ESTIMATED FINISH TIME 13.34

(STRENGTH CALCULATION)
MAX.BM(TM) 131549 (0.21)

FR.NO.	51	57	64	68	73	77	82	86	91	101	109
SF(T)	2640	327	-966	-376	986	227	-236	-1602	-1480	-1002	-395
	(0.22)	(0.02)	(0.07)	(0.02)	(0.07)	(0.01)	(0.01)	(0.11)	(0.11)	(0.10)	(0.03)
BM(TM)	100862	120807	110808	96134	100237	133392	130157	113660	74553	7358	4591
	(0.16)	(0.20)	(0.18)	(0.16)	(0.16)	(0.22)	(0.21)	(0.18)	(0.12)	(0.01)	(0.00)

PORT
CAPTAIN
C/OFFICER

FIG.6 DATA LOGGING

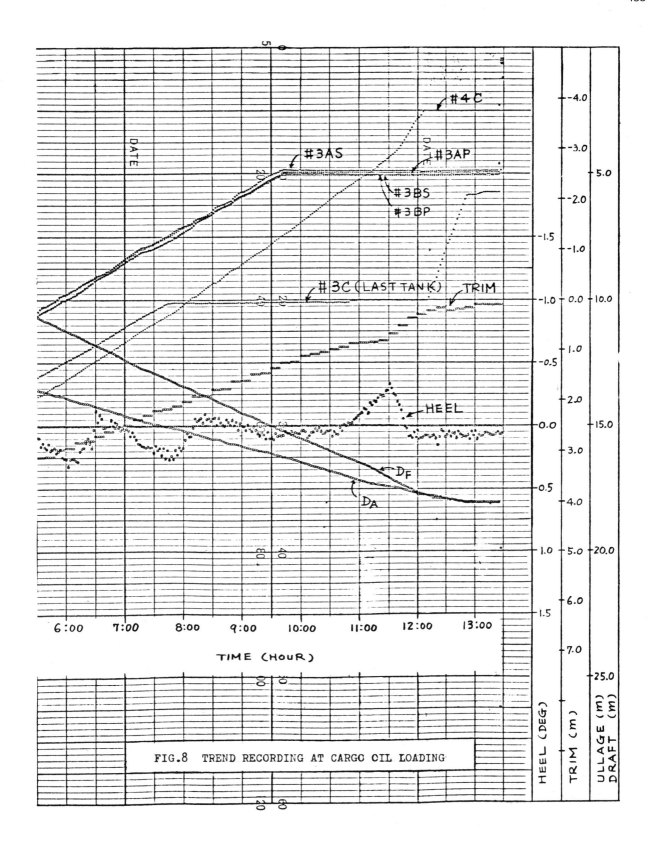

FIG.8 TREND RECORDING AT CARGO OIL LOADING

COMPUTERIZED SUPER-AUTOMATION SYSTEM OF
THE "TOTTORI MARU", TURBINE DRIVEN TANKER

Hideo Saito
Deputy Manager
Ship Engineering Department
Mitsubishi Heavy Industries, Ltd.

Sachio Okano
Staff Superintendent
No.1 Ship Designing Department
Nagasaki Shipyard & Engine Works
Mitsubishi Heavy Industries, Ltd.

ABSTRACT

The turbine tanker TOTTORI MARU is adopted the
centralized computer control system which controls
various systems for navigation, cargo handling and
turbine plant by one set of the process control
computer MELCOM 350-5S.
As to the navigation systems, the anti-collision
radar is provided the ship to enable her to avoid
collisions with other vessels, and the Omega Navigation Method is adopted to determine the ship's
position and also make various navigational
calculations.
As for the cargo handling system, cargo-handling,
ballasting and deballasting are automatically
controlled completely for the purpose of saving
labor, reducing the time required for cargo handling, and securing operational safety.
The turbine plant system is employed for monitoring and direct digital control of the main turbine,
preventing the black-out, hot-starting the boilers
etc. in order to securing safety and saving labor
in the plant operation.
Now, she is on her way of the 3rd voyage. The
super-automation system is operating successfully.

1. INTRODUCTION

Completed at the Nagasaki Shipyard & Engine Works
of Mitsubishi Heavy Industries, Ltd. on September
5, 1972 was the turbine tanker "Tottori Maru".
The vessel is a 237,383 ton d.w. oil tanker built
to the joint order of the Nippon Yusen Kaisha Ltd.
and the Taiheiyo Kaiun Kaisha Ltd. She is the
Japan's first fully computer controlled turbine
ship, and is in the service of transporting crude
oil between Persian Gulf and Japan, her super-
automated control system being in satisfactory
operating condition.

2. OUTLINE OF SUPER-AUTOMATION SYSTEM

2.1 Progress in development of super-automation system

In response to the Government's policy, since 1968
Mitsubishi Heavy Industries, Ltd. had pursued
researches on the super-automated ship jointly
with the Nippon Yusen Kaisha, Ltd.: in 1970 a
decision was reached to apply the results of the
joint researches to the turbine tanker to be
built at Nagasaki Shipyard & Engine Works.
In the course of the development, a high priority
was given to previous studies and experiments;
shipboard and shop tests were conducted to obtain
various characteristics of the plant; on the bases
of the experiments was made plant model with the
use of the analog computer belonging to the
Mitsubishi's Nagasaki Technical Institute; and
simulation tests were conducted on the model over
five months in combination with the computer
installed in an actual ship. The reliability and
practicability of the super-automated system could
be confirmed previously as mentioned above, and so
the system was generally in excellent condition
while at sea, and satisfactory results could be
obtained at an early stage of navigation.

2.2 Features of super-automation system

The super-automation system of the "Tottori maru"
was developed jointly by the Nippon Yusen Kaisha,
Ltd. and the Mitsubishi Heavy Industries, Ltd.
through the results of the researches conducted by
the S A Research Group. The purpose of the
development was to confirm through shipboard
experiments improvement in safety of navigation,
improvement in reliability, rationalization of
shipboard work, and effect of improved economy.
The system, however, not only meets the purpose of
experiments, but is highly serviceable for actual
navigation.
This system is characterized by the following.
(1) The computer (Mitsubishi Electric Co. - made
    MELCOM-350-5S) is so versatile as to centrally
    control various systems for navigation, cargo
    handling and turbine plant control, all by
    itself.
(2) All of the systems can be controlled from
    their respective convenient places. Namely,
    the navigation system from the wheel house, the
    cargo handling system from the cargo handling
    control room, and the turbine plant system from
    the engine control room.
(3) The computer and its equipment are so designed
    as to remain unaffected by the vibration,
    pitching and rolling of the hull, salinity,
    humidity, etc.
(4) The sensors and actuators used have all been
    subjected to severe testing, and are perfectly
    reliable accordingly.
(5) Even if there occurs power failure in the ship,
    power can be supplied from the buttery for the
    continuous operation of the computer.
(6) If the computer should go into trouble, the
    conventional device can automatically be

actuated without delay, thus securing the smooth and safe operation of the ship.

(7) Built to Nippon Kaiji Kyokai's MO requirements, the ship is navigable without the use of the computer.

3. COMPUTER SYSTEM

3.1 Hardware

(1) Computer:

The computer MELCOM 350-5S is provided with one 16K words core memory and three 32K words magnetic drums as memory units, and also with the high speed arithmetic unit which is so designed as to make complex, rapid calculations.

(2) Peripheral equipment:

There are connected one paper tape reader with the reading speed of 120 words per second, one paper tape puncher with the punching speed of 60 words per second and five sets of fixed carriage typewriters (FCT), two of which are capable of processing key input.

(3) The input/output unit:

(a) Analog input

Two sets of V/F converters are used in parallel, and are so designed as to read the input of over 200 points at the various signal levels.

(b) Analog output

The analog output of the rudder type, is used in setting revolutions, such as cargo pump speed control, etc.

(c) Digital input/output

The contact and level input/output are possible. As to the output, a number of momentary output are used for bumpless transfer at the time of computer troubles.

(d) Pulse input/output

The pulse width output, for instance the direct digital control of the main turbine, and various pulse inputs are connected to it.

(e) Interrupt input

The inputs for various program starting and stopping and trip sequence record of important machineries are connected.

(4) Man machine interface:

There are provided various operator consoles and typewriter desks, etc.

(5) Power Supply:

There is provided the uninterrupted power

source unit consisting of the motor and the generator, and so even in the case of power failure throughout the ship, the computer can be operated constantly.

(6) Ship's actual service:

The ship is on the third voyage; and especially, no troubles have occurred in the CPU and the memory unit (including the magnetic drum), proving that they are highly reliable. The paper tape reader and the puncher are all in very satisfactory condition. The typewriters were generally in good working condition, but the one for navigation system went into trouble only once. The input/output processing unit was also in satisfactory condition, and is frequently processing inputs and outputs correctly and accurately. On the maiden voyage, the relay cards for the analog input and the digital output went into trouble, but normal operation could be resumed after replacement with spare cards. The computer had a low percentage of troubles as compared with other electronic equipment; and it has been proved that the shipboard computer is very reliable.

3.2 Software

The software is intended for attaining the smooth operation of the entire systems, and consists of the following basic programs.

(1) Supervisor

The supervisor is used in controlling the peripheral input/output units, in handling the interrupt input and in the real-time execution of the application programs. A special consideration is given to the time sharing in order to avoid the delay of the application program due to waiting for the completion of the functioning of the peripheral instruments and also to reduce the frequent transmission of memories from the drum as far as possible.

(2) Executive control program

There are provided two different kinds of mode -- the auto. mode and the test mode. The auto. mode is the on-line control mode, and the test mode is the off-line mode by which the computer is completely disconnected from the plant. The hardware testing and the program debugging can be easily carried out by means of the test mode. In addition, the executive control program handles the stopping and starting of the entire systems and the remedial measures at the time of troubles. When, for instance, troubles occurs in the drum, the hardware and software for the system which uses the drum in trouble are disconnected, and after that, the operation is resumed. When the typewriter goes into trouble, automatic changeover to the substitute is carried out.

(3) Support program

There are provided an abundant support program in consideration of the control of the system specially required for a ship.

(a) On-line utility

It has functions required for registering and modifying the programs in the on-line mode.

(b) Function control

This is a program intended for treating in batch various tests of hardwares in the on-line mode.

(c) Load execution program

- This is used for reading various sorts of tapes by means of a push-button and punching paper tapes for data on particular areas.

(d) On-line debugging program

While in operation by means of the on-line mode, the dynamic function of the application program can be inspected; and the gathering and preparation of data required can be done.

(e) In addition to the above, there are provided the utility and debugging programs which are used in the off-line mode, and the assembler.

(4) Ship's actual service

The computer was required to function frequently at the time of ballast conversion carried out during navigation. At that time the waiting state of the task was measured by sampling period of 0.1 second, and as a result, it became evident that there was hardly any program in the state of waiting for starting. The system is so designed as to prevent the disorder of tasks due to waiting for the completion of work even when many logging programs such as noon logging were in function, and so there arose no problems at all. There occurred some disorder when the anti-collision radar was in frequent tracking operation, but it had no effect on the control programs such as the main turbine DDC, which functioned during a short period, by adequate selection of the priority of each programs. And the executive control program and the support program also functioned as was planned at the early stage, and especially, the on-line debugging and function control programs, etc. also proved to be effective.

4. NAVIGATION SYSTEM

4.1 Anti-collision radar

This radar has been developed jointly by Mitsubishi Heavy Industries, Ltd., Mitsubishi Electric Co., Ltd. and Anritsu Denpa Co. to prevent collision with other ships and objects floating on the sea. The system consists of the 5 centimeter wave radar for marine use and the control stand called "MARAC-

II". The radar video signal sent from within 2.5 to 7.5 nautical miles or 5 to 10 nautical miles away from the ship is processed by means of the special circuit; and the computer detects a target ship automatically and performs automatic trackings. The anti-collision program computes the CPA (Closest Point of Approach), the TCPA (Time required for approaching the closest point), the speed and sailing course of the target ship, display various data on the control stand, and also indicates the data on the dangerous ship, giving an alarm in the case that the target ship is estimated to approach within the limit of CPA. It is possible to perform simultaneous tracking of as many as 10 dangerous ships as target ships, and also possible to detect the target ship by manual operation.

When the ship was on her second voyage, the software and hardware were completely adjusted, and the normal function of all the units was confirmed. Especially, the radar video signal processing unit functioned satisfactorily, which was designed to avoid the reduction of the number of target ships due to several islands and low clouds acting as targets.

4.2 Position fixing by means of omega navigational system

The omega navigational system is used for the determination of the ship's position by means of the computer. The ship's position is obtained through the lane of position derived from the omega receiver and the correction data fed in advance. At the present time, however, the completion of the omega station is still behind the schedule, and cannot be used in determining the ship's position. Under the circumstances, the estimated position should be used as the data to be used for a logbook or the manual input is used after obtaining the corrected value of the ship's position by other means, for instance astronomical observation, radar, etc.

4.3 Navigational logging

There are the following records about navigation.

(1) Noon report
(2) Final report
(3) Omega fix
(4) Track and current

The loggings are made at regular intervals (at 1200 and 2000 hours SMT) or when necessary. It is necessary to have the input of corrected data, etc. at the initial stage of navigation or during the navigation. For that purpose is used the typewriter. To prevent the wrong input from the typewriter keyboard, the dialogue between the man and the computer is adopted. The items for key input are as follows.

(1) Initial data setting
(2) Corrected data input
(3) Relogging and report making

4.4 Navigational calculation program

(1) Mercator sailing method
(2) Middle latitude sailing method
(3) Great circle sailing method
(4) Calculation by means of astronomical observation

The data input required for the above calculations can be obtained from the typewriter keyboard like in the case of item 4.3 mentioned above.
The programs are effectively used for planning navigation and calculating the estimated position of a ship. And especially, the omega navigational method cannot be used, and so the calculation by means of astronomical observation is frequently used.

5. CARGO HANDLING SYSTEM

5.1 Basic programs

Fig. 3 shows the six basic programs.
These programs control the basic sequence of cargo handling ranging from the initial setting of valves prior to the pumping operation to the closing of the valves after the completion of the cargo handling, and also include the pipe line flushing to be specially carried out in the case of "single buoy mooring" off Kawasaki. In preparing the basic program, a special consideration was given to the versatility, the switching to computer control in the course of cargo handling operation, and the saving of time required for cargo handling.

(1) Versatility:

There are a great number of combinations of cargo tanks and pumps in handling two or three different kinds of cargo oils. This cargo handling system is so designed as to control any type of cargo handling operation. On the first voyage, the cargo oil was discharged at two ports, and two different kinds of oil were discharged at each port. The cargo oil discharge was completely controlled by the computer, displaying its versatility. On the other hand, the versatility leads to an increase in input required for specifying the type of cargo handling operation; and in the case of the unloading program, there are provided as many as 73 items. These are derived from several sorts of standard data tapes ready for use, and fed into the computer by means of the paper tape reader. Then, they are revised to fit the specific case by the operator console.

(2) Changeover to automatic operation during cargo handling operation:

The pumping work is a sequence of works lasting for 24 hours; and it is considered that during the pumping period there may occur an alteration and interruption in the cargo handling pattern. To cope with such cases, the basic program is so designed as to start performing in the course of a sequence of cargo handling works.
In the course of cargo handling on the second voyage, the computer needed to be stopped for

revision of the program, and resumed its controlling operation through this method of changeover to automatic operation.

(3) Saving time for cargo handling:

In conventional cargo handling operation, only about four tanks were loaded with cargo oil simultaneously, and so it was necessary to reduce the loading speed at a relatively early stage of cargo handling operation. In the case of this system, however, all of the tanks except for one for final loading can be simultaneously loaded with cargo oil, thus delaying the reduction in loading speed. And it is estimated that by so doing, approximately two hours could be saved.

5.2 Control program

During the pumping operation, a close watch is to be kept on the tanks for overflow and on the hull for trimming, heeling and strength. In case that the limits are exceeded, suitable tanks are to be selected, and control performed by opening or closing the valves fitted in the tanks. At Mizushima harbor where the unloading was carried out on the first voyage, a limit was placed on the upper deck height above the water level due to the height of the loading arm, and the rise of ship's side due to heeling could not be disregarded. The ordinary limited heeling of 0.5° could be successfully reduced to 0.2°. The unloading at Mizushima was carried out under very severe hull strength condition, and in that case both the bending moment and the shearing force nearly reached the limit. Without the computer, it was very difficult to make a check by calculating manually in the course of cargo handling operation.

5.3 Pump speed control program

The speed of the cargo oil and ballast pumps is controlled to prevent the cavitation attributed to reduction in suction pressure, to prevent the suction of air from the bell mouth in the cargo tank, to keep balancing at the time of parallel operation of the pumps, and to maintain the limited pressure in the onshore manifold and also to overriding for boiler pressure. Particularly, to prevent the cavitation and air suction, severe control is carried out according to the calculations made on the basis of the pump revolution and the cargo oil flow, and so more improvement in efficiency can be expected than in the case of the manual operation. On the first and second voyages, the reduction in the time was not very remarkable, because sufficient margin was provided for control. However, this is considered to be one of the programs very effective in labor-saving and safety.

5.4 Loading plan program

This program includes functions of various calculations, which are itemized as follows.

a) Calculation of optimum loading condition
b) Calculation of ship's condition
c) Calculation of specific gravity on the basis of API and temperature

d) Correction of ullage in the final-loaded tank (Loading)
e) Examination of final draft (Loading)

The calculation of the above Item a) was seldom made; and the ship's condition (draft, trim, heel, structural strength, etc.) mentioned in the above Item b) was calculated very often. There is no need for reducing the hull strength farther when it is sufficiently within the limits. And it is considered that even though many pattern of operations are prepared, ship's personnel only carry out operation in accordance with the pattern they could master. The Items c) and d) are very useful because they can be used for quick calculation of the final loading.

5.5 Other programs

There are provided the level gauge checking program to examine the float gauge which is liable to suffer damages in spite that it is one of the most important detectors.
The data logging program is used in logging at an interval of one (1) hour, and information is available at any time regarding trim, heel, the corrected ullage, the amount of cargo oil contained in each tank (quantity, KT, LT, NET, BBL), total amount of oil load or unloaded.
These programs are quite serviceable enough for labor-saving along with the other control programs. In normal condition of cargo handling there is no necessity for a duty officer to keep watch for cargo handling.

5.6 Detectors newly developed and improved

To control the cargo handling by means of the computer, the detector need to be newly developed and improved, and so the cargo oil pump flow meter, the overflow detector, the low level detector, etc. were developed and improved to get rid of their moving parts subjected to severe conditions.
The flow meter serves as an important detector for the pump speed control program. And the low level detector is able to eliminate the work which was conventionally done by the ship's crew by looking into the oil tank for confirmation, and serves to save labor at the busiest time of cargo handling.

6. TURBINE PLANT SYSTEM

The turbine plant system is intended for easy and safe operation of the plant.
All of the programs function independently, but are closely related to the conventional control devices, and consists of the following systems.
Figure 4 shows the component parts of the turbine plant system.

6.1 Data processing system

(1) Logging and efficiency calculation

As to loggings, the following are typed out by the logging or announcement typewriters.

(a) Logging at regular intervals
(b) Noon logging
(c) Voyage logging

(d) Demand logging

As to performance calculation, fuel consumption (expected values and actual values), boiler water consumption, mean shaft horsepower, mean revolution, etc. are calculated. It was effective that the typewriters were separately used in accordance with report making and recording of plant condition. And performance calculation was effective for forming a judgement of overall plant efficiency.

(2) Alarm scanning

The condition of the turbine plant is scanned at the intervals of 10 or 30 seconds in accordance with the characters of the data. When the plant is in abnormal condition, an alarm is given, and the message about abnormality (time, abnormal point, and data) is typewritten. There is also provided a monitoring device of the conventional type, simultaneous watch was kept by means of the two units. It has been experienced that the message about abnormality was quite serviceable for plant operation.

(3) Digital display

The data of the plant can be displayed at any time in the digital indicator through the operator's console. The displayed data are renewed every three seconds and so they are effectively used for watch at the time of severe load fluctuations that occur when the ship arrives in or departs from a port.

(4) Trip sequence recording

When the main turbine, main boiler, generator turbine and feed pumps are tripped, the tripping order is recorded by means of the typewriter to facilitate subsequent investigation into the cause of tripping. During a period of her voyages, the plant was in perfect condition, the program was never used.

6.2 Abnormality detection and prevention system

(1) Detection and prevention of abnormality of main turbine

This system is intended for safety operation of the main turbine.

(a) Detection of abnormal vibration

As soon as abnormal vibration of the high or low pressure turbine rotors is detected, an alarm is given and at the same time the speed increase is discontinued or the speed is reduced automatically according to the extent of abnormality and the operating condition.
In the region of high speed revolution, the vibration frequency can be counted; the vibration nature is analyzed; and the cause of the vibration is typed out.
In the region of low speed revolution, the turbine gland is monitored for contact by

means of the rub check monitor which has
been newly developed; and an alarm is given
in case of abnormal condition.

(b) Detection of thermal stress

The temperature outside and inside of the
flanged part of the high pressure turbine
casing is detected; the thermal stress
produced in the flanged part is monitored;
and when the thermal stress exceeds the
limit, the turbine speed is reduced
automatically. At the time of the speed
increase, a calculation is made of the
thermal stress which will be possibly caused by the speed increase; a maximum of
allowable speed is obtained from the
calculation.
The increase and decrease in the main
turbine speed of this ship is monitored and
controlled by this program; and it has been
confirmed that the program is perfectly
reliable. Figure 5 shows an example of the
operation of the turbine.

(2) Black-out prevention

This is intended for preventing power failure.
The operation of the turbo-generator and the
main condenser is monitored; and when the main
cause of the black-out is detected previously,
the auxiliary diesel generator starts and
synchronizes automatically.
In the ship, the plant was operated in perfect
condition throughout the voyages, and so this
program has never been used.

6.3 Direct digital control of main turbine

The starting and stopping, the changeover to ahead
and astern directions, the increase and decrease in
the shaft revolution are directly controlled from
the bridge or the engine control room by means of
the computer. The program has the same function
with the conventional remote controlling device.
And it is supported by the conventional remote
controlling device whose control lever, actuators
after the governor motor, revolution counter are
used common to the computer. Therefore, the
computer control can be changed over to the control
by means of the conventional remote controlling
device for bumpless transfer.

6.4 Recovery of plant operation

(1) Recovery from black-out

In case of power failure, recovery operation
such as power source recovery by means of the
auxiliary diesel generator, restarting of the
auxiliary motor etc. can be made by means of
the conventional automatic device. This
program starts functioning simultaneously with
the occurrence of power failure, monitor the
above-mentioned operation, and gives an alarm
in case of unsatisfactory operation, and type
out the operation guide to ask the crew for
correct operation. And when recovery of the
boiler is possible, the boiler hot starting
program starts functioning.

(2) Boiler hot starting

This program automatically controls the sequence
of the boiler hot starting. The function is
started through the order received from the
program of recovery from black-out or by means
of the push-button, and is finished through
various stages of preparations for lighting-off
(operation of valve, changeover from ACC to
computer control), lighting-off, pressure rise
and changeover to ACC. However, lighting-off
is carried out remote-manually by push-button.
The plant was always in satisfactory condition
through the voyage, and so the plant recovery
system was never used. However, the boiler hot
starting program has had the chance to perform
in Kawasaki from her first voyage. Although
the load was unsteady due to the cargo unloading, there arose no problems about the all
sequences. This program required no operation
and watch after the order for lighting-off is
given, and enjoyed popularity.

7. CONCLUSION

In this paper have been briefly discussed the super-
automation system of the Tottori Maru and the
results of its operation. In general, the system
was in satisfactory condition throughout the
voyages, and proved to be highly reliable and
practicable. It is, however, only a short time
since the super-automation system was put to
practical use.
Authors are intending to pursue further studies of
the computer controlled system to achieve its
completion and to realize the progress in the
automatic operation of ships.

440

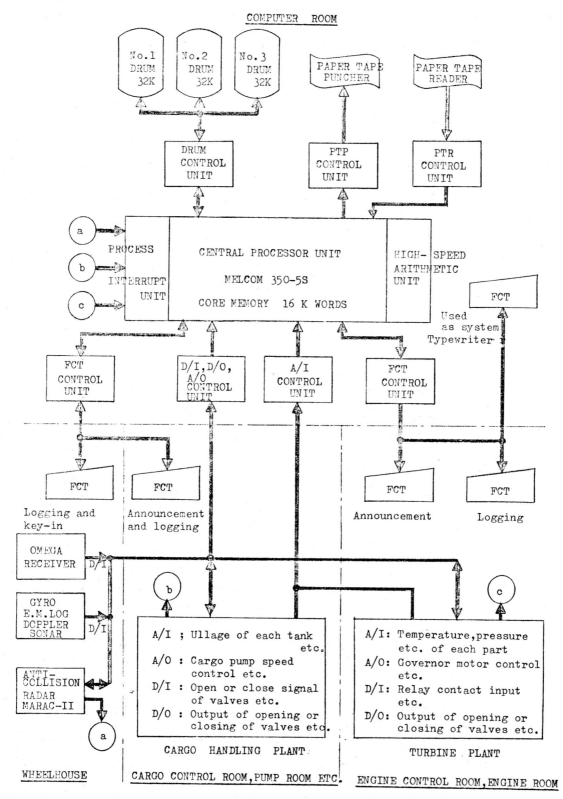

COMPUTER ROOM

No.1 DRUM 32K   No.2 DRUM 32K   No.3 DRUM 32K

PAPER TAPE PUNCHER

PAPER TAPE READER

DRUM CONTROL UNIT

PTP CONTROL UNIT

PTR CONTROL UNIT

a   PROCESS

b   INTERRUPT UNIT

c

CENTRAL PROCESSOR UNIT

MELCOM 350-5S

CORE MEMORY 16 K WORDS

HIGH-SPEED ARITHMETIC UNIT

FCT

Used as system Typewriter

FCT CONTROL UNIT

D/I,D/O, A/O CONTROL UNIT

A/I CONTROL UNIT

FCT CONTROL UNIT

FCT

FCT

FCT

FCT

Logging and key-in

Announcement and logging

Announcement

Logging

OMEGA RECEIVER   D/I

GYRO E.M.LOG DOPPLER SONAR   D/I

ANTI-COLLISION RADAR MARAC-II

a

b

c

A/I ; Ullage of each tank etc.
A/O : Cargo pump speed control etc.
D/I : Open or close signal of valves etc.
D/O : Output of opening or closing of valves etc.

A/I: Temperature,pressure etc. of each part
A/O: Governor motor control etc.
D/I : Relay contact input etc.
D/O: Output of opening or closing of valves etc.

CARGO HANDLING PLANT

TURBINE PLANT

WHEELHOUSE   CARGO CONTROL ROOM,PUMP ROOM ETC.   ENGINE CONTROL ROOM,ENGINE ROOM

FIG. 1   DIAGRAM OF HARDWARE FOR COMPUTER CONTROL SYSTEM

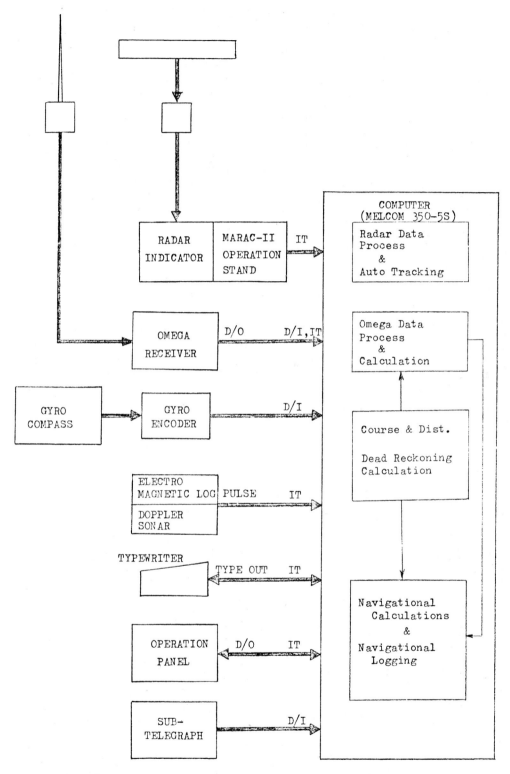

FIG 2   DIAGRAM OF NAVIGATION SYSTEM

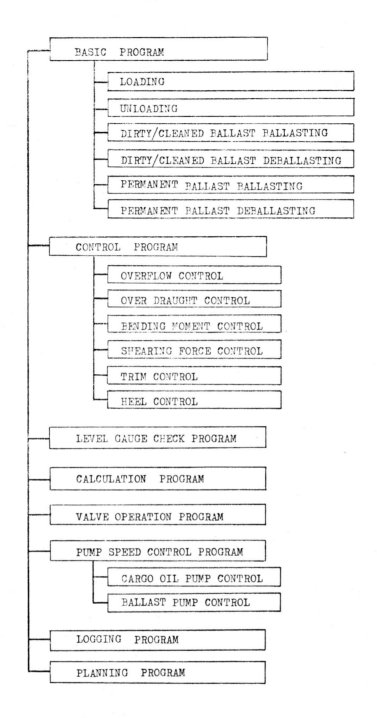

FIG. 3   DIAGRAM OF CARGO HANDLING SYSTEM PROGRAMS

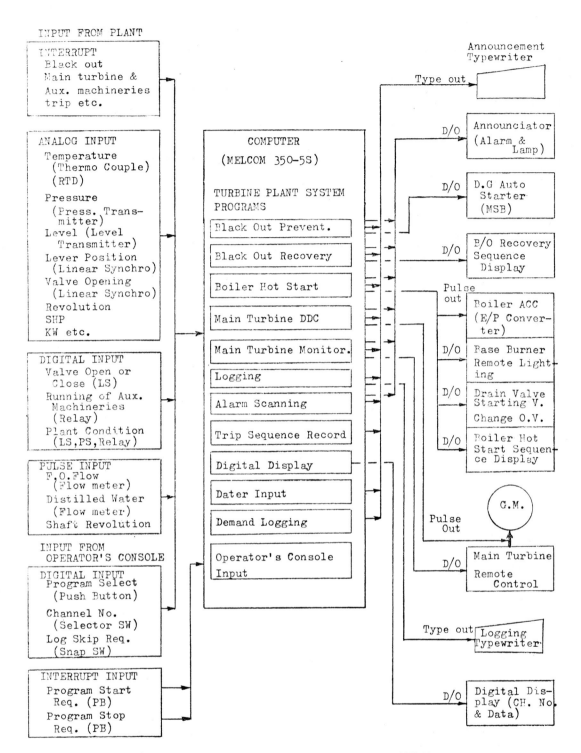

FIG. 4   DIAGRAM OF TURBINE PLANT CONTROL SYSTEM

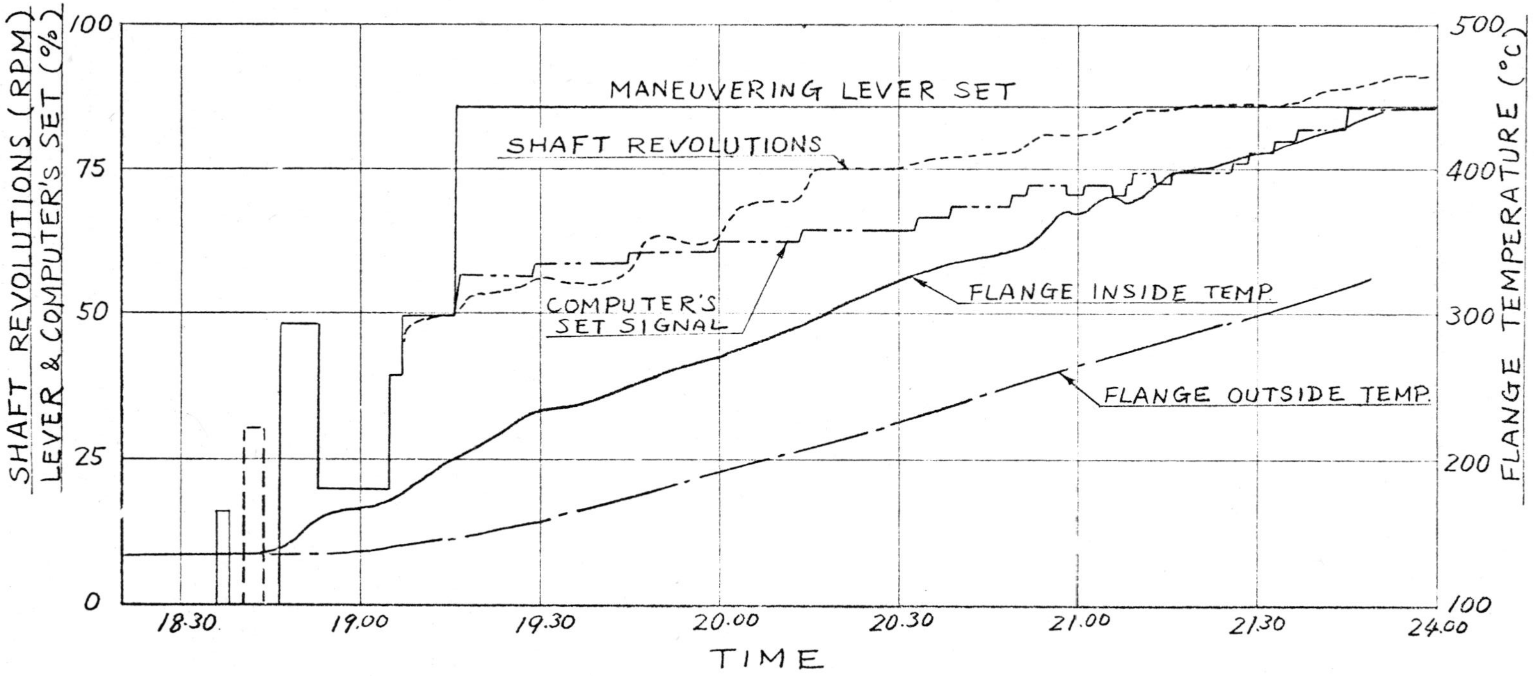

444

FIG 5 RESULT OF MAIN TURBINE START UP

COMPUTERIZED AUTOMATION OF THE CONTAINERSHIP LLOYDIANA

Giuseppe Sitzia
Director
CETENA
Genoa, Italy

Gianfranco Sartirana
System Analysis Dpt
CETENA
Genoa, Italy

ABSTRACT

The paper describes a practical application of general process computers in the integrated automation system of the container-carrier "LLOYDIANA" which will be delivered on the first months of 1973 by "Cantiere Navale Muggiano" for the owner "Lloyd Triestino".
The computer system is based on an IBM system 7 for the fast data acquisition and on an IBM 1130 for the mathematical calculations and disk operation and access : its task is to integrate the basic peripherical automatic systems and to perform some functions for which complex calculations are needed.
Details are given on the computer system configuration and procedures and on the tasks committed to the system in the Navigation, steam propulsion plant control and refrigerated cargo monitoring.
The computer System, is now operating on simulation in the yard.

1 - INTRODUCTION

Around 1965, when different groups started to study the possibility of installation of a computer on board, the uncertainty was not mainly concerning the tasks to be entrusted to the computer, but rather about its possibility of "surviving" well in the particular marine conditions. The usage has confirmed in fact that a computer which is installed with the same care as any nautical device has at least an equivalent viability. This is also the result sprung from the "Esquilino" Project conducted jointly by the Genoa University, "Lloyd Triestino" and CETENA, in which to a computer were entrusted several tasks on the automation of the ship.
The experimentation showed that the computer copes well with the different problems posed by its utilization on a ship. In addition, the "Lloyd Triestino", the owner of the "Esquilino", realized that the utilization of a computer could lead to essential economic and operatives advantages, due not to a reduction in the crew, but rather to an improved operation of the different systems on board. Because of that, there has been, in 1971, an agreement between "Lloyd Triestino" and the "Italcantieri" yards for the study and the development of a further application of computer on board the Containership "Lloydiana". This study and its realization was then committed to CETENA, that was able to take advantage of its previous experience and of Genoa University's. [1]

2 - DESIGN PHILOSOPHY OF THE COMPUTER SYSTEM

When the "Lloyd Triestino" decided to continue the experiences conducted on the M/s "Esquilino" by an application deeper inserted in the ship operation, it was considered useful to fix some conclusions derived from the preceding experience and to define, in full accordance with the shipowner's managers and technical staff, the development-lines of the new project. We can summarize the former and detail the latter, as follows :

A) The installation of a digital computer in the several functions concurring in the ship operation appeared feasible, though with different difficulties depending on the considered function. Also the implementation of these different functions in one or more computing units was possible, on condition that a proper software was prepared.

B) The previous considerations didn't necessarily imply that the computer had to be inserted in all those functions.
Instead, this meant that the functions distribution must be done taking into account of what the computer can do more and better, with regard to the available devices. Therefore, it was necessary to extend an investigation to all the subsystems composing the ship to examine what could be offered by the utilization of the computer more than by the conventional solutions. This examination has allowed to define the following general criteria of development of the "Lloydiana" system :

a) The installation of a computer can and must be initially justified by its capacity in concentrating and correlating the information, in providing rapidly essential data in case of emergency, and in supervising critically the consistency of the concurring data.
The computer ability in concentrating the information will relieve the ship officer tasks, since he will not receive a great and uncorrelated heap of data with a low density of information, but a reduced and selected series of elements, all necessary or, at least, useful to the decisional process. The typical case of this utilization is the computer capability to provide indexes of operation of the various components the steam propulsion plant; this possibility eliminated the necessity of a continuous monitoring of the functional variables of each apparatus.
The usefulness of concentrating the information becomes important in those cases of emergency in which the engineer must take operating decisions that may be essential in an extremely limited time. Therefore, if this operator will have at his disposal tho-

se few data whose knowledge is necessary to take the optimal decision or the minimum risk one, the computer, which will provide these data, will be a very important element for the ship safety.

At last, the computer capacity in correlating data coming from various information sources allows, through this correlation, to attribute to these data some "reliability indexes" connected to the consistency level of everyone with all the others. This will allow also a supervision of the "controlling system-controlled system" complex, so that it will be possible to distinguish between the former system anomalies and the second system ones. A typical case is the failures detection in perypherical sensors, which could cause wrong alarms and which, on the contrary, can be detected by the computer.

b) All that above referred don't exhaust, obviously, the possibilities of a computer, for which it is possible to foresee applications in various Direct Digital Controls and, finally, the passage to the optimal control of the various subsystems. That is, infact, the ultimate purpose of every application of computer process control. Nevertheless the authors believe that the introduction of a DDC done by the computer isn't its best application. This evaluation is suggested by some considerations about the total reliability of the system and it is valid if the loops on which the computer should intervene, are operating on stationary systems. On the contrary, if it is necessary to control system variability, and, therefore, also a variability of the control parameters, the use of a computer naturally adaptable, through the loaded program, to the variations of the controlled system, becomes justified. In this case the computer itself should determine these variations through proper identification programs. At this point, the passage to the optimization of the various controls is a natural one, at least theoretically. Then the computer itself will determine the values of the control parameters minimizing some objective function, in accordance with optimum criteria appropriately selected. This is the case, for example of an adaptive steering or of an optimal control of the various subsystems of a steam propulsion plant.

In any case, it is clear the necessity of valid mathematical models of the systems on which the computer intervention is thought useful. Nevertheless, generally, these models derive only from complex analyses operated on the behaviour of the variables of the system. Therefore, in our project, it is established an application sequency that foresees, at first, the utilization of the computer in identifying the systems which call for an optimal control. On the other hand, this is a common way to do in the ground-based computer process controls.

c) We thought to give no general answers to the open question of the different tasks subdivision between one or more computers.

The authors believe that, because of back-up problems, at least two computing units will be necessary on board. The tasks subdivision must be then tailored every time, taking into account that :

- the concentration of several functions in one unit allows a saving of central core storage, due to its utilization in time-sharing by different programs;
- this concentration complicates the operating systems that must manage these programs and besides puts problems of total reliability. Therefore, it is our opinion that the solution adopted on T/s "Lloydiana" is not only interlocutory, but also tailored to the particular philosophy of this design.

d) A special attention has been given to the resolution of I/O problems, especially with regard to the simplification of the man-computer interaction. In particular, the programs execution is generally automatic. In the extremely limited cases in which the operator has to start the execution of several programs and has to introduce data into the computer, we tried to avoid, as much as possible, the standard keyboards use and we have preferred thumbwheels and push-bottom methods.

Possible mistakes in data input will be detected by the computer whose programs will be therefore protected.

As regards the output operations, the prints are used only for the historical recordings; instead, electronic nixie-tubes are used for the normal outputs. In this way we think that, after the first running period, the interactive conversation procedures will not require particular knowledges about the computer.

3 - THE T/s "LLOYDIANA"

The Lloydiana is a container ship, the first built in Italy for Italian shipowners. The ship, for containers transportation only, has one propeller, powered by a geared turbine, with the power plant stern housed. The ship is divided in 10 compartements by 9 watertight bulkhead : 6 of the compartements are constituted by 6 holds for the containers transportation, with a capability of 1600 containers, of which 100 refrigerated.

The deadweight is 32.000 tons. The steam propulsion plant is consisting of a turboreductor AEG-De Schelde fed by two boilers Babcock-Wilcox, capable to furnish continuously a maximum power ahead of 32.500 HP (50% from the HP turbine and the other 50% from the LP turbine).

For this power plant, there are 4 types of control systems :
- automatic remote control from the bridge;
- automatic remote control from the control room, following the orders from the bridge telegraph;
- electrical control from the control room following the orders from the bridge telegraph;
- manual control of the maneouvre valves following the orders from the bridge.

Moreover, there is installed a general call and alarm system. The ship is provided with the most advanced electronic navigation aids, among which :
- Selenia-Raytheon A/C System connected with the radar;
- Receiver for the Transit satellyte signals;
- Decca navigator;
- Loran navigator;
- Sperry SRD 301 doppler log;
- Microtecnica gyro-compass
- AEG autopilot

The whole of the shortly described characteristics makes the T/s "Lloydiana" one of the most advanced and equipped units of the Merchant Marine and, therefore, it is one of the most qualified to be completed with the installation of a central computing unit realizing an integrated automation.

4 - THE COMPUTING SYSTEM

On the ground of the considerations exposed and of the systematic study of the functions described in the following, the central computing system has been configured and inserted on the operation of the "Lloydiana" as follows (see fig.1).

a) A computing unit IBM 1130, with the following characteristics and peripheral units :
- 16 K of core storage (16 bits)
- 3.6 μ s of memory cycle
- Typewriter
- IBM 1442 card reader-punch
- Magnetic disk with a capacity of 512.000 words
- A "storage access channel" for coupling in "multiprocessing" with the IBM S/7.

The unit is equipped with an operating system expecially studied for the operation in multiprocessing with the System 7.

b) An IBM S/7 system for rapid acquisition and preliminary treatment of data, wich consists of the following :
- a 5010-B08 central module with 8 K words (16 bits), a memory cycle of 0.4 μ sec, 4 priority levels (each with 16 sublevels) and 2 real-time cloks;
- an operator station 5028 (Keyboard-typewriter);
- a multifunction module 5012 formed by 128 bits of DI, 64 bits of DO and 2 analog outputs;
- two analog module 5014-B01, each formed by 1 variable-range amplifier (7 different ranges), one relay multiplexer with a scanning rate of 200 points/sec, and 128 analog input points.

This is the acquisition unit which is reserved especially for different process to be monitored.

c) Two printers for the output of the results of the calculations and measurements which have been made. They are driven by S/7 Digital outputs. The former is used for the prints referring to the steam plant, the second one for the reefed cargo monitoring.

d) A Nixie-tube digital display for the visualization of the value of a variable to be selected by thumbwheels.

e) A Nixie-tube digital display on the bridge for continuous visualization of the ship position.

f) A push-botton keyboard for starting some computer calculations and procedures. The keyboard will be in the control room of the steam-plant.

g) Two alarm panels related to the reefed cargo, the former on the bridge and the second one in the Control room.

h) Several interfaces between the computer and the peripherals.

With the solution which has been described, we think we have realized a flexible operation and a certain degree of back-up. The two units, S/7 and 1130 communicate directly at the level of the central unit and at the speed of the slower unit, that is 275.000 words/sec.

There is the possibility to "cold start" the S/7 from the 1130, thereby reducing the manual operation of starting up.

We would however point out that, if all the application programs and the operating system would be at the same time in core storage, the computer will have a dimension and a cost too much high for to be economic on board, even if the several functions will be divided between two different computers. There are, in addition, some applications requiring a recording of a relatively large amount of data (for example, the planned maintenance).

According to this considerations, we adopted a computing unit (the IBM 1130) with relatively little core storage, but provided with a direct access magnetic disk.

This allows to the computer to run with a turn over of programs based on the actual need of calculation at each moment.

5 - THE FUNCTIONS PERFORMED BY THE COMPUTER

It is possible to divide the functions managed by the computer in the following groups :
- Navigation (oceanic and coastal)
- Power plant monitoring
- Refrigerated cargo monitoring
- Ship calculations (stability, trim etc.).

5.1 Navigation

5.1.1 Oceanic Navigation

The task consists in deciding and controlling in real time the ship course. Therefore, first of all it is necessary a continuous and precise knowledge of ship position.

On the "Lloydiana" the continuous calculation of the ship position is done by dead reckoning, through the reading of the gyrokompass and doppler sonar log. This continuous fix will be automatically corrected by the signals coming from Transit satellites, acquired by a special receiver and elaborated by the central computer. This correction is executed, in medium, every 80 minutes. The average precision of the ship fix so obtained is about 0.1÷0.2 Nm [2]. Then, by the comparision between the ship fix obtained from the satellite and the contemporaneous estimated one, it is possible to evaluate every error on the second one. A mathematical treatment (Kalman filter) which correlates this error to wind, sea and current conditions will allow to value the influence coefficients on the course and speed. Then, the computer elaborates all the calculations relative to the fixed course to reach the port of destination in the minimum time. The computer course may be, by request, by great-circle, or loxodromic or by lines of loxodromic between points of great-circle.

When it is possible to foresee the environmental conditions in which the next navigation will be, the computed course will be corrected to take into account the influence of these conditions. In this way, it will be possible to follow in a more precise manner the chosen course and, therefore, to reduce the distance traveled and, eventually, to save fuel.

An interesting application of the computer, with regard to the oceanic navigation, is the optimal adaptation of the autosteering parameters. This is one of those control loops in which the introduction of the computer should produce some improvements. In fact, the problem of the authomatic steering is nowadays solved in a satisfactory way by the commonly utilized devices, on condition of changing appropriately the parameters of the control-loop taking into account of the cargo ship conditions and of the disturbances (sea, wind, current) whose effects must be contrasted. These variations are committed to the ship staff and therefore are based on a subjective evaluation too depending on the individual and on his personal experience. On the contrary, if this adaptation is committed to a computer that, after identifying the ship mathematical model and the disturbances, minimizes an objective function, it will be possible to have an adaptive regulation always really optimal, according to the scheme shown in fig.2.

To choose the objective function, it is necessary to consider that the task of an autopilot is to maintain the ship on a course as much straight as possible, taking also at a minimum the rudder movements.

In accordance with the above referred principles, the computer tasks will be the following :

- on line identification of the mathematical linearized model of the ship, in the actual boundary conditions (sea, wind, currents etc.).
- calculation of the feedback coefficients which minimized the objective function [3] :

$$J = \overline{\Psi}^2 + \lambda \; \overline{\delta}^2$$

That takes into account the mean square values of the heading and rudder angles.

It is also predisposed the possibility that the computer substitutes the autopilot, getting directly into the feedback regulation.

5.1.2 Optimal meteorological navigation

The problem is to determine, knowing the foreseeable meteorological conditions of the oceanic area, the course that minimized the crossing time, compatibly with the imposed boundaries.

The determination of these boundaries depends essentially on three parameters :

- the maximum available propulsion power;
- the maximum allowable value of every ship motion or of consequent phenomena (slamming, propeller emersion,etc);
- the maximum allowable structural stresses in safety conditions.

All the meteorological data are grouped as follows:

- Beaufort number (B);
- Waves motion direction;
- Steady currents speed
- Steady currents direction

Through the above referred data, it will be possible to define a maximum allowable speed, in each sea condition and for each angle of attach. Then, basing on these values, it's possible to determine the minimum time course, by the application in the computer of the Bellman optimization principle [4] [5].

5.1.3 Restricted waters navigation aids

It will be installed on board the radar anticollision system RAYSCAN (Selenia-Raytheon) that is programmed to perform the following functions :

a) Automatic tracking of up to 40 targets

b) CPA (Closest Point of Approach) and TCPA (Time of Closest Point of Approach) calculations.

c) Alarm for dangerous targets, whose CPA and TCPA are less than a fixed limit.

d) Suggestion of an avoidance manoeuvre.

e) Visualization on the PPI of the manoeuvre.

Moreover, it is foreseen an interface between this A/C system and the central computer, which will allow the interchange of the following informations:

- From the A/C system to the central computer:
  - X-Y coordinates and speed of all the controlled targets;
  - off-center coordinates of own ship;
  - scale range used (3÷24 NM);
- From the central computer to the A/C system :
  - X-Y coordinates, length and direction of the vectors to be visualized.

In this way, the central system will add to the peripherical one the following functions :

- fairways visualization

The shallow waters limits and navigation lines along the forecasted route will be stored on the 1130 disk. When the ship goes into the zone, the computer, knowing the ship position and comparing it with the coordinates of the fairways, decides if there are some lines to be visualized on the PPI.

- Calculation of the manoeuvre to go from a point A to a point B allowing for the manoeuvring characteristics of the ship, the presence of other ships, the grounding and local navigation rules.

This function, in order to be reliable in restricted and congested waters, needs the utilization of a rather complicated mathematical model. Moreover, this model requires the knowledge (by measure or calculation) of the rate of yaw and of the speed of surge. Therefore a rate gyro has been added to the already existing gyro.

The solution of the problem will be however useful for a large range of applications; that is :

a) Approaching a strait with given heading and speed.

b) Series of manoeuvres for a safe navigation in very winding and congested channells.

- Radar fix

The operating procedure will be :

a) Storage on disk of the coordinates of fixed points previously chosen.

b) Automatic transmission from the A/C to the computer of the radar data of the fixed point.

c) Calculation, by the computer, of the ship fix with reference to the fixed point.

- Decca fix

The Decca receiver will be connected to the computer, which, taking into account the phase differences between master and slave stations (whose coordinates are stored on it), will intersect two or three paraboloyds and calculate automatically the ship position.

The precision of the Decca fix is very high in the North Sea where the navigation is congested, then the procedure in that zone will integrate the Radar fix.

5.2 Steam plant monitoring

In this case, the computer, according to the already explained concepts, does not substitute but rather completes the control functions which are entrusted to the autonomous AEG system of automation. It is that the way followed also in the terrestrial power plants.

The variables sent to the computer, whether derived from the AEG panel or from special sensors that had to be added, can be seen in fig.3, that shows also a schematic view of the steam plant.

The choice of the variables has been done taking into account of the different utilizations that can be summarized as follows.

5.2.1 Logging

A printing of the most interesting measures is foreseen. This printing will be periodic or on request. There will be also the possibility to get an immediate visualization of the value of whatever controlled variable, by a digital display in the control room.

5.2.2 Trend analysis

For a choice of variables, such as the reductor bearing temperatures, a trend calculation will be done, after a filtering of the measurements. This will allow to get an early feeling, of some future dangerous situations. When some trend is out of limit, there is an alarm print.

5.2.3 Transients recording

During the manoeuvres will be recorded some variable variations. Those records will be after utilized to design a dynamic model of the different parts of the plant. Only having a reliable dynamic model of the systems, it will be possible to introduce the computer in the control loops.

5.2.4 Efficiency control

The computer is programmed to check continuously the conditions of exploitation and the yields of the steam plant and its components, with the goal of detecting any difference between the values considered optimal and the actual ones (deviation concept monitoring, see fig.4) [6].

A program of this type will permit the most economic and most effective exploitation as far as the following are concerned :

- Accomplishment of certain maintenance or periodic operations at an opportune time, such as blowing out the soot in the boilers, maintenance of the burners, cleaning of the filter, etc.
- Programming for replacement of certain devices or components at an opportune time.

The program has been prepared in close collaboration which AEG, the manifacturer of the propulsive plant and of its automation. It is divided in a series of subroutines, namely :

a) Boiler efficiency control. It will use the calculation of the efficiency for each boiler by the indirect method, that is :

$$\eta = 1 - \frac{Q_1}{Q_f}$$

where : Q_f = furnished energy to the boiler

Q_1 = lost energy from the boiler

It has been chosed the indirect method rather the direct one for, taking into account the errors of the different sensors, it is more precise. If the calculation shows an efficiency less than the foreseen one, a series of controls on combustion airflow and on the CO_2 percentage in the exhausts will be done in order to detect the reason of the bad operation among the following :

- Error in the combustion air rate
- Too much soot on the tubes
- Bad combustion

The results will be printed in the control room.

b) Condenser and sea water pump efficiency control.

The main problem is, in this case, the calculation of the heat exchanged between the exhaust steam, coming from the turbine, and the sea water. Because of the difficulty of measuring directly with a little error this heat, we will get its value by an indirect way. Then we consider the engine room as a system in which, in a steady state situation, the sum of the energy coming on will be equal to the coming out one (see fig.5).

Then we have :

$$Q_{cond.} = Q_{fuel} + Q_{fan} - (Q_{exhausts} + Q'_{fan} + Q_{LPst.} + Q_{PW} + Q_{prop})$$

The calculation of $Q_{cond.}$ allows the determination of the actual value of the transmission coefficient through the equation:

$$K = \frac{Q_{cond} \, \ell u \, \frac{T_s - T_1}{T_s - T_2}}{S \, (T_2 - T_1)}$$

where : S = total tubes surface

T_S = condensing temperature

T_1 and T_2 = Inlet and outlet sea water temperature

The difference $(K_{design} - K)$ is related to the operating conditions of the condenser.

When this difference indicates a bad operation, further controls allow to detect the causes, as :

- Dirtiness of the tubes
- Bad operation of the ejectors
- Air infiltrations

For the sea water pump monitoring, the displacements from its characteristic curve will be calculated.

c) Turbine efficiency control

The parameter chosen is the heat rate. Because of the lack of a direct measure of the steam flow at the turbine inlet, there will be a calculation starting from the feed water flow, from which will be subtracted the turbopump and turboalternator steam flow. The result will be compared with curves provided by the manifacturer, allowing for different conditions in :

- Superheated steam temperature
-      "   "   pressure
- Propeller r.p.m.
- First bleeder steam flow
- Third   "   "   "

5.2.5 Statistical analysis of the plant operating conditions as a means to improve the planning of the maintenance.

The cycles of maintenance for each trip will be stored in the auxiliary memory of the computer. At the established date, a print of each maintenance operation will be automatically done. The operating conditions of some principal components and auxiliaries of the steam plant will be controlled at fixed intervals. Each intervention on these components will be coded and introduced into the computer, as well as the failures and breakdowns. Then we will be able to obtain from the computer :

- the operating hours of each device or component;
- the interventions and failures which happened;
- the mean time between failures of all components.

Those data, introduced on a maintenance model taking into account the maintenance costs and the minimum level of reliability required, will allow to modify the intervention cycles so that the operating cost will be minimized.

5.3 Refrigerated cargo monitoring

To the computer is committed the measure and recording of the temperatures and pressures related to the refrigerated cargo. Should any variable be out of prestored limits the computer will activate an alarm and a print of the variable value. The monitoring will not be only devoted to inform about conditions of out of limit, but also to identify failures of sensors and cables. This is a tipical example of supervising critically the consistency of the data. The engineers will have also the possibility of simulating an alarm condition. This procedure will allow a further verification of the correct operation of the control system.

The system has been designed so that its precision is within ± 0.15° C in the measuring range - 3° C ÷ + 3° C and within ± 0.25° C outside, as required by "Lloyd Register of Shipping" and "Registro Italiano Navale".

5.4 Ship calculations

The computer calculates the methacentric height.

The calculation is based on a transport of water from a tank to another one and on the formulas of naval architecture.

Another method of calculation, less precise but more quick, is based on the measure of the rolling period on calm water. The computer will do also this one.

It will be done also a control of trim and deflections during the cargo operation.

- CONCLUSIONS

At the time when the authors are writing (January 1973), the project is at an advanced stage of realization. The computing system, after some 7 months of operation in the yard, during which several tests on application program and on operating systems have been performed, is now installed on board. The maiden voyage of "Lloydiana" is scheduled in the next April. Some months ago, the first of six computerized ships has been delivered by Kockums and the Seiko Maru, a japanese computerized ship, is travelling from the 1971. In all these applications, not all the possible functions are committed to the computer, but only a certain number of tasks carefully chosen. In the writers' opinion, this means that the first enthusiastic pioneers' age is maybe coming to its end. A new age is coming, in which the economical balances are more (or not less) important than the technical problems and the operating side is pushing the R.& D. advancements in well defined directions. In this "second age", we believe that the "Lloydiana" Project will find its place.

ACKNOWLEDGEMENT

The authors are very indebted to prof. Volta for his useful suggestions and hints in the development of the project. Also the support of his staff has been very useful in the study of some functions realized on the "Lloydiana".

REFERENCES

[1] Sitzia, Volta, Sartirana : "Progetto di automazione integrata della nave utilizzante una unità centrale di calcolo"
Convegno di Tecnica Navale ATENA, Trieste, 25÷27/3/1971

[2] Sartirana : "Il sistema di navigazione satellitare installato sulla T/n "Esquilino"
L'Automazione Navale - n.1 - 1971

[3] Koyama : "On the Optimum Automatic Steering System of Ships at Sea"
J.S.NA. Japan - Dec. 1967

[4] Zoppoli, Scarano, Molfino : "Ottimizzazione della rotta di una nave mediante programmazione dinamica"
Symposium on Shipbuilding Automation, Opatija, 22÷24/11/67

[5] Zoppoli : Minimum-time Routing as an N-stage Decision Process
Journal of Applied Metheorology, April 1972

[6] Salisbury : "Power plant Performance monitoring"
Journal of Engineering for Power, October 1961

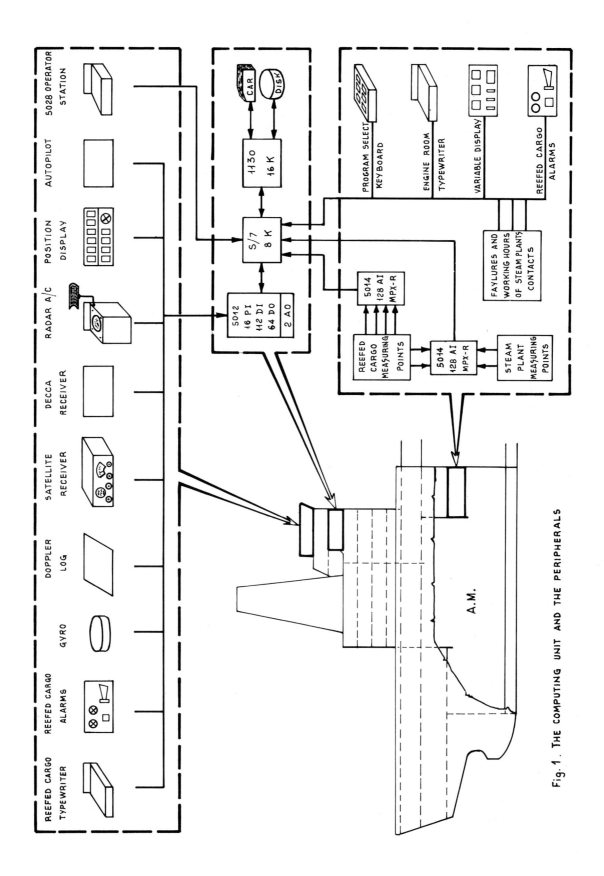

Fig. 1. THE COMPUTING UNIT AND THE PERIPHERALS

452

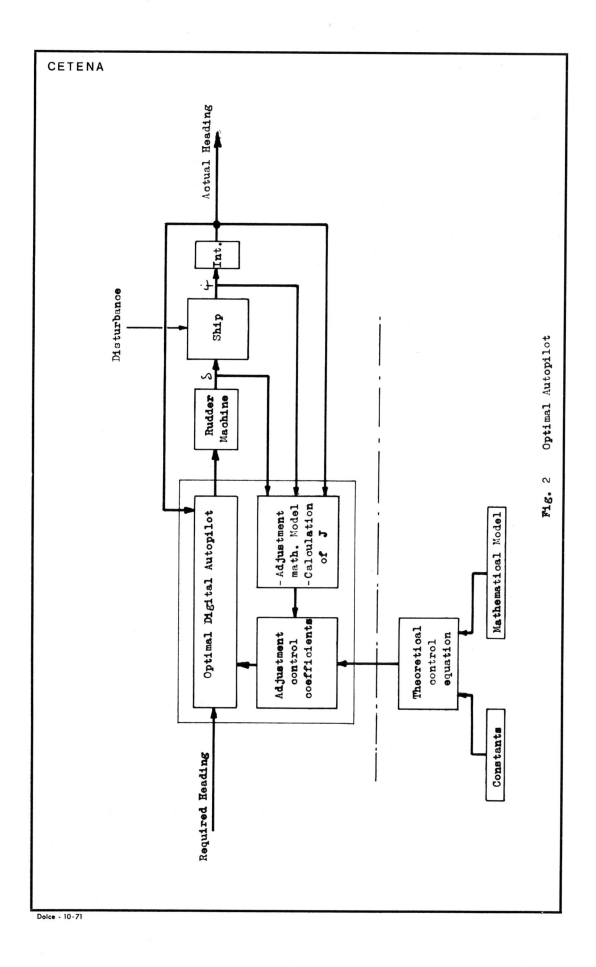

CETENA

Required Heading

Disturbance

Actual Heading

Optimal Digital Autopilot

Rudder Machine

Ship

Int.

Adjustment control coefficients

-Adjustment math. Model
-Calculation of J

Theoretical control equation

Constants

Mathematical Model

Fig. 2   Optimal Autopilot

Dolce - 10-71

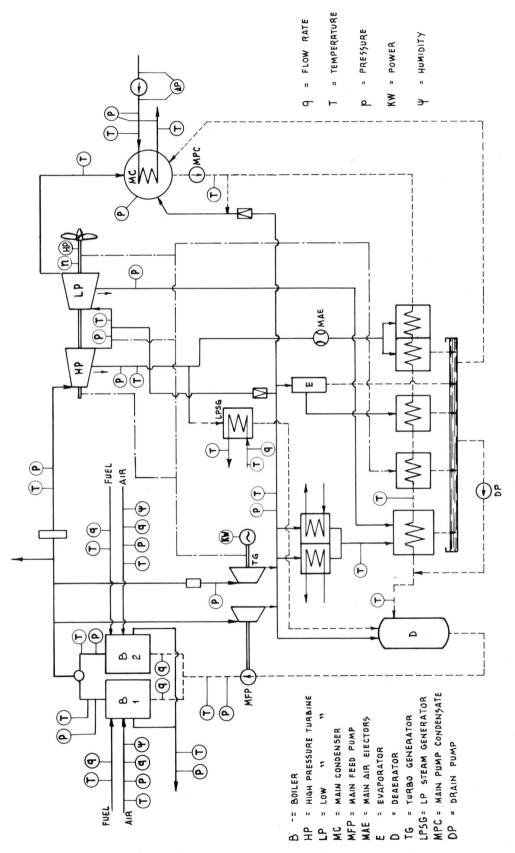

q = FLOW RATE

T = TEMPERATURE

p = PRESSURE

KW = POWER

ψ = HUMIDITY

B = BOILER
HP = HIGH PRESSURE TURBINE
LP = LOW " "
MC = MAIN CONDENSER
MFP = MAIN FEED PUMP
MAE = MAIN AIR EJECTORS
E = EVAPORATOR
D = DEAERATOR
TG = TURBO GENERATOR
LPSG = LP STEAM GENERATOR
MPC = MAIN PUMP CONDENSATE
DP = DRAIN PUMP

Fig. 3   STEAM PROPULSION PLANT AND SENSORS

454

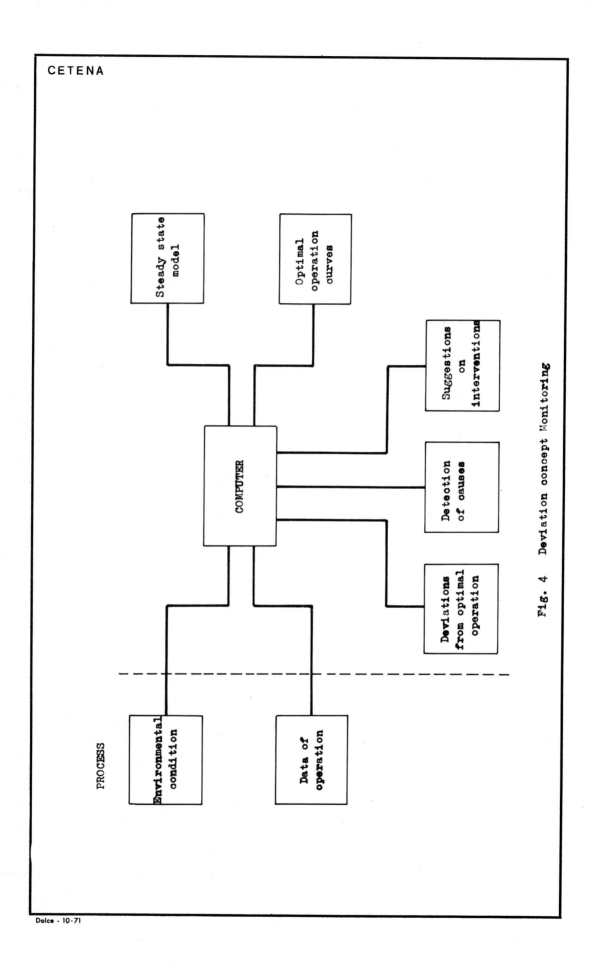

Fig. 4   Deviation concept Monitoring

Dolce - 10-71

CETENA

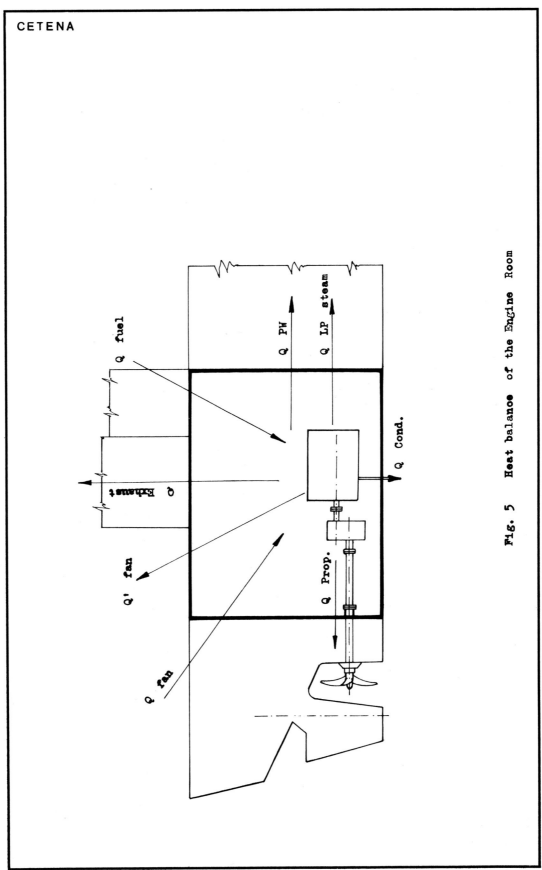

Q fuel

Q PW

Q LP steam

Q Exhaust

Q Cond.

Q' fan

Q Prop.

Q fan

Fig. 5   Heat balance of the Engine Room

COMPUTER-BASED SHIP AUTOMATION SYSTEM
FOR A POLISH CARGO SHIP

S.Zieliński and W.J. Martin
Ship Research Institute
Technical University Gdańsk

ABSTRACT

The paper presents some results of works being now in progress to develop a computerized system of complex automation for a Polish cargo ship. The philosophy of designing the system is discussed and the range of system functions and objectives analyzed. The proposed hardware configuration of the system is characterized and some more details of the Polish mini-computer K-202 given. The concept of system software is outlined. Finally the authors give some details of the future developments.

INTRODUCTION

The Polish shipbuilding industry shows constant growth in gross production output as well as in the assortyment of ships it manufactures. Semicontainers, 32,000 TDW and 55,000 TDW bulk carriers, great fishing ships are being build currently; construction of 105,000 TDW OBO ship has just started. In the nearest future construction of great tankers and special ships will be developed.One of the most important factors of the modern ship technology is automation. This is why also in Poland works have started in 1971 on one of the most recent aspect of ship's automation-computerized complex automation. This work is conducted by the Ship Research Institute of the Gdańsk Technical University, sponsored by the Shipbuilding Industry Research Centre. The paper presents some results so far obtained in the project of computerized ship complex automation.

DESIGN PHILOSOPHY

We call the computerized ships automation system complex because it performs concurrently a wide variety of interacting functions, such as: automatic control, optimization, interlocks, monitoring, data processing and so on. The design and implementation of such a system is relatively difficult. The difficulties are additionally amplified by the high reliability and environmental requirements.
The development of our system, as of any comlex system, can be divided into several stages.

More important of these stages are listed below (see also Fig.1):
1. Ascertaining the objectives of complex automation. This stage includes:
   - general analysis of the ship (considared as an object of the complex automation) and ships processes to be automatized, preliminary determination of the system functions as well as a concept of technical implementation of the system;
   - assessment of the profitability of the system based on the ship's operation economical analysis.
2. Functional analysis of the system. In this stage the designers have to analyze the functions of different subsystems in various operational modes such as continous operation, starting-up, manoeuvering etc. Particular attention should be paid to the interlocks and monitoring subsystems as well as the data gathering and processing subsystem.
3. Concept of the system. In this stage the overall structure and algorithms are specified for the control system, the interlocks and safety subsystem and for information gathering and preprocessing subsystem. The interdependencies of algorithms are also to be taken care of. As a result, descriptions and flow-charts of algorithms are made. It is a good plan to employ simulation techniques at this stage of design. Analogue, digital and hybrid mathods can be used. Digital simulation languages offer a very powerful and promising tool.
4. Design of the hardware implementation. Basing on the system structure and the algorithms obtained in stage 4, different hardware implementations of the system can be analyzed and compared. To select a proper hardware realization the following aspects should be taken into account: investment and operational costs, reliability, flexibility and possibility to introduce future extensions to the system, and others. It will be necessary at this stage to check and possibly verify some assumptions taken prewiously.
It can be easily seen from this short

description that the design stages are not independent - there is some feedback from later stages to earlier ones. The design is in fact an iterative process. Results obtained in later stages often call for corrections and even repeating previous analyses. Some of the more important feedbacks and intercomnections in the design process are shown in Fig.1.

It is obvious that designing of the ship complex automation system is very complicated and laborious task. It calls for collective work and close cooperation of specialists of different kinds. The efficiency of such a work vastly depends on very careful planning and good supervision. We intend therefore to employ PERT method as a help in managing the project.

THE EXTENT OF SHIP'S COMPLEX AUTOMATION

General assumptions. The design of the complex automation system for a Polish cargo ressel, described in this paper was carried out basing on the following assumptions:

1. Components of Polish manufacture should be employed in the system whenever possible. In particular - a Polish computer system should be used.
2. The ship to be automated has the following characteristics:

Type - general cargo ship with facilities to carry containers having 2 refrigerated holds.

Deadweight - 23 000 tons.

Main propulsion: - two GRND 90 Cegielski-Sulzer diesel engines, 17 400 BHP each, 122 rpm, - two variable pitch propellers.

Boiler instalation - two waste heat La Mont boilers and one oil burner boiler.

Generating plant - there motor - alternators, engines Cegielski-Sulzer 8A25 , 750 rpm, alternators type GD8, 1250 kVA, 50 Hz.

Bow thruster.

3. The engine-room operation should conform to the Polish Register of Shipping requirements for periodically unmanned engine-room 16/24 class . It is additionally assumed, that in the case of computer system failure it should be possible for the engine-room to be controlled by one person from the control stand by means of local control and alarm monitoring systems.

The general structure of the system is shown in Fig.2. The solid lines indicate "on-line" information flow; the dashed ones - "off-line" information flow. The more important functions of the blocks given in Fig.2 are discussed below.

Engine-room. The engine-room automation covers the following equipment: main engines and their ausiliaries, boiler installations, evaporating plant installations and starting air installation.

The computer system performs the following functions:
- Measuring the parameters. There are 420 quantities to be measured (240 analogue and 180 binary). Out of them over 100 are checked for off-limit values.
- Remote control. It is possible to set the system from the bridge into one of the four modes of operation: readiness, manoeuvre, continuous,operation, shut-off. The computer system effects its control by supervising the conventional local automatic systems and coordinating the execution of all engine-room programs.
- Program controlled attaining the desired load by the propulsion system.
- Starting and shutting-off the boilers.
- Starting and shutting-off the evaporating plant.
- Control of fuel oil systems.
- DDC of cooling water temperatures, lubricating oil temperatures, fuel viscosity, water levels.
- Calculation of exploitation indices, technical diagnostics and maintenance scheduling.

The generating plant. The general structure of the power plant subsystem is shown in Fig.3. It employs local control systems such as synchronizer, speed governors, voltage regulators etc. The computer performs basically two groups of functions-checking and interlock functions and control functions. The checking functions complement those of the local system. They cover measuring 76 quantities and checking them for off-limit values, periodical recording of some quantities as well as in some cases preserving several previous readings of the same quantity. All output generated by the computer, when performing the checking functions, goes to the monitoring and alarm block. The more important control functions are:
- starting and shutting down the motor - alternator sets,
- program controlled disconnecting and connecting selected power receivers in order to smooth out the load peaks,
- correction of frequency control and voltage control,
- load sharing control and reactive power sharing control.

The propulsion system. The task of this system is to set the engine rpm and the propeller pitch in such a way as to obtain maximum overall efficiency at the given load conditions. A simplified block diagram of this system is shown in Fig.4.

Displays and alarm system. This system gives the following facilities:
- The value of any parameter measured can be displayed on the CRT display set upon request.
- Specified parameters are recorded periodically for the engine-room log purposes.
- Alarms are monitored triggered either by off-limits parameters values or by protection systems violation.

The system has two modes of operation: for unmanned engine-room and for manned engine-room. An independent alarm system enables the engine room to be controlled by a single man in the case computer system fails.

Administration and raports. These functions represent to a great extent typical data processing They cover: inventory and materials system, preparing reports from the voyage, crew payroll etc. There are 6 data files and 15 processing programs provided to carry out these functions.

Medical diagnoses. The computer system is also employed as an aid in automatic recognizing illnesses. An algorithm has been selected which, given symptoms and patient's data provides one, or more, hypothetical diagnoses. These are thoroughly verified. Verification may meed additional information.

Navigation. There are two alternative solutions of the navigation subsystem. The first one involves a specialized, autonomous, computer based system exclusively for navigation purposes capable of performing a very extensive range of functions (particularly a comprehensive anti - collision system).

The second alternative, shown in Fig.2, covers the following functions:
- dead - reckoning based on EM - log and gyro - compass readings;
- position fixing, based on OMEGA and/or DECCA systems as well as astronomical, optical and radar observations;
- calculating great circle routes;
- simple anti - collision system;
- optimal routeing.

This alternative does not involve a separate computer. Its functions share the main computer system resources.

The computer system and software.

The hardware configuration of the computer system is shown in Fig.5. In selecting the configuration the reliability requirements played a significat role. To ensure a high reliability margin two processors are proposed and a substantial amount of core store. One of the processors is capable of performing on its own all the more important system functions. Therefore in the case of processor failure it is still possible for the system to perform all its basic functions. The disc memory and magnetic tape memories are not involved in any of the basic system functions. They are uded exclusively for the off-line programs and associated files, as well as for program storage. All the on-line programs and data fit into core store. This policy is based on very little practical experience in employing mass storage devices on board ships. Their inclusion into the system is partly aimed at gathering more operational experience.

The development of system software has just started and takes several parallel directions. The more important are listed below.
1. Development of on-line real time operating system, constituting an environment for application programs, including:
   - main scheduler;
   - program of synchronous reading process variables;
   - input - output routines;
   - operator language - commands language;
   - various checking and control programs;

- system special extracodes;
- interrupts servicing, and so forth.
It is intended to employ digital simulation in the design of operating system.
2. On-line and off-line application programs.
3. Various testing and maintenance programs.
4. Simulation system. In order to be able to test on-line applications programs it is necessary to develop a special simulation system, which will form an artificial environment for these programs.

To properly test the complete system a special laboratory stand is being prepared. This will include all the devices forming the computer system as well as simulators of various ship's processes.

THE DIGITAL COMPUTER CHARACTERISTICS

As the core of the computer system it is intended to employ a K-202 computer of Polish manufacture. Being a new computer it is not yet widely known. We give therefore below the basic characteristics of the K-202 system.
1. Central processor:
   - asynchronous, parallel;
   - word length - 16 bits;
   - number representation - binary, 2's complement, fixed point - 16 and 32 bit, floating point - 48 bit;
   - instruction set: 90 basic instructions - an instruction may occupy 1,2,3 or 4 words;
   - arithmetic: binary - hardware floating point unit available as an option;
   - two modes of operation - user mode and privileged mode;
   - 32 priority interrupt levels;
   - 7 fully programmable registers;
   - multiprocessing - up to 4 processors;
   - multiprogramming facilities available.
2. Main memory:
   - type: ferrite core memory;
   - cycle time: 0.35 to 2 microsec (standard 0.7 microsec);
   - memory capacity - 4k, 8k, 12k or 16k within main module; additionally up to 63 blocks 4k, 8k, 16k, 32k or 64k each - maximum capacity 64 x 64k; memory protection in blocks of 4k, 8k, 16k, 32k or 64k;
   - 2 independent interfaces:
     a. memory interface - 16 bit data bus, transfer rate 1 000 000 words/sec, with standard autonomous access facility,
     b. character interface - 8 bit data bus, transfer rate 200 000 bytes/sec, processor-controlled;
   - i/o devices - up to 8 channels, each capable of handling 8 i/o devices can be connected to character interface; 8 channels of 8 devices each to memory interface;
3. Physical structure - the system is modular. Module dimensions - 480 x 210 x 600 mm, weight - 32 kg, power consumption ca. 500 W - 220 V ± 10%, 50 Hz ± 1 Hz. The main module - processor module houses the CPU, 16k of core, or 12k and floating point hardware, interface control and character channel for 4 i/o devices together with operator panel, all the necessary power

supplies and interface connectors. Another
modules may house e.g. 64k of core store with
associated power supplies or 32k of core store
and 8-device character channel with power
supplies.
4. Reliability factors:
    MTBF - Mean Time Between Failures: not less
        than 10000 hrs;
    MTTR - Mean Time To Repair: less than 20
        minutes.
5. The standar software includes:
    - operating systems with debugging facilities,
    - comprehensive assembly language,
    - BASIC compilers,
    - FORTRAN IV compiler,
    - variety of application programs, mathematical
      routines and utility programs,
    There are other compilers and programs in
    development.
A small K-202 system is already installed in
the authors' Institute. The authors experience
prove it to be a very suitable tool for on-line
real-time applications.

CONCLUSIONS

The brief description of the computerized ship's
complex automation system given in the paper
shows the great complexity of the design and
implementetion process. It is intended to put
special emphasis on developing suitable shore
based laboratory installations with the purpose
of forming an environment for testing parts of
the system, and perhaps the complete system.
Another important point is writing a comprehensive, modular and flexible software for the
system.
Every effort will be made to obtain good
modularity and flexibility, even at the cost of
somewhat reduced efficiency. This should
facilitate introducing new functions to the
system as well as tailoring it to the particular
requirements.

REFERENCES

(1) "SEIKO MARU" computer navigation and
    automatic cargo handling. The Motor Ship,
    December 1970.

(2) Madesatera A., Process Computers on Ships
          - The "Sea Sovereign" -
          Project.
    New Ships/Die Neubauten,
    12/1, 1970/71.

(3) Mikalsen T., Computer Integrated Instru-
          mentation on Ships.
    New Ships/Die Neubauten,8,1969.

(4) Ship Complex Automation Project. Preliminary
    Analysis and Proposals. In Polish, 9
    volumes . Technical University of Gdańsk,
    Ship Research Institute. Gdańsk, 1972.

(5) Yourdon E., Design of on-line computer
          systems. Prentice-Hall, 1972.

460

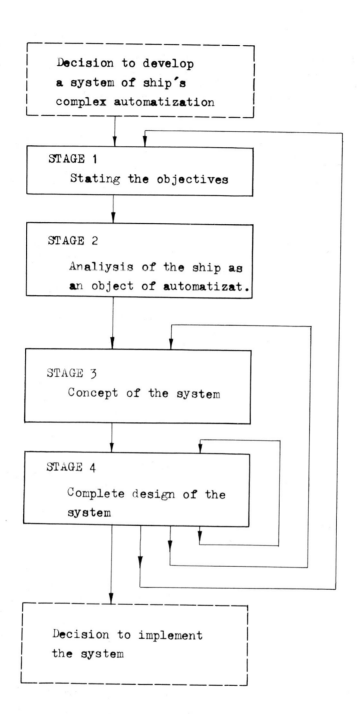

Fig. 1   Stages in system development

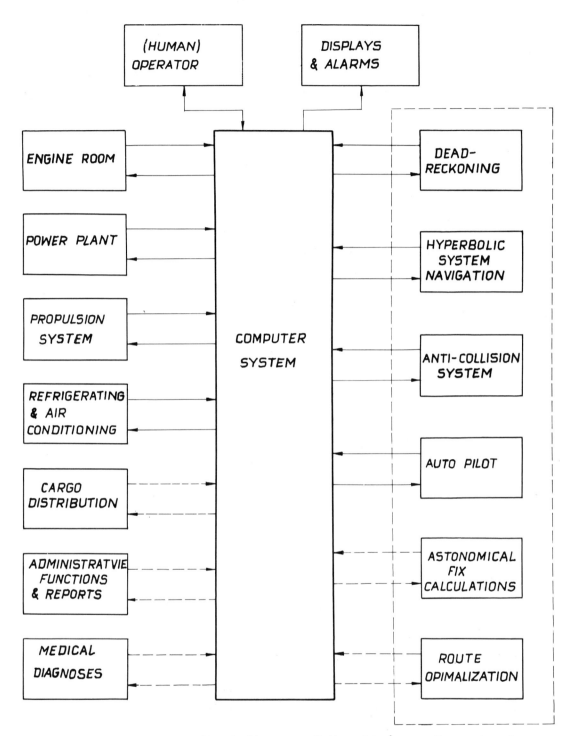

Fig. 2   General block diagram of the ship's complex automation
          system

462

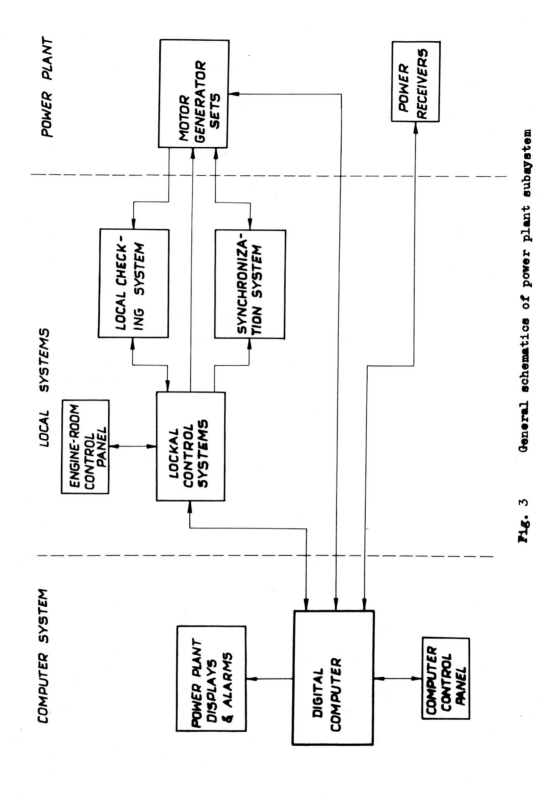

Fig. 3   General schematics of power plant subsystem

463

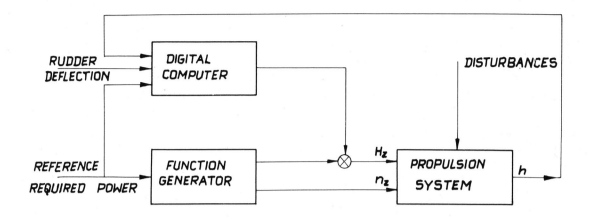

Fig. 4 Block diagram of propulsion system control

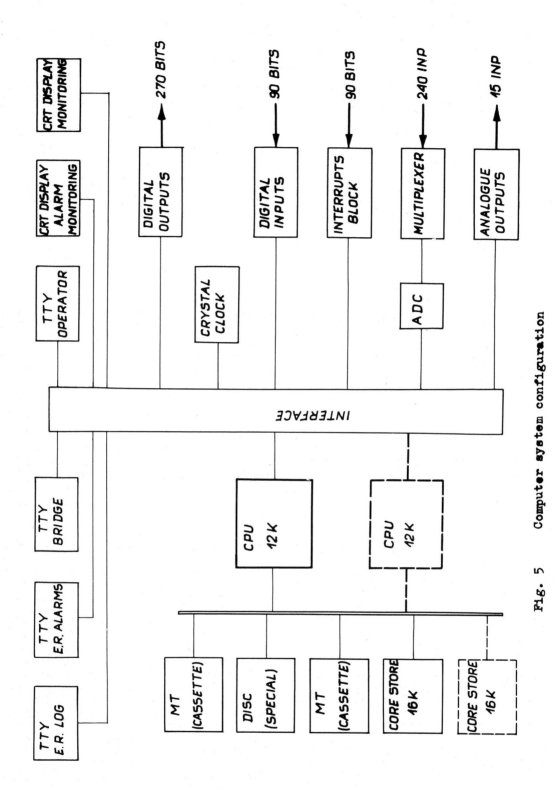

Fig. 5   Computer system configuration

THE COST CONCEPT RELATED TO SOFTWARE TASKS
IN EVALUATING SHIPBORNE COMPUTER SYSTEMS

Carsten Bøe
Det norske Veritas
Oslo, Norway

Gustav Dahll
Institutt for Atomenergi
Halden, Norway

Tor Heimly
Det norske Veritas
Oslo, Norway

ABSTRACT

This paper is an attempt to outline the most promising methodology for quantitative anlysis of shipborne computerized automation system found in a pilot study. Data for a cost function intended as a measure of the ship utility, are established for different failure modes of a computer system. Analysis on item level yields a cost estimate for the ship at large, as a function of the computer system reliability and availability.

The mode of proceeding utilizes the advantages of both qualitative and quantitative analysis techniques to give further insight into the important problem of safety onboard.

INTRODUCTION

In recent years, computers are frequently used in automation systems such as bridge control and control of machinery plant. Furthermore, the concept of multicomputer systems has been introduced in order to increase the flexibility and reliability of computer control. In the present paper the problem of finding the reliability and availability of a multicomputer system utilized in ship automation, is examined.

Conventionally the availability is defined as the expected percentage of a certain time period that a system is working. This definition is, however, restricted to systems with two states of performance, a working state and a failed state. Thus a system is in a working state until it fails, and then remains in a failed state until it is repaired.

Such a definition does not describe adequately the reliability characteristics of a multicomputer system, which may also be in reduced states of performance; states where the computer system can perform only some of its tasks due to failure in one or more hardware modules.

A property of a multicomputer system, which is different from for instance a mechanical system, is that a specific task is not performed by a specific hardware module.

PERFORMANCE OF THE ANALYSIS

To obtain a measure of the availability of a multicomputer system, the consept of an error cost function is introduced. This function is a measure of the expected cost associated to the loss of performance because of random hardware failures during a certain time period.

The resulting error cost function is of this form

$$C\ (T) = E(N_{ij})\ f_{ij}(t_j)$$

where the sum is over all hardware state transitions (from state i to state j), $E(N_{ij})$ is expected number of transitions $i \rightarrow j$ in the time period T, $f_{ij}(t_j)$ is the cost of the transition $i \rightarrow j$, which depens upon the expected time period (t_j) the system is in state j.

Fig. 1 shows the basic elements contained in the analysis. According to a certain ship system, a set of computer tasks are defined. Based on this, the computer system and the program strategy are chosen. Defining the program strategy comprises allocation of the computer programs to the various computer modules and specifications of action to take place in case of hardware failure. Based on the actual ship system to be controlled, the various tasks are assigned cost values according to their importance for the ship. Also the failure statistics of the computer system are evaluated based on the failure data of the various computer units. From this and a failure consequence analysis, the error cost function can be evaluated.

THE COMPUTER SYSTEM

Three computer structures have been examined: a one module computer system (OC system), a two module computer system (TC system) and a decentralized modular computer system (FC system).

The latter consists of four minicomputers. Each of these may be used as an independent unit and consists of a memory, a sentral processing unit (CPU), a local memory bus. In addition, all CPUs have access to the memories of all four computers via a duplexed global memory bus. The CPUs also have access to the peripheral units and the process variables via a duplexed global I/0 exchange.

The second system which is already installed aboard ship, consists of two computer modules, connected by a data channel. This channel enables computer no. 1 to take care of the high priority tasks whereas computer no. 2 takes care of the low priority tasks which are dependent on the performance of the tasks in computer no. 1. The data channel connecting the two computers allows computer no. 1 to read and write in the memory of computer no. 2, whereas computer no. 2 may only read from computer no. 1.

Finally a one module computer system has been examined for reference. All systems have been assigned the same peripheral units.

THE COMPUTER TASKS

A computer system shall perform a certain set of tasks. There are various tasks which can be performed in ship control systems. Increasing interest in the computerization of bridge functions like integrated navigation systems and anticollision systems have been observed. This paper, however, is limited to those tasks that relate to the propulsion system of the ship.

The computer tasks are divided into two parts: The high priority tasks, which are called the E0 tasks, and the low priority tasks, concerning condition monitoring (CM) of the machinery plant.

The E0 tasks consist of safety, alarm and automatic control systems in addition to remote control of the machinery plant from the bridge. The CM tasks consist of data logging and evaluation of certain parameters concerning the state of the machinery plant. This is the basis from which diagnostics are performed for predictive maintenance tasks. The CM tasks also make use of a CRT display.

In the OC system, all tasks are allocated to one computer. Regarding the MC system, it is natural to divide the E0 and CM tasks into subtasks. The programs performing those subtasks are then allocated to the different computer modules, and backup programs of the most important tasks may be allocated to other modules.

The subdivision of the tasks for E0 is: alarm $(E0_a)$, safety $(E0_s)$, control $(E0_c)$ and remote control of propulsion machinery from bridge $(E0_r)$. The latter task is not implemented in the TC system, but it is natural to include it in the more flexible FC system. Furthermore, the E0 tasks of FC will also include the control of a steam boiler.

For CM the subdivision is: datalogging (CM_l), evaluation (CM_e), diagnosis (CM_d), CRT-display (CM_c)

Both the E0 programs and the CM programs need input- output routines which are used frequently. Two sets of input-output routines are implemented, one for E0 and one for CM.

They are, however, made similar so that one can be used as back-up for the other in the case of hardware failure.

THE COST VALUES

A variety of circumstances will influence the assigning of cost values to the different computer tasks. The cost assignment is therefore a very difficult part of the analysis.

Because of the influence of environmental conditions the cost function depends to some degree upon the sailing schedule of the ship.

A typical voyage which is estimated to last one month, may consit of 24 days at open sea, 4 days in congested waters and two days in harbour.

Regarding loss of propulsion, the associated instantaneous cost for sailing in congested waters is greater than the cost for open sea by a proposed factor of 10. For manoeuvring in congested waters the corresponding factor is proposed to be 1000.

Assigning cost to the computer tasks can best be done by personnel with experience in and knowledge of ships and ship systems. The estimation of different cost values is independent of the computer configuration. Consequently, no knowledge of any computer system is required for the cost estimation, when the different tasks are given.

Fig. 2 shows a simplified diagram of the consequences for propulsion and auxiliary machinery resulting from loss of E0-tasks on the FC system. Probabilities of several occurences are stated at the input on some of the logical OR-gates. For example, the probability of loss of "unmanned machinery space" caused by loss of all E0-tasks is set to 1.0. Figures in brackets state probabilities for the different occurrences when the ship is in a manoeuvre situation. The figures should be multiplied by a factor of 10^{-1} and 10^{-3} for sailing in congested water and in open sea respectively.

Having established the diagram in fig. 2, and the different data connected to it, the associated cost values can be estimated. These are presented in table 1, which also included the estimated cost values for the CM tasks.

APPLICATION OF THE ANALYSIS METHOD

The analysis for the three different computer systems is performed as outlined in fig. 1.

A hardware state is defined as a certain combination of failed and working units. Thus there will be 2^n hardware states, n being the number of units. A transfer from one state to another occurs when a unit fails or is repaired. From the probabilities of failure and repair of the units one may evaluate the quantities which are of interest: the pointwise and interval availabilities of the hardware states, the expected numbers of state transfers in a time and the expected time between entrance and exit of a state.

It is assumed that the time period considered is long compared to the mean time to repair (MTTR), that the mean time between failure (MTBF) is much larger than MTTR, and that all hardware units are failing and are repaired independent of the states of other components.

The availability of a state n, where k units (no. 1 -- k) are failing, while the rest is working is then

$$S_n = \lambda_1 \ -- \lambda_k \mu_{k+i} --- \mu_n / q_1 -- q_n$$

where λ_i and μ_i are the inverse of MTBF and MTTR respectively, and $q_i = \lambda_i + \mu_i$

The expected number of transfers from state n to state m during the time period 0 - T_p is

$$E(N_{nm}) = S_n a_i T_p$$

where $a_i = \lambda_i$ or μ_i if the transfer was due to a failure in or repair of component no. i.

The average time of stay n is given as

$$t_n = S_n \cdot T_p / \sum_{\substack{\text{all states} \\ n}} E(N_{nm}) = 1 / \sum_{\substack{\text{all units} \\ i}} a_i$$

Today there exists, however, no statistical evaluation of the failure data of the units concerned. Furthermore, the data will depend upon the environmental conditions. The mean times to failure used in this analysis are estimated in communication with the designers of the systems. The repair data depend upon the amount of spare parts, tools and skilled personnel on board.
Table 2 shows failure and repair data used.

A failure consequence analysis as shown in Fig. 2 is performed for all three systems. The resulting cost values are shown in table 1. Using these cost values, the cost values for the specific hardware state transfers are found to be of the form:

$$f_{nm}(t_m) = k_{nm} + c_m t_m$$

where k_{nm} is the immediate cost from the loss of performance of some tasks due to a state transition. If a program is regained via a reconfiguration, the cost of the program being absent during the time of reconfiguration will also be added to k_{nm}. c_m is the cost of the inability of performing the programs which are absent in state m.

The total error cost function is:

$$C(T) = \sum_{nm} E(N_{nm}) \cdot F_{nm}$$

where F_{nm} is the sum of all the costs of one state transfer type.

The value of $C(T)$, with T = one month as the time for a typical sailing mission, is given in table 3.

The values for the FC system in the first column and the values for the OC and TC system in the third column are obtained using the data given in the text.

It turns out that failure in the process I/0 system gives a dominant contribution to the cost function. This suggests, that to utilize the features of the multicomputer structure, the process I/0 system should also have the same degree of flexibility. The second column shows that the error cost function is reduced by a factor of 50 when the I/0 system is duplexed.

The analysis also shows that the possibility of damage to the steam boiler, which is an immediate consequence, gives an essential contribution to the error cost. This suggest that this specific task should have more back-up or be removed. The latter is the fact in the remaining values for the error cost function shown in column III and IV of Table 3. These values are evaluated without and with duplexed process I/0.

It is seen that with a single process I/0 system, there is not much difference in the three systems, whereas the difference is more significant when the I/0 system is duplexed.

The analysis shows that the predominant part (almost 100%) of the error cost comes from the possibility of immediate loss of the E0 tasks.

The results should not be taken as absolute measures of reliability of the computer system, but rather as illustrative examples of the method and its possibilities.

CONCLUDING REMARKS

The main features of the analysis are the simplicity and the combination of economic and reliability characteristics to provide a better basis for decision making.

The method enables a clear division of the problem into one part that handles the computer hardware structure and its failure statistics, and one part that handles the tasks to be performed, and their cost values relating to the ship system. These parts are then, via the program strategy united into the error cost function.

This work is not intended to give a thoroughful analysis of the reliability of multicomputers used aboard ships, but rather to pinpoint some of the essential problems and suggest a way of attacking them.

REFERENCES

(1) Heimly, T., Dahll, G. and Bøe, C.
Reliability and Availability of Computer Systems onboard Ships.
Det norske Veritas, Machinery Department, 1972 (In Norwegian)

(2) Bøe, C., Heimly, T. and Mathiesen, Tor-Chr.
A Reliability Model using Markov Chains for the Utility Evaluation of Computer Systems onboard Ships.
1973 Winter Simulation Conference Proceedings, January 17 - 19, 1973.

468

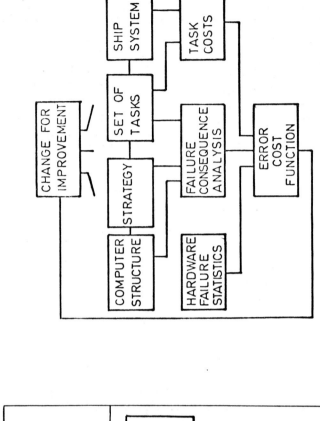

FIG. 1 PROCEDURE FOR EVALUATION OF ERROR
COST FUNCTION

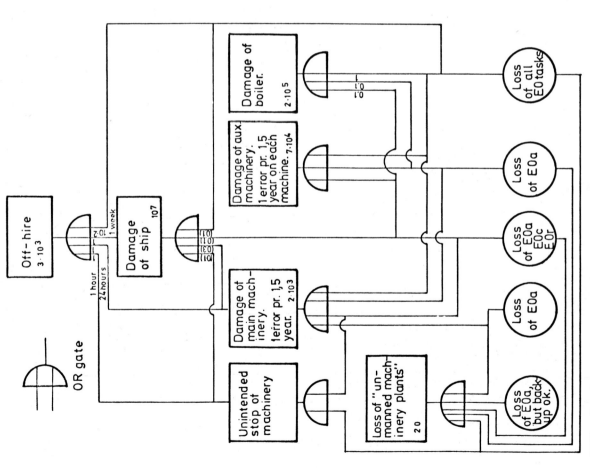

FIG. 2. SCHEMATIC DESCRIPTION OF CONSEQUENCES OF LOSS
OF PERFORMANCE OF THE VARIOUS COMPUTER TASKS
FOR THE FC SYSTEM.

LOSS OF TASKS		COST IMMEDIATE	COST TIME-DEPENDENT
FOUR COMPUTER SYSTEM (FC)	SAFETY SYSTEM WITH BACK-UP	$2.0 \cdot 10^4$	95
	ALARM SYSTEM WITH ONLY BACK-UP WORKING	0	20
	ALARM SYSTEM WITH BACK-UP	$1.5 \cdot 10^3$	80
	AUTOMATIC CONTROL SYSTEM WITH BACK-UP	$2.1 \cdot 10^4$	45
	BRIDGE CONTROL SYSTEM WITH BACK-UP	$2.8 \cdot 10^4$	20
	SAFETY, ALARM AND AUTOMATIC CONTROL SYSTEM WITH BACK-UP	$2.3 \cdot 10^5$	220
	ALL OTHER COMBINATION OF TASKS	LINEAR COMBINATION OF DIFFERENT COST.	
	DATA LOGGING	0	3
	EVALUATION	0	2
	DIAGNOSTIC	0	1
	DISPLAY	0	1
	ANY COMBINATION INCLUDING DATA LOGGING	0	1
OC AND TC SYSTEM	ALL EO TASKS	$2.7 \cdot 10^4$	136
	ALL CM TASKS	0	3
	ALL CM TASKS, EXCEPT DISPLAY	0	2
	DISPLAY	0	1

TABLE 1. ESTIMATED COST VALUES.

UNIT		MTBF HOURS	MTTR HOURS
ALL THREE SYSTEMS	PROCESS I/O	1000	6
	TELETYPE	1000	2
	OP. CONSOLE	30000	10
	CRT	3000	8
	TAPE READER		5
FC SYSTEM	MEMORY	5000	4
	GLOBAL MEM. BUS	20000	2
	CPU	20000	2
	I/O CHANNEL	20000	2
OC, TC SYSTEM	COMPUTER MODULE (OC)	5000	4
	COMPUTER MODULE (TC)	2500	4
	DATA CHANNEL	20000	10

TABLE 2. FAILURE AND REPAIR DATA

	I	II	III	IV
FOUR COMPUTER SYSTEM (FC)	$180 \cdot 10^3$	$34 \cdot 10^3$	$22 \cdot 10^3$	700
TWO COMPUTER SYSTEM (TC)			$25 \cdot 10^3$	3000
ONE COMPUTER SYSTEM (OC)			$29 \cdot 10^3$	7000

  I WITH CONTROL OF STEAM BOILER
  II WITH CONTROL OF STEAM BOILER AND DUPLEXED PROCESS I/O
 III WITHOUT CONTROL OF STEAM BOILER
 IV WITHOUT CONTROL OF STEAM BOILER AND DUPLEXED PROCESS I/O

TABLE 3. ERROR COST FUNCTION VALUE

EXPERIENCE WITH AN ADVANCED SOFTWARE SYSTEM
AS AN OPERATOR'S AID IN A SHIP COMPUTER SYSTEM

Holger Røkeberg
NORSK A/S PHILIPS
Oslo, Norway

ABSTRACT

The paper deals with the experience gained in operating a ship computer system. The system is designed with the objective of continued development after installation and start of operation on board. This objective has necessitated a software system which is more comprehensive than is usual for ship-borne computers. The software system is made up of three major parts: Application programmes, software development facilities, and operating system. Two categories of operators are defined. One category is mainly concerned with operation of the application programmes, another category is making use of the software development facilities in the work with application programmes. A brief system description is given to illustrate the nature of the duties of the operator. The operator's experience with the software system is a collection of incidents and impressions which for clarity are grouped according to the major modes of system operation.

INTRODUCTION

This paper deals with the software system for a ship computer installation. It is termed an advanced system because it utilizes a recently developed large operating system with extensive software development facilities and has a mixture of low and high language application programmes, which all together are advanced for ship computer systems. The system is installed on board M/T "BERGE FISTER", a large oil tanker owned by A/S Sig. Bergesen d.y. & Co.
The paper relates how such a system behaves in its working environment and the operator's experience from using it.

The software system may be divided into three parts:

1. The application programmes which carry out the objectives of the installation,

2. The software development facilities for future development of application programmes,

3. The operating system.

PRESENTATION OF THE USER

The installation is a development project. After installation and start of operation on board, a two-years trial period was commenced during which further development and studies of operational results should be carried out in cooperation with personnel from the ship owner and the system supplier.

This led to a situation where we now have to consider two categories of users. The first one includes the intended end users of the system: The officers and crew of the ship. The other category includes the personnel from Norsk A/S Philips participating in the project on board the ship. At the time of writing it is primarily the second group that is gaining the most experience. Since these persons are present on board they handle some of the work that will subsequently be handled by the ship officers.
The ship officers have not had any previous experience or training with computerized equipment when joining this ship. They have learned their part of the system operation by direct use. Any systematic training schemes are not readily carried out with the present high turnover of ship officers.
The personnel from Philips include persons with widely different backgrounds. Some are regular beginners in the trade of computers, others are professionals with several years of experience. It is natural that these different people have gained different impressions of the software system. Before getting into this subject, it is necessary to give a short account of what the installation con-

sist of, and what it is intended to do.

DESCRIPTION OF THE SYSTEM

1. Central Processing Unit.

There is one central processing unit, CPU, a 16-bits NORD-1. The CPU is interphased to a Philips ferrite core memory with 256k words' capacity. The memory has 18-bits words, using one bit for parity control and one as a spare.

By equipping the CPU with a memory bank switching circuit, the CPU operates with random access to all core locations with all the standard addressing modes available.

2. Peripherals.

The computer is installed in a cabin on the poop deck. This cabin is known as the EDP-room and is located in the ship office area. One teletype, one photo electric paper tape reader, and one fast paper tape punch are installed in this cabin. These peripherals are mainly intended for software development, but are also used in operation of the applications. In addition there are a teletype in the wheel house and one in the engine control room.

3. Instrumentation.

The instrumentation includes a large number of both analogue and digital sensors, mostly located in the engine room. For the present purpose it is only necessary to note that the sensors are sampled at intervals or by interrupts caused by an engine timing system.

4. Collision Avoidance System.

This is the most striking system component. It is a piece of hardware which is quite demanding on the computer, but demands little of the operator.

5. Omega Receiver.

One of the least conspicuous system components is the Omega receiver, which consists of one card drawer located in the CPU rack and a pre-amplifier in the antenna base.

OPERATING SYSTEM

The operating software system used in this installation is PHILTRAN, which is based upon SINTRAN II. It is tailored to the specific computer configuration described above.

PHILTRAN was developed to fulfil the following objectives: The operating system shall be used in a development project where new programmes and new versions of old programmes are being written and tested. The operating system shall make the generation of these programmes as simple as possible. After the programmes are written they shall be tested in a realistic environment, without chance of destroying or disturbing other running programmes.

PHILTRAN consists of the following main parts:

- Monitor
- Operator communication
- Loader
- Memory protect routines
- Library
- Input/output system
- FORTRAN run-time system
- FORTRAN compiler
- Assembler
- Editor

Figure 1 illustrates the arrangement of the memory. The memory is divided into eight banks, each of 32k words. One bank is used for the PHILTRAN system, hence named the system bank. The other banks are called application banks, although banks 6 and 7 are used for programme development facilities. The system bank is hardware protected from the other banks. Any instructions executed in the application banks which try to store into or jump to the system bank are checked for validity. The system bank links to one application bank at the time. There are no direct connections between any two application banks.

DESCRIPTION OF THE APPLICATIONS

1. Collision Avoidance System.

To the user this is essentially a radar display with a number of unusual controls. All communication is done through push-buttons and joystick, numerical information is displayed on an alpha-numeric display.

2. Navigation.

The navigation package, decribed in a separate paper to this symposium, is operated by teletype. The conversational programme is a real-time programme and is started on operator's command. The route planning is an interactive routine. Position finding, on the other hand, is automatic after the programmes have been

ous service programmes that are used as general tools or he may use some of the commands of the operating system which will give detailed history of past programme execution.

No diagnostic programmes have been deviced to monitor system operation, since the high activity level on board leads to detection of malfunctions in a short time. With all applications activated there will be even less need for particular diagnostic devices to halt operation in case of incorrect operation.
Besides, these are features that should be part of the operating system, and they are. The most important software safety measure is the memory protect routine, preventing improper access to the system bank.

2. The Interactive Functions.

The operator has full control of the operation of all programmes running under monitor control. Programmes operated at fixed intervals or initiated by hardware interrupts will normally not be touched by the operator after successful initiation.

In this mode of system operation the operator is concerned with the practical use of the applications. For the ship officers this means that they are performing familiar duties with a new and unfamiliar tool. The software system is a central part of this tool. The operator's contact with software is generally through communication routines. We have made some observations on our conversational programmes and what is commonly termed man-machine communication.

The operating system has a communication system which includes a selection of commands and inquiries to the system. Within each application programme separate communication routines had to be written. When several programmers write programmes without close coordination there will be differences in their communication routines, just as in their other types of programmes. We have avoided confusion, and our experience gives reason to be moderately satisfied. But we have learned the importance of giving these aspects full attention from the very beginning.

In assembly programmes it has been possible to write economic conversation routines with safe check on input validity. These formats do not

mix easily with formats available in FORTRAN programmes. The general facilities of input offered by FORTRAN have proved to be too flexible to be really useful. This refers in particular to the extra programming efforts required to make operator typing errors harmless and readily corrigible.

Generally, the communication routines will be directed to the teletype from which an application programme is called. The operator can use any one of the teletypes when communicating with an application programme. This part has been successful. Good organization of automatic messages is more complicated. Certain types of messages are buffered in ring buffers. Output of these messages need a certain priority to ensure that the ring buffer is not filled up and messages lost. This priority will be higher than some tabular outputs, and mixups on the same teletype may occur. Such situations can be avoided by using the system feature of automatic selection of alternate device if the programmed device is busy.
But such remedies are unsuitable because it means for instance that the chief engineer may get his messages in the wheel house.

3. Software Development Facilities.

These facilities are operator tools in a limited sense only. Being a central part of the development aspect of the installation, however, they still deserve some mention. The project schedule assumed software development after installation on board, and the overall impression is that this has worked satisfactorily.

The Philips personnel has had good opportunity to use the various software facilities, and the experience is that software development can run parallel to regular system operation quite smoothly. It is desireable that the operators are able to write simple FORTRAN programmes because there is often small jobs that can be handled by a few FORTRAN statements. An example of this could be a programme to log a measured value in a period when its value would be of particular interest. Because of the proved value of such possibilities and probably because of some curiosity, there is interest among the crew members for learning FORTRAN programming. This development is welcomed by all parties, and a floating programming school is in the making.

New programmes can be tested out. For FORTRAN programmes which are loaded into one of the application banks this has been successful. For assembler coded programmes which are loaded into the system bank, the experience has been mixed. A fair number of system failures have occured as a result of these manipulations. But out of these a majority is suspected to occur due to the less than careful practice which one is quick to adapt when live debugging is within comfortable reach. These practices, however, had to be restrained when parts of the system were commissioned.

Programming practice as mentioned above is limited to FORTRAN and is loaded in a bank where no harm can be done to the rest of the system.

4. Instrumentation Changes.

The PHILTRAN used in this software system does not contain facilities for operating instrumentation. Programmes for such purposes are formed as regular real-time programmes operated under monitor command.

The operator can, therefore, interfere with the operation of the instrumentation without interferring with the operating system. Most measurements are read at fixed intervals. Each measuring point is defined in a table where all particulars of the reading is gathered and where the status also can be found. This status consists of single bits set according to whether the particular measuring point is in alarm condition, or when it is disconnected.

The operator can operate on the instrumentation table directly by means of on-line assembler. The operator can alternatively make corrections in the source tape of the instrumentation table. This is quite simple as he has the EDITOR-programme available. The new source tape is read by the initiation programme. The drawback of this method is that the initiation programme also will reset any status bits that are set. Thereby any measuring point disconnected by the operator will be reactivated. Apart from that, the only consequence will be a printing of any alarm condition that existed. The instrumentation programmes themselves will operate undisturbed.

The operator's need for these possibilities will in the future be limited to changing conversion factors when calibration of new sensors are necessary. In a system under development, however, the uses are many. In addition to changing conversion factors, it is possible to move the measuring point to another real-time programme operating with different intervals. Digital filtering may be turned on or off and the degree of filtering can be adjusted. Furthermore, there are individual settings for low and high alarm limits.

5. System Hang-ups.

In a small software system it is possible to remove all programming errors. Such a system will be designed to allow well defined operations only, and it will react in some prescribed manner to situations it was not meant to handle. A large operating system will invariably contain programming errors for quite some time beyond the formal completion. In flexibility and ability to meet undesired operations it will greatly outdo a simple system, but never to perfection. System hang-ups will therefore occur from time to time. The operator will detect such situations in various ways, and as long as the operator communication is active, he has various means of interrogating the system. Hang-ups cannot be resolved by the average operator. Although he can determine that a programme is blocking a stack, or there is a clash of priorities of programmes, he is unable to repair the situation. Most likely he will wind up with a system break-down.

6. System Break-Down.

System break-downs occur, or appear to occur. The difference is of no concern as long as the operator is unable to see it. If in his opinion the situation is unrepairable, he has just one thing to do, and that is to start all over again.

In theory, some seemingly unrepairable situations may be recovered by a person with adequate system familiarity. We have found that keeping such personnel at hand continuously is not feasible. An expert of that kind would be idle most of the time since he would not be expected to do the other chores of operating the system. Our experience is that a ship is not the place to hunt for the last bugs in an operating system. On the other hand, how does one get equally demanding conditions back in the laboratory ?

properly initiated. The Omega receiver is fully automatic, calling a driver routine by interrupt.
Dead reckoning and course information by either great circle or loxodrome sailing are also automatic.

3. Engine Condition Monitoring.

    This application is intended to be active at all times. Every few minutes a complete analysis of the engine parameters is conducted and any interesting developments are noted. Eventual error messages are typed out in the engine control room. If there are alarms from the E0-system (unmanned engine room supervision), some of these may also initiate a condition analysis. Finally, the operator may call on parts of the system for some detailed or specific information.

4. Hull Fouling Control.

    This application consists of two major parts. The first collects data relevant to hull fouling and assembles these in records that are stored in the memory. Some of this information is entered by the operator. The second part is a conversational data selection and tabulation programme. The operator starts one real-time programme, the individual routines of the system are called by commands of the main programme.

5. Load/Unload Planning.

    This programme is independent of instrumentation and has no connection to real-time. It is, however, no different from real-time programmes. The operator gets contact with a conversational routine after calling the real-time programme.

6. Logging Functions.

    The system produces various logs. The manoeuvre log registers all manoeuvres and prints a standard record at intervals while the manoeuvre is being executed. The alarm log is a print-out of all E0-alarms and some other messages. The engine log is printed daily, giving readings for every 4-hour period of selected engine measurements.
    All these logging functions are operated without operator's assistance once they are initiated.

7. Administrative Functions.

    These are primarily payroll calculations and crew work load registration. These are operated through teletype with conversational routines similar to those of navigation and load/unload planning programmes.

EXPERIENCE

The system which is described above has at the time of writing been in operation on board for 16 months. During this time a certain operator experience has been accumulated. It is shared by several operators and has so far been dominated by the implementation of new application software. It has not had much chance of becoming routine. Experience is a picture consisting of many details, and the following account is organized according to the various modes of system operation which the operator will encounter. Some of these operation modes are daily occurrencies, some are occasional, and some we shouldn't miss at all.

1. Automatic Functions only operating.

    In this mode the operator is not taking part in the operation. Still, should he drop by the EDP-room there are several ways of checking the situation. The operating system is active at all times. If not doing anything else, the monitor activates a background programme, effectively a dummy programme continually incrementing a computer hardware register. However, the system is never continually idle. Every second a programme for reading a series of multiplexer channels is activated, another programme reads a group of hardware counters, and a calendar programme is called for updating local and GMT clock and calendar. Every minute additional instrumentation programmes are called. These programmes cause a typical pattern on the multiplexer panel lights which is an indication to the operator that the system is working normally. This situation is, however, known to exist although operator's communications can be blocked thereby making the system literally inaccessible. The operator can call the operator communication, and if the request is serviced he can ask for the time of day or ask for the monitor time queue. The top six programmes of the time queue are written out. These are mostly programmes running at one second intervals. There are in fact a number of things the operator can do to verify proper operation. He may call vari-

Having a complicated operating system can be a source of frustration for the skilled operator/programmer. He will not be able to understand the problems caused by the operating software, and is unable to take the proper corrective actions, or even better: Identify an error. For the operator without programming background it is of no concern, since he would not understand a simple system either and would be quite prepared to give up when the procedure in the book doesn't work.

We have accepted that the software system of a development installation will collapse at times. When this happens the operator needs means of getting quickly back to business. All software is therefore being kept stored on magnetic tape.
Thus the "starting all over"-procedure has been simplified to read a magnetic tape containing an operating version of the total system. The whole operation will take about 15 minutes if the complete memory is reloaded. Normally the software development facilities are exempted. This comparatively long period is a result of choosing a low-speed magnetic tape station for the installation. A shorter re-load-time is desireable, but not essential, since it is only part of the total down-time and the other parts having nothing to do with the speed of the magnetic tape station. The system break-down may first be experienced by an operator who himself does not have time to do anything about it. By the time somebody else has appeared in the computer room and have decided what to do, the job itself may be the least part of it.

7. Continuity.

So much about software break-downs. What are the consequences ? Ideally, a computer system should have 100% continuity of operation. The author is unfamiliar with anybody living in such comfort, and do not expect to find it in a prototype system. The system will stop at times. Hence, the operation is discontinued and the 100% goal is unattained. This does not necessarily result in discontinued applications. Few programmes must be permanently discontinued because of a system failure. With well-considered data storage a programme can carry on even if there have been disturbances since the last programme execution.

A programme may keep data in several places:

- In itself

- In a common area of the bank

- In the global area of the system bank

- In the data stack, temporarily while the programme is active

The operator has no way of choosing the place to store data, that is part of the programme. The experience with the various ways of retaining data is inconclusive, but in conjunction with the use of a magnetic tape station for programme back-up it is chosen to keep all current measured values in the global area and all data of extended interest are kept in common area. It is then part of the operator's work to look for indications of the soundness of this method.

8. Miscellaneous.

Core Access.

It is often practical to be able to insert values directly into individual core locations. This can be a hazardous practice in a system with moderately qualified operators. The operating system has a routine for examining an addressed location and subsequently loading a new content to the same address. This feature is operational in the system bank. It has proved to be safe in use, the deposit-command will only work if directly preceeded by an examin-command. The obvious drawback is that only octal integers are read, or can be written.

Individual locations in the application banks, as well as in the system bank, may be addressed by the assembler. Regular assembler operations are then available. An inexperienced operator is not expected to use this facility, which can easily be improperly used. In the hands of an experienced operator it is a powerful tool. The most valuable feature is perhaps the means of reading and writing floating point quantities. Few operators, or programmers for that matter, are able to convert floating point numbers to the corresponding three octal integers. There are many applications for these facilities. In a system of many programmes, there will be various initiation procedures. Some of these are formed as separate programmes. They are mainly circumstances where it is necessary to read a data tape. In some programmes the setting of a switch is the only requirement for differentiating between the first and subsequent programme executions. In such cases an initiation programme seems wasteful.

Conversion constants for most measurements may be changed by inserting floating point numbers in a location in a common area. Another obvious use of direct core access is during programme debugging.

DEVICE ALTERNATION

With operator communication through three teletypes at different locations, it is important that the operator can call any programme without knowing what is going on at the other two teletypes. If the called programme is busy, the operator's call will be placed in a queue and will be served as soon as the programme is ready. This is fine, except that the operator may have lost interest in the meantime. The sudden reply to a forgotten programme request may be awkward at times. There is a command for cancelling programme requests which would prevent such situations, it is just a matter of remembering to use it. The automatic switching to alternate device in a system with several output peripherals can cause housekeeping problems. The system has a couple of examples of this. A high priority warning being addressed to the teletype in the computer room will be readdressed to a different teletype if the former is busy, for instance with operator communication which itself has high priority. The message will probably go through on the alternate teletype even if this is writing a long table at the time.

Priority allocation is a difficult proposition. The hardware priorities are well established. They have been derived at by the speed of the devices and the response requirements of the application. Programmes with software priority only can give surprises. The priority of programmes calling other programmes must be selected so that the proper sequence of execution is assured. The operator can change the priority at any time, except for a programme already requested. The programme must be deactivated before its priority can be altered. The operating system has commands to handle this.

CONCLUSIONS

This paper could not be a complete and final report on the title subject. Experience with any undertaking will accumulate as long as the work is carried on. The nature of the job will determine whether new experiences will be gained all the time, or if all that can be learned is learned early, with nothing but repetitions thereafter. We have defined two major categories of operators according to their backgrounds. Experience is unevenly divided between the two categories. So far the category with the better computer qualifications has gained the bulk of the experience with the software system. This experience has proved that the extended facilities of an advanced software system is a valuable operator aid. It is possible to carry on development of both software and equipment with other parts of the system in regular operation, but the software system is both large and complicated and can also be a source of system stops. This is not surprising, and while efforts are made to remove the causes of such occurrencies, the operator has practical means of reducing their effects.

The second category of operators, which should rather be named users, is gaining experience more slowly and is less concerned with the software system anyway. The user will gain an overall impression of the practical value of an application, a part of this impression will be "ease of operation". If this part is large, it will mostly be so due to the software system. At the time of writing this particular experience is limited, but it is growing in the right direction.

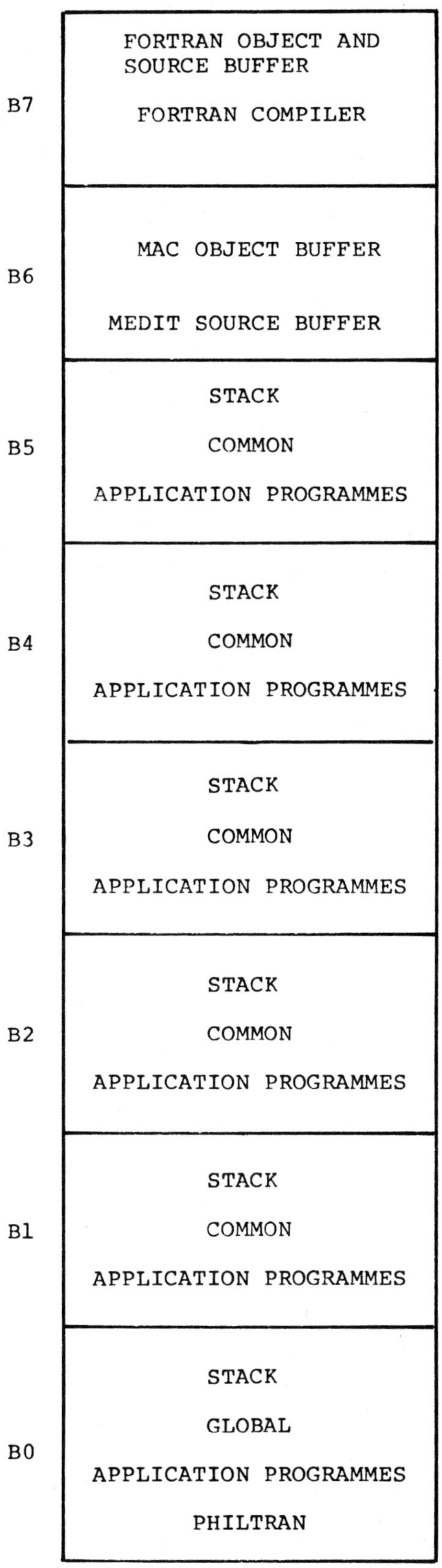

```
┌─────────────────────────┐
│   FORTRAN OBJECT AND     │
│     SOURCE BUFFER        │
│                          │
│     FORTRAN COMPILER     │
├─────────────────────────┤
│    MAC OBJECT BUFFER     │
│                          │
│    MEDIT SOURCE BUFFER   │
├─────────────────────────┤
│         STACK            │
│         COMMON           │
│  APPLICATION PROGRAMMES  │
├─────────────────────────┤
│         STACK            │
│         COMMON           │
│  APPLICATION PROGRAMMES  │
├─────────────────────────┤
│         STACK            │
│         COMMON           │
│  APPLICATION PROGRAMMES  │
├─────────────────────────┤
│         STACK            │
│         COMMON           │
│  APPLICATION PROGRAMMES  │
├─────────────────────────┤
│         STACK            │
│         COMMON           │
│  APPLICATION PROGRAMMES  │
├─────────────────────────┤
│         STACK            │
│         GLOBAL           │
│  APPLICATION PROGRAMMES  │
│        PHILTRAN          │
└─────────────────────────┘
```

B7, B6, B5, B4, B3, B2, B1, B0

Figure 1   MEMORY ALLOCATION

RELIABILITY IN ONBOARD COMPUTER SYSTEMS,

EQUIPMENT SELECTION AND SYSTEM DIAGNOSTICS

Kåre Harald Drager
Project Leader   and
Det norske Veritas
Oslo, Norway

Morten Heldal Haugerud
Cand. real
A/S Computas
Oslo, Norway

ABSTRACT

When a computer system is used for process control, it is of primary importance to obtain reliability and some degree of fault-tolerance. The process control reliability depends on the computer system design and the back-up philosophy. This paper describes a computer system designed for process control and predictive maintenance onboard a Norwegian gas tanker. A dual computer system which operates in a real time/batch configuration was chosen. This resulted in low software overhead and made it possible to obtain computer back-up for the highest priority jobs.

A diagnostic system was developed to detect errors and initiate the necessary operations in case of failure. The diagnostic system consists of both hardware and software parts. High priority diagnostic routines check the hardware and the software parts of the system. In case of errors, the hardware takes the appropriate action.

If a system error occurs which affects the process control, the diagnostic system disconnects the output system and establishes a "fail-safe" condition for the process. The system has been in operation onboard the Norwegian tanker, M/T Høegh Multina, since October 1971 and the experience achieved during the first period is reviewed.

Finally, ideas are discussed to increase future system availability and insure minimum down time due to hardware failure. Important factors to consider in this case are on-line maintenance diagnostic, print-outs to ease trouble determination and location, and permit hardware repair and check-out concurrent with live operations.

INTRODUCTION

Computers are used for process control in several industries and onboard ships today. It is a convenient tool because of its ability to solve complex problems with great speed and flexibility. Many different systems has been developed, from the simplest minicomputer to sophisticated multi-processing systems.

However, anyone designing a computer system for process control has encountered the problem of computer system failure. The computer often represents a system centralization, and in case of hardware or software failure, unacceptable damage can be done, hence some kind of back-up system is necessary. This has often resulted in the use of a complete conventional automation system as back-up. Thus the total system costs have been extremely high. Therefore an evaluation of various aspects of installing a computer system is needed.

1. System complexity
2. Necessary back-up
3. The total system reliability
4. The total system cost/ benefit ratio

When using a computer system for critical process control, it is also important to insure minimum computer system down time. To achieve this, on-line maintenance diagnostic can be implemented to ease trouble shooting and location of the failures. In case of errors, easy repairability can then be achieved by replacable system modules.

A computer system developed for process control of a large bore diesel engine onboard a Norwegian gas tanker will be described to illustrate those steps which were found necessary to insure safe engine room operation during computer system failure.

A ship is an isolated unit during its seagoing period, and there is a limitation to the amount of spare parts available onboard and the possibility of carrying out repairs at sea. The need for automatic monitoring and process control of the machinery is therefore obvious. However, various failures in a large bore diesel engine cannot be monitored by conventional instrumentation only. The need for some special instrumentation is necessary. Moreover, to evaluate the data from both conventional and special instrumentation, requires thorough process knowledge and elaborate data handling.

This was the basis of the need for a project for development and installation of the computer system for monitoring and process control of the engine room as well as predictive maintenance of the propulsion machinery onboard the Norwegian ship M/T Høegh Multina. The main aim was to obtain a reliable, flexible, and economic installation. The project partners were the shipping company Leif Høegh & Co. A/S, the Moss-Rosenberg Shipyard and the Norwegian classification society Det Norske Veritas, with some financial support from The Norwegian Council for Scientific and Technical Research.

The project work was divided into three subprojects:

1. Development and evaluation of diagnostic routines and methods to achieve an optimal maintenance of the propulsion machinery

2. Development of instrumentation, sensors and electronics for direct measurement of the main diesel engine's condition

3. Development of a computer hardware and software system for process control and predictive maintenance based upon results from the other subprojects

When introducing the computer as a system component onboard, this complex equipment had to be handled by people without education in this field. The project objectives were no extra crew onboard to take care of the computer system. The need for reliable equipment, easy repairability and on-line diagnostic for instructive maintenance was therefore obvious. The design of the computer system therefore became an important part of the project work, and the philosophy and steps which were taken to achieve computer system integrity will be discussed in the following sections.

SYSTEM DESCRIPTION

To obtain a more complete understanding of the subject a short description of the process and the computer system seems necessary.

The process in question is the ship's engineroom, which consists of the following main parts:

1. The main engine for the ship's propulsion

2. Auxiliary smaller diesel engines to run the generators

3. Steam system with donkey boiler and exhaust boiler for delivery of steam for heating

4. Generators for electric power supply

5. Compressors for delivery of compressed air for main engine starting and manoeuvring

6. Purification system with separators for cleaning of fuel and lubricating oil

7. Pumps for delivery of fuel, cooling water and lubricating oil to the main and the auxiliary engines

Figure 1 shows those parts of the process which were included in the computer control system, and those parts which were conventionally automated.

The engine room was to be operated according to the ship classification society's recommendations for unmanned engine room (EO-Class Notation), and the classification society divides the process control into three levels of automation:

1. Control loops   (Temperature control, etc.)

2. Monitoring   (Alarm warning, etc.)

3. Safety functions   (Shut down, slow down, etc.)

The three levels of automation are not allowed to have any common hardware. This is due to the requirement of safe operation. If the controllers and the monitoring system are in-operative, the safety function hardware can still prevent damage of the equipment.

The triple control system solution was easy to implement with a conventional automated system. For complete computer control however, it would be necessary to have three separate computers; one for each level of automation. This would make it hard to compete with conventional systems. Therefore a compromise was made and only parts of the process were computer controlled. The large investment however, made it necessary to consider the problem very carefully to see which automation parts could be implemented without breaking the rules for safe operation for the engine room.

Under the constraint that the engine room must be operated safely in case of computer system failure the following solution resulted.

Operated by conventional hardware:

1. All shut down safety functions)
2. All analog control loops   )   EO-
3. Remote control of the main en-)   system
   gine   )

Operated by computer system:

1. Monitoring   ) EO-
2. Digital control   ) system
3. Start-up safety functions)

4. Predictive maintenance   ) PM-
   system   ) system

A block diagram of the predictive maintenance system is shown in Figure 2.

The input/output load on the system is
quite large and the dynamic process data
for the predictive maintenance system requires sampling interval as short as 100
microsecond. The variety of tasks from
high priority process control routines to
interactive teletype communication routines also laid heavy demand on the computer
system's flexibility and execution speed.

The objective for selection of the computer hardware was also minimum down time
and easy repairability in case of hardware
failure. A single computer system did not
seem to give the necessary performance,
and a multi computer system was considered.
A dual computer system seemed to meet the
requirements both from an operational and
a system performance point of view. If the
software overhead could be kept at a reasonable level, this seemed to solve the
problems.

Figure 3 shows the chosen hardware configuration. Two small digital computers
each with a 16K 16 bit memory were used.
The minicomputers were connected via two
data channels and had a memory cycle of
1.5 microsecond. A common input/output system gave either computer access to the
process. Two teletypes, one fast tape reader, one fast tape punch, a CRT-display
and a hardwired communication panel were
chosen as peripheral equipment.

One of the computers was chosen for real
time operations performing the process
control PAC (Process-data Aquisition Computer) and had highest priority. The other
computer DAC (Data Analysis Computer) operated in batch mode and was designed to do
the predictive maintenance tasks for the
diesel engine. All jobs in DAC were either
activated automatically from PAC or manually through teletype communication.

HARDWARE SELECTION

One objective was that special accomoda-
tions should not be necessary for the
computer system. It had to work in the
control room in the engine room, where
the temperature could reach 50-60°C with
high humidity and constant viberations.
The need for ruggedized equipment was obvious. Both computers were tested for
climatic conditions according to Det

Norske Veritas' recommendation for instrumentation onboard.

One important part however, was the power
supply for the computer system. There is
always a possibility for ship black-out
and in that case the computer system is
important for error diagnostic. When power
is back, the computer is needed for stand
by automatic and sequence start of the
pumps and auxiliary equipment. Much effort
was therefore put into the design of the
computer power supply system. Figure 4
shows a block diagram of the chosen design.

The normal supply is by inverter to insure
continous supply in case of ship black-
out. During inverter failure it is possible to use ship 220V~ supply. The computers therefore also were tested for
electrical disturbance, according to Det
Norske Veritas' recommendations.

To insure information of power failure,
the alarm system for the power supply is
hardware and independent of the computer
system. In case of need for redundant
power (inverter failure), the switch over
must be done manually, but power failure
software routines do automatic start-up
of the computer system when redundant power is connected. This insure minimum
down time of the computer system and few
operational problems for the operator.

The low voltage power supplies are fed
from the battery, and they are divided
into three main groups; EO, IO and PM.
Different action is taken automatically
during failure for the different groups
and teletype messages make it easy for
the operator to locate the failing power
supply.

All electronic equipment was mounted in
the back section of the control desk in
the control room, to make easy access for
the operator in case of failure. The
equipment with connections out in the engine room, such as steering relays and
sensors, were made short circuit safe by
electronic fuses. There is also a possibility of connection of wrong voltage
during installation. To insure as little
damage as possible of any electronic
equipment if this should happen, this
electronic equipment was tested for high
voltage to see when damage would appear
and the system was improved according to
this.

As a conclusion it can be said that all
reasonable steps were taken to avoid damage of the electronic equipment during
installation and operation onboard.

SOFTWARE SYSTEM

The software objectives were to keep the

software over-head down, make the system
flexible, easy to handle, and insure high
software reliability. Figure 5 shows a map
of the software for the system. PAC-soft-
ware is operating in real time and DAC-
software in batch mode. Either computer
can run either jobs. A short description
of the most important software parts will
be given below.

The PAC real time monitor administers the
execution of the process routines. The
real time clock gives an interrupt every
10th millisecond, which is the system's
basic time. A maximum execution time can
be specified for each routine. If any job
uses more time than specified, the monitor
aborts the job and gives a message to the
computer diagnostic system, which takes
any necessary action. In its idle loop,
the monitor calculates the time load of
the system, which can be displayed for the
operator, to give him an idea of the system's performance.

Because of the system configuration (real
time - batch) it is necessary to have a
communication system between the computers.
This is done through the data channels.
Each computer can read and write in the
other computer's memory without disturbing
the CPU-execution. The effect is a doubling of the memory cycle time.

In this configuration, the real time system PAC has the highest priority, and the
DAC computer was not allowed to disturb
the PAC system by mistakenly writing an
error in the PAC memory. Therefore DAC is
only allowed to read from PAC's memory,
but PAC can read and write in DAC's memory.

The communication between the two computers is implemented by two message buffers
in each computer. The PAC computer with
the ability to read and write, transmits
the messages between the buffers.

DAC does no real time jobs. Its tasks are
teletype activated or automatically activated from the PAC computer. All teletype
jobs need manual data input, and an interactive teletype communication system is
therefore implemented in DAC. Every teletype job has a name starting with the
character #. By writing the job's name
followed by carriage return, the computer
starts the question sequence. After this
is finished, the job is executed. If the
operator makes a mistake, the computer
interrupts him and rewrites the question.
The operator can also interrupt a job himself by writing the character @. The computer will then interrupt the job and indicate that it is ready for new jobs.

Because either software systems, PAC or
DAC, can be executed on either computer,

the DAC computer is therefore a back-up
for the PAC-system. The back-up is of the
"short-break" type. This means it is necessary to restart PAC after loading the back-
up computer with the paper tape containing
the PAC system. The system could have been
reloaded from a disk or a magnetic tape,
but in either case it would have been a
short break. A secondary memory would also
have introduced higher system costs and
more system software. However, the system
is flexible enough for installation of a
secondary memory later if it is found necessary.

COMPUTER DIAGNOSTIC SYSTEM

The dual computer system has introduced a
higher reliability and greater flexibility.
However, in case of a computer system
failure, it was still possible to do serious harm to the process because either
computer has access to the common input/
output system. It was therefore necessary
to analyse the majority computer system
failures and their possible damage. This
resulted in the construction of a hardware/
software diagnostic system which carries
out the appropriate action if an error
occurs in the computer system.

By looking at the hardware configuration
shown in Figure 3, it is clear that the
sensor data has to pass many "intersections" before being "safe" in the computer.
Any hardware failure of the multiplexer,
analog/digital converter, input/output system, or software failure will lower the
computer system's performance.

It is therefore important to detect and
avoid any failure that may influence the
process control. Three important items can
be listed:

1. A "fail-safe"-condition must be
   defined for the process

2. Every system failure must be detected and reported

3. When any system failure occurs,
   which has no back-up, the "fail-
   safe" condition must be established

The first step is to define the "fail-safe"
condition for the process. This is the engine room condition that must be established automatically in case of a computer
system failure which may influence the PAC
system process control. This is defined as
the safety condition for the engine room,
which represents the best safety condition
for the total ship.

Every unit which is operated by the computer system, will be forced to its "fail-
safe" condition.

To fulfill the requirements for safe operation of the ship, the computer system down time must be as short as possible. This can be achieved with computer system self checking and on-line diagnostics. In case of failure, a printout of failure description and location will help the operator in his maintenance and restart of the system. It is impossible to detect all computer system failures which may influence the process control, but the most important ones, found necessary to track, are listed below.

1. Sensor failure
2. Multiplexer and A/D-converter failure
3. I/O-system failure
4. Power supply failure
5. Data channel failure
6. Software failure

PAC is necessary to maintain the EO-functions, and has the highest priority. In case of a PAC failure, a short break will be necessary before the PAC system can be activated on the other computer. The DAC system however, is not critical and may be stopped.

PAC can operate independently, but DAC's operation depends on the PAC system (tandem configuration). Any failure in the PAC system hardware and software must therefore result in the "fail-safe" condition until the other computer can take over. During DAC system failure however, only blocking of the DAC system is necessary.

Sensor failure and relay failure must influence neither the PAC nor the DAC system, but only the routines using the failing device. The system behavior in an error situation can therefore be divided into three levels of hierarchy.

1. Fail-bit

Blocking of an actual routine operation is done by software. All sensors are sampled by an interface routine for input. If a failure occurs, the interface routine marks a fail-bit for the particular sensor. This fail-bit is sensed by the application routine which is then terminated. The alarm-system will warn the operator and give an alarm message identifying the sensor, and the software routines will not use the sensor before the fail-bit is reset.

The same operation occurs for a routine, if it fails to activate a steering relay. A message is given to the operator to identify the relay with an alarm warning. The routine will not try to activate the device again before the alarm is manually reset. This operation is limited to the actual software routines and have no influence on the rest of the system.

2. IOTE-blocking

The philosophy here is that if a DAC system error occurs, it is important to avoid the execution of any output orders from the DAC computer. This is done electronically by blocking the IO-enable signal (IOTE) for the particular computer. This will only influence the DAC computer output and the PAC computer system will continue operation.

3. Master-relay

The top level of the safety system is the "fail-safe" condition. Every steering relay for the process has a main power supply. By disconnecting the power supply, every steering relay will be disengaged. This established the "fail-safe" condition of the process, and makes a galvanic break between the computer and the process, because the master-relay (MR) is the main gate for power to the steering relays. This relay is operated by the computer diagnostic system.

Only the process output signals will be blocked by disengaging the master-relay. The rest of the system (man/machine, input, alarm, etc.) is in operation and can tell the operator what is wrong. This helps the operator in his trouble shooting. The block diagram in figure 6 shows schematicly the computer diagnostic hardware system.

The list below shows the errors that will establish the "fail-safe" condition (PAC-failures).

1. Power failure PAC computer
2. I/O-system and sensors power supply failure
3. I/O-system transport failure
4. Multiplexer and A/D-converter failure
5. Maximum time exceeded for a software routine (selective watch dog)
6. Too high time load for the PAC-system (limit-timer)

The appropriate list for DAC errors is:

1. DAC-computer power failure
2. Failure of the power supply modules for the PM-sensors
3. Data channel failure
4. Time load too high for the DAC system (DAC watch-dog)

These error signals will be checked by the control logic and the DAC computer IOTE-signal will be blocked.

Different messages will appear as teletype printouts under the different failure situations. These will help the operator in his trouble shooting and insure minimum down time of the computer system. Below is given a short description of the different printouts.

1. PAC POWER FAILURE
2. DAC POWER FAILURE

Identifies main power failure of the computers.

3. PS EO FAILURE
4. PS IO FAILURE
5. PS PM FAILURE

Power supply (PS) failure
EO - Group of power supplies for EO-equipment
IO - Group of power supplies for IO-equipment
PM - Group of power supplies for predictive maintenance (PM) equipment

6. IO EO BITS 004251 FAILURE
7. IO PM BITS 000002 FAILURE

Input/output (IO) transportation failure. EO and PM identify each a 256 bit block and the code identifies the module.

8. MP EO FAILURE
9. MP PM FAILURE

Multiplexer (MP) failure. Two channels of each multiplexer (EO and PM) are used for checking the marginal voltages (0 V and 1 V).

10. ROUTINE NO 01 ABORTED

Real-time software program failure. One real time routine has exceeded its time limit and is aborted. This can be due to software errors, CPU or memory failure.

11. PAC COMPUTER FAILURE
12. DAC COMPUTER FAILURE

The overall watch-dog has been activated. This is a limit-timer set by the lowest priority routine. This failure can be due to software errors, CPU or memory failure.

13. ACM PAC BITS 001200 FAILURE
14. ACM DAC BITS 011000 FAILURE

Data channel (ACM) transport failure. The code indicates the failing bits.

15. ACM PAC FAILURE
16. ACM DAC FAILURE

Data channel addressing failure.

DIAGNOSTIC SYSTEM PANEL

Because both computers can run either jobs, PAC or DAC, it is necessary to indicate which computer runs which job. This is done by a software identification routine in each computer. This routine tells the control logic which computer shall be blocked when errors occur. A service panel was installed to give the operator this information.

As mentioned earlier, the objective for the system design was easy operation of the system and unambiguous presentation of data and information to the operator. The man/computer communications panels were therefore made easy understandable and easy operationable.

On the service panel each computer has a key-switch and four lamps. The key-switch is shown in Figure 7. The lamps above the key-switch identify the job which is actually being executed by that computer. The two lamps beside the key-switch tell the operator if the output system is connected to that computer. The lamp above (MR) lights (green) when the master-relay is activated and the PAC system is in normal operation. The other lamp lights (red) when this computer's IOTE signal is blocked.

The operator must manually reset the computer diagnostic system after a failure. This is done by the key-switch. A 10 millisecond pulse is generated by operating the switch. This is enough for the diagnostic system to establish a run situation if the system is performing correct.

Figure 8 shows a picture of the service panel. Power to the different power supplies (computer, instrumentation, I/O-system, etc.) can be checked and switched on and off at this panel in addition to the diagnostic system operation. Computer 1 (to the left) is doing the PAC job in the picture. The master-relay (MR) is activated as indicated by the light (green). The IOTE-lamp for computer 2 (right) lights (red) because this system is not yet enabled. The operator is just trying to connect the output system of this computer by operating the key-switch. If he succeeds, the IOTE-lamp will be dark and the total PAC-DAC system will be in operation.

In addition the operator has more detailed information of the failure on the alarm panel. The total control desk with the alarm panel is shown in Figure 9. The service panel is mounted on the rear of this panel.

EXPERIENCE WITH THE SYSTEM

During system debugging and start-up, the dual system had many advantages. The system development had to be done before the ship left the shipyard, and system testing and debugging by two operators on a computer each with access on-line the process was therefore convenient.

The PAC system was first connected on-line because of the EO-functions. The PAC core was filled with application routines, and the other computer was conveniently used for debugging the PAC system by use of the data channel.

The computer system has been in operation since October 1971 and the diagnostic system has proven its worth. All self-check functions have carried out their mission at least one time. In particularly power supply failure, I/O system transport failure, multiplexer and A/D-converter failure, and data channel failure, which have been quickly corrected because of error information given to the operator.

The maximum time set for real time routines and the limit-timer needed some corrections during the test-out period. This was also expected because it was difficult to estimate the right time before the system was actually used on-line.

The importance of a self-check system separated from the main application system is obvious. This is not fully accomplished in the described system, because this diagnostic system is a mixture of hardware and software with the hardware as an overall safety device. With microprogramming, however, the self-check or diagnostic system could probably have been fully separated, and it would have been easier to implement in the system.

CONCLUSIONS

The paper has described a dual computer system for process control. The computer diagnostic system found necessary to achieve a safety level of process operation is outlined. The dual system appears to be a flexible and reliable computer system solution. However, the dual system has introduced a more complex diagnostic system to insure the safe operation of the process during computer system failure.

By sharing the jobs between the two computers in a real time/batch system, a savings in the software overhead was achieved. This is because the computers do two different jobs without overlap, and use the data processed by the other computer when necessary. It is also possible to control the system execution time by putting large jobs in DAC and hence not disturb the real time processing. In addition this gives a computer back-up for the high priority jobs in PAC.

The objectives have been total computer system integrity, and overall protection of the process. In case of critical computer system failure, the computers are disconnected from the process to insure no damage due to such failures. The operator is helped in his trouble shooting by printouts of computer diagnostics to minimize computer system down time. But the operator himself must manually restart the system when the failure is corrected.

The philosophy of manual restart is probably not useful in the future. If critical decisions must be made within seconds, the computer system must probably have built in redundancy which can immediately take over in a computer failure situation, and the computer system must be self repairable to some degree. Many systems are also on-line continously and shut down of the system is undesirable. To do maintenance on this system it is desirable to change erroneous modules concurrent with live operations. The erroneous modules must also point themselves out by printouts from on-line diagnostics to minimize trouble shooting time. The self repairable system with this feature can then by regular maintenance increase its mean time between failure (MTBF) and lower its mean time to repair (MTTR) considerably.

Very few computer systems except for computer systems for space crafts have any built in redundancy and self repairability to day. This is due to considerable cost increases with such features to day.

However, this will change in the future. The competition in the computer market is keen, and the users are concerned with their computer system performance and are looking for high reliable systems. Hopefully this results in more reliable computer systems with built in redundancy, on-line diagnostics and some degree of self repairability. This will increase the computer systems' reliability and performance to a desirable level required for equipment used for critical process control.

KEY WORDS

Ship automation
Process control
Multiprocessing
Computer diagnostic
Computer communication
Man/computer communication

BIBLIOGRAPHY

Drager, K.H. and Liland, H., "A computer System for Process Control and Predictive Maintenance of a Diesel Engine on a Sea-going Vessel". Proceedings of the 27th Annual ISA Conference, New York - October 9 - 12, 1972.

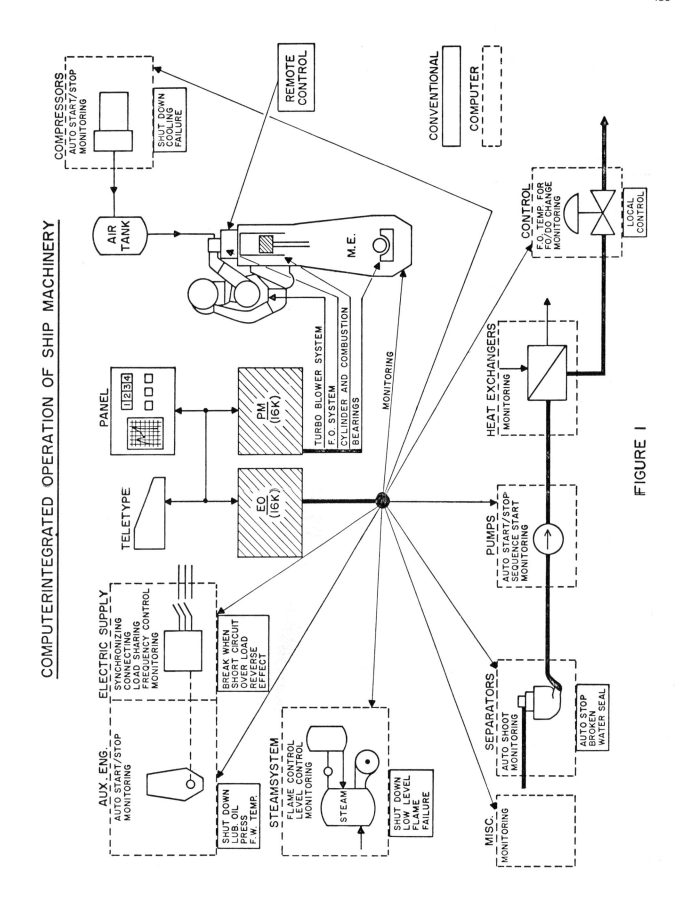

COMPUTERINTEGRATED OPERATION OF SHIP MACHINERY

FIGURE 1

486

COMPUTERINTEGRATED OPERATION OF SHIP MACHINERY

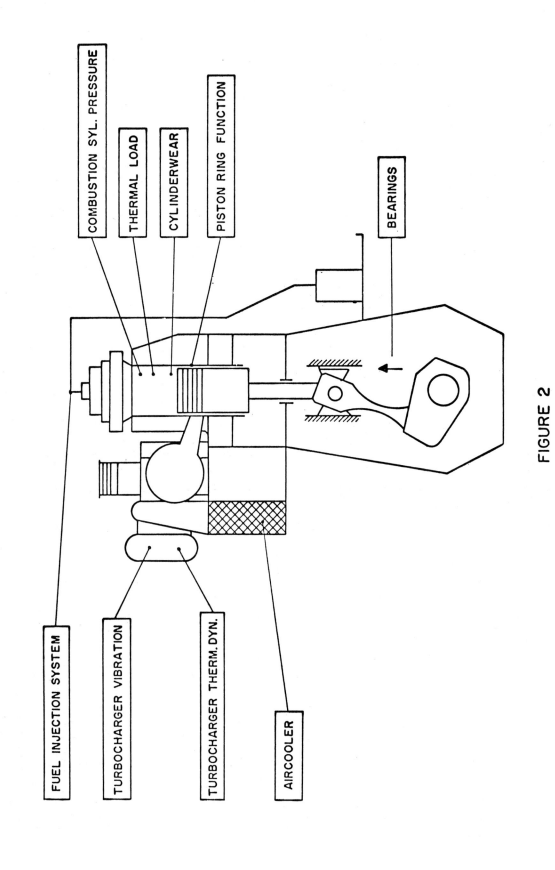

FIGURE 2

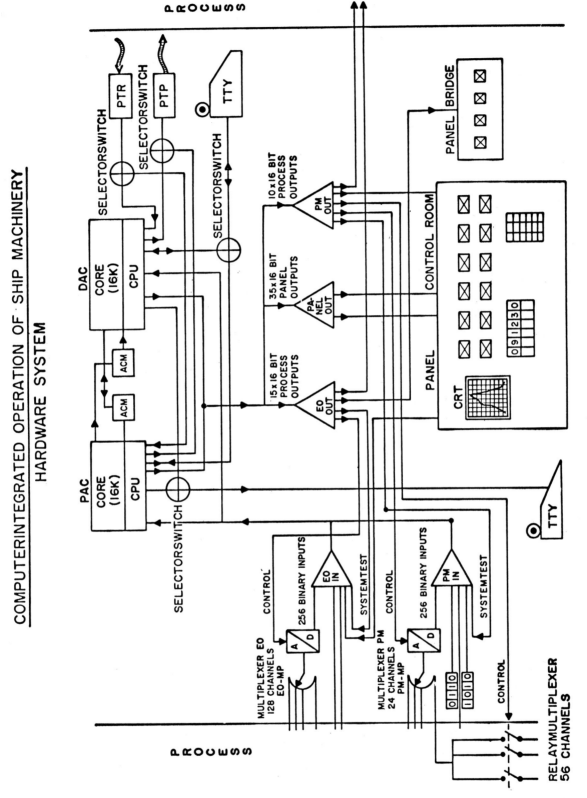

COMPUTERINTEGRATED OPERATION OF SHIP MACHINERY
HARDWARE SYSTEM

FIGURE 3

488

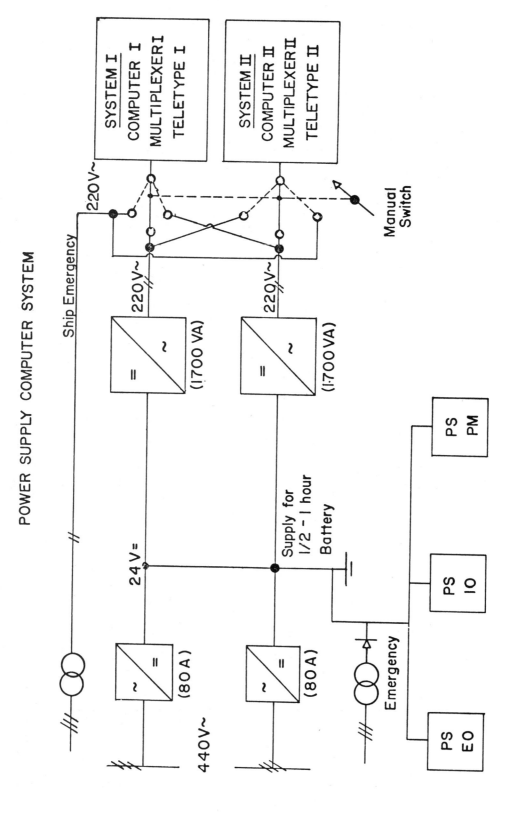

POWER SUPPLY COMPUTER SYSTEM

SYSTEM I
COMPUTER I
MULTIPLEXER I
TELETYPE I

SYSTEM II
COMPUTER II
MULTIPLEXER II
TELETYPE II

220V~

Ship Emergency

Manual Switch

220V~

220V~

~

(1700 VA)

~

(1700VA)

=

=

24 V=

Supply for 1/2 - 1 hour
Battery

~
=
(80 A)

~
=
(80 A)

440V~

Emergency

PS
PM

PS
IO

PS
EO

Figure 4

489

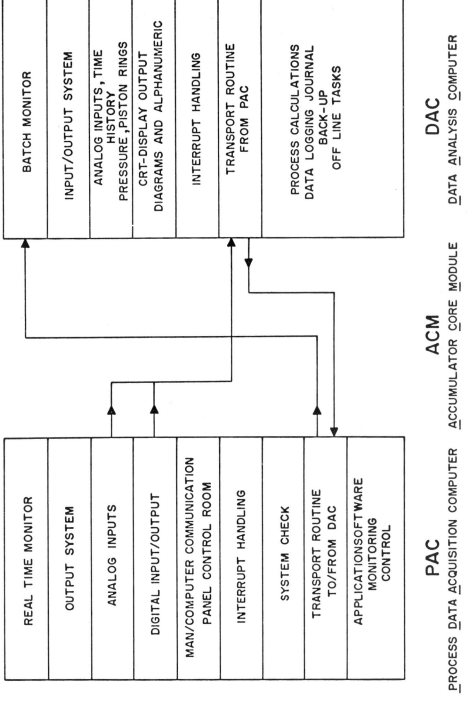

COMPUTERINTEGRATED OPERATION OF SHIP MACHINERY

SOFTWARE SYSTEM

FIGURE 5

PAC   ACM   DAC

PROCESS DATA ACQUISITION COMPUTER   ACCUMULATOR CORE MODULE   DATA ANALYSIS COMPUTER

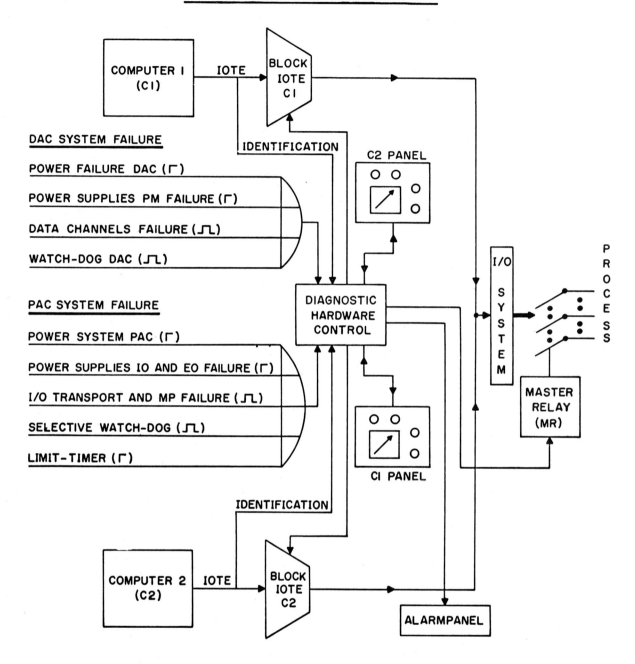

FIGURE 6

KEY-SWITCH FOR THE SAFETY CHECK SYSTEM

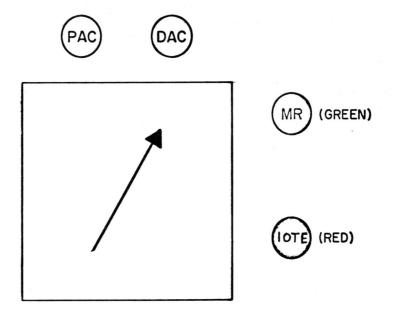

FIGURE 7

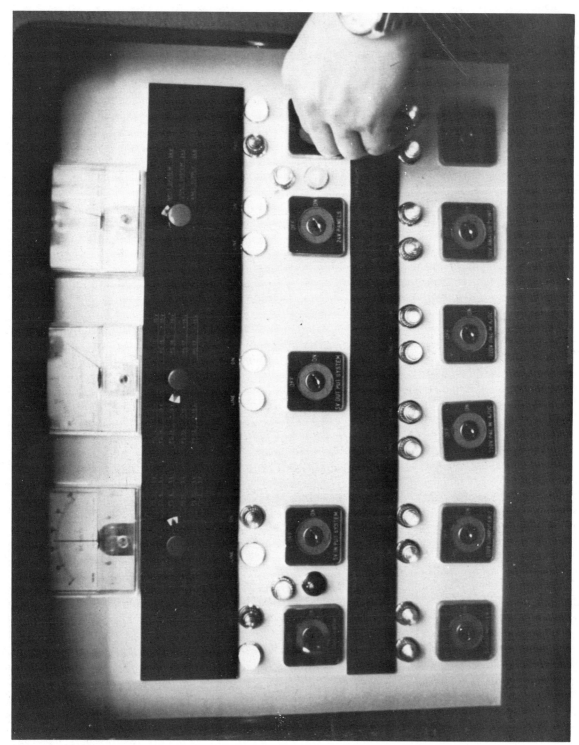

FIGURE 8

FIGURE 9

ELEMENTS OF RELIABILITY ENGINEERING
APPLIED TO SHIP AUTOMATION

Carsten Bøe and Tor Heimly
Det norske Veritas
Oslo, Norway

ABSTRACT

This paper is an attempt to state some of the general background of reliability engineering as a part of modern system theory. It is shown how certain simple reliability analysis thechniques yield valuable information on system reliability and availability. Particular emphasis is placed on failure modes and effects analysis applied to part of a ship automation system. Further, reliability computations are performed, as an example, for some items within this system. It is shown how the analyses give valuable information related to decisions on system design and choosing between design alternatives.

INTRODUCTION

Reliability is a term used in everyday life. Most people have an appreciation of what it means, although there are often slightly different views on the term. Thus misunderstandings arise when someone applies the concept of reliability to system safety, and another applies it to system availability.

A definition of reliability, suggested by ANSI (1), states that:

"Reliability is the ability of an item to perform its required function at stated conditions for a specified period of time".

Speaking quantitatively, reliability means the probability of successful operation of an item for a specified period of time at stated conditions. Availability means operational effectiveness or relative operational success.

The reliability of a component or a system is no longer a subjective and obscure concept, but a property which can be manipulated and expressed numerically together with other physical properties. This approach to reliability is the discipline of reliability engineering.

Reliability engineering belongs to the field of modern system analysis. After its origin in the second world war, the application of reliability engineering has mostly been in the field of electronics, space aviation and atomic energy. In recent years, however, the trend towards more complicated ship automation systems has brought reliability engineering techniques into the focus of ship designers and operators.

RELIABILITY AND MARINE ENGINEERING

An old and basic principle in the ship design process has been to develop simple and rugged systems, inherently reliable at a relative moderate cost. However, the last decade has seen a more rapid application of new technology than before. The increasing size of ships, more complex and advanced systems for propulsion, navigation and cargo handling has developed the need for application of reliability engineering in order to assess the utility of the new technology.

It is evident that reliability and availability of the propulsion and navigation units are of vital importance for the economical results when operating large, modern ships. Operational breakdowns and system failures mean not only loss of time and money. They also involve possible spill of high-risk cargo and pose danger of collision or grounding in areas of heavy traffic or in congested waters.

Reliability engineering is a discipline providing tools for the evaluation of all kinds of failures and their consequences. It is, however, important to note that reliability engineering does not imply improving reliability but quantifying reliability. It presents a systematic approach to solving design problems, evaluating existing designs and estimate future system performance.

Performing reliability analyses means asking oneself "what happens if .... ?, and such a question is often very difficult to answer. The designer of a system most often asks himself "Which functions are to be performed?", and this is a different attitude from that of the reliability assessor who in addition will ask whether a system really will perform its tasks, how long it will perform, what happens if something goes wrong and what can go wrong in a particular system.

Analysis Methods

A person performing reliability analysis has two kinds of tools to help him. The first one comprises the qualitative analyses, telling him whether one

design alternative may be better than other alternatives, what kind of failures may occur and what
the consequences of these failures will be. Qualitative analyses enable the assessor to judge failure criticality, estimate maintainability and evaluate failure sequences leading to particularly dangerous or costly events.

The second category comprises the quantitative
analyses, telling the assessor just how much
better one alternative is compared to another,
how often the different kinds of failures will occur
and give a numerical estimate on the probability
of events expected to take place in future. Quantitative analyses give answers to questions in terms
of numbers, thus enabling direct comparison
between designs on an objective basis.

Some of the most important analysis methods
within each of the two categories are:

Qualitative analyses:

Failure mode and effect analysis
Corrective maintenance analysis
Fault-tree analysis

Quantitative analyses:

Markov analysis
Simulation analysis.

In this context the failure mode and effect analysis
and Markov analysis will be demonstrated.

Failure Mode and Effect Analysis

Failure mode and effect analysis (FMEA) represents a simple, but effective design tool. It can
be applied almost without any particular training
and consists of systematic and formalized evaluation of failure information. FMEA is a mental
exercise, performed on a piece of paper, and the
end result may provide important input to maintenance planning, spare provision planning as well
as quantitative reliability analyses. By asking
"What can happen?"the failure modes are obtained,
and then their effects on system and installation
performance are evaluated by answering the question "what happens if....?".
An FMEA will assist to provide a high degree of
achieved reliability or availability prior to finali-
zation of a design by identifying the failure modes,
their effects and evaluate corrective actions that
will eliminate or reduce the effects of the failure
modes.

Markov Analysis

Markov models seem to be a mathematical model
providing simple and effective means for analysing
repairable as well as non-repairable systems.
Although the components contained in a system
subject to analysis by Markov models, must have
exponentially distributed times to failure and to
repair, the assumption of a Markov process represents a very useful way of analysing the behaviour
of alternative system designs. It is also a simple
way of determining the contribution from each of
the system elements to the total unreliability or
unavailability of a given system configuration.

Reliability Data

Reliability calculations cannot be mentioned without touching on the subject of reliability data. In
most papers on reliability analysis, the distressing
lack of data is emphasized. This is particularly
true for mechanical components and equipment in
contrast to electronic components where at least
some data exist, e.g. (2). It is convenient to
conclude that feasible data for reliability and
maintainability analyses are not obtainable for
mechanical components. However, several efforts
are being made to obtain such data. It seems that
only field data from similar items obtained during
normal operational use, and field data from generi-
cally similar items used in a variety of applications, are considered feasible for mechanical components. Today and in the future one has to rely
mainly on field data on similar components for the
evaluation of reliability characteristics of mechanical equipment.

Data Collection Activities

In 1966 Det norske Veritas initiated a data collection on equipment in automation systems aboard
ships. This collection is still going on, and much
valuable information has been extracted, and used
especially in connection with type approval of
instrumentation equipment.

Another data collection effort should also be mentioned. In 1972 a data collection was initiated in
order to obtain reliability data on components and
systems in the machinery space onboard ships.
This data collection is part of the activities of a
project called the DRAM-project, which is a cooperative reliability development project joined
by several Norwegian institutions.

At the end for 1972 a data collection on reliability
data for important navigational equipment was
started. This collection has been initiated by Det
norske Veritas in connection with research work
on systems for navigation of ships, and investigations into the reliability characteristics of such
systems.

These reliability data collection activities are motivated from the urgent need for numerical data
concerning shipborne components and equipment,
especially mechanical items. It is also felt that
these activities will expand in the future, as they
are the backbone of quantitative reliability analysis and assessments of designs.

RELIABILITY ANALYSIS IN PRACTICE

A demonstration of the features and the utility of
reliability analyses is best done by showing a practical example on the use of such analysis methods.
The objective is to demonstrate how simple techniques demanding little effort, will help to give a
systematic evaluation of a design.

Description of Sample System

The sample system is a manual and automatic remote steering system. The functional block diagram is shown in fig.1, where the gyro and stee-

ring gear are omitted on purpose. The system has four operational modes:

- Hand I ⎤ non follow-up
- Hand II ⎦
- Auto I ⎤ automatic pilot
- Auto II ⎦

In the following, part of an FMEA and a Markov analysis will be shown applied to this sample system. A purpose of the FMEA is to draw attention to critical parts within the system in an inquizitive manner, and the analysis performed in this example does not emphasize the many positive properties of the system.

The system shown in fig. 1 has to a certain extent built-in redundancy. Basic operational modes are Hand I and Auto I. Hand II is a back-up operational mode for Hand I, and this results in an easy obtainable back-up for the basic automatic operational mode, namely Auto II. However, Auto II does not represent a complete back-up system for Auto I as neither electronic auto pilot nor feedback unit are duplexed.

Application of FMEA

An FMEA covering the part of the system within the dotted line in fig. 1, is shown in table 1. The FMEA on this subsystem is performed to a level of detail determined by the main physically and functionally independent items. Table 2 shows another FMEA covering some parts within the subsystem covered by table 1. In this case the level of detail is carried one step further in order to demonstrate effects on the system of failures in smaller components.

As anticipated, the critical units are those that are common for all four operational modes. The hydraulic power cylinder and the feedback unit seem to represent bottle-necks because they are single units, and operation in all four modes depends on these items working correctly. The change-over switch, consisiting of switch I and II including switch gear, becomes a critical component when a failure has occured in one of the other components. Restoring system performance by changing to a back-up operational mode, depends on correct operation and function of this switch.

The FMEA performed may be used to indicate design alternatives or alterations in order to obtain balance of the reliability characteristics through the system. In this sample system it may be considered to provide means for simple manual corrective actions or operations on the critical items. Additionally the use of a duplexed hydraulic power cylinder should be considered together with independent oil supply to the two cylinders. The cylinders should also be arranged so that a mechanical failure in one of them does not impair the function of the other.

A more extensive instrumentation in the purpose of monitoring the system would give a higher level of availability. Extra alarm covering the hydraulic system should be considered, because failures in this subsystem in most cases makes the total system inoperative. Other alarms should cover power failure alarms to indicate a.o. unintended pump

motor stops.

Application of Markov Analysis

In quantitative reliability analyses of complex systems, the aid of a programmable digital computer is necessary. The computer is therefore considered a natural tool in performing reliability calculations.

Fig. 2 shows the state space transition diagram for the entire sample system according to fig. 1. In this case the normal operational mode of the system is Hand I. The different states are identified in Fig. 3 which also shows the steady-state probabilities, i.e. the state availabilities. These state probabilities are calculated by a revised version of the computer program STAVAN (3).

The state space transition diagram shows the expected failures and operational states into which the system is supposed to enter. The transitions between the states are determined by the failure and repair rates of the fifteen physical units within the system.

This particular example is not based on a detailed research on meantime between failures (MTBF) and meantime to repair (MTTR), but on estimates and engineering judgement. These estimates enable calculations of different transition rates between any state in the diagram to be performed.

By assuming constant failure and repair rates and every piece of equipment failing independently, a Markov process will represent an adequate failure behaviour model. The results of the calculations are shown in fig. 3, and it is seen that for 98,9% of the operational time, the system is expected to be working normally in mode Hand I. The calculated state probabilities also show the contribution from each item to the total system unavailability. It is seen that power failure alarms may be justified to install. Depending on repair facilities and maintenance actions the results can be worsened or improved. Decisions on spare parts provisioning and maintenance planning should, however, be based on both the qualitative and quantitative analyses performed.

CONCLUSION

Reliability engineering consists of systematic system evaluation based on failure analysis. Failure mode and effect analysis is a formal technique for system assessment requiring little effort and almost no reliability data. The special FMEA form provides good documentation of such a failure analysis, and it may be extended to cover other points as failure detection techniques, actions reducing failure effects and surveying instructions. It has been shown how the FMEA represents a systematic way of thinking in terms of failure, and how it can be used to point out design deficiencies and weaknesses.

The features of the FMEA have induced Det norske Veritas to include this analysis in its classification rule requirements (6). Especially regarding automation systems where complex electronic equipment, as for instance a computer, plays a major part, it is felt that failure mode and effect analysis is necessary as part of the system documentation to provide a proper evaluation of a given design.

Application of Markov analysis has been found to constitute a very convenient tool in quantifying the reliability of systems. This is because the concept is easy to understand, easy to use and computer analysis takes only a few seconds of computer time.

Providing adequate data are available, comparisons between alaternative designs and evaluation of a given system configuration can be performed on a quantitative basis.

REFERENCES

(1) ASQC (ANSI) Standards
    A2 - 1971 (Z 1.7 - 1971)

(2) Reliability Stress and Failure Rate Data for
    Electronic Equipment.
    MIL-HDBK-217A, 1 December 1965.

(3) Tor-Christian Mathiesen: "Reliability Engineering and Ship Machinery Plant Design".
    Lic. Techn. Thesis.

(4) Bøe, C., Heimly, T. and Mathiesen, Tor-Chr.
    A Reliability Model using Markov Chains for
    the Utility Evaluation of Computer Systems
    onboard Ships.
    1973 Winter Simulation Conference Proceedings, January 17-19, 1973.

(5) Heimly, T., Dahll, G. and Bøe, C.
    Reliability and Availability of Computer Systems onboard Ships.
    Det norske Veritas, Machinery Department
    1972 (In Norwegian).

(6) Det norske Veritas, Rules for the Construction
    and Classification of Steel Ships, Supplement
    No. 1-73, Chapter XV, Section 8, Computer
    System in Machinery Plants. Tentative Rules.

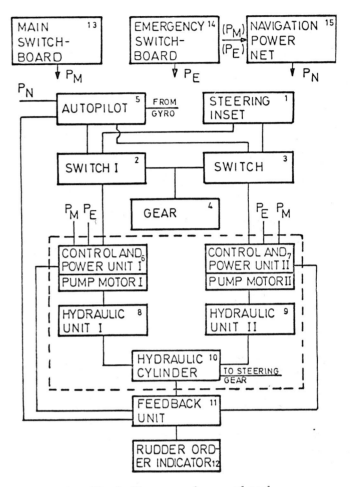

Fig. 1. Block diagram of manual and automatic remote steering system.

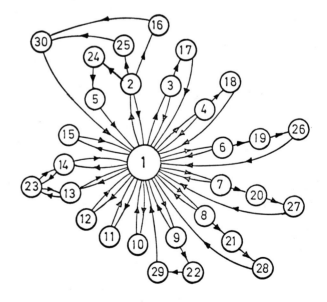

Fig. 2 Transition diagram.

STEADY-STATE AVAILABILITY ANALYSIS BY USE OF MARKOV PROCESSES
WITH DISCRETE STATE SPACE AND CONTINUOUS TIME PARAMETER.
****

PROJECT: RELIABILITY INVESTIGATION OF NAVIGATIONAL EQUIPMENT
BY: CARSTEN BWE AND TOR HEIMLY. SYSTEMS DEP.

SYSTEM: MANUAL AND AUTOMATIC REMOTE STEERING SYSTEM

	SYSTEM STATES	SYST. PROB.
1	SYSTEM WORKING CORRECTLY	.9890+00
2	STEERING INSET FAILURE	.9888-04
3	SWITCH 1 HAS FAILED	.9889-04
4	SWITCH 2 HAS FAILED	.9889-04
5	AUTOPILOT FAILURE	.3516-07
6	CONTROL AND POWER UNIT 1 FAILURE	.3295-03
7	CONTROL AND POWER UNIT 2 FAILURE	.3295-03
8	HYDRAULIC UNIT 1 FAILURE	.2966-03
9	HYDRAULIC UNIT 2 FAILURE	.2966-03
10	HYDR. POWER CYLINDER FAILURE	.1582-03
11	FEEDBACK UNIT FAILURE	.2967-03
12	RUDDER INDICATOR FAILURE	.1187-03
13	MAIN SWITCHBOARD FAILURE	.2967-02
14	EMERGENCY SWITCHBOARD FAILURE	.2967-02
15	NAVIGATION POWER NET FAILURE	.2967-02
16	STEERING INSET AND SW. GEAR FAULT	.9888-08
17	SWITCH 1 AND SWITCH GEAR FAULT	.9889-08
18	SWITCH 2 AND SWITCH GEAR FAULT	.9889-08
19	CONTR/POW. UNIT 1 AND SW.GEAR FAULT	.3295-07
20	CONTR/POW. UNIT 2 AND SW.GEAR FAULT	.3295-07
21	HYDR. UNIT 1 AND SW. GEAR FAULT	.2966-07
22	HYDR. UNIT 2 AND SW. GEAR FAULT	.2966-07
23	MAIN AND EMERGENCY SWITCHB. FAILURE	.8901-05
24	STEERING INSET AND AUTOPILOT FAILURE	.4395-08
25	STEERING INSET AND FEEDBACK FAILURE	.2966-07
26	CONTR/POW. UNIT 1 AND MODE 1 FAULT	.1647-06
27	CONTR/POW. UNIT 2 AND MODE 1 FAULT	.1647-06
28	HYDR. UNIT 1 AND MODE 1 FAILURE	.8898-07
29	HYDR. UNIT 2 AND MODE 1 FAILURE	.8898-07
30	STEERING INSET AND HAND MODE FAILURE	.1538-07

| SUM OF STATE PROBABILITIES | .1000+01 |

Fig. 3. Printout from revised version of STAVAN

DESCRIPTION OF ITEM		FAILURE DESCRIPTION			FAILURE EFFECTS			CLASS-IFICA-TION OF FAIL-URE	CORRECTIVE ACTIONS	FAILURE DATA			REMARKS
NO	IDENTIFICATION/FUNCTION	MODE OF OPERA-TION	FAILURE MODE	FAILURE CAUSE/MECHANISM	DETECTION OF FAILURE	EFFECTS ON OTHER ITEMS	EFFECT ON PRI-MARY (IMPORTANT) FUNCTIONS	RESULTING OPERATIONAL MODE			RELA-TIV FREQ.	MTBF	MTTF	
6-10	CONTROL AND POWER UNIT, INCL. PUMP MOTOR AND HYDR. CYLINDER	HAND I (HAND II)	NO STEERING, NO MOVEMENT OF SERVO CYLINDER	STICKING OF CYLINDER, FOREIGN MECH. MATTERS IN HYDR. SYSTEM.	BY OPERATOR	PUMP MOTOR MAY BE OVERLOADED	LOSS OF STEERING FUNCTION	NON OPERA-TIONAL	AIII/BI	(SEE REMARKS)	H	8100	4	LOSS OF BOTH HAND I, II AND AUTO I, II
				BY-PASS VALVE FOR STAND-BY SYSTEM STICKING IN BY-PASS	AS ABOVE	AS ABOVE	AS ABOVE	AS ABOVE	AS ABOVE	(SEE REMARKS)				LOSS OF BOTH HAND I, II AND AUTO I, II
				CONSTANT-FLOW VALVE CLOSED	AS ABOVE	AS ABOVE	AS ABOVE	AS ABOVE	AII/BI	HAND II (I) OR AUTO II (I)				
				FOUR-WAY VALVE STICKING IN CENTER POSITION	AS ABOVE	AS ABOVE	AS ABOVE	AS ABOVE	AII/BI	AS ABOVE				
				STOP VALVE STICKING/OPEN	AS ABOVE	AS ABOVE	AS ABOVE	AS ABOVE	AII/BI	AS ABOVE				
				NON-RETURN VALVE DEFECT (CLOSED).	AS ABOVE	AS ABOVE	AS ABOVE	AS ABOVE	AII/BI	AS ABOVE				MAY RESULT IN LOSS OF BOTH HAND I, II AND AUTO I AND II
			NO STEERING-MOVEMENT,FREE MOVEMENT OF SERVO UNIT	BY-PASS VALVE STICKING IN "BY-PASS"	BY OPERATOR (OR OVERLOAD ALARM)	PUMP MOTOR MAY BE OVERLOADED	LOSS OF STEERING FUNCTION	NON OPERATIONAL	AII/BI	HAND II (I) OR AUTO II (I)	L/M			
				SAFETY VALVE DEFECT (OPEN)	BY OPERATOR		AS ABOVE	AS ABOVE	AII/BII	AS ABOVE				
				STOP VALVE DEFECT	BY OPERATOR OR OVER-LOAD ALARM	PUMP MOTOR MAY BE OVERLOADED	AS ABOVE	AS ABOVE	AII/BII	AS ABOVE				
				PUMP MOTOR STOP	BY OPERATOR OR SEPARAT ALARM		AS ABOVE	AS ABOVE	AII/BI	AS ABOVE				PROVIDED THAT IF POWER FAILURE, PUMP MOTOR AND STEERING ENGINE ARE SUPPLIED BY A SEPARATE POWER SUPPLY
				OIL PUMP DEFECT	BY OPERATOR	PUMP MOTOR MAY BE OVERLOADED	AS ABOVE	ABOVE	AII/BI	AS ABOVE				
				BROKEN COMPEN-SATING PIPE	AS ABOVE		LEAKING OF OIL MAY CAUSE LOSS OF FUNCTION		AI/BI					MAY BE DANGEROUS IF MULTIPLE FAILURE
				NON-RETURN VALVE DEFECT, OPEN	BY OPERATOR OR OVER-LOAD ALARM	PUMP MOTOR MAY BE OVERLOADED	LOSS OF STEERING FUNCTION	NON OPERATIONAL	AII/BI	AS ABOVE				
				LEAKAGE IN HYDR. SYSTEM	BY OPERATOR		AS ABOVE	AS ABOVE	AIII/BII					SWITCH TO HAND II OR AUTO II MAY NOT BE USEFUL IF LOSS OF OIL IS CONCERNING BOTH SYSTEMS, E.G. BROKEN PIPE BETWEEN HYDR. CYLINDER AND BY-PASS VALVE.
			NO STEERING-MOVEMENT TO STB. (PORT)	ONE DIRECTION MOVEMENT OF FOUR-WAY VALVE	BY OPERATOR		LOSS OF STEERING FUNCTION	NON OPERATIONAL	AII/BI	HAND II(I) OR AUTO II(I)	L			RUDDER MAY ONLY MOVE TO PORT (STB.)
				STOP VALVE DEFECT	AS ABOVE		AS ABOVE	AS ABOVE	AII/BI	AS ABOVE				RUDDER MAY ONLY MOVE TO PORT (STB.)
			TOO SLOW STEE-RING MOVEMENT	FLOW VALVE DEFECT	BY OPERATOR		PARTLY LOSS OF STEERING FUNCTION	NON OPERATIONAL	AIII/BI	HAND II(I) OR AUTO II(I)	M			NOT EASY TO DISCOVER
				REDUCED EFFECT FROM PUMP MOTOR TO PUMP	AS ABOVE		AS ABOVE	AS ABOVE	AIII/BI	AS ABOVE				NOT EASY TO DISCOVER
			TOO SLOW STEE-RING MOVEMENT	LEAKAGE OF OIL	BY OPERATOR		PARTLY LOSS OF STEERING FUNCTION	NON OPERATIONAL	AIII/BI	HAND II(I) OR AUTO II (I)				MAY REGARD BOTH HAND AND AUTO
				PUMP FAULT	AS ABOVE		AS ABOVE	AS ABOVE	AIII/BI	AS ABOVE				
		AUTO I (AUTO II)	ANALOG TO	HAND I (HAND II), BUT WITH A CHANGE IN "CLASSIFICATION OF FAILURE" FROM AII TO AIII										

Table 1. Part of FMEA on system level for a manual and automatic remote steering system.

DESCRIPTION OF ITEM		FAILURE DESCRIPTION			FAILURE EFFECTS			CLASS-IFICA-TION OF FAIL-URE	CORRECTIVE ACTIONS	FAILURE DATA			REMARKS
NO	IDENTIFICATION/FUNCTION	MODE OF OPERA-TION	FAILURE MODE	FAILURE CAUSE/MECHANISM	DETECTION OF FAILURE	EFFECTS ON OTHER ITEMS	EFFECT ON PRI-MARY (IMPORTANT) FUNCTIONS	RESULTING OP-ERATIONAL MODE			RELA-TIV FREQ.	MTBF	MTTF	
(6) (7)	PUMP MOTOR WITH TRANSFORMERS, CONTRACTORS AND SWITCHES	HAND I	NO EFFECT FROM PUMP MOTOR TO OIL PUMP	COUPLING BETWEEN MOTOR AND PUMP PUMP	BY OPERATOR		LOSS OF STEERING FUNCTION	NON OPERATIONAL HAND I, AUTO I	AII/BI	HAND II OR AUTO II	M	15000	5	
				POWER FAILURE IN MAIN SUPPLY	ALARM		AS ABOVE	AS ABOVE	AII/BI	USE OF EMER-GENCY SUPPLY SYSTEM				IT IS ASSUMED THAT ONE HYDR. POWER UNIT AND ONE STEERING GEAR MOTOR ARE SUPPLIED VIA EMERGENCY SWITCH BOARD.
				FAILURE IN POWER CONTACTOR FOR SERVO SYSTEM	AS ABOVE		AS ABOVE	AS ABOVE	AII/BI	HAND II OR AUTO II				
				FAILURE IN INTER-LOCKING CONTACTOR	AS ABOVE		AS ABOVE	AS ABOVE	AII/BI	AS ABOVE				
				FAILURE IN SELECT-OR SWITCH	BY OPERATOR		AS ABOVE	AS ABOVE	AII/BI	AS ABOVE				
				OPEN/SHORT CIRCUIT, GROUND CONNECTION	BREAK OF MAIN FUSE, ALARM	MAY CAUSE DAMAGE BEFORE BREAK OF FUSE	AS ABOVE	AS ABOVE	AII/BI	AS ABOVE				
				PUMP MOTOR FAIL-URE	BY OPERAT-OR OR OVER-LOAD ALARM	BREAKDOWN OF MOTOR IF OVERLOAD ALARM FAILS, OR NOT RECOGNIZED BY OPERATOR	AS ABOVE	AS ABOVE	*	AS ABOVE				* MAY BE SERIOUS IF OVER-LOAD IS CAUSED BY FAULT IN HYDRAULIC POWER UNIT, PUMP MOTOR FOR HAND II MAY THEN ALSO FAIL.
				ALL THREE STEERING ENGINE MOTORS STOPPED	SEE REMARKS									MULTIPLE FAILURE IF NOT INTENDED. IF INTENDED, NO POWER TO PUMP MOTORS, BUT NOT ALARM FOR "POWER-FAILURE".
			REDUCED (WRONG) EFFECT FROM PUMP MOTOR TO OIL PUMP	PUMP MOTOR WORK-ING AT SINGLE PHASE (PARTIAL POWER FAILURE)	BY OPERA-TOR (MAY CAUSE OVER-LOAD ALARM	SLOW MOTION OF HYDRAULIC POWER CYLINDER	"SLOW MOTION" STEERING FUNCTION	NON OPERATIONAL HAND I, AUTO I	AIII/BI	HAND II OR AUTO II	M			MAY ALSO CHANGE TO EMERGENCY SWITCHBOARD.
				PUMP MOTOR FAILURE	AS ABOVE	AS ABOVE	AS ABOVE	AS ABOVE	AIII/BI	AS ABOVE				
		HAND II AUTO I OR II	ANALOG	AS FOR HAND I, BUT WITH CHANGE "CLASSIFICATION OF FAILURE" FROM AII TO AIII FOR AUTO I AND II										
		HAND I	VARIABLE EF-FECT FROM PUMP MOTOR TO OIL PUMP	BAD CONTACT IN MAIN CONTACTOR, INTERLOCKING CON-TACTOR, SELECTOR SWITCH	BY OPERA-TOR, AND NO POWER FAIL-URE ALARM IF ONLY ONE CONTACT POINT FAIL-URE	MAY CAUSE OVER-LOAD ALARM ON PUMP MOTOR	MAINLY LOSS OF STEERING FUNCTION	MISOPERATING	AIII/BI	HAND II OR AUTO II	M			
		AUTO I(II)	VARIABLE EF-FECT FROM PUMP MOTOR TO OIL PUMP	BAD CONTACT IN MAIN CONTACTOR, INTERLOCKING CON-TACTOR, SELECTOR SWITCH	BY OPERA-TOR, AND NO POWER FAIL-URE ALARM IF ONLY ONE CONTACT POINT FAIL-LURE	MAY CAUSE OVER-LOAD ALARM ON PUMP MOTOR	MAINLY LOSS OF STEERING FUNCTION	MISOPERATING	AIII/BI	HAND II OR AUTO II	M			

Table 2. Part of FMEA on subsystem level for a manual and automatic remote steering system.

TROUBLE SHOOTING WITH B.I.T.E. ON

MARINE CONTROL SYSTEMS

C.H. Collingwood, B.Sc.,C.Eng.,M.I.E.E.,
Assistant Chief Engineer
Marine and Engine Controls
Hawker Siddeley Dynamics Engineering Ltd.,
Hatfield, Herts.

M. MacPherson
Design Engineer
Hawker Siddeley Dynamics Engineering Ltd.,
Hatfield, Herts.

ABSTRACT

The problems of maintenance of shipboard controls are being intensified by the increasing complexity of these systems, so that the capital cost of equipment is often insignificant compared with the support costs. It is essential that the reliability and maintainability be considered at the design stage in terms of the Mean Time Between Failures (M.T.B.F.) and the Mean Time To Repair (M.T.T.R.). A system which fails once a year but has a repair time measured in hours or days may be unacceptable in relation to a system with a higher failure rate but faster repair time.

INTRODUCTION

Built in Test Equipment (B.I.T.E.) provides the maintainer with a valuable tool for the diagnosis of a fault to the level of a replaceable item. A sequence of tests may be carried out automatically or semi-automatically to test the system fully in all normal modes of operation. The failure of any test would result in the display to the maintainer of the suspect item. The component or assembly may then be simply replaced and the tests repeated to confirm correct operation.

JUSTIFICATION

The M.T.B.F. or reliability of equipment has been improved by modern design and circuit technology, assembly and testing techniques; but however great an improvement is made, failures will occur and in complex systems fault diagnosis becomes more difficult. The M.T.B.F. of a piece of equipment is calculated from the individual failure rates of each component which makes up a total equipment. The individual failure rate for each component is predictable for a given stress level and range of environment. The figures used in these calculations are based upon the failure rates experienced in a wide range of application.

When a population of equipments or components is put into service the failure rate in the early period is high (Figure 1). This is the 'early failure period' where, components with hidden defects fail, design defects are highlighted and general learning of the use and servicing of the equipment is taking place. If the population is increasing with time then this early failure period is extended.

After the early failure period there is a time where the failure rate is constant and defects occur in a random manner. Where a large population of components is considered these defects are approximately evenly spread during the useful life period. The end of the useful life period is marked by an increase in failure rate due to the wearout of components.

With the knowledge that all equipment will be subject to failure the fitment of built in test equipment may be justified under the following headings.

1. Reduced fault location and repair times.

2. Reduced skill levels.

3. Consistent testing.

4. Comprehensive testing.

5. Essential to complex equipment.

The reduction in times for fault location and repair is the primary argument for the fitment of B.I.T.E. A system may be tested, the faulty component or module located and replaced, and a confirmatory test carried out in times measured in minutes. Short test times are ensured by giving the maintainer simple controls and instructions, automating the testing sequence and presenting the result of tests in a clear display.

The maintainer does not need to have a full knowledge of the system under test, the diagnostic power being largely supplied by B.I.T.E. The testing is consistent and not dependent on the subjective analysis of readings taken by the operator. Tests which require a variety of inputs and conditions may be readily carried out and comprehensive testing ensured.

The rapid advances in circuit technology have

resulted in large improvements to the reliability of electronic equipment. Traditional manual methods of test can become totally impractical with complex systems utilising MSI or LSI technology. An LSI chip may contain several hundred circuit elements and have a reliability figure comparable with a simple integrated circuit element. The testing of the complex circuit element would necessarily be more complicated; but may be readily accomplished by automatic testing.

SYSTEM CONSIDERATION

It is important when considering the role of B.I.T.E. to keep system availability (Reliability and Maintainability) as the key criteria. B.I.T.E. will ensure a minimum M.T.T.R. but could result in a reduction of M.T.B.F. and hence reduce the system availability.

System availability may be defined as the proportion of time that a system is operable when it is called upon to operate.

i.e. $S.A. = \dfrac{M.T.B.F.}{M.T.B.F. + M.T.T.R.} \times 100\%$

The fitment of complex failure detection equipment integral with the system can significantly increase the failure rate whilst it can also complicate the diagnosis, as a failure in the detection equipment cannot always easily be differentiated from a system failure.

It follows that it is essential that any B.I.T.E. equipment should contain a self test facility and should not reduce the reliability of the system. This aim may be largely achieved by building simple failure detection circuitry into the system and by having the diagnostic B.I.T.E. facility available on a plug-in basis.

Figure 2 shows an integrity diagram for a system with standby control and manual reversion. The main channel comprises Blocks A, B, C and D, the standby system Blocks E, C and D and the manual control Blocks F and D. A failure of the main control (Block A) will be detected by the fail freeze circuit (Block B) and control transferred to the standby control (Block E). The failure rate of the fail freeze circuit is small compared to the main control and therefore does not significantly reduce the M.T.B.F.

Failure rate main channel
$$\lambda_m = 45.75 \times 10^{-5}$$

Failure rate standby channel
$$\lambda_s = 3.28 \times 10^{-5}$$

Failure rate manual control
$$\lambda_c = 1.07 \times 10^{-5}$$

It may be shown that the probability of both the main and standby systems failing in a given period is controlled by the reliability of the common items (Blocks C and D) provided that they are both functioning prior to that period. It is therefore important when running on the main system to carry out periodic checks on a standby system.

The probability of a failure occurring in both the main and standby systems in an hour is almost the same as the failure rate of the common items (2.18×10^{-5}). In racing terms the chances of a failure are about one in fifty thousand against.

The correct operation of the main system is continuously monitored by the fail freeze circuitry and observation by the operator. When a failure occurs the B.I.T.E. is used to diagnose the defect such that the faulty element may be replaced. To ensure that the test equipment can diagnose a fault rapidly and reliably in a system it is essential that B.I.T.E. has a full self test facility. The possibility of faults in the diagnostic equipment must be removed if repairs are to be effected rapidly and with confidence. It is essential that the system being tested is muted and effectively removed from control, whilst it is under test.

B.I.T.E. SYSTEM

Figure 3 illustrates the basic elements which make up the test system. The system to be tested is connected to B.I.T.E. through the interface unit (A5). This unit is essentially a routing system such that the stimulus (A3) and measurement (A4) devices can be connected to the system under test.

The operator controls and monitors the test sequence via the control and display panel (A1). The control signals are fed to the central control (A2) which effects the correct test sequence and feeds signals back to the display panel. The operator is informed through the display of the result of the test and if required the most probable corrective action.

The B.I.T.E. system has a self test facility included which must be periodically exercised to ensure that the B.I.T.E. system is functional prior to the testing of a suspect system. The system to be tested is simply connected to B.I.T.E. and identified by coding of the connectors. Three lines coded in binary are used to identify the system; this eliminates the possibility of an operator selecting the wrong test sequence for the system under test. The insertion of the connector mutes the system, effectively taking it off-line.

Once the system has been connected, 'System Test' is selected and the test sequence started by pressing the select test button. The central control then sets up the first test in the sequence. The routeing is set up such that appropriate stimulus and measurement devices are connected to the system under test.

The measurement is taken and the result compared to alarm levels and a pass or fail determined and displayed to the operator.

The operator selects the tests in sequence until a failure is indicated or the sequence is completed. When a failure occurs the indicated faulty module is replaced and the test sequence repeated. On successful completion of the testing, the connectors are removed and the system may be re-selected for control.

The B.I.T.E. system described in this paper has been developed to meet a particular requirement but in principle can be applied to a wide range of systems.

CONTROL AND DISPLAY PANEL (A1) AND OPERATION

The Control panel (Figure 4) is the interface between the test system and the operator. This panel is laid out to ensure simplicity and ease of operation. It is mounted in the machinery control console adjacent to the systems requiring test.

The system test socket (SKT2) carries the connections such that a system may be fully tested. When a connection is made from this socket to any system or the 'Self Test' socket (SKT1), the B.I.T.E. system will automatically carry out the tests on the selected system or on the test equipment itself dependent upon test mode selected.

The mode switch is a four position rotary switch which selects the appropriate mode of operation.

Position 1 ... OFF

2 ... Self Test 1. Lamps and Display Checks.

3 ... Self Test 2. Stimulus and Measurement Checks.

4 ... System Test.

With the mode switch in position 2, and the Select Test button depressed, the displays are automatically checked. The test number starts at '00' and runs up to the full test number count, and any discrepancy will be indicated to the operator.

With the mode switch in position 3, and with SKT1 linked to SKT2, a full check of the stimulus and measurement devices is carried out. The test sequence is then identical to that for a normal system. The self test facility is normally concealed under a flap so that operation of the panel is not confused.

With the mode switch in position 4, and with the system to be tested linked to SKT2, the system test is carried out. When system test is selected the 'Off Line' lamp is illuminated confirming that the system under test is muted. The first test is selected by pressing the

'Select Test' button, the result of test (i.e. pass or fail) is displayed and the affected module or minimodule indicated. Testing is continued by pressing the 'Select Test' button again and observing the results.

The ability of a system to drive an actuator is checked by a rotating drum indicator. The direction of rotation is checked by the operator against the 'opening' or 'closing' lamp, the correct sense being illuminated. This is essentially a measurement device but is mounted on the display panel for convenience.

STIMULUS & MEASUREMENT DEVICES A3 and A4

The number and type of stimuli required have been kept to a minimum by careful consideration of the requirements when drawing up the test schedules. The stimuli fall basically into two types, namely analogue and logic signals.

Logic signals are applied to the system under test to simulate the condition of various machinery state-inputs. Up to 24 bits may be applied for a given test, or any part of the 24 bit word applied for each test over the sequence. All inputs can be fed with a logic '1' or '0' signal or be left open circuit, depending upon the requirement of the selected test.

A range of fixed frequency signals and a variable frequency generator are available as inputs to the system. Programmable d.c. signals as well as defined d.c. voltage levels can be selected and applied.

The signals returned from the system under test, are measured to check whether they fall within the programmed limits. Both analogue and logic signals are processed in parallel and the result displayed as a pass or fail. The type of test is specified, that is whether an analogue voltage, logic level or combination of these is to be toleranced.

Associated with most measurements there is an inherent time delay to ensure that all voltages reach their correct levels prior to results being sampled. Logic results may be taken in programmable windows, a logic '1' state, for example, may be required for a given signal between 100ms and 200ms after stimulus signals have been applied.

All d.c. signals are scaled prior to measurement so that the analogue to Binary Coded Decimal (B.C.D.) converter does not require a change of range. The three digit B.C.D. number is compared with the upper and lower tolerance limits which are programmed in B.C.D., and the pass or fail determined.

CENTRAL CONTROL UNIT (A2)

Figure 5 shows a block diagram of the Central control unit. The controller receives the commands from the control and display panel and routes the programme information to the peripheral devices and supplies all the necessary timing signals. It consists of three main blocks, test sequence controller, test programme controller and the Pass/Fail detector.

The test sequence controller (A2.1) produces a master timing signal and a test count, the latter being output on the test control bus. The test sequence is controlled by the 'Select Test' switch; depressing the switch initiates a test. This action is synchronised with the master clock, the test count is incremented and a start test signal generated. During the test the 'Select Test' switch is inhibited until the sequence is completed. A system test signal generated in the interface unit ensures that testing is inhibited in the event of an inadvertant 'self test' selection when a system is connected.

The test programme controller (A2.2) receives as its main inputs, the test number and the system select information and outputs the commands to set up the stimuli and take the measurements. The programme information relevant to the selected system and the particular test is extracted from the memory and output to the various devices. This information is held in 8 bit words in the memory and is output sequentially under the control of the master timing lines.

The Pass/Fail detector (A2.3) receives the test results compares these with the programmed upper and lower tolerance levels and determines whether the test has passed or failed.

PROGRAMME STORAGE

Various methods of programme storage were considered for the application. A 'Read only Memory' (ROM) was chosen because it is a non-volatile storage medium and not subject to the environmental limitations of a conventional core store. Input of programme information by paper or magnetic tape was rejected because these are subject to damage and require careful maintenance.

Whilst it is recognised that a ROM provides an excellent storage medium, it has the disadvantage that any change to the programme is relatively expensive, as tooling charges are incurred to produce a new mask. This problem is overcome by utilising a 'Programmable Read only Memory' (PROM) in the system. The PROM has all the virtues of the ROM with the additional facility that it can be programmed at relatively low cost. Changes are readily introduced by fitting a replacement PROM, programmed with the modified information, in the place of the existing device. It should be noted that a PROM can be erased, i.e. the memory cleared, and re-programmed with new information. This procedure requires high intensity ultra violet light over a long period of time which cannot occur under operating conditions.

Figure 6 shows a typical map of a PROM. This particular device, shown diagramatically, contains 2048 bits of information arranged in 256 eight bit words. The PROM, when addressed with the test number and system select information outputs the eight bit word on the data highway. The figure shows that this particular PROM carries the upper and lower most significant digits for 32 tests in up to eight systems. This technique enables all the programme information to be simply and reliably stored.

FUTURE CONSIDERATIONS

The B.I.T.E. facility is flexible in that the effect of modifications to the system which it tests are in most cases confined to software, that is, to the programme. Alterations can be readily accommodated by changing the PROM. Extra stimulus and measurement devices may be added to the system to increase its applicability.

The flexibility could be increased by replacing the hard wired logic of the central control by a micro-computer. This would allow more efficient use of the memory and would simplify the operation. Additional advantages would arise in the commissioning stage and programme modifications would be more readily incorporated than with the hard wired system.

CONCLUSIONS

B.I.T.E. gives the operator a reliable and rapid diagnostic tool, which helps to minimise repair times and ensures maximum system utilisation. The diagnostic skills of the system designer are built into the equipment, which minimises the required level of understanding of the operator. A full self test facility is incorporated which allows the equipment to be used with confidence.

The authors wish to thank the Ministry of Defence (Procurement Executive) and the Directors of Hawker Siddeley Dynamics Engineering of their support and assistance.

The authors gratefully acknowledge the help provided by colleagues in the preparation of this paper.

504

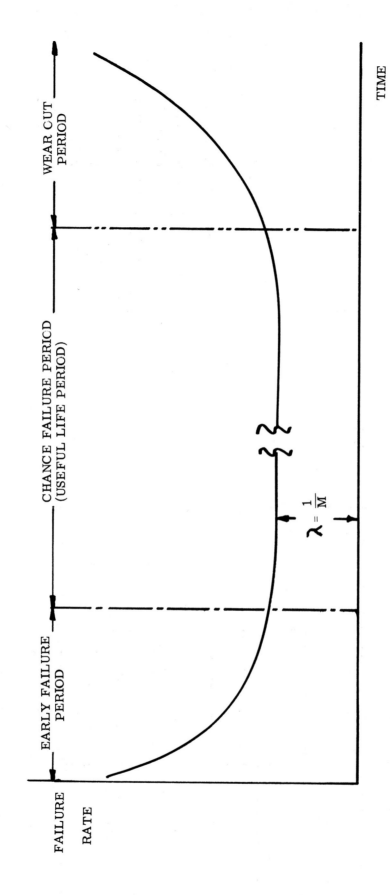

FAILURE RATE vs LIFE

FIG. 1

λ = FAILURE RATE

M = MEAN TIME BETWEEN FAILURE

505

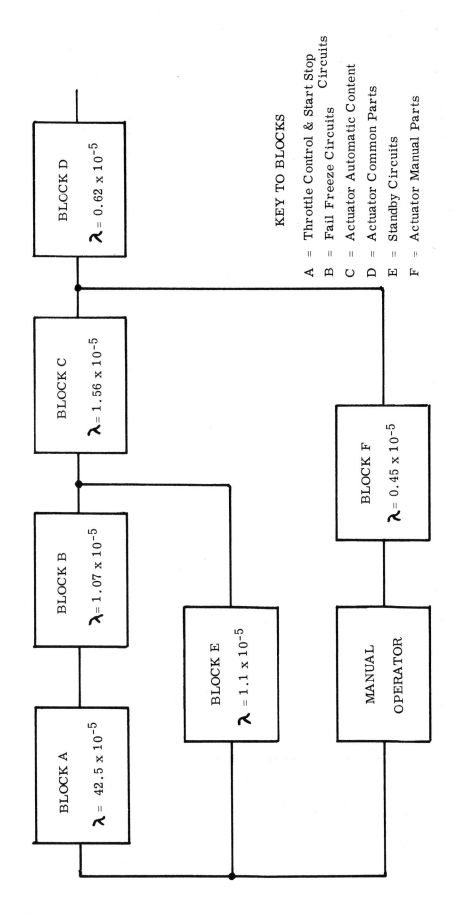

KEY TO BLOCKS

A = Throttle Control & Start Stop
B = Fail Freeze Circuits Circuits
C = Actuator Automatic Content
D = Actuator Common Parts
E = Standby Circuits
F = Actuator Manual Parts

INTEGRITY DIAGRAM NAVAL ENGINE CONTROL

FIG. 2

506

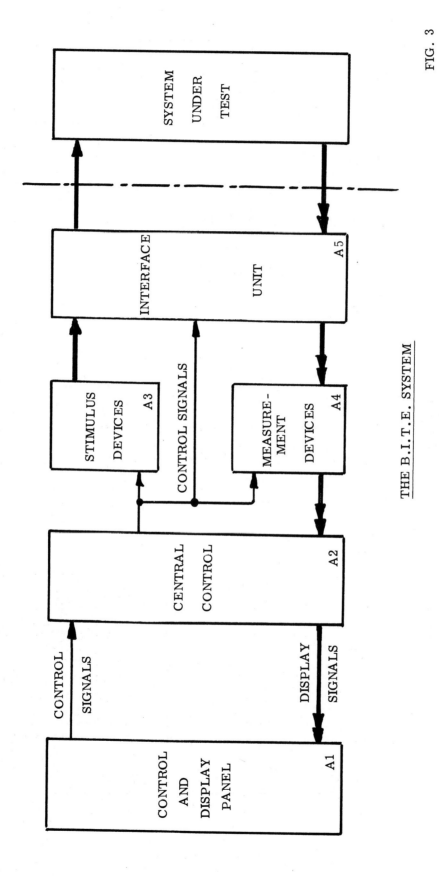

FIG. 3

THE B.I.T.E. SYSTEM

507

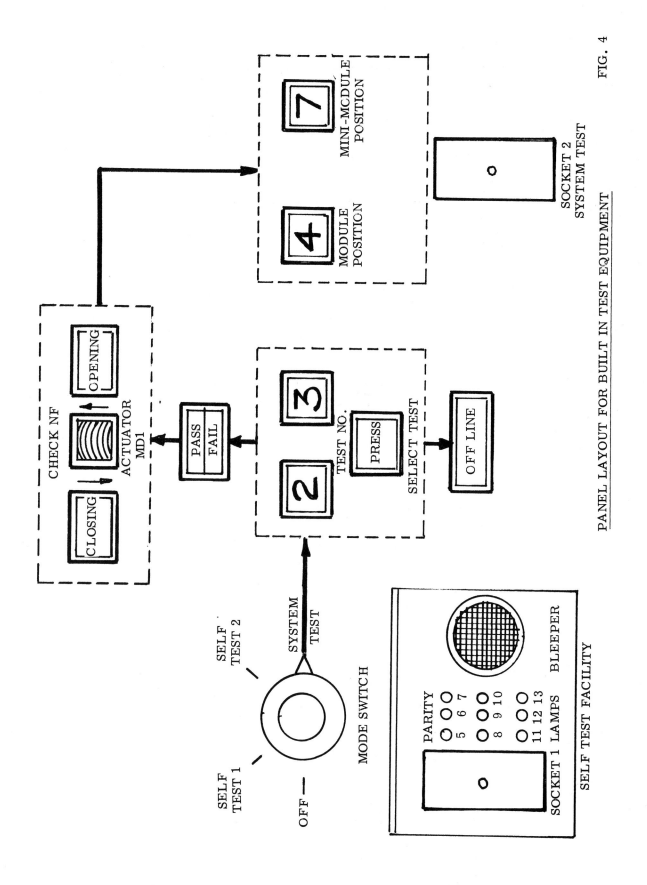

PANEL LAYOUT FOR BUILT IN TEST EQUIPMENT

FIG. 4

508

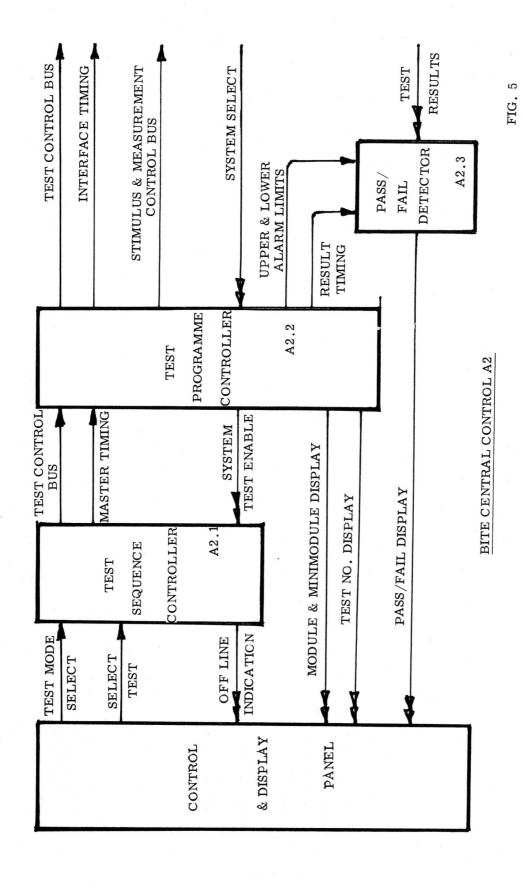

FIG. 5

BITE CENTRAL CONTROL A2

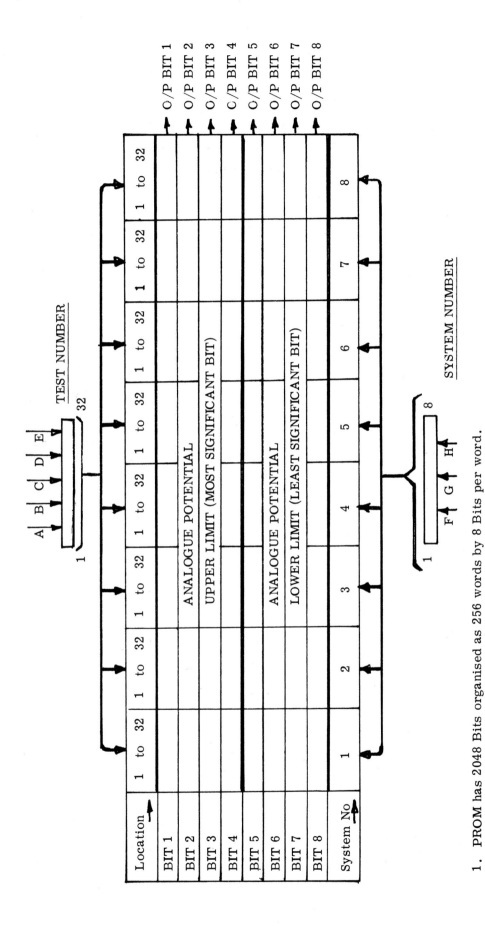

FIG. 6

PROM PROGRAMME STORAGE

1. PROM has 2048 Bits organised as 256 words by 8 Bits per word.

2. The 256 words are divided into 8 blocks having 32 words per block.

Trouble Shooting
on electronic automation Systems
on ships

Oberingenieur
Walter Langhans
Technical manager
Automation marine departement
Siemens Aktiengesellschaft
Erlangen, Germany

Why does an engineer think of a trouble
or fault whenever a technical installation is concerned? In my opinion, this
is an attribute of the foresighted engineer to be prepared for all eventuali-
ties though he is convinced that his
installations are absolutely safe and
reliable.

Is there no discrepancy between these
statements? The answer is no! When developing new systems, all possible faults
that may occur in this connection will
have to be envisaged an especially the
way of locating and eliminating these
faults.

In particular on ships where the staff is
entirely dependent on itself during the
passage, these installations must enable

- an easy location of the fault and

- replacement of the defective part.

The introduction of electronic automation
equipment on ships was met with great dis-
trust in the problems of fault location
and elimination from the shipowners and,
in particular, the concerned ship's crew.
For that reason, the manufacturers
strived to facilitate and simplify fault
location and elimination when developing
their electronic automation systems. The
target envisaged in this connection must
logically be realized in two ways, videlicet:

1) Furnishing of the systems with equipment for fault location (simulators)
   and a

2) design facilitating trouble shooting.

The furnishing of the units and systems
with technical facilities for trouble
shooting depends to a high degree on the
scope of the respective installation.
Voluminous electronic control and regulating devices should be equipped with
special simulators, if necessary. With
this type of simulating devices the individual functions of the system can exact-

ly be simulated and as a consequence the
operating sequences be traced step by step.

Fig. 1) (simulating device) EE47/72f260e

Of course the use of such simulating devices conditions the provision of suitable
indicators for visual display of the correct or faulty state of the operating sequences in the electronic circuitry. Fig.1
shows such a simulating device for an
electronic automatic remote control for
Diesel engines incorporated in the control
cubicle of the respective system. With the
aid of this simulator it is possible to
execute two different types of tests,
videlicet:

a) Testing of the whole installation including the external elements, e.g.
   position transmitters, actuators,
   solenoid valves, and limit switches

b) Testing of the electronic control
   and regulating system without external components.

The test procedure according to it.a) can
only be realized with stationary Diesel
engine and closed main starting air valve,
i.e. in the harbour. The test of the electronic control system without external components is provided for trouble shooting
during the passage with running Diesel
engine, in which case the engine must be
operated manually.

The above example demonstrates that the
operational concerns on board must be giv-
en due weight when designing the simulating device.

All these testing and simulating devices,
of course, require a certain knowledge of
the ship's personnel charged with the performance of these tests. To keep the expenditure for training purposes as low as
possible it is necessary that appropriate
manuals are placed at the disposal of the
tester enabling him to perform a systematic trouble shooting.

Fig. 2) (flow diagram for testing)
        EE 47/722307e

Fig. 2, for example, represents a flow diagram for testing the actual value (actual speed) of an electronic remote control for Diesel engines with the aid of the shown simulator. In addition to the above flow charts, the manuals contain details conserning the necesarry preparations before the test procedure and the supply voltages required in the individual branches of the system. These instructions render it possible, even to a less trained personnel, to trace positively an occurring fault.

Faults experienced, in the main, in electronic systems are:

a) early failures of electronic components, videlicet during the first weeks after commissioning

b) failures caused by overvoltages, e.g., the electronic system is erroneously connected to a ship's system voltage of 220 V or 440 V

c) long-time failures of electronic components.

In the event of the early failures, the cause of trouble cannot be detected. The reason why must be found in the component part itself. The responsible manufacturers strive to locate these failures by subjecting the components to a short-time service test prior to the delivery in order to obtain troubleproof products.

According to the experience gained by the classification societies and the electrical industry during the preceding years, the percentages of failures in electronic systems is below 10%.

The greater part of these faults occurred on the external units equipped with contacts, e.g. limit switches on Diesel engines which can be affected by the following faults:

a) mechanical damages

b) contact faults caused by oil and dirt.

Endeavours are made to eliminate these sources of trouble by an increased use of limit switches for contactless switching operating on the proximity principle.

Fig. 3) (Simatic-test unit) EE47/722302e

In addition to the fixed simulating and testing equipment there exist portable test sets, such as our "Simatic Test" equipment. This unit may be used as well on board as on shore in the service shops and may assume the following tasks:

1) Performance test of printed-circuit boards.

2) Testing the interoperation of two printed-circuit boards

3) Measurement of signal duration with digital indication of the measured time

4) Current and voltage measurement in 6 measuring ranges each

5) Indication of 28 signal states

6) Storage and indication of 4 short-duration signals, minimum duration 15 μs

7) Digital indication of an Aiken-coded number

8) Summation of pulses with two-digit digital display of the summation value

9) Wiring continuity test

10) Formation of two independent pulse trains, of Aiken-coded numbers, and of bounce-free signals for testing counters and registers.

Fig. 4) (Simatic test unit, chassis removed from the housing)
        EE47/722303e

Simularly to the electronic tube ore valves tester, the inputs and outputs of the test objects are connected over crossbar distributor. Punched test cards facilitate the programming.

A special test specification gives the required information about the stepwise proceeding when testing the individual printed-circuit board. By this way performance tests are obtained capable of being compared with each other.

When measuring signal times, the pulses produced are summed up in a counter during the signal duration. The count is indicated and is proportional to the measured time. All printed-circuit boards are tested under rated load conditions.

The equipment with test cards and test specifications depends practically on the printed-circuit boards used in the corresponding system. These devices and information respectively enable a detailed trouble shooting up to the individual faulty component.

Once the fault is located by means of the simulating devices, test sets etc., the defective module needs only be replaced by a corresponding spare assembly, and therewith the selection of suitable spare parts for the appropriate installations on board comes up for discussion. As regards this task, the following points should be observed in addition to the relevant regulations of the classification societies:

a) Design of the installation
b) State of training of the respective personnel.

Considering the statements made at the
beginning, the number of spare parts
increases with the number of the different modules used in the systems. An adequate designing of the electronic
systems may already favour trouble shooting and the extent of spare parts required. The use of integrating circuits,
compact subassembly, and miniatur printed
boards is of great advantage. Nevertheless it will be necesarry to equip the
different electronic systems with an
appropriate number of different modules.

When reflecting on the arrangement of
systems using standard modules and those
built up of special assemblies, it must
be ascertained that the price of the
system is in inverse ratio to that of
the spare parts. To put it plainly:

 -A system comprising a small number of
  different standard modules costs more
  than an installation built up of specially designed modules matched to the
  requirements.

  The extent of spare parts is small and
  cheap.

 -A system using special modules of
  different design and in a great number
  is cheaper, since only the features
  and functions required for this installation are available.

  The scope of spare parts is considerable and expensive.

In practice endeavours are continuously
made to design system built up of standard modules with a low number of variet-
ies.

When selecting the spare parts and determining their scope, the state of training of the operating personnel is of
importance insomuch as the possibility
of carrying out repair work on the modules on board depends on it. If this
should be the case, spare parts in the
form of components, such as resistors,
transistors etc., can be delivered to
the ship. In such a case the extent of
spare parts can be kept down.

These considerations make clear that the
number of spare parts required should be
carefully examined before determining
their extent. An adequate number of spare
parts available on board is just as important as a suitable equipment for
trouble shooting.
The location of a fault is practically
to no purpose, if it cannot be eliminated on account of missing spare parts.

As already mentioned, appropriate arrangements should be made to simplify trouble
shooting and reduce the extent of spare
parts for the service on ships. Unfortunately
two demands are opposed to each other
when designing electronic systems.

With regard to the provision of adequate
spare parts, standard modules (printed-
circuit boards) from electronic switching
systems should preferably be used. By this
means the various individual functions of
the system are allotted circuitwise to
several flat modules.

This circuit arrangement, of course, renders trouble shooting difficult, since a
far-reaching localization is required before eliminating the defective component.
Another solution is the combination of
components on the individual modules to
form functional groups. The objection to
this method is that the use of special
modules is mostly required, which will
have to be made specially to the assigned
duty. This will result in a great expenditure as regards the provision of spare
parts at the shipowner's (on board) and
manufacturer's.

This circuit arrangement facilitates
trouble shooting. You have only to find
out which printed-circuit board accommodates the defective component by localiz-
ing the disturbed partial function. A
further location on board is not required,
since the whole module is replaced and the
necessary repair of the affected printed-
circuit board performed by the maker.

This problem is chiefly met with systems
built up of discrete components. When
developing these installations, the problem of applying standard or special modules should be solved by way of a compromise, i.e. by using preferably standard modules and for some special functions
specially designed modules.

Fig. 5) compact subassembly, EE47/71787e
The changing over to the integrated circuit technique gave rise to considerable
alterations in this connection.
The miniaturization of the components enables the change to other designs. The
so-called modular assembly renders it
possible to form functional groups by using standard boards. The design of the
modular assemblies is such that several
boards are arranged as cross box (by plug-
ging) on a flat module in European size.

The boards in question are standard boards
of the Simatic C3 Switching System which
are connected to each other on the module
to form functional groups. The advantage
of this method is founded on the fact that
the elimination of the defective function-

al group will do in the event of trouble
shooting. After detecting the faulty
functional group the corresponding modular assembly can be replaced. Following this the defective board within the
modular assembly can calmly be located
either on board or in a service shop on
shore. Then the defective boards may be
substituted for standard boards as listed in the catalogue. Therewith the modular assembly is fully operative and may
be reused as stand-by unit on board.

The above statements make clear that the
integrated circuit technique facilitates
trouble shooting which is simplified in
addition where a less profound fault
location will do. In cases where a whole
small-size installation is combined in a
single modular assembly, a simple replacement of this assembly will suffice in the
event of a fault without preceding
trouble shooting.

The purpose of these examples is to explain, how the trouble shooting on board
can be influenced by a corresponding design of the systems.

As already state at the beginning, the
introduction of the electronic automation equipment was confronted with a certain prejudice on the part of the user,
in particular with respect to trouble
shooting.

Experience gained during the preceding
years has shown that these prejudices
have yielded to an objective judgment
for al long while. Both parts, electrical industry and ship's crew, were instrumental in making the electronic automation systems so adapted for the use on
ships.

Trouble shooting, if any, on automation
equipment has considerably been improved
by the use of

        simulating and testing equipment
        and

        by a thorough knowledge of the
        concerned ship's personnel of
        electronic systems on board

We can say in conclusion that the electronic equipment on ships can now be
classified under standard and familiar
technical equipment as are the mechanical
installations.

514

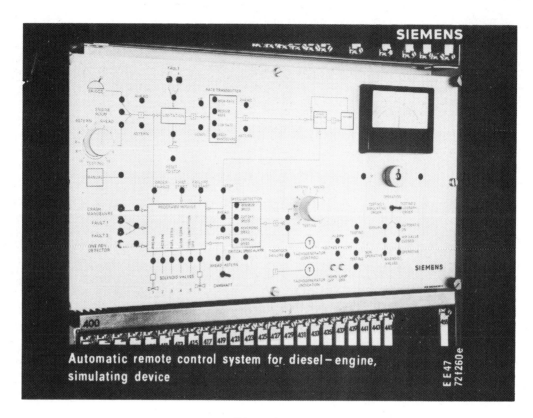

Fig. 1

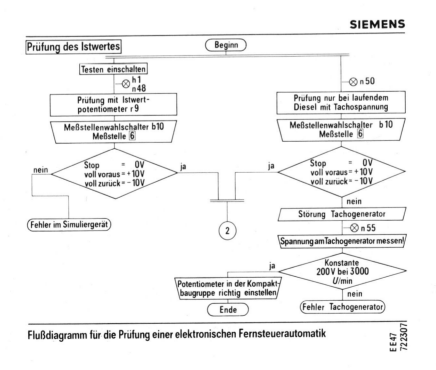

Flußdiagramm für die Prüfung einer elektronischen Fernsteuerautomatik

Fig. 2

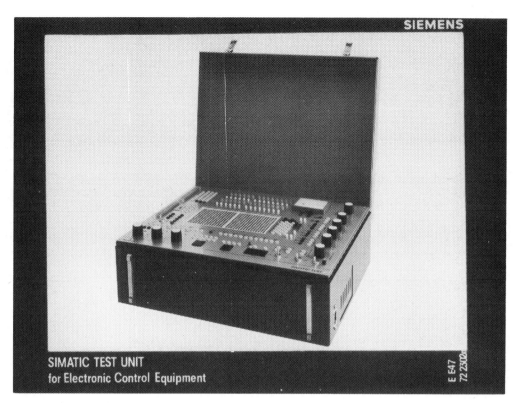

Fig. 3

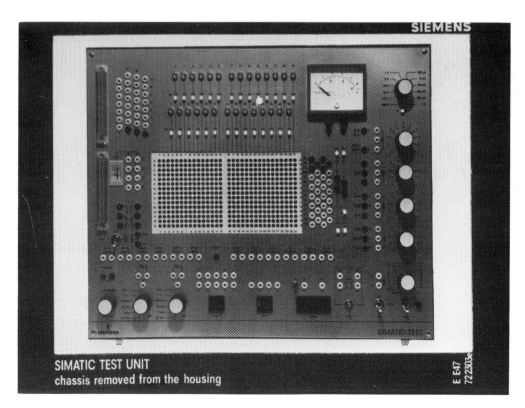

Fig. 4

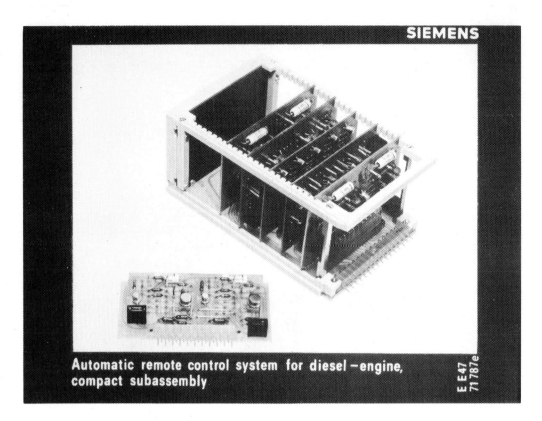

Fig. 5

ELECTRONIC SYSTEM FOR INTRINSICALLY SAFE
INSTRUMENTATION AND MONITORING

Hans-Christian Oppegaard
Engineer
Marine Department
Automation section
A/S NORSK ELEKTRISK & BROWN BOVERI
Oslo, Norway

INTRODUCTION

During the last ten years there has been a great extension in the development of intrinsically safe apparatus. The increasing need for advanced instrumentation and process control equipment in general also applies to the intrinsically safe apparatus. We do not need to go too far back in time to find the first registrated regulation for intrinsically safe equipment. British Standard No. 1259 from 1945 has often been mentioned in articles and books concerning this matter, to be the first regulation about intrinsically safe equipment in coal mines etc.

The main reason for the necessity of todays advanced circuitry has been the continuous increase of marine transport of oil and gas. Oil transportation does not require any large instrumentation, but it is of great importance on a Liquified Natural Gas carrier or a Liquified Petrol Gas carrier (LNG/C - LPG/C). This kind of instrumentation is the main subject for this lecture.

As mentioned above there are two different kinds of gas carriers, the LPG and the LNG.

The only difference is that the LPG/C can take a lot of various liquified gases, the LNG/C liquified natural gas only. The LPG/C has compressors for cooling the cargo, the LNG has none and a continuous boil off is unavoidable.

SYSTEM DEFINITION AND REGULATIONS

On board a LNG/C the instrumentation equipment will normally be installed in an air-conditioned gas free control room and do not need to be intrinsically safe. Outside this control room the area will be classified as zone 1, (periodical explosive atmosphere) and the sensor circuits must be secured as " intrinsically safe circuits".

The British Approval Service for Electrical Equipment in Flamable Atmospheres, (BASEEFA) has the following definition of the expression: "An intrinsically safe circuit".

"A circuit in which any spark or thermal effect produced either normally or in specified fault conditions, is incapable under prescribed test conditions of causing ignition of a given gas or vapour."

Similar definition is given for intrinsically safe apparatus and systems.

In addition to equipment definitions there is also a group system for various kinds of gases and vapour and another for the presence of explosive mixture of gas and oxygene expressed as

Zone 0: Area where an explosive mixture of gas and oxygene always must be considered present.

Zone 1: Area where an explosive mixture can occur, but not always is present.

Zone 2: Area where an explosive mixture seldom, and only for a short time, is present.

This grouping of presence of explosive atmosphere given by the International Electrotechnical Committee, (IEC) is basic for the estimation of the use of zeener barriers.

Zone 0 requires a complete galvanic separation between the sensor circuit and the electronic system.

Zone 1 and zone 2 requires regular zeener barriers to be used and this group covers for example the deck area of a LPG/LNG carrier.

Further, there are several other regulations and specifications the designing engineer

must take into consideration when he constructs intrinsically safe circuits.

For the specified system on the LNG carrier and as a general guidance in the following, we will give our attention to the
Verein Deutsche Elektroingenieure (VDE)
regulations 0165 and 0171. These regulations are similar to other international
regulations in this field.

Earlier the equipment to be used in explosive dangerous areas, was made explosion
proof. This quality was achieved by building the whole part into a solid housing
and secure it with sand filling, oil filling or by making the housing solid enough
to be a protection itself. Later on, the
complete intrinsically safe circuit (Ex)i,
has been used more and more in control and
monitoring systems.

According to VDE 165/4.66 §8 the complete
circuit in all parts must be as follows:

1. Each component must be of (Ex)i appro-
    ved type according to VDE 0171/2.65.

2. Intrinsically safe cables or terminals
    must be at least 50mm from non intrin-
    sically safe equipment at any place in
    the circuit.

    By the use of shielding or other kinds
    of insulation this distance can be re-
    duced.

3. Conductors in the intrinsically cir-
    cuit must be kept separated from
    others.

4. Water-, dust- and touch-safety must be
    in accordance with P20 in DIN40050.

5. Earthing or shorting of circuits should
    only be done where this is clearly
    specified in the PTB certificate,
    (Physikalisch-Technische Bundesanstalt).

6. Conductors must be of insulated type
    only and test voltage between conduc-
    tors and conductors against ground
    must be at least 500VAC.

7. Marking colour on intrinsically safe
    conductors in the cabinet etc. should
    be of clear blue colour (RAL5015).
    This colour must not be used on any
    other kind of equipment or cabling in
    the same cabinet.

8. Shielding and revolved conductors
    should be used to protect the circuit
    from influence from the ambient area.

9. Complete spesification for the circuit
    limitations regarding allowed inducti-
    vity, capacity and resistance must al-
    ways be present and available.

In each case there is a special formula.
($E_S = 1/2 \ CU^2$) for the capacity and
($E_S = 1/2 \ LI^2$) for inductivity. The total
circuit energy must be kept below a limit,
specified to be 2/3 of the total ignition
energy. All components in the complete
circuit must be considered against ambient
vapour chemical influence, and against
sparks initiated by direct mechanical
affect.

This relation have been taken into consideration by VDE in the regulation 0171d/
2.65, covering the depending components
in the intrinsically safe circuit.

In circuits where zeener barriers are used,
the barriers must be type approved by a
serious test laboratory as BASEEFA, PTB,
in West Germany where the test is done
according to VDE regulations 0171/1.69
(Ex)i 05, or others.

The Zeener Barrier.

Brown Boveri & Cie (BBC) has been producing
zeener barriers for several years. Fig. 2
is a general diagram for the type mostly
used. The zeener barrier is not a galvanic
separator and consists of two zeener diodes,
one fuse and some resistors. The basic
prinsiple is to give limitations to the
voltage and/or current in the attached
circuit.

The output voltage U_2 is limited according
to the permitted capacity in the circuit.
The resistors in the barrier will give
limitations to the current according to
permitted inductivity.

This kind of barrier is designed for single
polarity and DC only. Barriers for AC and
dual polarity is available too.

If the specified voltage limit is exceeded
the fuse will blow due to shorting through
the zeener diode and without exceeding the
specified circuit limitations.

We have designed and built this type of
equipment for some years, and always there
is one general problem present. Due to
the various regulations and certifying
institutions involved, it is difficult to
know whether your solution is correct in
all details or not. The first conclusion
made is that we need a concentrated collection of specifications, some sort of an
extraction of all kinds of regulations and
limitations. Within some years there
should be a possibility to achieve an international collection of regulations at
least for equipment to be used on board
vessels.

PRACTICAL USE

Through its great flexibility and applicability the electronic system will meet almost all kinds of instrumentation requirements. In addition, the electronic system can be connected to an unlimited number of registrating instruments etc. Direct shut down and regulation functions are available too.

For use on board LNG/C's, a special claim has been given to accuracy. Temperatures in the cargo tanks must be measured with an accuracy better than 0,5% of the full scale, that means, better than 1^{0}C at -163^{0}C which is the normal cargo temperature. When using high quality calibration devices, the accuracy should, if possible, be increased by more than 50%.

For pressure measuring, the tank and void space pressures against atmosphere should be measured with a total system accuracy of 1,5%. Here the complete alarm limit hysteresis is taken into calculation, because these limits are used in direct operation of relief valves, shut down functions and so on.

To be able to give a better description of the system I have made a simplified diagram of a regular system, see fig. 1. The figure is horizontally divided by means of the zeener barriers, and an intrinsically safe circuit is indicated with one Pt500 and one on - off sensor.

All kinds of analogous sensors can be used if the total circuit inductivity and capacity is kept within the specified limitations at a certain voltage and current.

The electronic system is divided into several separate parts. First of all the analogous converter where the various sensor or transmitter signals are converted to a standard 0-1V signal. For direct reading of the analogous value, this signal is transferred to a regular moving coil instrument or via a selector panel to a high quality digital instrument. In addition each signal can be used by all kinds of chart recorders, logging equipment or other additional equipment for registration of analogous parameters.

When value limits are necessary for alarm, safety or control functions, a limit value card will watch both high and low values and give a simple on-off signal to the other part of the electronic system, the on-off central. In addition to directly connected signals from regular level switches, pressure or thermo switches, the on-off signals will initiate a lamp function, a group alarm system or a relay for external control function.

CIRCUIT DESIGN

Fig. 3 is a constant voltage circuit for a pressure transmitter. For this actual transmitter, a constant voltage of 5,8V is necessary.

Fig. 4 is a more accurate type of circuit which is used for temperature measuring in the cargo tanks. As sensing element, a high class Pt-500, is used to achieve a high grade of accuracy at the extreme low temperature whereas a regular Pt-100 element has a too low resistance, see fig. 6.

Fig. 5 is a diagram of a regular on-off circuit. A constant voltage of approximately 20V is fed to the barrier. By using a separate supply, the circuit can be watched relative to fault conditions if grounded.

Fig. 6 is a regular constant current circuit with a Pt-100 element as temperature sensor. The intrinsic safety is achieved by use of only one zeener barrier.

FUTURE INTRINSICALLY SAFE EQUIPMENT

The primary subject in all remote reading of variable parameters is how to transfer the produced signal. There are two main systems in use as intrinsically safe transmission of signals, electrical or pneumatical. Several ships are sailing with both systems working together. It will probably always be so, but electronic systems are taking over a continuously increasing part. The trend is electronic systems for instrumentation and pneumatic systems for operation and control.

The electronic system described here is what we make to-day. Tomorrow another and new design will take over, to-day known as optoelectronics, ready invented and developed, tomorrow taken into industrial production to an acceptable price. Then a new era in the field of electronic intrinsically safe aparatus will start.

We will never see the end of new inventions and possibilities in the world of electronics. There are always some people developing new methods. The intention is to dig up problems in the process and find new ways to go. To-day we have special educated personell within each field. The problem is to make them co-operate to achieve an optimum of possibilities.

Let this be an invitation to search for new methods and products.

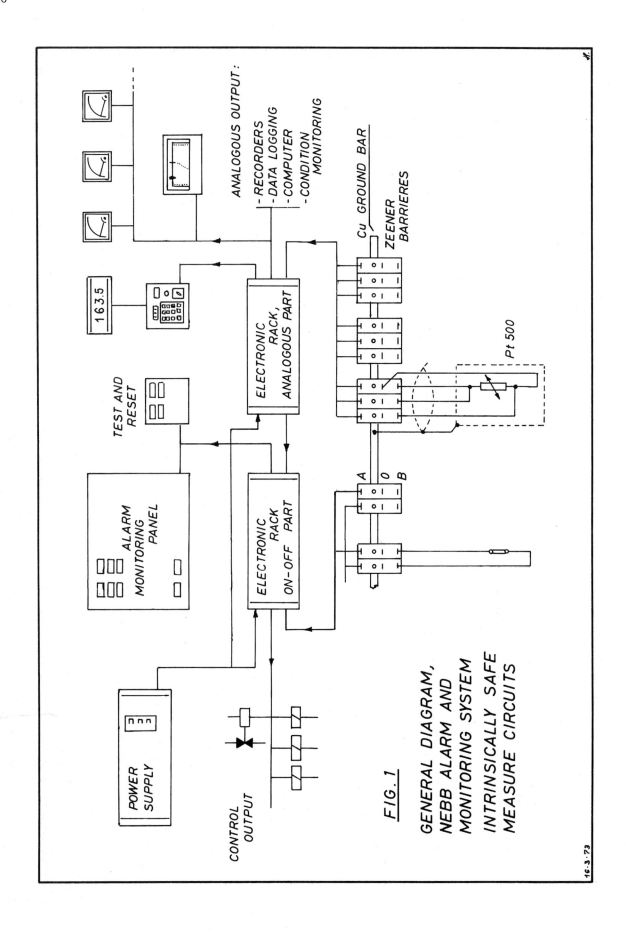

CONTROL OUTPUT

POWER SUPPLY

ALARM MONITORING PANEL

TEST AND RESET

ELECTRONIC RACK ON-OFF PART

ELECTRONIC RACK, ANALOGOUS PART

163.5

ANALOGOUS OUTPUT:
- RECORDERS
- DATA LOGGING
- COMPUTER
- CONDITION MONITORING

Cu GROUND BAR

ZEENER BARRIERES

Pt 500

A
0
B

FIG. 1

GENERAL DIAGRAM,
NEBB ALARM AND
MONITORING SYSTEM
INTRINSICALLY SAFE
MEASURE CIRCUITS

16-3-73

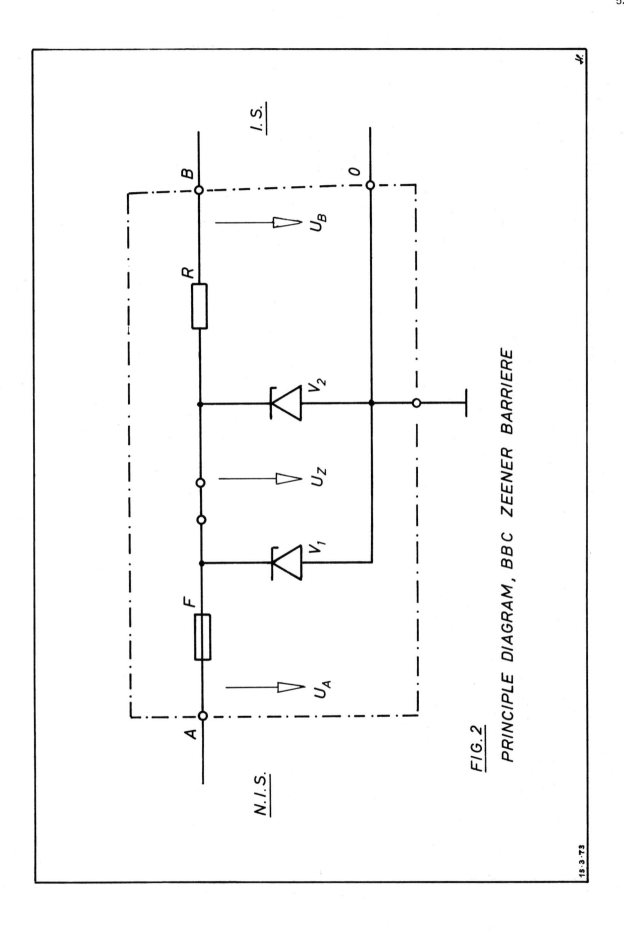

FIG.2   PRINCIPLE DIAGRAM, BBC ZEENER BARRIERE

522

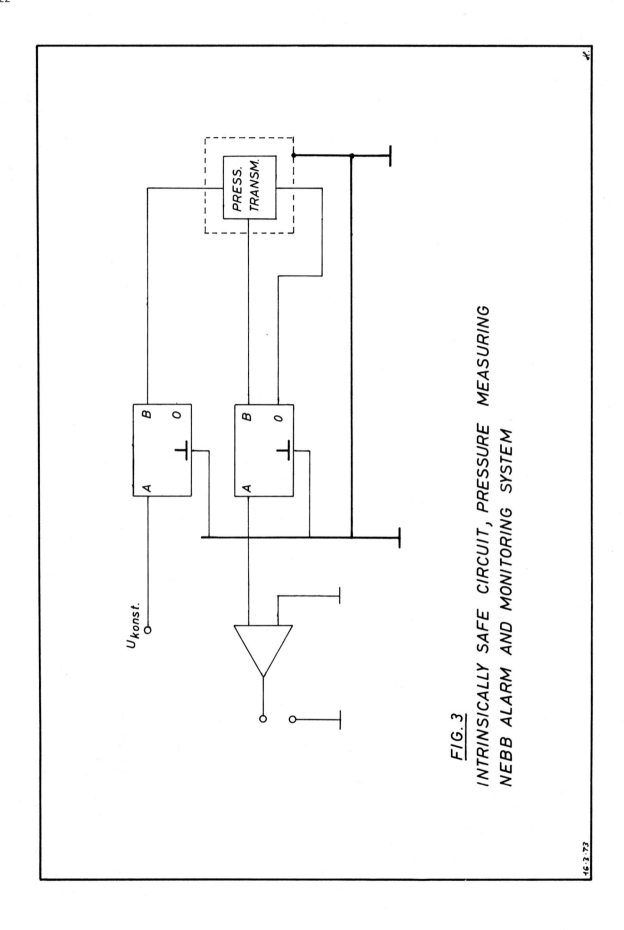

FIG. 3

INTRINSICALLY SAFE CIRCUIT, PRESSURE MEASURING
NEBB ALARM AND MONITORING SYSTEM

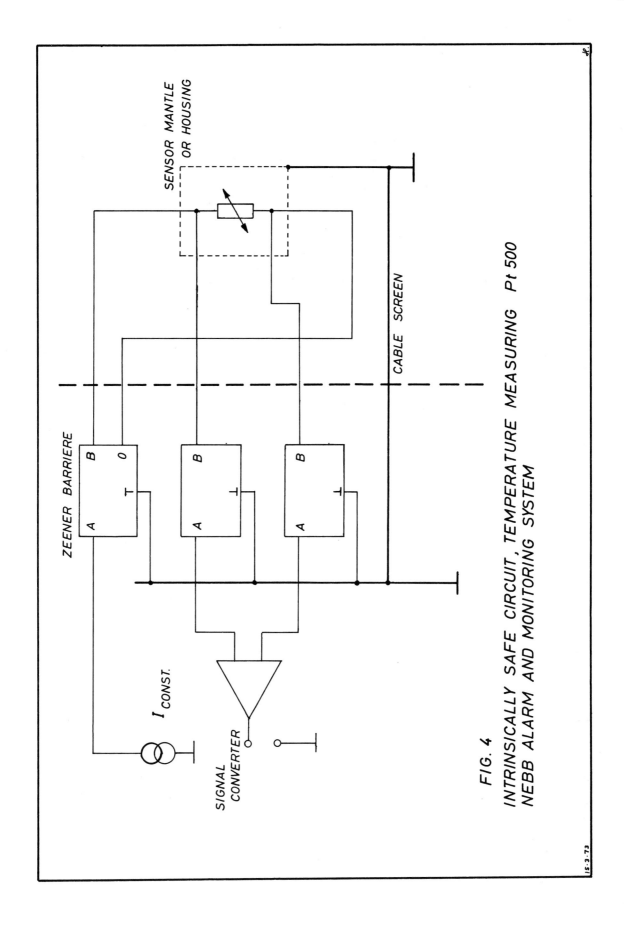

FIG. 4

INTRINSICALLY SAFE CIRCUIT, TEMPERATURE MEASURING Pt 500

NEBB ALARM AND MONITORING SYSTEM

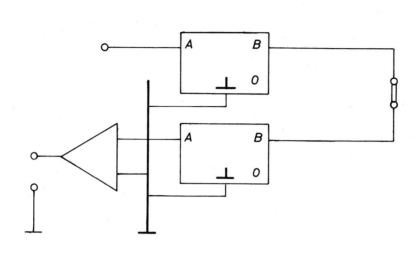

FIG.5

ON-OFF REGISTRATION

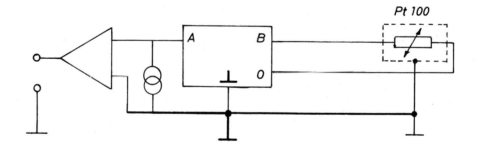

FIG.6

TEMPERATURE MEASURING, Pt 100
SINGLE ZEENER BARRIERE

- INTRINSICALLY SAFE CIRCUITS,
- NEBB ALARM AND MONITORING SYSTEM

HIGH VOLTAGE, THE ANSWER TO INCREASING POWER DEMAND ON BOARD SHIPS AND OILPLATFORMS.

Thor Erik Thorsteinsen
Technical Manager
AC-ELEKTRO A/S
Storgaten 38,
Porsgrunn, Norway.

In connection with large power demand and also relatively long distance between power generation and power consumers, there have been built or are being built ships and oil-offshorerigs where high voltage (H.V.) that is 3 to 7,2 kV has been choosen for generation and distribution to large power consumers.
In the following high voltage (H.V.) is used for the voltage 3 to 7,2 kV although internationally medium voltage is often used for these voltages.

WHY HIGH VOLTAGE SYSTEM:

a) The generating capacity and the short circuit capacity is so high that the short circuit currents at 440 V becomes so large that it is difficult to commercially obtain breakers which safely can handle the arising short circuit currents.
Short circuit forces becomes so large that busbars, connection-bars and links etc. in switchboards and elsewhere in the circuits have to be made with great care to be able to stand the mechanical forces in case of a short circuit.

A short circuit at the high current levels in question almost certainly results in an open arc. The thermal effects of such a high current arc are rather disasterous and may for example burn through metalplates in the front of the switchboard in less time than 0,1 sec. In other words, before a main breaker has sufficient time to operate.

The effects of these high short circuit current also involves danger to personell which should not be neglected.
With regards to available circuit breakers for 440 V it becomes as mentioned difficult to get suitable circuit breakers and maintain the selectivity in a complex system when the short circuit currents rises above 50 to 100 kA dependent of the rated current. This means generating capacities of 4-7 MVA at 440 V.

The mechanical forces on parallell conductors are proportional to the square of the current and inversely proportional to the distance between the conductors.
The forces between parallell conductors are

$$F = \frac{2}{d} i^2_{max.}$$

d is the distance in cm between the conductors and i is the peak value of the current in kA. This gives F in kp/m.

At 50 kA symetrical short circuit current in a 440 V system with a minimum of 20 mm distance F is about 5000 kp/m and at 100 kA F is about 20000 kp/m.

From tests it is well known that open arcs above 25 kA_{rms} easily burn through sheet steel and cause heavy burning on the equipment depending on the time it is allowed to burn.

b) The distance between the generators and the power consumers is so long that high voltage distribution becomes economical due to savings in cable costs.
At 6,6 kV the cable costs are only about 5-10% of the cable costs at 440 V at the same transmitted power for the power level in question.

CHOICE OF VOLTAGE:

The chosen voltage should be somewhere between 3,3 to 7,2 kV.
Technically and economically there are not much difference within this range of voltage.
It is therefore very important to standardize on a voltage.
To save as much as possible in conductor costs 7,2 kV should be chosen according to IEC recommendations. 7,2 kV is the maximum service voltage and normal service voltage should be 6,6 kV.

This voltage is a normal voltage widely used on land in Europe.
The cost of switchboards will be approx. the same at 3,3 or 6,6 kV. Whereas breakers and contactors will be somewhat more expensive at 6,6.

526

The motors and generators may be in the order of
5 % more expensive at 6,6 kV than at 3,3 kV.
On the other hand the cables will be cheaper as
half the cross section area is sufficient at
6,6 kV compared to 3,3 kV.

At 6,6 kV service voltage a 630 A current rating
is equivalent to 7200 kVA 3 phase power.A short
circuit current of 40 kA at 440 V is equivalent
to 2,7 kA at 6,6 kV.

TEST VOLTAGES:

An electric system in a ship is not exposed to
atmospheric overvoltages. A normal impulse test
with wave 1,2/50 should therefore actually not be
needed.
A power frequency test voltage should be
sufficient. On the other hand it would, from a
standardisation point of view, be simplest to
use the same test requirements as have been laid
down in the IEC recommendations for similar
equipment.
This means impulse as well as power frequency
testing for the apparatus and the switchboards,
power frequency test for generators and motors
and dc tests for cables.
Equipment which has been manufactured and tested
according to the excisting IEC test regulations
has shown excellent service reliabillity in the
industry and it is no need for using equipment
with higher or different insulation strenght on a
ship than on land.

GENERATORS:

There are no special requirements for a H.V.
generator in a ship apart from the fact that
the generator must be "shipshape" and fullfil
the requirements laid down by the different
authorities. Special care should be taken to
keep the windings dry and clean.

MOTORS:

The squirrel cage motor is robust, simple,
easy to manufacture and attractive in price.
This type of motor can be used in most cases
where speed regulation is not required.
The starting torque of the squirrel cage motor
is relativly low between 0,5-0,9 of the rated
torque with starting current 4-5,5 times the
rated current.

For pumps, centrifuges, compressors, motor-
generators, ventilators and other machinery where
the start is not heavy the squirrel cage motor
is very suitable.
In cases where the start is rather heavy the
motor can be built with so called double cage
rotor. This type of motor has a starting torque
of approximate 2 times the rated torque at a
starting current of 5-7 times rated current.
Almost all the equipment where H.V. motors
would be used have a light start. Even a bow
thruster with variable pitch propeller will
normally be possible to start with a squirrel
cage motor.

According to different H.V. motor manufacturerers
the minimum power limit for 6,6 kV motors
varies from 100 - 500 kW.
For the H.V. motors for the applications in
question there are no practical upper limit as
regards the power.
The best solution although expensive when speed
is required, is to use thyristor controlled
rectifiers and dc motors. This gives an exellent
speed regulation. On drilling platforms where
as an example a number of motors require speed
regulation, a centralized thyristor unit may be
of advantage.

On a ship, squirrel cage or double cage motors
will normally fullfil the requirement for the
H.V. motors.

START OF SQUIRREL CAGE MOTORS:

Direct start of a squirrel cage motor gives as
mentioned above starting currents 4 - 7 times
rated current for a period varying from 1 to 30
sec. dependent on the time it takes to accelrate
the motor.

The influence of the starting current on the
system is dependent on the relation between the
starting current and the available short circuit
power.
Furthermore it is a question of how large
voltage dips that can be tolerated.
From a technical point of view a short voltage
drop of 20 % can be accepted. However, on a
passengership this might not be acceptable seen
from the point of view of comfort to the
passengers.

If a direct start gives to large voltage drop
the following solutions can be used:

a) Start with separate starting busbar (fig.1a).

b) Start with autotransformer   (fig.1b).

c) Start with inductance in series with
   the motor,   (fig.1c)

Separate starting busbar (fig. 1a) is the most
flexible solution, however, it is also the most
expensive solution.
When a big motor is started all load is transferred to one of the busbars. One generator and
the motor to be started is left on the other
busbar which is disconnected from the rest of
the system.
The motor is then started either with direct
start or the generator is run from standstill to
full speed with the motor connected to the
generator. The latest procedure is the most safe
one. Modern equipment is, however, built to stand
a direct start which is by far the simplest and
can be used with advantage.
As soon as the motor is in normal service the
two busbars are phased together again.

Starting with autotransformer (fig. 1b)means
starting at reduced voltage.
There are different methods in connecting the

autotransformer.
In fig. 1b a rather simple method is shown.

1) at starting the breaker bn is closed where-
   after breaker bb is closed and the motor
   starts at reduced voltage.

2) bn opens and the autotransformer functions
   as an inductance in series with the motor.

3) bs is closed and the motor is directly
   connected to the busbar.

Starting with an inductance in series with the
motor, fig. 1c, is normally carried out in two
steps.

1) With the full inductance in series.

2) Short circuiting the full inductance in
   one operation.

The method with starting inductance is cheaper
than starting with autotransformer.

BREAKERS:

For H.V. installations on board a ship, only
breakers with the best electrical properties
should be used. This means that breakers of
the "airbreak" type is the most suitable. In
airbreak type breakers the interruption takes
place in air at atmosphereic pressure instead
of in oil, compressed air, SF_6 or vacuum.
The advantages of the airbreak type breakers
are the following:

1) Overvoltages.
   Minimum oil breakers or airblast breakers may
   create high overvoltage at interruption of
   inductive load. Interruption of motors during
   start or at low load means breaking of
   inductive current. A minimum oil breaker or
   airblast breaker may give overvoltages of the
   order of 4 times the peak value of the
   voltage phase to earth i.e. k factor = 4,
   whereas an airbreak breaker does not give
   higher overvoltages than k factor = 2.
   By using minimum oil breakers or airblast
   breakers it is therefore a risk that so high
   overvoltages arises that the motor- or
   generator-insulation may be weakened with
   earthfault or short circuit as a result.

2) Breakerexplosion.
   Both minimum oil and airblast breakers may
   in case of failure of the breaker explode and
   cause considerable secondary damages.
   The airbreak breakers do not contain any
   medium which can give rise to an explosion.

3) Firehazard.
   Although the oil content in the minimum oil
   breakers is small there still exists a firehazard with this type of breaker.

4) Maintenance and revision intervals.
   The airbreak breakers are very simple in
   construction and maintenance. There are no
   critical tolerances and parts. The breaker
   can, dependent of type, stand more than 5000
   operations between revisions. This means that
   the motorstarter normally can be omitted and
   the breaker used as a starter.
   Minimum oil and airblast breakers contain
   seals and other details which must be
   checked.

   Furthermore the oil in minimum oilbreakers
   will be polluted by the interruptions.
   The minimum oil- and airblast-breakers must
   therefore be maintained more carefully than
   the airbreak breakers.

The principle of the airbreak breaker is as
follows:

The breaker looks like an isolator with large
arcing chambers over the contacts, see fig. 2.
During interruption the arc is blown by the
electromagnetic forces into the arcing chamber.
The chamber consists of a number of smaller
chambers of inflamable and insulating material.
The arc is lengthend and cooled against the
cold walls in the arcing chambers.
At the first zero passage of the current after
the arc has blown out into the chambers the arc
is interrupted and deionized. Between the
contacts the voltage-withstandstrength has built
up so that the arc does not restrice. The
current is definitly interrupted.
The long arc during interruption constitutes a
rather high resistance.
During interruption in inductive circuits the arc
resistance reduses the phase angle between
current and voltage.
Therefore at current zero when interruption
takes place the voltage also is nearly zero.
This is the reason why the airbreak breakers
give so small overvoltages.

TRANSFORMERS:

The transformers should be air cooled with "dry
type" insulation so that oil or other insulation
medium can be avoided.
The sizes and types in question are available.

CABLES:

H.V. cables for normal installation should be
sheet steel armoured or metal screened.
However, for cables in steel tubes it seems
reasonable to use cables without steel or metal
armouring.
The cable ends must be handled with care
especially if cables with semiconducting layers
on the conductor insulation are used. Semiconducting layer is used to equalize the voltage
stresses on the insulation.
There are suitable cables for voltages up to
7,2 kV in the market. These cables have EPR
(etylen-propylen-rubber) insulation and are not
specially made for use on board ships.

NEUTRALPOINT EARTHING:

Directly earthed neutralpoint gives high
earthfault currents and normally also rather
large damages due to arcing and heating at the
point of failure.
The failure is easily located and the faulty
feeder disconnected provided that the
selectivity scheme for the breakers are correct.
This is also a disadvantage as every earthfault
results in an instantanous service interruption
of the faulty part of the system.
Directly earthed neutral point gives defined
and stable voltage reference to earth. There
excist no risk of overvoltage in connection
with earthfaults. The voltage stresses on the
insulation are reduced to a minimum.

Isolated or unearthed neutral is normally
used on 440 V systems and has the advantage that
the system can be run for sometime with a one
phase earthfault. However, an earthfault in an
unearthed network can under special circumstances when the arc is striking and restriking
(arcing grounds) cause high overvoltage on the
sound phases, theoretically up to 7 times the
peak value of the phase to earth voltage.

In an H.V. system where the insulation margins
are not as large as for 440 V such overvoltages
may lead to damages.

It seems that a resistance earthed neutral point
would be most advantageous. This would lead to
a reduced earthfault current in case of a
failure to earth. If the resistance in the
neutral point is dimensioned to give an earthfault current in the order of 10 A the damages
of earthfault current will be very limited.
Further the risks of overvoltages as in an
unearthed system will be avoided. At around 10A
a selective arrangement for disconnecting the
faulty feeder is fully possible.
From the security point of view a resistance
earthed system may be regarded as safe as, or
even safer than an unearthed system due to the
fact that a rapid disconnection of the failure
can take place.

ONE LINE DIAGRAM:

In figure 3 an example of a one line diagram
is shown. The main generators and motors down
to 100-500 kW should be connected to the high
voltage side. The emergency generator should be
connected to the 440 V side.

The busbar arrangement is partly dependent on
what kind of starting arrangement is chosen for
the motors. In fig. 3 a double busbarsystem with
breakers in all branches is shown. This is an
exspensive but flexible system with 100 % back-

H.V. SWITCHBOARD:

The H.V. switchboard should be equipped with
truck mounted withdrawable breakers. For
inspection and maintenance the breakers can
easily be taken out of the compartement.
When the breaker is taken out of the compartement
shutters should automatically screen any live
parts so that no live parts can be touched even
with the compartement door open. The switchboard
should also have earthing devices which can only
be operated at no voltage.
The outgoing and incoming cables shall be
arranged in such a way that these cables can be
screened off from busbars, contacts etc. under
voltage so that the cables can be connected or
disconnected with the rest of the switchboard
in service.
The switchboard should also be built so that, if
an open arc due to a failure is developed,
venting of the overpressure shall occure in such
a way that personell will not be in danger.
That means that the doors, inspection windows etc.
in the front must withstand the overpressure
which is built up by the gasses.
Furthermore the equipment, busbars etc. should be
arranged in such a way that the arc does not
burn through the front.
Breakers should be preferred instead of fuses
and contactors. If, for economical reasons, fused
contactors is used the arrangement should be such
that the contactors with fuses must be disconnected (truck or drawout system) before
changing of fuses can take place.
The switchboard should preferably be without
disconnecting switches.

The requirements of the regulations of a visible
isolating distance in a circuit that is going to
be earthed, can be fulfilled by arranging the
truckmounted breaker in such a way that it can
be moved a sufficient distance for isolation
between the fixed contacts in the compartement
and the contacts on the breaker truck.

Mechanical and electrical interlocks should
prevent the moving of the breaker before it is
opened.

DEGREE OF AUTOMATION:

A H.V. system does not require any higher degree
of automation than a 440 V system. If a H.V.
system is chosen the electric system will normally
be large, which may justify an extensive
automation, such as for example automatic load
sharing, with automatic start, synchronisation
and stop of generators.
However, the degree of automation is dependent
of the type of ship and the requirements of the
shipowner.

REGULATIONS AND CLASSIFICATIONS:

The classification authorities Lloyd´s and Bureau Veritas have some requirements for H.V. system in their regulations, but each installation has to be studied separately.
Each country has their own national requirements with regards to the safety of personell, and these requirements have also to be fulfilled.

A technical comittee within the IEC is working with regulations:"Medium voltage for A.C.systems on ships".
It will, however, take some years before we can expect to have the necessary regulations established.

QUALIFICATIONS OF PERSONELL FOR OPERATING A H.V. SYSTEM:

An important question is the qualifications that should be required of the personell which will be allowed to do maintenance and service on the H.V. equipment on board. If the H.V. system is laid out as proposed in this paper, there will be very little work which has to be carried out on the H.V. system.
The breakers or contactors are of draw out (truck type) and the service on these items will be carried out outside the compartements. Such a service is mainly a mechanical job. Other maintenance on the H.V. switchboard should not be necessary between the classification intervals.

Any maintenance of the H.V. generators and motors is naturally always carried out during standstill.

With regard to the H.V. cables it seems very unlikely that any of those have to be changed out by the personell on board.

The maintenance on the H.V. system will as stated above be very limited.
It is therefore proposed that ordinary ship-electricians should, after a short theoretical and practical course, be authorized to do the limited maintenance needed on the H.V.system.

CONCLUSION:

The equipment needed for building H.V. systems for ships is available, and there are not any complicated design problems attached to such systems.

A H.V. system with a switchboard built in accordance to the proposed design principles is not more dangerous to the personell than a conventional 440 V system.

On the countrary it can be claimed to be safer and more reliable in service as much more emphasis is laid on safety in the H.V. switchboards.

The number of H.V. systems will certainly increase during the next years, and the fields for H.V. systems may increase.
For example is the use of H.V. system for propulsion an interesting application for ships with high power consumption in harbour, such as cruiseships or refrigerating cargoships.

It is therefore important that the IEC regulations for such systems are finished as soon as possible. When those regulations are ready it will also be easier to establish the requirements needed for the personell operating the H.V. system on board a ship.

REFERENCES:

1) M.J.A. Bolton: The electrical power system in Queen Elizabeth 2 - Design and operational experience. The Institute of Marine Engineers, Transactions, Vol 83 Part 11, 1971.

2) IEC-document 18A (Secretariat) 27 (May 1971), Draft - Cables intended for medium-voltage installations in ships.

3) IEC-document 18 (Secretariat) 529 (June 1971), Draft-Proposal on medium-voltage a.c. systems of supply (three-phase a.c.).

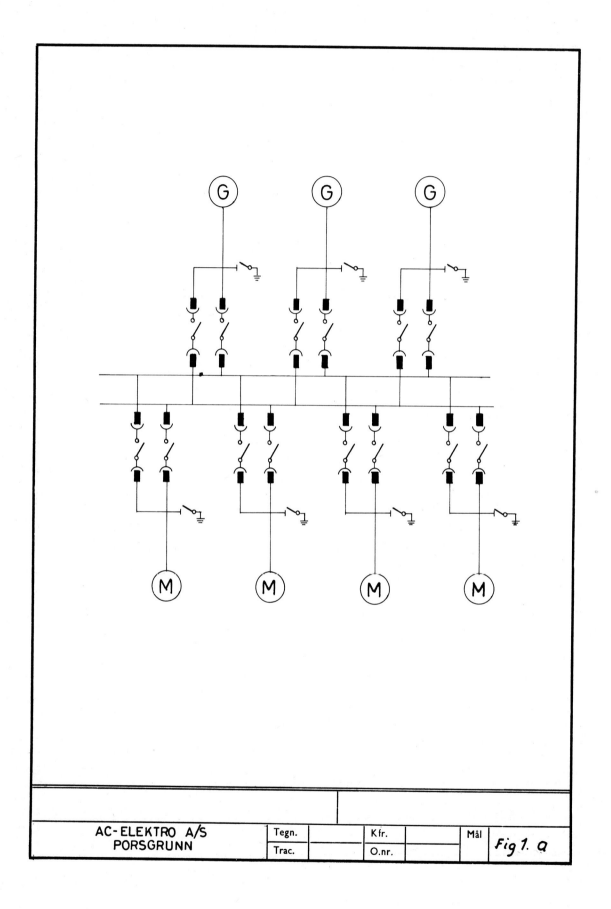

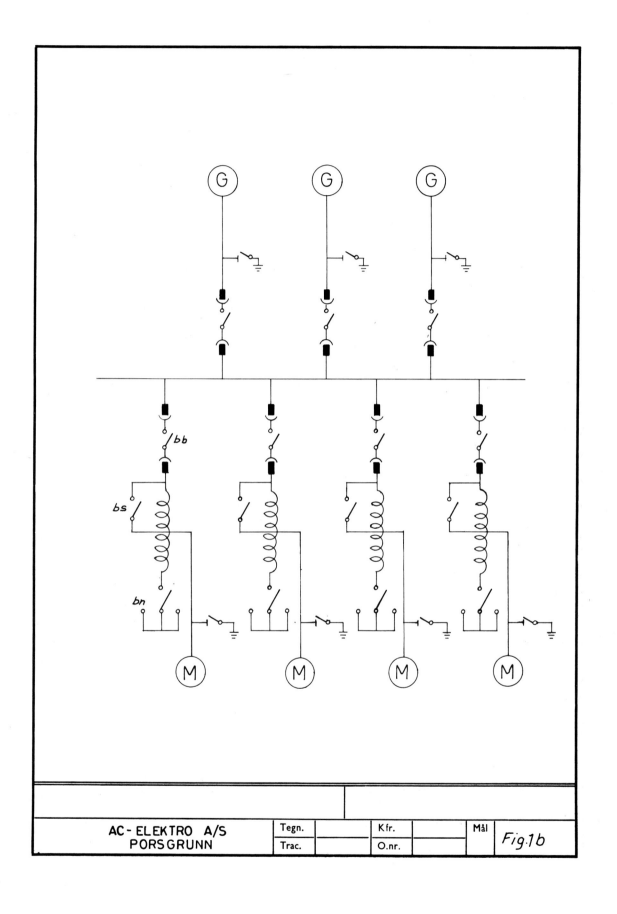

AC - ELEKTRO A/S	Tegn.		Kfr.		Mål	*Fig.1b*
PORSGRUNN	Trac.		O.nr.			

532

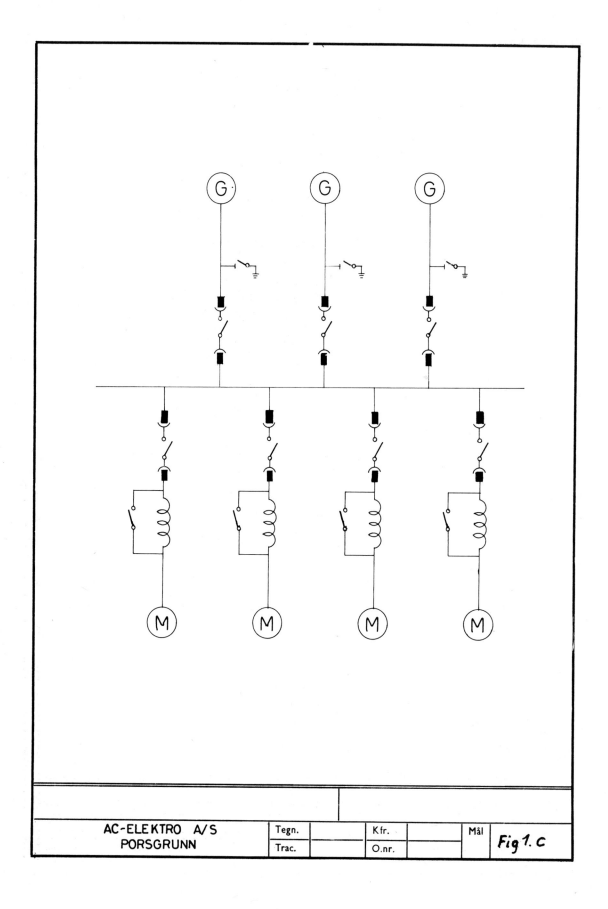

533

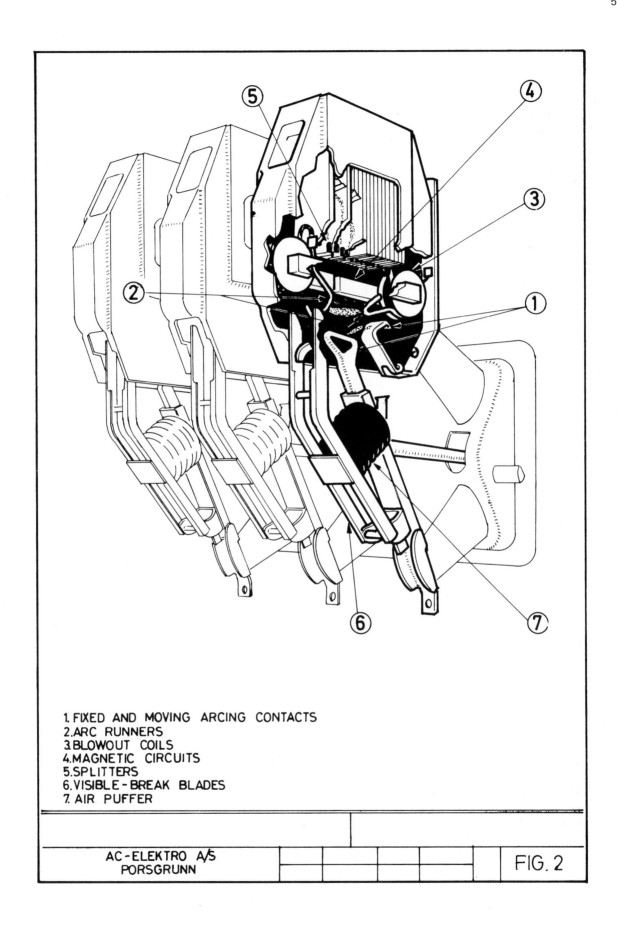

1. FIXED AND MOVING ARCING CONTACTS
2. ARC RUNNERS
3. BLOWOUT COILS
4. MAGNETIC CIRCUITS
5. SPLITTERS
6. VISIBLE-BREAK BLADES
7. AIR PUFFER

AC-ELEKTRO A/S
PORSGRUNN

FIG. 2

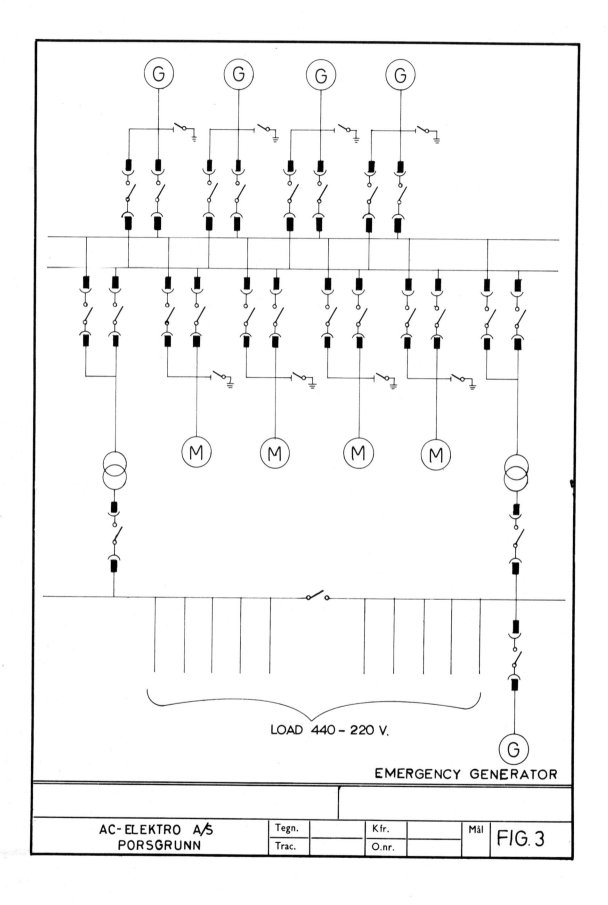

LOAD 440 – 220 V.

EMERGENCY GENERATOR

AC-ELEKTRO A/S	Tegn.		Kfr.		Mål	FIG. 3
PORSGRUNN	Trac.		O.nr.			

ELECTRONIC CONTROL OF MARINE GAS TURBINE ENGINES

J. M. Binns
Chief Performance Engineer (Fuel Systems)
Hydromechanical Group
Lucas Aerospace

M. J. Joby
Performance Section Manager
(Electronics)
Hydromechanical Group
Lucas Aerospace

SYNOPSIS

The advantages of electronic controls in terms of accuracy and adaptability to differing require- ments have been recognised for a long time. The application of these controls to gas turbine engines, has in the past been inhibited by their unreliability when compared with that of hydro- mechanical systems. Recent developments in con- structional techniques of electronic controls however, have altered this situation, and control systems are now available which give reliabilities comparable with those available with the hydro- mechanical systems used hitherto.

Electronic controls operate by modifying the fuel flow to the engine, and the interface equipment to perform this function must be chosen with care, taking account of the necessary speed of response and the requirements for modes of failure.

The wide range of fuels which are burned in gas turbine engines and the possibility of salt-water and other forms of contamination pose peculiar problems in the design of the pumping element which have been successfully solved.

In this paper a practical example is given of a control system for a gas turbine engine used for ship propulsion. The type of control, the control interface and the pump design are all discussed, and typical test results are published showing the control system performance during engine starting, steady running and transient operation. A brief description of the constructional tech- niques for the electronic control is also given.

1.0   INTRODUCTION

The Gas Turbine Engine is being used increasingly for Naval and general marine propulsion purposes. Control of the Marine Gas Turbine engine poses a number of interesting problems for the Control Engineer. Many Marine Gas Turbine Engines are derived from aircraft engines and it is possible to take the existing aircraft control system and with some modification use it for controlling the Marine version of the engine. This however, normally has a number of disadvantages due to the very different marine environment and the often unnecessary complexity of the control.

Electronic controls are becoming more widely accepted for aircraft and non-aircraft gas tur- bines. They offer a number of advantages over hydromechanical systems particularly in flexibil- ity and ease of adjustment and matching the diff- erent engine requirements. With the development of higher reliability and integrity electronic devices it is possible that electronic controls will displace fully hydromechanical systems on future marine gas turbine engines.

Aircraft gas turbine engine control systems have been intensively developed over the past 30 years. Lucas Aerospace provided fuel systems for the ear- ly Whittle engines in 1941 and since then for the vast majority of the European built civil and military engines. These control systems have been mainly of a hydromechanical nature but an electronic control was flying as early as 1949. In more re- cent years the greatly improved reliability ach- ieved by modern electronic solid state integrated circuits, has made electronic control much more attractive and feasible. Such equipment is now utilised on the Olympus 593, RB211 and RB199 engines. From this aircraft engine electronic con- trol equipment has been derived low cost, high reliability electronic controls for vehicle gas turbines such as the Leyland lorry engine which is fitted with a Lucas electronic control and it is this basic background which has lead to the work described in this Paper in developing a low cost, high reliability electronic controller for use on Marine Gas Turbine Engines.

In parallel with the evolution of this electronic controller has been the development of pumps and control valves to work with fuels of a low lub- ricity and of a corrosive nature. With the com- bined electronic and hydromechanical package for a Marine Engine, the hydromechanical parts are as simple and robust as possible to deal with the salt water laden fuel, with all the sophistication built into the electronic control.

The requirements for a Marine Gas Turbine Engine can be divided into the following main areas.

(a) Starting

Some form of fuel flow control is required during starting. This can take the form of a schedule of fuel flow versus engine shaft speed, a fast acting temperature control, or a ramp of fuel flow against time. The choice of starting schedule depends upon the engine requirements but an electronic control can encompass any of these functions with relatively little complication. For the Marine Olympus engine around which much of the fuel control development work has been carried out a simple schedule of fuel flow versus engine shaft speed has proved adequate.

(b) Engine Steady Running Requirements

For ship propulsion a measure of engine power is normally required. There are a number of engine functions which can be used for this and one of the prefered functions would be engine compressor delivery pressure. An approximate measure of power from the engine would be the use of gas generator speed and further alternatives would be the use of compressor pressure ratio, non-dimensional speed, or power turbine speed.

The use of compressor delivery pressure would present the ship's watchkeeper with an unfamiliar parameter and involve the use of a high cost pressure transducer. A compromise parameter is engine gas generator shaft speed (in the case of a two shaft gas generator like the Marine Olympus low pressure shaft speed is utilised). Gas generator shaft speed is equally applicable to fixed pitch and variable pitch ship's propellors and is generally prefered by ship's officers to the alternative of power turbine governing. The use of power turbine governing can result in substantial changes in gas generator speed with the ship's propellor load due to ship motion. Gas generator governing gives the watchkeeper a selectable engine power and engine shaft speed.

The system described in this Paper while working on engine shaft speed in line with current Naval requirements is equally operable on compressor delivery pressure if this should be required in future.

(c) Engine Acceleration and Deceleration

It is necessary to be able to accelerate or decelerate the engine avoiding compressor stall, over-temperature or flame out. In general on a Marine Gas Turbine the acceleration time can be longer than that normally required for aircraft engines providing it is stall free and does not over-temperature the engine, but a rapid controlled deceleration is a requirement, more so than for aircraft engines to cater for sudden unloading of the engine in such cases as the ship's propellor coming out of the water as the ship pitches.

(d) Engine Limiters

A number of limiters will normally be required for engine protection purposes and these can be divided into the following categories:

(a) Engine Shaft Speed Limiters. Normally a maximum limiting control will be required on each shaft of the engine to prevent overspeed.
(b) Free Turbine Maximum Speed Limiter. This will be required to cover potential failure cases, and any sudden unloading of the ship's propellor due to motion of the ship.
(c) Turbine Entry Temperature Limiter. For turbine protection the maximum value of turbine entry temperature has to be limited. On some engines this temperature limiter can also be used as a start control set at a higher than normal datum. On other engines this limiter can sometimes be dispensed with if the engine has a very wide stall margin and where the turbine inlet temperature can be inferred from the engine shaft speed.
(d) Overspeed Trips. On some applications an over-speed trip mechanism may be required to shut the engine down to idle.

This Paper describes a combined electronic and hydromechanical fuel system suitable for marine applications which has been built and tested on an Olympus 201 engine. Details are given of the performance of this system on the Lucas engine test facility showing its suitability as the control system for marine engines.

2.0 DESCRIPTION OF SYSTEM

2.1 Pumping System

A variety of different types of pump are available for pumping typical fuels used for Marine applications. Extensive experience is available of piston pumps, gear pumps and centrifugal pumps on a variety of different aircraft applications. Careful consideration of characteristics of all these different types of pump has led Lucas to recommend variable displacement piston pumps for engine mounted pumps on Marine gas turbines. These pumps have the advantage of some hundreds of millions of flying hours and the resulting high state of development. Their variable displacement feature enables them to operate efficiently at part load conditions without putting excessive heat into the fuel. Extensive running on salt water laden diesel fuel and low lubricity Light Virgin Naptha fuel has led to the development of a pump to give a target life of eight thousand hours between overhaul on Marine fuels. The Marine standard of pump has now been developed to a higher standard than the aircraft pump and is fitted with Tungsten Carbide port inserts, carbon lined piston bores and a number of anti-corrosion features.

The output of the fuel pumps is controlled by a fuel operated servo system which alters the angle of a swash plate thus altering the displacement of the pump pistons.

2.2 Fuel Flow Interface Valve

The emphasis on the hydromechanical part of the Lucas Marine fuel system has been on keeping this as simple and robust as possible. It is considered desirable for a Marine engine that any electrical failure shall cause the engine to either fail frozen or shut down.

If the engine failed frozen engine speed would remain constant and it would then be possible to revert to manual control whereby the ships engine room staff will be able to increase or decrease engine speed by means of a lever or wheel. The alternative of engine shut down implies that failure causes the engine to be shut down and for the engine room staff to be able to control the engine directly by means of local battery power or engine mounted generators. To enable the fail frozen capability to be achieved a throttle valve driven by an electric actuator is arranged such that in the event of an electric failure the motor stays in its last position before failure and the manual control then is able to move the control independent of the actuator. A simple pressure drop unit is arranged across the throttle valve which acts on the pump servo system to regulate the fuel flow to the engine to keep a constant pressure drop across the throttle valve. Such a system is shown on Fig 1.

If there is no requirement for the system to fail frozen the throttle valve can be removed from the fuel line and the electronic control can be arranged to position the pump servo directly with the system stabilised by a suitable feedback of servo position, fuel flow or compressor delivery pressure.

In addition to the pump and flow interface some form of simple pressurising valve would be present in the system both for providing sufficient pressure to work the pump servo and also to divide the fuel between pilot and main burners if required. A shut off cock would also be provided with both a manual input from the engine operator and facility for rapid shut down if required.

2.3 Electronic Controller

The electronic controller described below is a development from aircraft and vehicle fuel system designs. It is based on the slave datum principle (reference 1). The unit provides the following control features:

(a) Automatic starting

(b) Range gas generator speed control of the LP shaft.

(c) Engine HP shaft speed limiting.

(d) Power turbine speed limiting.

(e) Power turbine inlet temperature limiting.

(f) Acceleration and deceleration control.

(g) Fail frozen capability.

The engine mounted transducers used for the control are variable reluctance speed probes for detecting the various shaft speeds and a thermocouple harness for detecting power turbine inlet temperature. The transducers used in the engine programme were essentially similar to normal aircraft standard transducers. The variable reluctance pick-offs provide an alternating output signal whose frequency is directly proportional to speed.

The thermocouple harness uses standard Chromel-Alumel thermocouples which are arranged around the engine to obtain a good average temperature signal. The controller incorporates a servo which is used to position the fuel control unit throttle. The controller is shown in block diagram form in Fig 2. Under normal operating conditions the control system operates in one of four modes.

(a) Starting

Engine LP shaft speed is measured using a variable reluctance transducer. The resulting signal is demodulated, providing an analogue type signal directly proportional to speed. This signal is fed to a function generator in the starting loop which sets a throttle demand against LP shaft speed schedule. The output of the function generator is compared in a lowest wins gate with the output of the main control system, and since the former is the smaller signal during the starting sequence it sets the throttle position demand. The throttle position servo receives position and velocity signals from transducers connected to the throttle. The outputs of these transducers are amplitude modulated a.c. signals. These are demodulated, compared with the throttle demand and then amplified, chopped and fed to a power amplifier, which drives the control winding of a two phase servo motor which positions the throttle. When the engine starter operates, the engine fuel flow rises along the line set by the engine pumps until the flow schedule takes over. As the engine speed increases the fuel flow similarly increases, giving a positive feed-back action, and the engine runs up to idle. At idle, the main control takes over.

(b) Range Gas Generator Speed Control

The watchkeeper selects gas generator speed by means of a conductive plastic film potentiometer. This signal is compared with the gas generator speed as shown, and fed to a lowest wins gate, where it is compared with error signals derived from the three engine limiters. Under normal operating conditions the engine is running at a speed which does not bring the limiters into operation. The LP speed error is thus the smallest signal, and is fed through the acceleration control limiter, integrated and compared with LP shaft speed as shown. The resulting signal sets the throttle demand. The integrator ensures that isochronous control is obtained. The small signal response of the system depends on the speed of the throttle position servo and fuel control unit, since this limits the gain which can be set in the so called fast loop of the control.

(c) Engine Limiters

Gas generator HP shaft speed, power turbine speed and turbine inlet temperature limiters are provided, and operate via the slow loop of the control. Fixed speed and temperature datums are generated within the unit and compared with the measured values of the parameters. Resulting errors are compared, with the range speed control errors, in a lowest wins gate. Under particular load or ambient conditions the maximum gas generator speed

selected by the watchkeeper could cause one of
these limits to be exceeded, in which case the limiter error is smaller than the range speed control
error and takes over control through the slow loop.
It is relatively easy to ensure the stability of
these limiters as individual dynamic compensation
can be applied to them.

(d)   Acceleration and Deceleration Control

The engine acceleration control is the slave datum
system.   A dual gain limiter is shown in the slow
loop of the control system.   When an error above
a preset value is fed into the slow loop, the output of the limiter becomes fixed and the output of
the integrator following it becomes a ramp.   This
signal is known as the slave datum and acts as an
input to the fast loop of the control.   It is inherent in the behaviour of feedback control systems that the fast loop signal, the engine LP shaft
speed, should try to follow this datum.   The output of the integrator under these conditions is
thus a speed demand, and so the input to the
integrator, which is the limiter output, represents
an acceleration demand.   Direct closed loop acceleration control is thus obtained.   Relatively
complex acceleration schedules can be generated
by varying the limit as a function of various engine and ambient parameters if this is required.
In the present application it was not required to
accelerate the engine from idle to maximum in less
than 8 seconds, and a fixed acceleration datum was
found to be quite adequate.   As the engine runs
up to speed the error signal reduces and when it
falls below the limiter value a conventional dual
gain integral loop is restored which tends to reduce the error to zero.   The dual gain characteristic is used to put the control onto its maximum
accelerating rate for relatively small error signals.

The deceleration control is required to be quick
acting, but to avoid causing flame out.   Two
controls are used to accomplish this, firstly a
deceleration limiter with a fixed value is provided
in the slow loop, and secondly a minimum flow
limiter.   When a rapid deceleration is required
the throttle closes down at a maximum preset rate
until the minimum flow condition is reached.   This
level is maintained until the engine runs down to
idle and the steady running control takes over
again.

3.0   SAFETY CIRCUITS

The control system is designed so that no hazard
to the engine occurs for any single failure, and
so that dormant faults can be detected on a routine
maintenance basis.   The main areas of the controller requiring check out are the datum signals, the
transducer signals, the throttle position servo
and the operational amplifiers, which in effect
make up the remainder of the control.

There are a variety of reactions which can be built
into the safety circuits.

1.   The circuit can cause the engine to shut down
     completely.

2.   The circuit can cause the engine to shut down
     to idle.

3.   The circuit can cause the system to freeze.

4.   The circuit can cause the faulty circuit to
     be isolated so that control may be resumed.

5.   The presence of a fault can be shown on a
     warning light.

Failure of a main control circuit necessitates
reversion to manual control, whereas a circuit
used as a limiter can be isolated, a warning
light switched on to warn the operator, and control resumed with out the limiter interfering. If
an actuator or actuator transducer fault occurs
then manual reversion is necessary.   The appended
list indicates how typical transducer faults can
be detected.

Speed Transducers

a)   Open or Shut Circuit

     Detection is by passing a current through the
     probe.   The voltage across it is compared to
     the voltage generated over the normal range
     of speeds.

     Failure of transducer used for control
     necessitates manual reversion.   Failure of a
     transducer used for limiting necessitates in-
     hibiting the channel because it could run the
     engine down.

b)   Earth Faults

     Earth faults have no effect on standard
     circuits.

Temperature Transducers

a)   Open Circuit

     Detection is by comparing the signal to a
     maximum value, open circuit causing a very
     high apparent temperature.

     The temperature channel has to be muted be-
     cause it would try to shut down the engine.

b)   Short Circuit

     If the temperature signal disappears for some
     N_H greater than a set value then a short
     circuit is indicated.

c)   Earth Faults

     The signal would go outside the normal range
     unless transformer coupling is used.

Catastrophic failures in the operational amplifiers are readily detected by monitoring their
summing junctions and outputs.   A simple multiplexed arrangement is used in the present system
which can detect output saturation, or a voltage appearing at an amplifier summing junction
for any required number of amplifiers.   The detection of such faults causes the safety circuits

to operate.

The throttle position servo is easily checked out by summing the throttle demand, position and velocity signals in an operational amplifier, and comparing the output signal with the equivalent signal in the control loop. Any significant discrepancy between the signals causes the safety circuits to operate.

The loss of any datum signal causes the engine to shut down. Drift would be detected by built in test equipment on a production unit. Built in test equipment would be used to check out the system as a part of the start sequence, and operates when the unit is switched on and tests the functioning of the safety circuits and integrity of the warning lamps. This consists of sequentially injecting false signals and checking for the appropriate fault warning and action. In the event of the monitoring circuits not checking out satisfactorily the start sequence is inhibited.

4.0   CONSTRUCTIONAL TECHNIQUES

Special hybrid circuitry has been evolved to meet the requirement of engine mounted gas turbine control systems. This application necessitated the development of a system of circuit construction capable of providing great accuracy and stability of calibration, and of functioning, with very high reliability in hostile environments of high and low temperatures and high vibration stress.

Thick film resistor networks as shown in the photgraph Fig. 3 are used rather than printed circuit boards for mounting circuit components. This system produces printed resistor and conductor networks on alumina substrates. Discrete components of most types can be added by soldering to the conductor film.

Printed resistor networks offer the greatest economic savings compared with discrete component assemblies in networks with larger numbers of resistors, or when adjustment of resistor values is necessary for correct functioning. Resistors can be trimmed after component assembly and with power supplies connected. This eliminates Select-on Test procedures and the need for high accuracy components.

The printed resistor network also provides a high thermal dissipation substrate, thus lowering component temperatures to improve reliability. The substrate also provides a high structural rigidity.

The tiles are mounted on metal trays with a layer of viscoelastic material interposed. The trays are then stacked on suitable mounting posts and a low thermal resistance path is provided to the mounting pad which can take the form of a finned heat sink or fuel cooler.

This arrangement allows the components to be mounted in areas of high temperature or vibration without excessive component temperatures occurring.

5.0   ENGINE TEST RESULTS

A series of engine and rig tests were carried out to evaluate the electronic control system. The engine used was a R.R. Olympus 201 which is in effect the gas generator section of a Marine Olympus engine. The fuel control unit was run on a rig and the servo control was set up with the aid of a transfer function analyser. The engine parameters were measured similarly using a transfer function analyser, and on the basis of these measurements preliminary control parameters were built into the electronic unit. Previous test runs provided data concerning the stall region of the engine, and suitable starting flow schedules were supplied by Rolls Royce (1971) Limited (Marine and Industrial Division).

The control was then used to run the engine. It was found that little adjustment was required owing to the previous test runs, the main regions requiring some attention being the take-over between the starting and steady running controls at idle, and the acceleration and deceleration control settings. The full scale acceleration time was set to be approximately 8 seconds and the deceleration time which was of the order of 13 seconds was as fast as could be obtained on the engine used without flame out occurring.

The enclosed engine test results show the performance of the engine during starting and as a range speed control. A temperature limiter was also successfully run, but power turbine governing could not be tried out since it was effectively only the gas generator which was being used in the tests. A power turbine speed limiter of the type described has however been run most successfully on a gas turbine truck engine. Fig. 4 shows the engine starting on its flow schedule and running up to idle on the gas generator LP shaft speed control for Aviation kerosene and diesel fuels. Fig. 5 shows the performance of the engine as an acceleration and deceleration control. The Nichols chart Fig. 6 gives the overall frequency response of the LP shaft speed control system and engine at high and low speed conditions.

6.0   CONCLUSIONS

A control system is described in this Paper which has been designed, manufactured and tested on an Olympus 201 engine basically similar in characteristics to the gas generator portion of the Marine Olympus TM3. engine. This successful test programme shows the availability of an electronic control system for present and future marine gas turbine engines.

7.0   ACKNOWLEDGMENTS

The authors wish to thank the directors of Joseph Lucas for permission to publish the information in in this paper and also acknowledge the work carried out by colleagues of Lucas Aerospace Hydromechcanical Group in designing, building and testing the equipment described.

REFERENCE
British Patent 946111

540

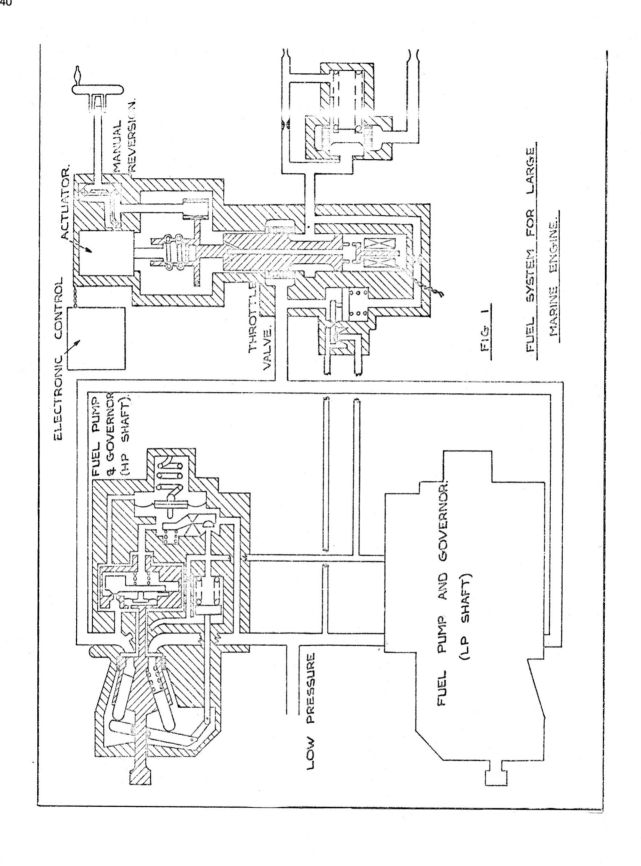

ELECTRONIC CONTROL.

ACTUATOR.

MANUAL REVERSION.

THROTTLE VALVE.

FUEL PUMP & GOVERNOR. (HP SHAFT).

LOW PRESSURE

FUEL PUMP AND GOVERNOR. (LP SHAFT)

FIG I

FUEL SYSTEM FOR LARGE

MARINE ENGINE.

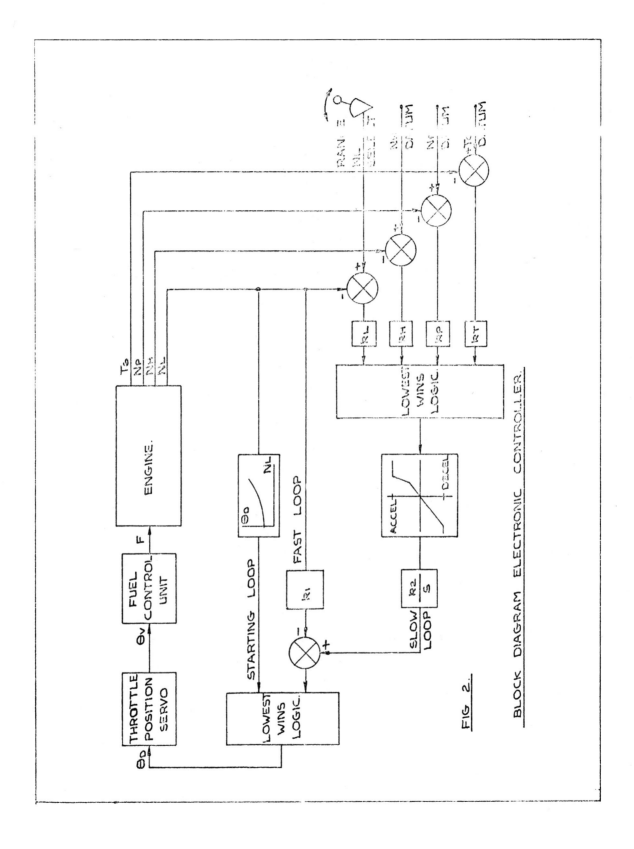

FIG 2.

BLOCK DIAGRAM ELECTRONIC CONTROLLER.

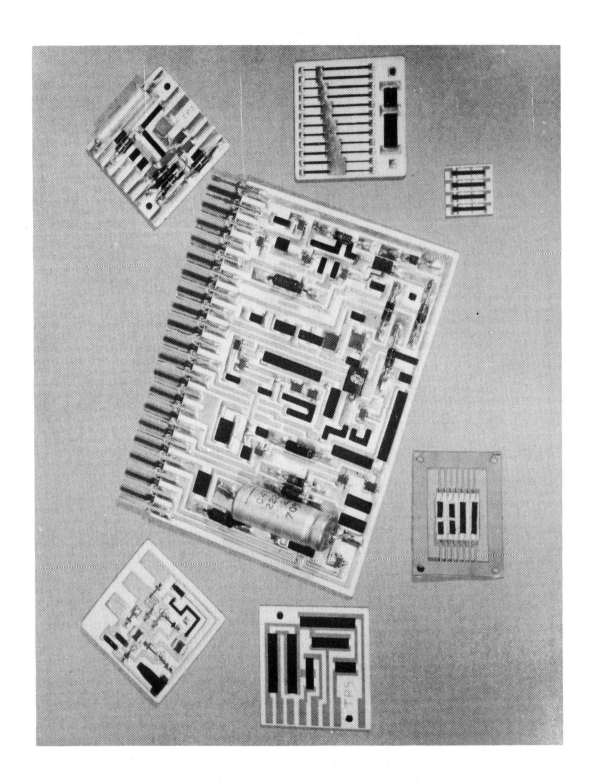

FIG. 3.

THICK FILM CIRCUIT MODULES (55575C)

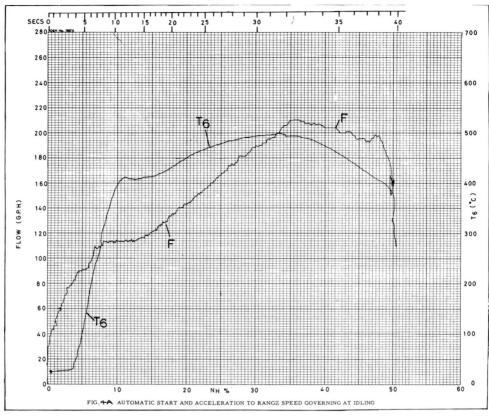

FIG. 4-A AUTOMATIC START AND ACCELERATION TO RANGE SPEED GOVERNING AT IDLING

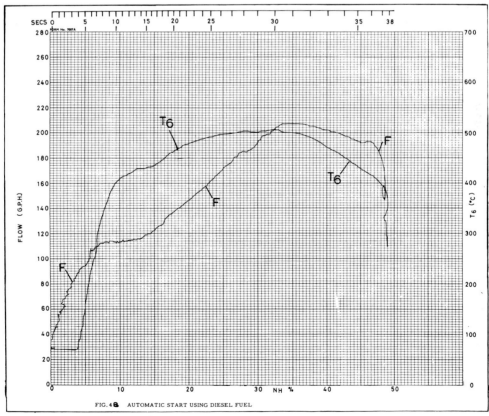

FIG. 4-B AUTOMATIC START USING DIESEL FUEL

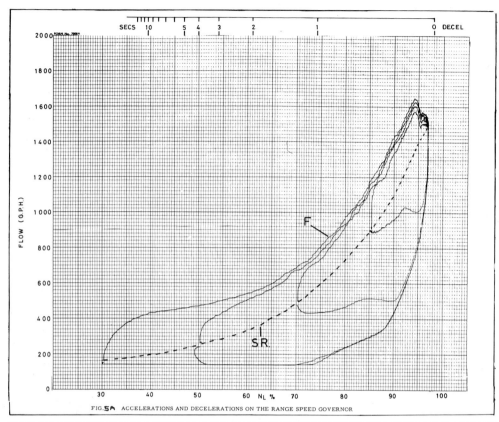

FIG.5A ACCELERATIONS AND DECELERATIONS ON THE RANGE SPEED GOVERNOR

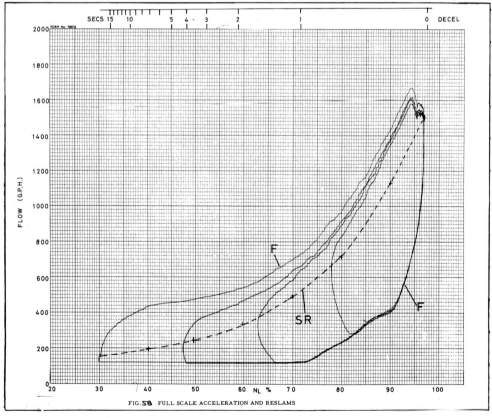

FIG.5B FULL SCALE ACCELERATION AND RESLAMS

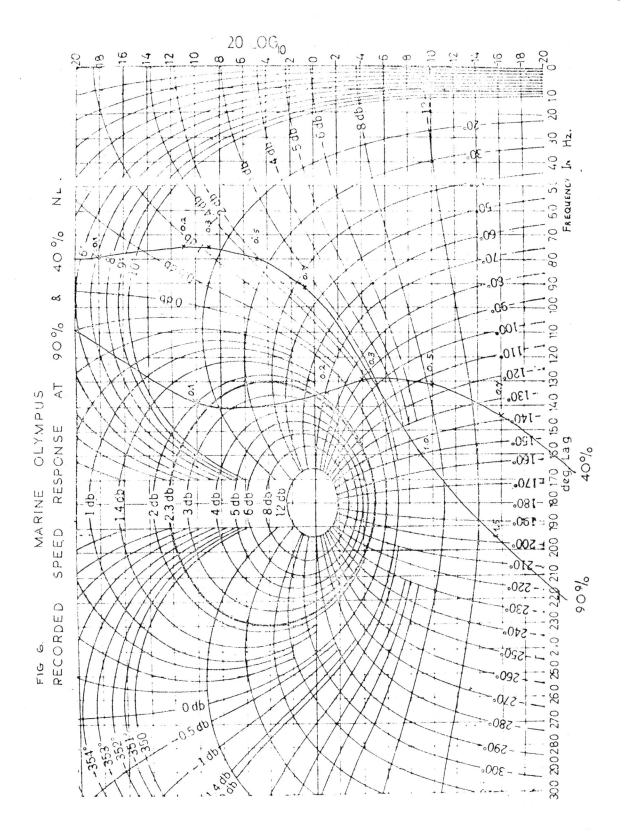

FIG 6.   MARINE OLYMPUS

RECORDED SPEED RESPONSE AT 90% & 40% N_L.

AUTHOR INDEX